CONTENTS

CONTRIBUTORS

John W. Ashbaugh
Vice President
Human Services Research Institute
2336 Massachusetts Avenue
Cambridge, Massachusetts 02140

Pat Beeman
Communitas, Inc.
P.O. Box 374
Manchester, Connecticut 06045

Bruce C. Blaney
Senior Research Analyst
Human Services Research Institute
2336 Massachusetts Avenue
Cambridge, Massachusetts 02140

Elizabeth Monroe Boggs
19 Henderson Road
Hampton, New Jersey 08827

Jean N. Bowen
Western Connecticut Association for Human Rights
11 Lake Avenue Extension
Danbury, Connecticut 06811

Valerie J. Bradley
President
Human Services Research Institute
2336 Massachusetts Avenue
Cambridge, Massachusetts 02140

Kathleen Carmody
Ray Graham Association
340 West Butterfield Road
Elmhurst, Illinois 60126

Susan B. Covert
31 Cottage Street
Contoocook, New Hampshire 03229

Agnesanne J. Danehey
Research Project Coordinator
Community Support and Access Unit
University of Maryland at Baltimore
630 West Fayette Street
Baltimore, Maryland 21201

Regina DeMarasse
5 Grandview Street
Wolcott, Connecticut 06716

George Ducharme
Northspring Consulting
185 Pine Street, #002
Manchester, Connecticut 06040

Derrick Dufresne
Community Resource Associates
736 Crab Thicket Lane
Des Peres, Missouri 63131

Anne Farber
Office of Child Development
Policy and Evaluation Program
University of Pittsburgh
121 University Place
Pittsburgh, Pennsylvania 15260

Elissa L. Freud
18 Samuel Parlin Drive
Acton, Massachusetts 01720

Raymond J. Gagne
Keystone Residence
2336 North Third Street
Harrisburg, Pennsylvania 17110

James F. Gardner
Chief Executive Officer
The Accreditation Council on Services for People with Disabilities
8100 Professional Place
Suite 204
Landover, Maryland 20785

Robert M. Gettings
Executive Director
National Association of Directors of Developmental Disabilities Services
113 Oronoco Street
Alexandria, Virginia 22314

Cheryl Jorgensen
Institute on Disability
Center for Health Promotion and Research
312 Morrill Hall
University of New Hampshire
Durham, New Hampshire 03824

Michael Kendrick
Assistant Commissioner for Program Development
Department of Mental Retardation
160 North Washington Street
Boston, Massachusetts 02114

Madeleine Kimmich
Human Services Research Institute
7910 Woodmont Avenue
Suite 912
Bethesda, Maryland 20814

Jerry Kiracofe
Former Executive Director
Human Services Institute
5430 Lynx Lane
Columbia, Maryland 21044

James A. Knoll
Developmental Disabilities Institute
Wayne State University
Justice Building
Room 326
6001 Cass Avenue
Detroit, Michigan 48202

Bob Laux
Creative Management Association
P.O. Box 5488
Portsmouth, New Hampshire 03801

Ruth Luckasson
Professor of Special Education
College of Education
University of New Mexico
Albuquerque, New Mexico 87131

Cathy Ludlum
46 James Street, #16
Manchester, Connecticut 06040

John D. MacIntosh
24 Montgomery Street
Concord, New Hampshire 03301

Kristen Magis-Agosta
292 South Edward Road
Monmouth, Oregon 97361

Kay Marcel
Community and Family Support System Task Force
713 North Lewis Street
New Iberia, Louisiana 70560

Beth Mount
25 West 81st Street, #16B
New York, New York 10024

Jane A. Nisbet
Institute on Disability
Department of Education
312 Morrill Hall
University of New Hampshire
Durham, New Hampshire 03824

Connie Lyle O'Brien
Responsive Systems Associates
58 Willowick Drive
Lithonia, Georgia 30038

John O'Brien
Responsive Systems Associates
58 Willowick Drive
Lithonia, Georgia 30038

Stephanie Powers
Office of the Assistant Secretary
Employment and Training Administration
United States Department of Labor
Room S-2307
200 Constitution Avenue, NW
Washington, DC 20210

Julie Ann Racino
Community and Policy Studies
2103 South Geddes Street
Syracuse, New York 13207

Donald L. Shumway
Director of Division of Mental Health and Developmental Services
105 Pleasant Street
Concord, New Hampshire 03301

Gary Smith
Director of Special Projects
National Association of Directors of Developmental Disabilities Services
6893 South Miller Street
Littleton, Colorado 80127

Michael W. Smull
Director
Community Support and Access Unit
University of Maryland at Baltimore
630 West Fayette Street
Baltimore, Maryland 21201

Deborah Spitalnik
Executive Director
University Affiliated Program of New Jersey
and
Associate Professor of Clinical Pediatrics
University of Medicine and Dentistry of New Jersey
Robert Wood Johnson Medical School
Piscataway, New Jersey 08855

Don Wesely
Senator
and
Chairman
Health and Human Services Committee
Nebraska State Legislature
State Capitol
Lincoln, Nebraska 68509

PREFACE

This book on systems change grows out of a deep commitment on the part of the authors to ensure that the vision of inclusion moves beyond rhetoric and becomes a reality for people with mental retardation and other significant disabilities around the United States. It grows out of a recognition that this task must be approached from multiple perspectives and that an ideal as basic and profound as true inclusion must be operationalized at all levels of the service system in order to be fully realized. We are convinced that if the "new way of thinking" about supports in inclusive homes and jobs is to become a "new way of doing," there remains much hard work to be done to create the needed legal, regulatory, financial, and organizational foundation.

Our collective experience has taught us that inclusion cannot be accomplished through aggregate approaches that minimize individuality and choice—it must take place one person at a time. However, we have also learned that without significant change in the governmental, agency, and organizational structures that dictate the funding and shape of systems, the gains made to date will continue as walled-off islands of excellence unavailable to the majority of people with mental retardation and other significant disabilities. Therefore, this book covers a variety of operational contexts, such as the state, local, regional, agency, and individual levels, and a variety of instrumentalities, such as funding, quality assurance, program design, and personal futures planning. It is an expansive resource of import to policy-makers, system administrators, program developers, service coordinators, service providers, program planners, social workers, advocates, consumers, and all others committed to interdependence and inclusion in the community for all people with disabilities.

It is not time to declare victory and leave the field. Acceptance of the importance of inclusion and its entailments of community presence, participation, choice, and respect are by no means unanimously endorsed or legitimized in practice. Where states have made gains in the phase-down of institutionalization and the creation of significant community opportunities, the impetus often came from litigation and not from a consensus among policy-makers. This is true in New Hampshire, Connecticut, Minnesota, Michigan, Pennsylvania, Maine, West Virginia, and Rhode Island. Though administrators and policy-makers in these states can take credit for the ways in which court mandates were implemented, most would admit that without litigation, the powerful opponents of deinstitutionalization (including unions, institutional suppliers, parents, and bond holders) would have severely constrained their ability to accomplish the changes that have taken place.

That progress has been achieved in large measure through litigation aimed at institutions is borne out by the increasing plight of people with mental retardation who have grown up in communities. Their aspirations to live independent and inclusive lives have been put on hold in many states. Waiting lists are growing; real relationships between people with developmental disabilities and others in our communities are still limited; and very few people with developmental disabilities have satisfying, paying jobs. There are also serious questions being raised about the continuing viability of community residential programs.

The field of mental retardation has been characterized by rapid changes and a continuing reassessment and reevaluation. People in the field have the ability to reinspect and renew their vision. However, the flux that they face also requires the continuing reconfiguration and reshaping of the legal and regulatory superstructure that governs the provision of services as well as the development of new service delivery and administrative strategies. Unfortunately, given the vagaries of public policy, such reform usually lags behind metamorphoses in vision and aspiration. This book, therefore, is an attempt to capture the major steps that must be taken to bring about this fundamental change.

ACKNOWLEDGMENTS

The editors would like to thank all of those who contributed to the completion of this book, including Paul Nurczynski at the Human Services Research Institute, who cajoled the computer into producing uniform copy from multiple formats and who served as an affable traffic cop for the many stages of production, and Victoria Thulman and Natalie Tyler at Paul H. Brookes Publishing Co., whose good humor and patience supported and guided us often-harried editors to the finish line. We would also like to salute all those individuals who are struggling with change but who have not lost sight of the ultimate goal—community membership for all people with developmental disabilities. Finally, we would like to thank all the authors in this book, whose collective wisdom is a powerful and persuasive force.

This book is dedicated to the memory of Jerry Kiracofe,
who worked for change and who helped agencies and
communities to respect and embrace the gifts of people
with developmental disabilities.

CREATING INDIVIDUAL SUPPORTS FOR PEOPLE WITH DEVELOPMENTAL DISABILITIES

I

HISTORY AND RATIONALE

1

INTRODUCTION

Valerie J. Bradley

Change and the desire for continual improvement in the field of developmental disabilities is a constant and is not the property of any generation—not even the one forged in the radical politics of the 1960s. In fact, the aspiration for reform and the hope for revolutionary change have existed for several decades. Evidence of the longstanding nature of such hopes can be seen in a speech that Gunnar Dybwad delivered in 1960 at the Golden Anniversary White House Conference on Children and Youth:

> We need residential facilities in different sizes, in different locations, for different types of residents, and above all we need courage on the part of state governments and our established private institutions to experiment with and test some new projects . . . [that embody a] radical departure from existing patterns. (Dybwad, 1964, pp. 231–232).

Dybwad went on to point out that in 1950, 10 years earlier, Joseph P. Weingold, a distinguished leader in the field of mental retardation, exhorted the founders of the National Association of Retarded Citizens (now known as the Arc) with the following call to arms: "There may be some doubt as to how much we can change our children for the sake of the world, but there can be no doubt as to how much we must change the world for the sake of our children (Dybwad, 1964, p. 232).

The differences between earlier periods in the history of the field and the post-modern realities of the 1990s are not so much in aspiration but in complexity. In the period before the mid-1960s, service systems at the state level were highly centralized, and changes required the approval of a limited number of actors. Budgets were made up primarily of state funds, and the only real constituencies were professional guilds, institutional employees, and an embryonic parents' movement. During the 1970s and 1980s, the system became much more complex as a significant part of the emerging community service system was contracted to private, voluntary and for-profit organizations. These contracted providers in turn became a potent political force (Bradley, 1981). Also during this period came a proliferation of advocacy organizations including protection and advocacy agencies, developmental disabilities councils, and a multiplicity of disability-based professional and parents' organizations. Sources of funding for services to people with developmental disabilities also became more complex as the federal government began to contribute to state services through a variety of new federal programs including Title XIX (Medicaid) and Title XX (Social Services), and local governments in many states also became key fiscal players. Thus, while the impetus for reform remained strong, the process of bringing about change was no longer a unilateral, but a multilateral endeavor.

Today, bringing about reform is further complicated by the emergence of new interests and the depth of the change being contemplated. The new interests include people with disabilities themselves who are organizing as self-advocates. They also include local citizens, schools, generic social services agencies and civic organizations whose participation will be needed to ensure that people with disabilities become supported and welcomed members of their communities. Furthermore, the change from a system based on services to one based on supports (see Bradley, chap. 2, this volume), requires a profound shift from a professional/provider-dominated system to one that is driven by the choices and preferences of people with disabilities.

The complexity of the task at hand is apparent. However, unlike previous reforms, which were of a more incremental character, the changes contemplated by the new paradigm cannot be accomplished using the methods and techniques of the past. Methods such as litigation, regulatory reform, and top-down mandates will not bring about the type of collaborative endeavor required and will not build the capacity needed in communities to support people. The next generation of change must, therefore, be governed by the following new set of assumptions:

- Change in a pluralistic system will require concerted action on multiple fronts and a conscious effort to expose all key actors to the values as well as the methods of providing supports.
- The implementation of change must be a participatory process involving all key actors, especially people with disabilities and their families.
- Changing laws and regulations will not be enough; changes will also be needed in the ways in which agencies are organized and the roles played by front-line staff.
- Change must be driven by explicit federal and state policies, including those that govern quality assurance.
- Movement to a supports-oriented system must begin at the local grassroots level, where decisions should be made and community connections forged.
- Funding mechanisms must be altered to allow for more individualized supports.

- People with disabilities and their families should be supported in their roles as decision-makers and as participants in policy-making arenas.

The purpose of this book is to face head-on the various areas in which changes must take place to transform the current service system including: 1) an overview of the factors that have contributed to change in the past and that are at work currently, 2) a review of the changes required in concepts and assumptions, 3) an outline of the multiple levels of the system that must be addressed, 4) a look at the challenges entailed in creating a truly customer- and family-driven system, 5) a discussion of the methods that can be applied to enhance and stimulate change, and 6) an examination of the implications for the future.

HISTORY AND CURRENT REALITIES

At the heart of the changes anticipated in this book is a so-called paradigm shift. Such a description rightly implies a break from a previous theoretical framework. Bradley argues, in Chapter 2, that this departure from past practices is both the logical extension of the "subversive" value of normalization as well as a realistic response to resource and staffing limitations. However, those who preach the coming of the new paradigm should beware of the hubris that comes from an uncritical acceptance of what is still an idea with limited application. In Chapter 3, Boggs points out the dangers of becoming immune to dissenting views and convincing "ourselves that for the first time in history we have grapsed a truth that will endure." She also warns of the unintended consequences of reform that inevitably lead to the oscillation between "cacophony and consensus" that for Boggs characterizes the process of change. Finally, Smull and Danehey, in Chapter 4, expand on the earlier monograph *Crisis in the Community* (Smull, 1989) and point to the specific challenges entailed in individualizing services and honoring and supporting personal choice and self-determination.

CHANGES IN ASSUMPTIONS

The new paradigm clearly will require a "new way of thinking" (Minnesota Governor's Planning Council on Developmental Disabilities, 1987), which in turn will necessitate a reconceptualization of key aspects of the system. The most important concept has to do with the way in which mental retardation is defined. In the past, the field has defined mental retardation as an unvarying state determined by deficits in intellectual and adaptive behavior and measured by normed assessment scales (American Association on Mental Deficiency, 1983). In Chapter 5, Luckasson and Spitalnik, two of the contributors to the 1992 revised definition (American Association on Mental Retardation, 1992), describe the changes that have taken place in the view of mental retardation from the 1980s into the 1990s.

Specifically, they explain that mental retardation is no longer seen as an inborn and immutable condition; rather, it is seen as a function of the interaction between the individual and her or his environment. This approach provides a strong underpinning for the support paradigm since it emphasizes the individual character of mental retardation and the potential for ameliorating some of its debilitating effects through environmental supports and adaptations.

Mount, in Chapter 6, describes the changes that must take place in the concept of individual planning in order to reinforce the centrality of the personal preferences and choices of the person with a disability and to build support networks that can assist in the realization of these choices. In Chapter 7, O'Brien and O'Brien provide further impetus for the need to *think* differently about the ways in which to provide assistance to people with disabilities and the importance of reconceptualizing the substance and ultimate aim of the system. Finally, Blaney, in Chapter 8, raises a provocative issue with resonance beyond the field of disabilities as he punctures the stereotypes of aging with an exhortation to reinspect not only the constructs in this field but also those that pertain to the larger society. He argues that a surrender to the stereotypes inevitably will result in the resegregation of people with disabilities.

CHANGE THROUGHOUT THE SYSTEM

To bring about change from a system of services to a system of supports, reform must be undertaken at the federal, state, local, agency, and neighborhood levels. In Chapter 9, Gettings lays out some of the reforms in regulations and funding that must take place at the federal level in order to allow for more flexibility and to reverse the institutional bias of the 1970s and 1980s. Racino, in Chapter 10, provides an overview of change at the state level and reinforces the importance of change that builds on local control and capacity. In Chapter 11, Covert, MacIntosh, and Shumway, focusing on state-level change, describe the systematic planning, policy and community development that led to the ultimate closure of the Laconia State School and Training Center, leaving New Hampshire as the only state in the nation without a public institution for people with mental retardation. Nisbet, Jorgensen, and Powers, in Chapter 12, highlight the methods that will be necessary to bring about true inclusion in public schools and provide specific examples of successful reform. Blaney and Freud, in Chapter 13, also discuss changes that will be necessary in communities in order to ensure that children and adults with disabilities can participate in the same recreational activities that their peers without disabilities enjoy.

In addition to changes at the federal, state, and local levels, individual organizations that provide services to people with disabilities will also need to reexamine their mission in order to bring their practices into alignment with a supports orientation. Magis-Agosta, in Chapter 14, describes the process of transforming sheltered workshops into programs that support people in competitive employment, and, in Chapter 15, Dufresne and Laux expand on these themes in their discussion of changes they have helped to facilitate in residential as well as employment agencies. In Chapter 16, Kiracofe, likewise, describes the steps that he and his colleagues have undertaken to assist a number of different agencies in making the transformation to supporting rather than servicing and emphasizes the importance of showing people within an organization the ways in which the new approach can work for specific individuals. Finally, Knoll and Racino, in Chapter 17, provide a ground-breaking examination of the role of paid staff in the supports paradigm and speculate on the shape and content of training curricula and the possible location of this training regimen in an academic context.

SHIFTS IN POWER RELATIONSHIPS

The adoption of the supports paradigm portends a profound change in the relationships between service customers and those who provide the services. Because the emerging values place the preferences of people with disabilities at the center of any considerations about where these individuals live, work, or seek recreation, it is important to understand their perspectives and the ways in which their voices can be heard more forcefully. Gagne, in Chapter 18, a longtime advocate for people with disabilities, describes his own journey from being a resident of an institution to being an independent, self-made man. Bowen, in Chapter 19, describes the richness of the self-advocacy movement and the journey of self-discovery that a group of self-advocates in Connecticut have undertaken. Self-discovery and self-determination are important aspects of any system design, but attention should also be paid to the development of interdependence between people with disabilities and supportive members of their communities. One means of accomplishing the development of these relationships is through circles of support, a concept described by Ducharme, Beeman, DeMarasse, and Ludlum in Chapter 20.

Leadership among people with disabilities and their families will be an important ingredient in the support systems of the future. However, such leadership must be nurtured and developed at the grassroots level to ensure that new, more participatory approaches do not result in tokenism or pre-emption. In Chapter 21, Kendrick speaks powerfully about the importance of leadership development models that will guarantee a critical mass of consumers ready to take on decision-making roles in their own lives as well as in the system as a whole. Farber and Marcel, in Chapter 22, describe what can happen when parents and people with disabilities are exposed to leadership training, specifically, the development and passage of a comprehensive bill creating individual and family supports in Louisiana.

THE LEVERS OF CHANGE

There are many mechanisms and approaches that can be, and in some instances must be, used to support and accelerate change. One crucial mechanism has to do with collaboration. As noted earlier, the nature of the changes being contemplated in this book cannot be realized by mandates from centralized authority but must be worked out in participatory processes using all major constituencies, including people with disabilities and their families. In Chapter 23, Ashbaugh lays out a theoretical framework and rationale for collaboration and explains the importance of balancing participation in the process in order to ensure that people outside of the formal system have substantial representation. Kimmich, in Chapter 24, adds to Ashbaugh's discussion and provide specific examples of the strengths and weaknesses of collaboration in action.

Another critical system lever that must be employed to facilitate employing the supports paradigm is quality assurance. In Chapter 25, Kimmich and Bradley argue that a failure to reform current rule-bound quality assurance approaches will constrain the growth of individualized supports and perpetuate "institutionally-referenced" quality criteria. They posit that quality assurance needs to reflect the new paradigm as well as the needs and desires of the next generation of people with disabilities, who never will have been institutionalized. They also provide concrete examples of how such reforms have complemented system change. Chapter 26 is a related chapter in which Gardner argues that quality assurance must become "continuous quality improvement" and enhancement. He further suggests that any definition of quality lies in those outcomes that are valued by the customer and supported rather than dictated by professional staff.

In Chapter 27, Wesely, a state legislator from Nebraska, describes how the legislative process can be used to bring about broad-based reform. Carmody, in Chapter 28, shows how regulatory change provides an opportunity for innovation she uses taking advantage of the requirements of the Omnibus Budget Reconciliation Act of 1987 (PL 100–203) to move people with disabilities out of nursing homes and into individualized living arrangements with a range of supports. Smith, in Chapter 29, describes the various ways in which federal and state funding streams can be reshaped to support new paradigm system changes. Finally, in Chapter 30, Ashbaugh, Bradley, and Blaney discuss implications of the new paradigm for the future.

The chapters in this book provide a beginning blueprint for change. However, the material and concepts conveyed should be viewed as only the first wave of information from a very exciting movement, a movement in which there is still much more to be learned about how to change systems. Most important, the instruction must come from the real experts—people with developmental disabilities themselves.

REFERENCES

American Association on Mental Deficiency. (1983). *Classification in mental retardation*. Washington, DC: Author.

American Association on Mental Retardation. (1992). *Mental retardation: Definition, classification, and systems of supports*. Washington, DC: Author.

Bradley, V.J. (1981). Mental disabilities services: Maintenance of public accountability in a privately operated system. In J.J. Bevilacqua (Ed), *Changing government policies for the mentally disabled* (pp. 193–208). Cambridge, MA: Ballinger Publishing Company.

Dybwad, G. (1964). *Challenges in mental retardation*. New York: Columbia University Press.

Minnesota Governor's Planning Council on Developmental Disabilities. (1987). *A new way of thinking*. St. Paul, MN: State of Minnesota Planning Agency

Smull, M.W. (1989). *Crisis in the community*. Alexandria, VA: National Association of State Mental Retardation Program Directors.

References

[illegible]

2

Evolution of a New Service Paradigm

Valerie J. Bradley

It would seem that the one constant in the field of developmental disabilities is change, which has not come without conflict and contention. The purpose of this chapter is to provide a context that will counter the perception of this change as random and unpredictable or, worse, the reflection of a field veering from one fad to another. The conceptual framework drawn suggests that a thread of continuity runs through the events of the early 1990s in the field and connects the earlier notions of normalization to the contemporary aims of community membership. It will also explore the reasons why the changes on the horizon are more challenging to the status quo than the ideology and policy that have characterized previous decades.

Specifically, this chapter addresses the theoretical variations that have precipitated change from the 1960s to the 1990s, the long-range challenges that this change entails, how these challenges will redefine organizational values and culture, and the critical implementation issues that lie ahead.

BACKGROUND

Hallmarks of Change

From the early 1980s to the early 1990s, the movement to increase the integration and inclusion of people with disabilities has been hastened by strong federal policy, including PL 99-457, the Education of the Handicapped Act Amendments of 1986; PL 98-527, the 1987 changes in the Developmental Disabilities Assistance

---

Parts of this chapter were adapted from Bradley and Knoll (1990).

and Bill of Rights Act; revisions in the Rehabilitation Act; and PL 101-336, the Americans with Disabilities Act of 1990.

Against the backdrop of these national mandates, other events have taken place that have moved the field closer to the ideal of normalization. These include a decline in institutional populations from a peak of 194,659 in 1967 (Lakin et al., 1989) to only about 75,000 in 1992 (Gettings, 1992); significant changes in the orientation of nationally recognized accreditation standards (Accreditation Council on Services to People with Developmental Disabilities, 1992); identification and dissemination of information about emerging best practices around the country (Taylor, Bogdan, & Racino, 1991); and continuing refinements of the notion of integration by progressive thinkers and advocates (e.g., O'Brien & Lyle, 1984, 1985).

Evolution of the Normalization Principle

Change has also been spurred by a deepened understanding of the ideal of integration and its link to the overall concept of normalization first articulated in Scandinavia by such people as Bank-Mikkelsen (1969), Nirje (1969), and Grunewald (1969). These ideas were introduced in the United States by Gunnar Dybwad (1969) and Wolf Wolfensberger (1971, 1972). Wolfensberger, in his 1972 formulation of normalization, discusses two types of integration—physical and social:

> If integration is one of the major means for achieving and acknowledging acceptance, as well as for accomplishing adaptive behavior change, then we must distinguish between and elaborate upon its dimensions and components. First of all, let us define integration as being the opposite of segregation; and the process of integration as consisting of those practices and measures which maximize a person's (potential) participation in the mainstream of his culture. . . .
>
> Ultimately, integration is only meaningful if it is social integration; i.e., if it involves social interaction and acceptance, and not merely physical presence. However, social integration can only be attained if certain preconditions exist, among these being physical integration, although physical integration by itself will not guarantee social integration. (pp. 47–48)

Wolfensberger's warning that physical integration was not sufficient to guarantee social integration has been heeded by planners and policy-makers only since the late 1980s. Instead of moving to accomplish physical and social integration simultaneously, the field has focused first on physical integration and is only now learning Wolfensberger's lesson that integration is more than just the opposite of segregation. People can be desegregated and be as isolated and as out of the mainstream as they were in their segregated settings, even though they may be living, working, or attending school in the community. Being *in* the community is not necessarily being *a part of* the community.

As Bersani and Salon (1988) have noted, the process of integration can be thought of as a hierarchy along the lines suggested by Nirje (1980):

> We can understand integration as a process which begins with physical presence (physical integration), and progresses through interactions within a setting (functional

integration), to the establishment of relationships (social and personal integration), to the highest levels of participation as a citizen (societal and organizational integration). (Bersani & Salon, 1980, p. 7)

A Change in Paradigms

Central to the changes in the field of developmental disabilities has been a shift in the conceptual framework or paradigm that provides the rationale for practice. According to Kuhn (1962), such a shift occurs when the consensus regarding the paradigm of any field of endeavor breaks down and another emerges. This sort of conceptual deconstruction and reconstruction is happening in the field of developmental disabilities.

The initial metamorphosis began in the late 1960s and is frequently described as a shift from the medical model of care to the developmental model or from the custodial model to the rehabilitation model. This transition was the first inkling of what Kuhn has called a paradigm shift. Only now, in the 1990s, is it possible to view the full outlines of the shift as the dust raised by a quarter century of constant turmoil is beginning to settle.

This evolutionary process can be broken into three distinct stages. In the first stage, the era of institutionalization, dependence, and segregation (ending roughly in the mid-1970s), the governing norms were primarily medical and the objective was to separate people who were designated sick and vulnerable from the rest of society. This era ended with the advent of the developmental model and a growing body of research showing the inadequacies of institutional care. This ushered in the second stage, the era of deinstitutionalization and community development (beginning in the mid-1970s), which was marked by the creation of group homes and sheltered workshops that were physically integrated in the community but that emphasized the provision of specialized services in socially segregated settings. The third and emerging stage is the era of community membership, which is marked by an emphasis on functional supports to enhance inclusion and quality of life as defined by physical as well as social integration.

As shown in the ensuing discussion, the emergence of each of these phases is not the result of a series of random occurrences or the expression of fickle and impatient ideologues; rather, it is the rational progression of a complex theory. This progression was anticipated by Karl Grunewald, one of the architects of the Swedish mental retardation system, in a speech before the World Federation for Mental Health in 1971. He predicted that the full realization of normalization would come in four stages: 1) diagnostic, with a focus on the diagnosis and formulation of needs; 2) specialization, with a tendency toward centralization; 3) differentiation, with standardization becoming increasingly difficult and individualization being stressed; and 4) decentralization and integration. In using Grunewald's model to describe the development of services in the United States, it is fair to say that the state of the service system is somewhere at the third stage, differentiation, and that it aspires to the fourth stage, decentralization and integration.

Another way of viewing this progression is to break down the components into a continuum from idealism to formalism to realism. The period of idealism coincides with the burst of optimism attendant on the emergence of the developmental model and the promise of new teaching and behavioral technologies for the growth of people with developmental disabilities. Formalism equates with the growth of regulation and standardization foreshadowed by Grunewald in his stage two, of specialization. The period of realism coincides with the growing recognition that there is a discrepancy between the cost of current service models and the finite amount of money and resources available to respond to unmet demand. Grunewald saw this as the third stage in the progression and called it differentiation. Finally, it will be argued that the field is once again embarking on a period of idealism tempered by the reality of the need for continuing reassessment and the values of community membership. This emerging phase can be tied to Grunewald's fourth stage, decentralization and integration. In the next section, each phase is explored and the essential characteristics of the emerging perspective are highlighted.

INSTITUTIONAL REFORM AND THE BEGINNING OF THE ERA OF OPTIMISM

Until the 1980s, people with disabilities had to leave home and take up residence in a public institution in order to receive publicly financed long-term support. As a result, the institutional population in the United States peaked in 1967 at almost 200,000 and nursing home populations also soared (Lakin et al., 1993). The only alternatives to public institutions were private institutions and hospitals for families or individuals who had the private resources to support such care. As shown in the questions in Figure 2.1, services were organized around a facility, and the model of care was rooted in medical/custodial approaches.

By the late 1960s, the deterioration of institutions and the increasingly apparent limitations of the custodial approach precipitated a reappraisal of the efficacy

Who is the person of concern? *The patient*	How are services planned? *Through a plan of care*
What is the typical setting? *An institution*	Who controls the planning decision? *A professional (usually an M.D.)*
How are the services organized? *In facilities*	What is the planning context? *Standards of professional practice*
What is the model? *Custodial/medical*	What has the highest priority? *Basic needs*
What are the services? *Care*	What is the objective? *Control or cure*

Figure 2.1. Focal questions of the era of institutional services. (Adapted from Knoll, 1992.)

of institutionalization. One of the major forums for this exploration was the federal courts, as a parade of plaintiff representatives around the United States began to spell out the woeful shortcomings of institutional care in a number of key class action suits. Nearly identical accounts of abuse surfaced at Willowbrook in New York, Partlow and Bryce in Alabama, Northampton and Belchertown in Massachusetts, Beatrice State Hospital in Nebraska, Sandhaven in North Dakota, Pennhurst in Pennsylvania, Solomon State Hospital in Maryland, and Cloverbottom in Tennessee.

The end of the institutional era was signaled by the acceptance of a new set of theoretical assumptions collected under the rubric of the "developmental model." This model was based on the assumption that all people, regardless of the severity of their disabilities, could grow and develop. These notions were actively employed in the creation of complex teaching approaches designed to assist people with disabilities in acquiring skills. Curricula were developed and ordinary skills of daily living were broken down into their most minute parts in order to facilitate learning among people with intellectual limitations.

In addition to the emerging learning and therapeutic technologies, another major reason for the rejection of institutions as the primary service modality was the growth of behaviorism, which assumes that behavior occurs because it is reinforced; change the conditions, that is, eliminate or refocus the reinforcement, and the behavior changes. This basic insight and its implications radically transformed the lives of many people with severe disabilities because it provided human services practitioners with an alternative to mere custodial care. As experience was gained in using this approach, clinicians realized that with the right interventions they were able to manage or control almost any behavior.

Thus, the institutional era ended on a note of extraordinary optimism about the possibilities of people with disabilities given the promise of the new teaching and behavioral technologies. This optimism spawned a sense of idealism that made the normalization principle seem not only possible but inevitable.

DEINSTITUTIONALIZATION AND THE SEARCH FOR ACTIVE TREATMENT

The era of optimism resulted in a major investment in community alternatives to institutions, including community residential and day programs, individualized programming, and the consequent ascendancy of the professional in the field of disabilities (Bradley, 1978). As the utilization of public institutions declined, the numbers served in small community-based settings almost quadrupled, growing from 40,424 in 1977 to 161,962 in 1991 (Lakin, Blake, Prouty, Mangan, & Bruininks, 1993). These new programs were seen as avoiding the pitfalls of the old, isolated institutional model of service. However, in the process, persons with disabilities became objects to be trained, habilitated, socialized, screened, assessed, and assisted through a continuum of educational, vocational, and residential settings. Furthermore, standards were written at the state and local levels that, over time, sought to regulate virtually every aspect of the service enterprise. As this period unfolded, the diaphanous promise of the previous era was transformed into formalized rules and standardized practices.

The court cases that were filed in response to the deplorable conditions in institutions resulted in court-imposed standards to bring custodial facilities into line with minimal care standards. Often the court decrees included very specific guidelines articulating, for example, staffing ratios, daily schedules, professional qualifications, number of residents per toilet, and the nutritional content of meals (see e.g., *New York State Association for Retarded Children et al. v. Carey et al.*, 1975; *Wyatt v. Stickney*, 1972). While some standards responded to specific issues in a particular court case, most represented an effort to assure that the physical, social, and psychological deprivation in all these types of settings would be corrected (Lottman, 1990). (See Figure 2.2.)

In the next generation of cases, plaintiffs requested that alternatives to institutions be developed in the community. (See *Halderman v. Pennhurst*, 1979.) Court-ordered standards in these cases regulated the character of community residences and work programs and also addressed administrative issues such as planning, quality assurance, and appeals mechanisms. Though seen as a significant stimulus for reform at the time the decrees were drawn, as time wore on, the courts' regulatory presence froze some systems in earlier models of service delivery.

The emphasis during this period was to maximize the people's potential for growth and development through the application of specialized services in keeping with developmental and behavioral theories. Small intermediate care facilities for people with mental retardation (ICFs/MR), group homes, developmental maximization units, and other residential alternatives spread rapidly around the United States. Because they were smaller, they were heralded as home-like settings. The

Who is the person of concern?
The client

What is the typical setting?
A group home, workshop, special school, or classroom

How are the services organized?
In a continuum of options

What is the model?
Developmental/behavioral

What are the services?
Programs

How are services planned?
Through an individualized habilitation plan

Who controls the planning decision?
An interdisciplinary team

What is the planning context?
Team consensus

What has the highest priority?
Skill development, behavior management

What is the objective?
To change behavior

Figure 2.2. Focal questions of the era of deinstitutionalization. (Adapted from Knoll, 1992.)

belief was that they had to be better than institutions because they were scientifically designed, professionally staffed, and organized according to an individual habilitation plan. These notions became enshrined in the ICF/MR regulations promulgated in the late 1970s, which boiled down the scientific approach to one phrase, "active treatment."

The basic motivation for these programs was to provide a specialized treatment environment where problems could be worked on, therapies delivered, and skills developed. The underlying assumption was that once people had achieved a higher level of functioning they could move on to a less restrictive setting, typically to a group home or other community facility.

The result was elaborate teaching regimens and lock-step progressions through pre-articulated learning objectives. Skills were taught without regard to context in many instances, and progress through the continuum of living arrangements and day and work training programs became contingent on the acquisition of the appropriate abilities and the mastery of requisite tasks.

The behavior specialist became a surgeon of human behavior with the attitude, "Show me a maladaptive behavior and I can cut it out." This attitude was guided by good human motivations: to improve the quality of life available to people by eliminating those actions that tended to alienate them from other people. Unfortunately, this technique was also frequently used for the primary purpose of facilitating the management of groups of people in large facilities.

Typically, the behavioral clinician identified the behavior that interfered with a person living in a community setting and then developed a program to remove that behavior from his or her repertoire. The person went into the behavioral hospital or specialized setting to have these treatments applied. Afterward, he or she could move to a less specialized setting where the treatment could be prescriptively reapplied if the symptoms reappeared.

Unfortunately, as people like Lovett (1985) have shown, this was a basic misdirection of behaviorism because it ignored the total context of behavior and usually did not recognize or respond to the point of view of the "client." When the individual's view is overlooked, this reflection is given to the complex network of factors that influence behavior. The restrictive, unstimulating, and frequently dehumanizing situations that society has forced upon people diagnosed with severe disabilities are, therefore, not always credited as primary stimuli for challenging behavior. Thus, during this time of active treatment, the practice of behaviorism became an end in itself bound by rigid regimens and incapable of responding to root causes.

Like the behavioral model, the traditional developmental model also assumed that skills could be learned in isolation from the ultimate reality of community living. It also presumed that true integration is earned after multiple hurdles in a therapeutic sequence of treatment. As in the routinization of behaviorism, practices growing out of the developmental model came to focus on the means and neglected the outcome of the treatment.

RETRENCHMENT AND A REALISTIC REAPPRAISAL

By 1990, New Hampshire and the District of Columbia were without public institutions, 38 public facilities had been closed since 1984, and it was anticipated that another 43 institutions would close in the next 5-year period (Lakin et al., 1991). However, the growth in the number of people being served by the public sector has been increasing by an average of only .5% per year (Gettings, 1992) since 1967. Furthermore, it is becoming increasingly obvious that the highly specialized and increasingly expensive models of residential and days services developed during the 1970s and early 1980s cannot be supported in ever increasing numbers.

The figures above suggest that the rapid expansion of services in the 1970s and 1980s was aimed primarily at deinstitutionalization and the accommodation of people moving back into communities. In the meantime, the aspirations of thousands of people with developmental disabilities who have never been institutionalized have been put on hold in many states. In a 1987 publication by the Association for Retarded Citizens of the United States, the number of individuals with mental retardation on waiting lists for community services nationwide was 132,967. By 1991, the University of Minnesota estimated that this figure had grown to 196,000 (Lakin et al., 1993). Given the continuing revenue shortfalls in many states, it is reasonable to assume that this is now a conservative figure.

Gettings (1992) has estimated that to meet the residential demand alone, states would have to increase their residential budgets by a full 20%. In reflecting on the fiscal realities at the federal and state levels, Gettings makes the following observation:

> The resources are simply not available—and not likely to be available in the foreseeable future—to sustain the growth rate in spending which the field experienced during the past decade. Further expansions and improvements in services to people with developmental disabilities, therefore, will be largely dependent on the capacity of advocates, providers and state officials to join hands in charting a new course that emphasizes more efficient utilization of available human and fiscal resources. (p. 16)

Furthermore, an assessment of the outcomes of developmental disabilities services shows that there is still substantial distance between the vision of integration and inclusion and the reality of people's lives. For example, the preliminary results of the consumer survey mandated as part of the 1990 report requirements in the 1987 amendments to the Developmental Disabilities Assistance and Bill of Rights Act suggest that real integration and real relationships and participation are still limited to very few people (Jaskulski, Metzler, & Ames-Zierman, 1990). In the 37 state surveys analyzed to date, 60% of the people with developmental disabilities who responded said that they had loneliness in the recent past. This compares with only 15% of the general population.

In addition, though the number of opportunities for people with developmental disabilities to secure real jobs has certainly expanded, there are still thousands of people with mental retardation and other severe disabilities who are confined to make work day programs. The 37 state surveys analyzed indicated that the average amount of money earned by respondents was $45 per week, 38% of the respondents earned less than $10 per week.

There are also serious questions being raised about the continuing viability of community residential programs. Bradley and Allard (in Jacobsen, Burchard, & Carling, 1992) noted in their study of the stability of residential programs that many residential providers surveyed reported serious financial and staffing problems, and a substantial number of state directors of mental retardation services expressed concern about the financial fragility of the community service system. Additionally, in states like California and Massachusetts where community providers are experiencing severe financial problems and, in some instances, cutbacks, people with developmental disabilities have been returned to institutions.

Smull and Bellamy (1989) reiterated the fact that this gap exists between aspiration and reality in a monograph on the crisis facing the system of services to people with disabilities:

> The symptoms of the crisis are problems of scarcity and quality. There are insufficient funds, staff, and program alternatives. Demands and expectations have risen far faster than resources. The slack in the system that was used to cope with unanticipated problems is gone . . . most state institutions [have] plans to reduce their census . . . many community programs are unable to attract staff at current salaries and they have few vacancies and no plans to expand. Wait lists for services are growing rapidly, and the families of individuals who are waiting have little hope for assistance. (p. 3)

Thus, a demand for more responsive community services has been created, but the supply is woefully inadequate.

Another issue that has begun to nag at policy-makers and advocates alike is the lack of options that people with developmental disabilities and their families have to chose from. This lack of options is, in some respects, the negative consequence of the successful privatization of the service system. The rapid expansion of many agencies in the 1970s and 1980s has led to the creation of a large and sometimes monopolistic private sector industry in many states and localities.

Another consequence of the rapid growth of the disability industry is the loss of community connections. Agencies that began as indigenous local organizations are now covering large geographical areas, with management often located outside the community.

Finally, the oversight of services is ameliorated as regulations from each era of reform are heaped on top of the requirements of the previous period. This exponential expansion of regulations provides the political anthropologist with an extraordinary laboratory within which to view the assumptions and mistakes made since the 1970s. As Clarence Sundram observed at a meeting on quality assurance sponsored by the National Association of Mental Retardation Program Directors in 1992:

> After two decades of experience with the existing regulatory system, it is abundantly plain that we have spent far too much time encouraging people to look at the ferns on

> the forest floor and have missed the forest itself. This tendency to drown both the regulator and the regulated in a mountain of data and an avalanche of paper seems to have clouded our vision rather than enabling us to see clearly what is going on. I have seen too many IHPs with detailed task analyses, and reams of measurable observation data, cataloguing a several year long effort to teach someone to tie his shoelaces. Hasn't anyone thought about buying velcro sneakers and letting the person get on with his life? (p. 7)

This period of realistic reassessment has pointed out the ways in which the field has strayed from the original optimism and idealism that sprang to life more than 20 years earlier and the ways in which the field has failed to fully understand and internalize the overarching value of normalization. These judgments, however, provide an opportunity to return to a period of idealism tempered by a clearer understanding of limitations and the dangers of losing touch with the most important goal; to improve the quality of life and inclusion of people with developmental disabilities in their communities.

COMMUNITY MEMBERSHIP AND A RETURN TO FIRST PRINCIPLES

To realize a true paradigm shift, the reality check described above suggests that the slavish focus on professional services and specialized programs to the exclusion of supports that enhance social presence and relationships has to change. Surrounding people with professionals inadvertently isolates them from friends, family, and community. Teaching skills without asking whether the skills have any functional meaning perpetuates skills acquisition for its own sake rather than to aid increased community participation. Requiring people to move through a service continuum denies their ability to take control of their own lives. The key questions in the future should be: Are people with developmental disabilities really any better off as a result of intervention? Has society provided assistance in ways that support the way the person wants to live, work, and socialize?

Instead of thinking about how to surround people with services in specially designed and constructed homes, the movement should be toward moving support to where people live. Instead of concentrating on how to make the individual adapt to the environment, ways of adapting the environment and supports to the individual should be explored. The concept of functional supports offers an alternative to the continuum of services and the obsession with program slots. Rather than focusing on putting people into community programs, this developing focus emphasizes creating a network of formal and informal supports that a person with a disability needs to meet day-to-day demands (Ferguson & Olson, 1989; Taylor, 1988; Taylor, Racino, Knoll, & Lutfiyya, 1987). (See Figure 2.3.)

Another way of capturing the spirit of an instrumental or functional approach to services is to think of all interventions as being holistic. To apply holistic principles is to examine the roles people play in their environment, the match between individuals and the demands of the environment, and the complex interplay of

Who is the person of concern? *The citizen*	How are services planned? *Through a personal futures plan*
What is the typical setting? *A person's home, local business, the neighborhood school*	Who controls the planning decision? *The individual*
How are the services organized? *Through a unique array of supports tailored to the individual*	What is the planning context? *A circle of support*
What is the model? *Individual support*	What has the highest priority? *Self-determination and relationships*
What are the services? *Supports*	What is the objective? *To change the environment and attitudes*

Figure 2.3. Focal questions of the era of community membership. (Adapted from Knoll, 1992.)

forces that influence individual behavior and learning. Rather than seeing behavior as caused either by some internal drive or the mechanistic response to external stimuli, the initial formulators of what has become the holistic perspective took their lead from Kurt Lewin's classic statement that behavior is a function of the interaction between a person and the environment (B = f{PE}) (Lewin, 1935, p. 73). In the years immediately after World War II, a group of researchers used Lewin's earlier work and undertook a psychosocial examination of the lives of people with physical disabilities (Dembo, Leviton, & Wright, 1956). This work led to the conclusion that most of the limitations of people with disabilities are imposed by society rather than being intrinsic to an individual's functional deficit. Bronfenbrenner (1979) and his colleagues further developed this theory of behavior by highlighting the need to see individual behavior and the definition of that behavior as the product of a series of complex interactions. From this perspective, not all of the elements that contribute to a behavior are immediately present in the setting where it occurs.

William Rhodes (1967) was the first to describe the value of a holistic approach for practitioners in special education and related disciplines. Speaking specifically of students labeled emotionally disturbed, he pointed out that educators had come to see disturbance as something residing in the student. Hence, their interventions were exclusively geared toward remediating the flaw within the person. As a more practical educational alternative, he proposed a holistic approach that focused on the interactive nature of the problem behavior and saw disturbance as residing in the tension between the individual and the demands of the environment.

Many now believe that undesirable behavior has a meaning. In other words, even the most troublesome behavior may serve a function for the person even if its purpose is not initially understood. This suggests that to deal with problem behaviors a functional adaptive behavior must be found to fill the need served by the maladaptive behavior. Lovett (1985) and others contended that this type of orientation is more reflective of the promise of behaviorism. This holistic perspective on human behavior is also sometimes called an ecological approach.

A number of authors have explored the theoretical and programmatic implications of a holistic analysis of people with disabilities in United States society (Algozzine, 1977; Apter, 1982; Hobbs, 1975, 1980; Swap, 1974, 1978). Following Rhodes' lead, most of these authors have focused almost exclusively on the need to see challenging behavior as resulting "from a discrepancy between . . . skills and abilities and the demands or expectations of . . . [the] environment" (Apter, 1982, p. 2). Similarly, the ecological approach has been used as a model for the most innovative programs for individuals with severe disabilities (Bricker, 1985; Brown et al., 1980) and as a framework for viewing issues in community services for people with disabilities (Hitzing, 1987; Lovett, 1985; Smull, 1987). From this broader view of disability there are three possible areas for intervention: 1) changing the person, 2) changing the environment, or 3) changing social attitudes and expectations. Many efforts in the past have focused on changing the person. Currently, exploration focuses more on ways to change the environment and attitudes.

Finally, a major implication of a holistic approach is giving up the search for a magic answer to the problems of people with disabilities. Instead, the field must begin to think about problems in the system and increase understanding of the interaction between the individual and the environment (Apter, 1982).

Another characteristic of the era of community membership is an emphasis on liberating people with disabilities from the stigma of being clients and providing supports that are in line with typical expectations concerning freedom and control over one's own life (Biklen & Knoll, 1987; McKnight, 1987). The central idea here is to ensure people with disabilities a quality of life that is congruous with the way society in general views good quality of life. The concept of quality of life is so pervasive that even individuals who have reservations regarding the community integration movement recognize that considering quality of life in program evaluation is crucial (Landesman, 1986; Robinson, 1987).

People with disabilities as well as their families are increasingly making their feelings known about what they want in terms of a quality of life. As early as 1970, a group of people with developmental disabilities issued a statement of "beliefs, questions, and demands" that was drafted by adults with mental retardation at a conference sponsored by the Swedish Association for Retarded Children. The following demands are among those made at the national conference in Malmo, Sweden:

> We wish to have an apartment of our own and not be coddled by personnel.
>
> We want the right to move together with the other sex when we feel ready for it, and we also want the right to marry when we ourselves find the time is right.
>
> We want to have more personal freedom.
>
> We who live at home have found that it is largely good, but one ought to move out

when the time is right to a sheltered apartment or hostel; one cannot for his whole life be dependent on his parents.

We demand more training in a wider range of vocational fields so that we can have larger freedom of choice in determining our vocations.

We do not want to be used on our jobs by doing the worst and the most boring tasks we do at present.

We think that we should be present when our situation is discussed by doctors, teachers, welfare workers, floor men, etc. Now it feels as if they talk behind our backs. (cited in Wolfensberger, 1972, pp. 190–193)

It has taken more than 20 years, but the developments in services for people with disabilities have reached the point where professional providers and policy-makers can hear the testimony of Malmo and reassess services in terms of the instrumental contribution they make to the achievement of these basic human objectives.

The keystones of this emerging paradigm are commitment to community and families, human relationships, functional programming and individualization, and flexibility and individualized supports (Taylor et al., 1987).

Community and Families

A key element in the emerging paradigm of support is a commitment to the community as the place where people should live. From this perspective, the community is not some sort of nirvana, but a place where everyone has a right to live. The job of the practitioner in this framework is to help remove the barriers that keep the individual from participating in his or her chosen community.

Where this perspective has been adopted people no longer speak of community alternatives or community-based services because there is no alternative to the community. A second part of the commitment to community has to do with providing support to people with disabilities in their families. In addition to recognition that moving people out of their home communities to specialized facilities severs important ties with natural supports, there is also acknowledgment that removing people with disabilities from their families, especially when they are children, ignores the commitment of the family, disrupts family connections, and deprives the child of the experience of growing and developing in a family unit.

Human Relationships

Commitment to physical presence in the community must be accompanied by tangible social connections in the community. Being part of a community means that individuals have enduring relationships with people other than those paid to be with them. With real friendship come natural systems of support that are often able to forestall relatively minor problems or prevent them from becoming insurmountable difficulties. Most people have these natural supports, but people who have been in the service system for years frequently have lost them to professional intervention.

There is no question that finding a methodology for developing relationships is a challenge. It is not the kind of issue that has traditionally been addressed in professional preparation. Indeed, overinvolvement of professionals in the process of developing relationships might lead to the development of a routinized friendship therapy. The best practices in this area seem to be marked by sensitivity and intuition, and an understanding that any approach to developing community linkages must include idiosyncratic elements.

Functional Programming and Individualization

The demands of an agency or the nature of a program should not dictate the individualized goals for people with disabilities. A functional approach concentrates on developing the skills that are required by the demands of each individual's unique life situation. The interdependence of housemates or workmates and the demands of each individual's daily routine dictate the components of his or her functional program.

Functionality begins with the attempt to understand how an array of adaptations can be created to assist a person in gaining control over his or her everyday life. These adaptations may be mechanical, such as an augmentative communication device or specially tailored hearing implements, or involve a person like a personal care attendant. Functional programming does not obviate the need for learning but does assess the necessity of acquiring skills against the roles that these skills will play in enhancing community presence and integration.

With respect to controlling or modifying behavior, a truly functional approach is a positive alternative to behavioral interventions that attempt solely to control or eliminate behavior. Service providers and behavioral consultants should look to a person's life in an effort to understand his or her behavior. They attempt to identify new, adaptive, functional skills that satisfy the same need as a problem behavior, while also serving a real purpose in daily life. Admittedly, all behaviorists will say this is what they do. The difference lies in the fact that most traditional behaviorists take a very narrow focus when they identify the antecedents and consequences of a behavior. From a holistic perspective, the full context of an individual's life is considered.

Individualized planning is key to functional programming. Such planning, to be responsive, brings together all of the people whose cooperation is essential for assuring the future quality of life of the individual of concern. O'Brien (1987) offered a forum for this approach to planning which he calls "Personal Futures Planning." Some service providers who have implemented this approach have found that it is a particularly useful tool with an individual who poses many challenges to the service system. O'Brien describes five planning perspectives: 1) community presence, 2) choice, 3) competence, 4) respect, and 5) community participation. It is his thesis that most people use these five elements in defining the quality of their lives. Applying these principles results in a shared vision of the unique situation of a specific individual and a plan of action for moving toward improving that person's quality of life.

Flexible and Individualized Supports

With individualized and flexible supports, all natural environments can be open to people with disabilities, including persons with severe disabilities. These supports are critical to facilitating social integration. Documented best practices in the field have shown that individuals with developmental disabilities, when provided with supports, can be fellow classmates, good neighbors, contributing coworkers, and involved citizens.

Flexible supports, including individualized housing and work options, encourage persons with disabilities to exercise control and choice. Supported living means that people live where they want and with whom they want, for as long as they want, with the ongoing support needed to sustain that choice (Ferguson & Olson, 1989). Some exemplary supported living programs include: Options in Community Living, in Wisconsin; Centennial Developmental Services in Evans, Colorado; and the Supported Placements in Integrated Community Environments (SPICE) program in Illinois. Features shared by these programs include: 1) paid support provided by live-in or on-call staff, roommates or companions, attendants, or neighbors; 2) individualization and flexibility; 3) a focus on the individual; 4) a belief that people live in homes not facilities; and 5) consumer and family involvement in planning and quality assurance (Nisbet, Clark, & Covert, 1991).

Options, a private nonprofit agency in Madison, Wisconsin provides residential support services to 95 men and women who have developmental disabilities. In operation since 1981, Options provides support and coordinates services to enable adults to live on their own in small, dispersed settings in the community. The agency works with people to help them make their own choices and reach their own goals, with support available to them as often and as long as they need it. Options is the oldest of such programs in the United States and is considered to be the leader of this growing movement of residential support.

The state of Colorado has several supported living programs in operation successfully assisting adults with disabilities to live in residential settings of their choice. In Illinois, the SPICE program is actively moving people with disabilities out of nursing facilities into their own one- or two-person homes. SPICE was designed to demonstrate that people with multiple and severe disabilities can live outside of congregate settings if they are provided with appropriate services and supports and to demonstrate a more individualized approach to residential services. Funded through a Medicaid waiver, SPICE serves 40 people throughout the state and has targeted people with multiple and severe disabilities who have not traditionally been considered for community placements.

These pockets of excellence suggest that it is possible to support people in ways that more closely conform with the imperatives of normalization and that avoid the pitfalls of the deinstitutionalization period. How to spread this new or more fully realized paradigm nation-wide while minimizing the inevitable formalism of the previous period is the challenge of the foreseeable future.

IMPLICATIONS FOR THE FIELD

As noted in the introduction to this chapter, change has been a constant in the field of developmental disabilities for over 25 years. However, the values that underpin community membership are potentially more revolutionary than the values that spurred deinstitutionalization and that characterized major federal legislation and court decrees in the 1970s and 1980s. Those earlier values—maximization of individual potential, placement in the least restrictive environment, and individual rights—represented a significant departure from previous norms associated with the institutional period, but they placed the professional very much in charge of the direction and content of services and led to a dramatic expansion of the disability industry in the community. In fact, many of these values increased the preeminence of professionals since they reinforced the virtues of active treatment and enshrined the importance of specialized, and ultimately special, services in the individualized education program and the individual habilitation plan.

The values associated with community membership, when realized, will totally alter the power relationships between providers and people with developmental disabilities and their families. They will make the person the subject rather than the object of intervention and tie success to quality of life rather than the completion of a treatment regimen. In other words, they will undo professional hegemony forever which is why this particular period of transition is so threatening. These threatening values are listed below:

- Individualization
- Consumer choice and self-determination
- Community connections
- Integration and inclusion
- Emphasis on families
- Real lives in real homes

These values have grown out of the continuing reassessment and reevaluation that characterizes the disability field. However, bringing about the changes that these values inspire will require a reconfiguration and reshaping of the legal and regulatory superstructure that governs the provision of services as well as the development of new service delivery and administrative strategies. Unfortunately, given the vagaries of public policy, such reform usually lags behind metamorphoses in vision and aspiration. Bradley first noted this discrepancy in 1978:

> In a sense, the move to integrate developmentally disabled persons into programs and settings as nearly normal as possible is still in its adolescence. Attempts to improve

> services continue to show little evidence of the strategic precision needed to ensure that changes are successfully integrated into a mature, predictable, and ongoing system. Maturity will come only when actual practice and application catch up with—or at least substantially reflect—commonly held values. (p. 7)

This observation in many ways remains true a decade and a half later. The overriding values associated with normalization are still at war with the ways in which service systems are organized, staffed, designed, and funded.

Implications for Providers

Unlike previous phases of reform, the era of individualization and choice makes very different demands on organizations. A review of those provider characteristics that have traditionally been valued and rewarded suggests that the stereotypical organization may not be equipped to shift to a supports orientation. Some of these traditional characteristics are listed below:

- A compliant attitude and the ability to understand and follow regulations
- Fiscal accountability
- Skillful documentation of all relevant activities
- A strong management philosophy and a structure keyed to specialized functions
- The ability to expand rapidly
- The capability to replicate services in a uniform fashion

These virtues were reinforced by funders, administrators, and quality assurance officials during the deinstitutionalization period. However, such virtues are not necessarily the ones that will ensure that people with disabilities will become true members of communities. Taylor et al. (1991) wrote about the characteristics that are associated with organizations that have been successful at providing community supports. They are listed below:

- A philosophy and mission that permeates everything the organization does and is not just a veneer
- An openness to change and self-examination and an emphasis on learning from one another
- A nondogmatic and nondefensive attitude
- An assumption that the organization is one of a kind and its creativity and uniqueness cannot be franchised
- A participatory spirit that includes people with disabilities and families and that leads the organization to take advantage of the individual strengths of people who work there
- A committed and caring leadership
- A greater concern about what the organization does rather than how it looks on paper
- A broad definition of purpose and a desire to influence others

In many respects these two sets of characteristics are almost diametrically opposed and suggest a struggle that will carry into the twenty-first century as agencies and policy-makers rethink the configuration and meaning of the service enterprise.

Taylor et al. (1991) also highlighted some important characteristics displayed by the management of these support organizations. Some of these are listed below:

- Keeping the values alive
- Creating a spirit of self-evaluation
- Guarding against bureaucracy
- Empowering staff
- Facilitating collaboration
- Protecting flexibility

Again, these characteristics presage a qualitatively different approach to the administration of support agencies that reflects a less hierarchical management structure, more emphasis on front-line staff, and an openness to change and self-reflection.

Implications for Staff

Staff of support organizations must also have characteristics that are different from those that are taught in more traditional programs. Some of these qualities have been identified by the Family Empowerment Project at Cornell University for people engaged in generic family support (Cochran, 1990). These also are the competencies that will be required to support people with developmental disabilities in their homes, at work, and in their communities. They are listed below:

- Ability and commitment to identifying strengths in people and groups
- Genuine respect for diverse perspectives and life styles
- A capacity to listen and reflect
- An ability to subordinate one's own ego (to put one's self aside in the interest of the group)
- Skill and creativity in helping people become more aware and confident of their own abilities
- Appreciation of when to step back and the ability to help the individual or group assume decision-making and action
- Ability to analyze power relationships and help others to do so
- Knowledge about how to gain access to information
- Ability to reflect on and criticize ongoing processes, including one's own role in those processes (p. 25)

These characteristics capture the collaborative nature of the emerging supports paradigm and focus on facilitation rather than on assessment and prescription. Since the new supports organization will have to rely in part on individuals who are already part of the service system and whose training may be at odds with the new focus, retraining at all levels will be required. Furthermore, nontraditional staff who are familiar with the community's resources and opportunities can make major contributions to a supports organization.

Implications for the Service System

There are several other changes in policy, funding, and structure that will be necessary to nurture support organizations and move toward the supports paradigm. These are listed below:

- Retraining of case managers and other staff to introduce the new supports paradigm and its ramifications and implications
- Changes in quality assurance that move the monitoring function closer to the person, that rely on the value of services to the customer, and that focus on quality-of-life issues
- Increases in interagency collaboration at the local level to assure access to the full range of supports that will be needed
- Changes in role of the state government away from provider of direct service to keeper of the vision or mission, provider of technical assistance, and evaluator of outcomes
- Increases in local control over the shape and content of services
- Development of cross-disability constituencies
- Letting go of earlier models by eliminating the regulations that supported and reinforced them
- Development of flexible funding mechanisms that allow for individually-tailored services and innovation at the local and provider level
- Emphasis on collaborative planning and policy-making involving people with disabilities and their families as well as providers, administrators, and other professionals
- Increased tolerance for variations in the design and content of services from one local community to another

CONCLUSION

Clearly, it is not time to declare victory and leave the field. Accepting the importance of integration and the community presence, participation, choice, and respect that this entails are by no means unanimously endorsed or legitimized in practice. Some observers still fail to see the importance of integration as a means of reinforcing the common humanity shared with people who have disabilities and therefore continue to judge the quality of the lives of people with mental retardation and other severe disabilities using limited and crude criteria.

It is time to concede that an ideological paradigm shift must be accompanied by a reconceptualization of the way services are designed and developed. As Smull and Bellamy (1989) noted: "If we are to ensure quality in the existing system and provide a reasonable array of services to those people who are waiting, a more fundamental change in service design is required" (p. 5). This book attempts to describe the major steps that must be taken to bring about this fundamental change at different levels (e.g., state, local, regional, agency, individual) and through different instrumentalities (e.g., funding, quality assurance, program design, and personal futures planning).

The changes to come may cause significant dislocation in existing service structures and appear incoherent for those comfortable with the routinization of service provision. Far from incoherent, however, these shifts will move the reality of practice closer to the goal of normalization and closer to the dreams of people with disabilities and their families.

REFERENCES

Accreditation Council on Services to People with Developmental Disabilities. (1992). *Outcome based performance measures: Field review edition 1992*. Landover, MD: Author.

Algozzine, B. (1977). The emotionally disturbed child: Disturbed or disturbing? *Journal of Abnormal Child Psychology, 5*, 205–211.

Apter, S.J. (1982). *Troubled children, troubled systems*. New York: Pergamon.

Association for Retarded Citizens. (1987). *A national status report on waiting lists of people with mental retardation for community services*. Arlington, TX: Author.

Bank-Mikkelsen, N.E. (1969). A metropolitan area in Denmark, Copenhagen. In R. Kugel & W.W. Wolfensberger (Eds.), *Changing patterns in residential services for the mentally retarded* (pp. 227–254). Washington, DC: President's Committee on Mental Retardation.

Bersani, H.A., & Salon, R. (1988). *(Mis)understanding integration: A review and critique*. Syracuse, NY: Research and Training Center on Community Integration, Center on Human Policy, Syracuse University.

Biklen, D., & Knoll, J. (1987). The disabled minority. In S.J. Taylor, D. Biklen, & J. Knoll (Eds.), *Community integration for people with severe disabilities* (pp. 3–24). New York: Teacher's College Press.

Bradley, V.J. (1978). *Deinstitutionalization of developmentally disabled persons: A conceptual analysis and guide*. Baltimore: University Park Press.

Bradley, V.J., & Allard, M.A. (1992). The dynamics of change in residential services for people with developmental disabilities. In J.W. Jacobson, S.N. Burchard, & P.J. Carling (Eds.), *Community living for people with developmental and psychiatric disabilities* (pp. 284–302). Baltimore: Johns Hopkins University Press.

Bradley, V.J., & Knoll, J. (1990). *Shifting paradigms in services to people with developmental disabilities*. Unpublished manuscript, Administration on Developmental Disabilities, United States Department of Health and Human Services, Washington, DC.

Bricker, R.P. (1985). Curricula without recipes: A challenge to teachers and a promise to severely mentally retarded students. In D. Bricker & J. Filler (Eds.), *Severe mental retardation: From theory to practice* (pp. 208–229). Reston, VA: Division on Mental Retardation of the Council for Exceptional Children.

Bronfenbrenner, U. (1979). *The ecology of human development*. Cambridge, MA: Harvard University Press.

Brown, L., Falvey, M., Baumgart, D., Pumpian, I., Schroeder, J., & Gruenewald, L. (1980). *Strategies for teaching chronological age appropriate functional skills to adolescent and young adult severely handicapped students (Vol. 9), Part 1*. Madison: Madison Metropolitan School District.

Cochran, M. (1990). The transforming role. *Networking Bulletin, 1*(3), 25.

Dembo, T., Leviton, G.L., & Wright, B.A. (1956). Adjustment to misfortune—A problem of social psychological rehabilitation. *Artificial Limbs, 3,* 4–62.
Dybwad, G. (1969). Action implications: USA today. In R. Kugel & W.W. Wolfensberger (Eds.), *Changing patterns in residential services for the mentally retarded* (pp. 383–428). Washington, DC: President's Committee on Mental Retardation.
Ferguson, P.M., & Olson, D. (Eds.). (1989). *Supported community life: Connecting policy to practice in disability research.* Eugene: Specialized Training Program, Center on Human Development, University of Oregon.
Gettings, R.M. (1992, May). *Responding to a changing policymaking and programmatic environment.* Keynote address to the North Carolina Council of Community Mental Health, Developmental Disabilities and Substance Abuse Programs.
Grunewald, K. (1969). A rural county in Sweden: Malmohus County. In R. Kugel & W.W. Wolfensberger (Eds.), *Changing patterns in residential services for the mentally retarded* (pp. 255–287). Washington, DC: President's Committee on Mental Retardation.
Grunewald, K. (1971). Speech given at the World Federation for Mental Health, Dublin.
Halderman v. Pennhurst State School and Hospital, 446 F. Supp. 1295 (E.D. Pa. 1977).
Hitzing, W. (1987). Community living alternatives for persons with autism and related severe behavior problems. In D.J. Cohen & A.M. Donnellan (Eds.), *Handbook of autism and pervasive developmental disorders* (pp. 396–410). New York: John Wiley & Sons.
Hobbs, N. (1975). *The future of children: Categories, labels, and their consequences.* San Francisco: Jossey-Bass.
Hobbs, N. (1980). An ecologically oriented, service-based system for the classification of handicapped children. In S. Salzinger, J. Antrobus, & J. Glick (Eds.), *The ecosystem of the "sick" child* (pp. 271–290). New York: Academic Press.
Jaskulski, T., Metzler, C., & Ames-Zierman, S. (1990). *Forging a new era: The 1990 report on persons with developmental disabilities.* Washington, DC: National Association of Developmental Disabilities Councils.
Knoll, J. (1992). From community-based alternatives to inclusion communities. *Inclusive Communities, 1*(1), 9.
Kuhn, T. (1962). *The structure of scientific revolutions.* Chicago: University of Chicago Press.
Lakin, K.C., Blake, E.M., Prouty, R.W., Mangan, T., & Bruininks, R.H. (1993). *Residential services for persons with developmental disabilities: Statistics and trends through 1991.* Minneapolis: University of Minnesota, Center for Residential Services and Community Living, Institute on Community Living.
Lakin, K.C., Jaskulski, T.M., Hill, B.K., Bruininks, R.H., Menke, M., White, C.C., & Wright, E.A. (1989). *Medicaid services for persons with mental retardation and related conditions.* Minneapolis: University of Minnesota, Institute on Community Integration.
Landesman, S. (1986). Quality of life and personal life satisfaction: Definition and measurement issues. *Mental Retardation, 24,* 141–143.
Lewin, K. (1935). *A dynamic theory of personality.* New York: McGraw-Hill.
Lottman, M.S. (1990). Quality assurance and the courts. In V.J. Bradley & H.A. Bersani (Eds.), *Quality assurance for individuals with developmental disabilities: It's everybody's business* (pp. 149–169). Baltimore: Paul H. Brookes Publishing Co.
Lovett, H. (1985). *Cognitive counseling and persons with special needs: Adapting behavior to the social context.* New York: Praeger.
McKnight, J. (1987). Regenerating community. *Social Policy, Winter,* 54–58.
New York State Association for Retarded Children et al. v. Carey et al., 393 F. Supp. 715 (E.D. NY 1975).
Nirje, B. (1969). The normalization principle and its human management implications. In R. Kugel & W.W. Wolfensberger (Eds.), *Changing patterns in residential services for*

the mentally retarded (pp. 179–195). Washington, DC: President's Committee on Mental Retardation.

Nirje, B. (1980). The normalization principle. In R.J. Flynn & K.E. Nitsch (Eds.), *Normalization, social integration, and community services* (pp. 31–49). Baltimore: University Park Press.

Nisbet, J., Clark, M., & Covert, S. (1991). Living it up! An analysis of research on community living. In L.H. Meyer, C.A. Peck, & L. Brown (Eds.), *Critical issues in the lives of people with severe disabilities* (pp. 115–144). Baltimore: Paul H. Brookes Publishing Co.

O'Brien, J. (1987). A guide to life-style planning. In G.T. Bellamy & B. Wilcox. *A comprehensive guide to The Activities Catalog: An alternative curriculum for youth and adults with severe disabilities* (pp. 175–189). Baltimore: Paul H. Brookes Publishing Co.

O'Brien, J., & Lyle, C. (1984). *Mapping community presence and community participation.* Atlanta: Responsive Systems Associates.

O'Brien, J., & Lyle, C. (1985). *Community presence and participation.* Atlanta: Responsive Systems Associates.

Rhodes, W.C. (1967). The disturbing child: A problem of ecological management. *Exceptional Children, 33,* 449–455.

Robinson, N. (1987). Direction for person-environment research in mental retardation. In S. Landesman-Dwyer & P. Vietze (Eds.), *Living environments and mental retardation* (pp. 477–486). Washington, DC: American Association on Mental Deficiency.

Smull, M.W. (1987). Systems issues in meeting the mental health needs of persons with mental retardation. In J.A. Stark, F.J. Menolascino, M. Albarelli, & V. Gray (Eds.), *Mental retardation and mental health* (pp. 394–398). New York: Springer-Verlag.

Smull, M.W., & Bellamy, G.T. (1989). *Community services for adults with disabilities: Policy challenges in the emerging support paradigm.* Baltimore: University of Maryland.

Sundram, C.J. (1992, December). *Reinventing quality: The role of quality assurance.* Speech given at the National Association of State Mental Retardation Program Directors, Alexandria, VA.

Swap, S. (1974). Disturbing classroom behavior: A developmental and ecological view. *Exceptional Children, 41,* 162–171.

Swap, S. (1978). The ecological model of emotional disturbance in children: A status report and proposed synthesis. *Behavioral Disorders, 3*(3), 156–186.

Taylor, S.J. (1988). Caught in the continuum: A critical analysis of the principle of the least restrictive environment. *Journal of The Association for Persons with Severe Handicaps, 13,* 41–53.

Taylor, S.J., Bogdan, R., & Racino, J.A. (Eds.). (1991). *Life in the community: Case studies of organizations supporting people with disabilities.* Baltimore: Paul H. Brookes Publishing Co.

Taylor, S.J., Racino, J., Knoll, J., & Lutfiyya, Z. (1987). *The nonrestrictive environment: A resource manual on community integration for people with the most severe disabilities.* Syracuse: Community Integration Project, Center on Human Policy, Syracuse University.

Wolfensberger, W. (1971). Will there always be an institution? II: The impact of new service models. *Mental Retardation, 9*(6), 31–38.

Wolfensberger, W. (1972). *The principle of normalization in human services.* Toronto: National Institute on Mental Retardation.

Wyatt v. Stickney, 344 F. Supp. 387 (M.D. Ala. 1972).

3

Benchmarks of Change in the Field of Developmental Disabilities

Elizabeth Monroe Boggs

There is a tide in the affairs of men,
Which, taken at the flood, leads on to fortune.
(Shakespeare, Julius Caesar, IV, iii)

This Shakespearean aphorism was quoted by Leonard W. Mayo to President John Kennedy in the Rose Garden of the White House on the occasion of the inauguration of the President's Panel on Mental Retardation in October 1961.

EBB AND FLOW

The tidal image is understood today, as in Shakespeare's day, to invoke the common understanding that there are cycles in our lives. We are all familiar with the manifestations of cycles in the physical and biological world, with tides and seasons, the invasions of the gypsy moth, birth rates that fluctuate, and epidemics that run their course and return at a later date. We also anticipate experiencing cycles in our individual lives—some ripples, some waves, our personal circadian rhythms, our own life cycles of growth and decline.

Then, too, there are cycles of which we may be less aware. When on a ship at sea, one may experience rough weather, yet not sense the concurrent rise and fall of tides or the course of the jet stream. Waves having long periods are often experienced as moving in only one direction if one's period of observation is shorter than the wave's cycle. A creature who lives only 6 hours can die believing that the sun always shines. Similarly there are phases in the cycles in human history that are longer than the life experience of any individual and hence may not be perceived, let alone fully understood, by those who do not outlive them. The concept of the very long wave—one measured in centuries, a secular tsunami—has been popularized in American culture by futurist Alvin Toffler in his book, *The Third Wave* (1980).

Citing the transition from nomadic to agricultural civilizations as the first wave, and the gradual ascent of the industrial revolution as the second, Toffler envisions a third wave now coming that has the potential to reconcile and synergize certain characteristics of both antecedents, thus creating a new, even more uplifting confluence, one that indeed can "lead on to fortune." Similar images of possible new futures shaped by our new command of information are evoked by other modern renaissance authors, such as Bronowski (1973) in *The Ascent of Man*, Naisbitt (1982) in *Megatrends*, and Drucker (1989) in *The New Realities*.

The implications of these scenarios for societal institutions, especially for work and government, are mind boggling. In some respects, they are being felt already. Computers have improved the productivity of homemakers and students as well as car manufacturers and photographers. Attorneys who finished law school after 1985 do their work differently. In short, more is being accomplished by fewer people in many lines of work. This suggests that consideration must be given to " a gradual, planned redistribution of the shrinking amount of work required as automation displaces human labor." With this may come "alternative systems for production, distribution and exchange of goods or . . . alternative ethics or cultural values" (Cornes, 1987, p. 4) replacing the traditional work ethic.

Today's philosophers think globally with broad concepts of an evolving biophysical/social ecology, but most of the rest of us, while listening to them, are, nevertheless, constrained to act locally. Our localities are defined not so much by location on a map as by the intellectual and moral neighborhoods we choose to inhabit.

Social movements also vary in their intensity, from a gentle undulation that raises all boats to the destructive crashing of the Great Wave of Kamakura, Japan or the Civil War in the United States. For many centuries philosophers have recognized and praised the ideal of moderation, the Aristotelian mean, the ability to maintain a dynamic balance between the yin and the yang, to move in a way that directs energy in the most constructive manner, to accommodate diversity, to favor a dynamic peace rather than war. Those movements and cultures thrive best that build with vision but avoid the crushing crescendo. This was also Mayo's style.

In 1961 Mayo's choice of the metaphor of the tide taken at the flood was apt in the short run and also prophetic in ways that even he could not have appreciated fully at the time. Not only was Mayo launching the Kennedy era of the field of mental retardation, he was also, with all his contemporaries, standing on the brink of social upheavals that reversed trends prevalent during his life up to that time.

The first two thirds of his life coincided with the first two thirds of the twentieth century, an era that has been identified in retrospect by social historians as the Progressive Era. The Progressive movement is seen in part as a response to the social dislocation associated with industrialization in the nineteenth century; that dislocation was characterized by the rise of new underprivileged classes. The progressives were reformers seeking a benevolent social policy toward the needs of people they called those less fortunate. This outlook was carried forward at first by voluntary action and philanthropy, but later, in the face of the disaster of the Great Depression, its proponents began to rely more heavily on government, on the state, as parens patriae, a paradigm reinforced by the New Deal.

The durability of the Progressive movement suggests that it had its roots in something deeper than political necessity. On careful inspection it appears that this, like many other cyclic themes, has its basis in a centuries old, recurring, but never entirely resolved ethical dilemma: the tension between two partial goods, in this case, paternalism and autonomy. The Progressive movement leaned toward a benevolent paternalism, while avoiding an extremist position and maintaining a centrality for many decades (Rothman, 1978). The unrest of the late 1960s is now beginning to be viewed not only as a protest against an illegitimate war (Vietnam) but, more fundamentally, as one symptom of a profound change in the dominant presumptions of public morality that had shaped social policy as Mayo had known it up to that time. Benevolence toward others began to give way to a passionate attachment to individual autonomy and personal freedom. In respect to people with developmental disabilities, this transition was expressed succinctly in the theme of the 1972 Congress of the International League of Societies for People with Mental Handicap held in Montreal: "From Charity to Rights."

Another diadic tension that has been recognized by social historians is that between compassion and remediation, that is, alleviation of the immediate woes experienced by people who are suffering, and investing in the treatment of the underlying social or medical conditions (Pumphrey, 1980). This tension creates a dilemma, especially where resources must be rationed. A discussion of this ethical dilemma in an international disability context has been lead by Ruth Purtilo (1981). The history of people considered to have mental retardation over the twentieth century shows that several cycles have occurred in the shifting of emphasis between compassion and remediation as contenders for resources.

Within cycles, especially long ones or complex ones, the critical events, the turning points, may be difficult to identify at the time they occur. Often, it is only in retrospect that we can fully appreciate the shape and force of the ideological tide we may have been riding. This chapter attempts to cast light on the changing fortunes of people with mental retardation within the larger social contexts of the twentieth century. The chapter begins with a look at how the ways we experience change have themselves changed.

THE PACE OF CHANGE IN THE TWENTIETH CENTURY

The Effect of Technology

In his contribution to *The Year 2000 and Mental Retardation,* Harold A. Linstone (1980), director of the Futures Research Institute at Portland State University, discusses two concepts that apply directly to a contemporary consideration of social change. Linstone noted first, "It is not the case that our society is much more complex than ever before. This view must be regarded as a conceit that every generation has savored. Cultures have been complex for thousands of years." He went on to observe that what has changed is the pace: "the explosive growth of population and technology is overwhelming our ability to learn and to manage societal change" (pp. 125–126).

Nowhere is the effect of technology more dramatic in daily life than in the areas of knowledge generation and communication. Communication from person to person is an ancient human experience, yet even interpersonal communication modalities have been dramatically changed in our lifetimes by the personal computer and the fax. The potential impact of new means for propagating ideas and opinions, as well as information, to large numbers of people was well demonstrated by the 1992 independent presidential candidate, Ross Perot. And we are promised still more.

In the field of developmental disabilities, awareness of contemporary change has been enhanced dramatically by the new capabilities for computerized data management and analysis. In 1971, when President Richard Nixon announced as a national goal for the year 2000 the transfer to the community of at least one third of the population of public institutions for people with mental retardation, no one had the data to confirm that the decline in population had already begun in 1967. When Earl Butterfield (1976) described the contemporary scene for the 1976 edition of *Changing Patterns of Residential Services for the Mentally Retarded,* the latest data available to him were 5 years old. In 1993, by contrast, the Center for Residential Services and Community Living at the University of Minnesota was able to publish very detailed national and state data as of June 1991, together with some preliminary data for 1992 (Lakin, Blake, Prouty, Mangan, & Bruininks, 1993). Similarly, Braddock's group at the University of Illinois at Chicago has been able to deliver multifactorial, state specific, comparative fiscal data that enable advocacy groups and policy-makers to make real time course corrections (Braddock, Hemp, Fujiura, Bachelder, & Mitchell, 1990). Also, computers have revolutionized publishing, again shortening the gap between the creation of knowledge and its wide dissemination.

These techniques transmit complex messages in a fraction of the time that it used to take to convey the same information in spoken or written form. Yet our personal human capacity to assimilate the information, to comprehend its significance, has not necessarily improved. Furthermore, the capacity to tolerate change varies significantly from person to person, group to group, state to state, and even from country to country. Despite the extraordinary adaptability of humankind, we continue to evolve only very slowly, and even the most advanced of us are still limited in rate and scope of comprehension and hence in the rate of change that each of us can tolerate. For these reasons, precipitous change may have negative or even explosive consequences, as confirmed by the fall of communism in Europe in the 1990s.

As noted by Linstone and experienced by many of us, with the acceleration in the propagation of ideas as well as information, the dominant social cycles are becoming shorter. Now more paradigm shifts occur during a single lifetime, and there is more attitudinal space between successive, coexisting generations. Paradoxically, while new foci of consensus emerge more rapidly (e.g., the phenomenon of the rise of 1992 presidential candidate, Ross Perot), so also do they dissolve. Not only do the same people have different views at different times, but different people have different views at the same time; indeed the most fertile and creative periods are those in which different views are permitted to coexist and contend in the market place.

Periods of cacophony may not, however, be the periods of greatest productivity if productivity is measured by concurrent apparent and tangible social progress. Indeed, one of the many faces of cyclical change is the alternation of cacophony and consensus, two phases of the same cycle, reflected in the old saw, "Planning without action is futile; action without planning is fatal."

The Propagation of Ideas

It takes some measure of consensus (expressed in a common plan) to bring about constructive social action. A lack of consensus stimulates debate but inhibits accomplishments in the debated field.

Another way of looking at the reciprocity between the spread of ideas and the intensity of action is to note that ideas are propagated in much the same way as are communicable diseases; a person who has one comes into close contact with someone else who is susceptible. This analogy has several dimensions. One can note that just as international travel has accelerated the spread of infectious diseases from one part of the world to others, so the technical advances in communication have facilitated close personal intellectual contact, and hence have accelerated the proliferation of ideas. Some ideas spread in epidemic proportions in a relatively short time; these are the ones that may subside just as rapidly. Other ideas are adopted at lower prevalence rates. In either case, a substantial proportion of the population may remain unaffected.

In embracing an idea, one develops a certain temporary immunity to counter positions. This suspension of skepticism or receptiveness is necessary if people, as individuals or groups, are to move from cacophony to consensus, and hence to act with confidence and conviction. If we see ourselves as change agents, we have to believe that our goals are the right goals. We support our goals with what we believe are facts. Once accepted, we are reluctant to repudiate our assumptions, even though, when we dare to think about it, we recognize that there is always more to know. During the period of immunity to critical appraisal, we even manage to convince ourselves that for the first time in history we have grasped a truth that will endure.

One of the few contemporary observer participants in our current cacophony who is prepared to admit publicly that our current truth is not necessarily enduring is David B. Schwartz. In his book, *Crossing the River: Creating a Conceptual*

Revolution in Community and Disability (1992), he recognized, "The developmental disabilities field shows clearly that the process of conceptual change is a constant one. One reason for this is that ideas, even visionary ones, are inevitably subject to deterioration in actual social practice" (p. 100). Thus, after working at a change for a while, a few people, and then more and more people, begin to see that the reality they have been creating is, in fact, diverging from their visionary intent and expectation; skepticism returns, restoring once more their susceptibility to new ideas, and thus making the time ripe for another paradigm shift.

It is important to bear in mind that the recognition of a new paradigm does not necessarily mean the obliteration of all preexisting ones. There are varying degrees of compatibility among paradigms, and they may jockey for recognition, but, like multiple windows on a computer screen, several can remain in sight and on call even though only one may be in the forefront at a given moment. In current representation of the major trends in this field, these overlapping and even interacting influences must be included (Rowitz, 1992). Just as the tides are not high at the same moment around the globe, so time does not become ripe in every jurisdiction simultaneously, even on the same issue. This concept is illustrated by Braddock's data on the progress of communitization in each of the 50 states and the District of Columbia (Braddock et al., 1990), examples of which are shown in Figure 3.1. Figure 3.2 shows the same data aggregate for the nation as a whole. Comparing these two figures shows clearly that the national aggregate lacks the heuristic qualities of the more diverse display. A similar pattern could be constructed around the growth of the Medicaid funded Home and Community-Based waiver (Smith & Gettings, 1993).

Simply aggregated national data may also lead to oversimplistic hypotheses about the nature of change. For instance, what was assumed by many to have been a major exodus of adults from large institutions for people with mental retardation into group homes between 1977 and 1989 turned out, on fuller examination, to be attributable at least as much to a reduced rate of admission of children that started in the mid-1960s, as to people leaving institutions. The former has continued into the 1990s when residents under age 22 account for less than 9% of the total (Lakin et al., 1993). The lower rate of admissions of young people reflects in part the decline of the high post–World War II birthrate but appears also to include the tangible effect of the increased availability of special education services in day schools (Boggs, 1987; Lakin et al., 1993; White, Lakin, Bruininks, & Li, 1991).

Like the spread of an epidemic, arriving at a new paradigm by consensus is a complex process that may proceed fitfully and not predictably. It can be influenced as much by extraneous factors as by purposeful leadership. In any case, there is frequently a hiatus, a latency period, between the time that people come together around an idea and its actual realization, however imperfect. For example, in the United States, nearly a century intervened between the declaration that all men are created equal and the enactment of the 14th amendment guaranteeing equal protection under the law.

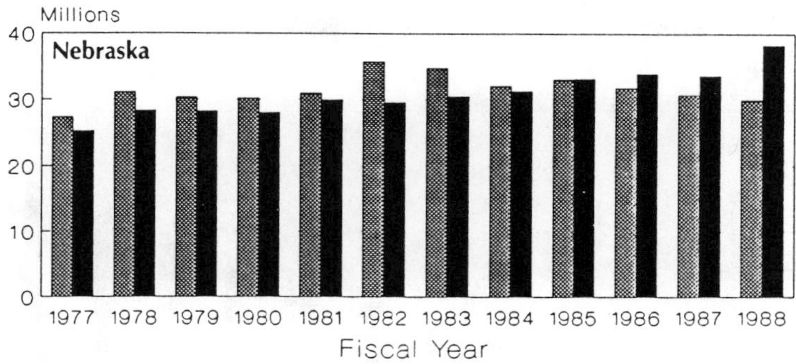

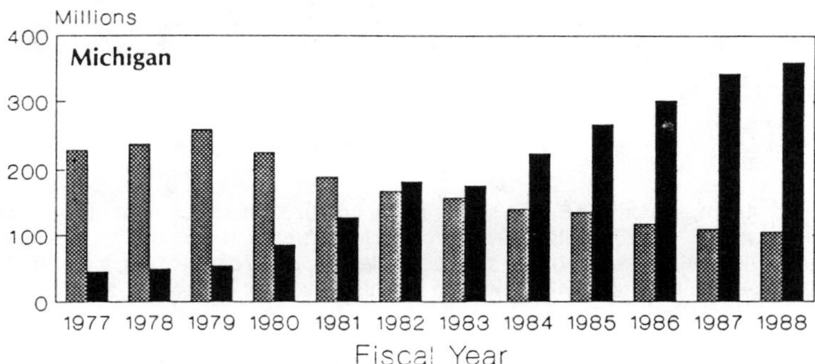

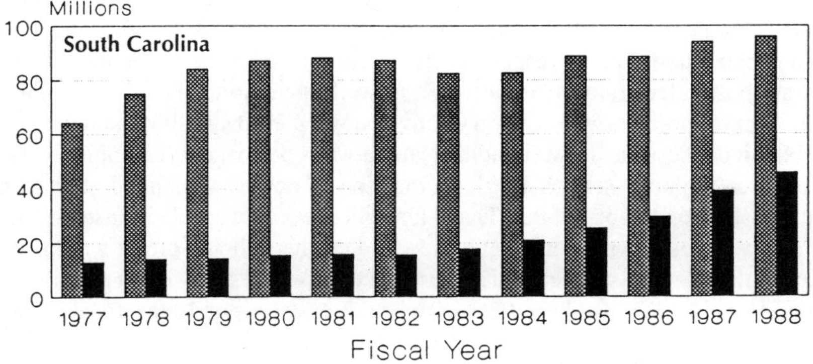

Figure 3.1. Adjusted mental retardation/developmental disabilities spending for congregate residential and community services in three states: Fiscal years (FY) 1977–1988. The vertical axis of each chart illustrates spending in millions of dollars; scales differ. (From Braddock, D., Hemp, R., Fujiura, G., Bachelder, L., & Mitchell, D. [1990]. *The state of the states in developmental disabilities*, pp. 285, 239, 405. Baltimore: Paul H. Brookes Publishing Co. Reprinted by permission.)

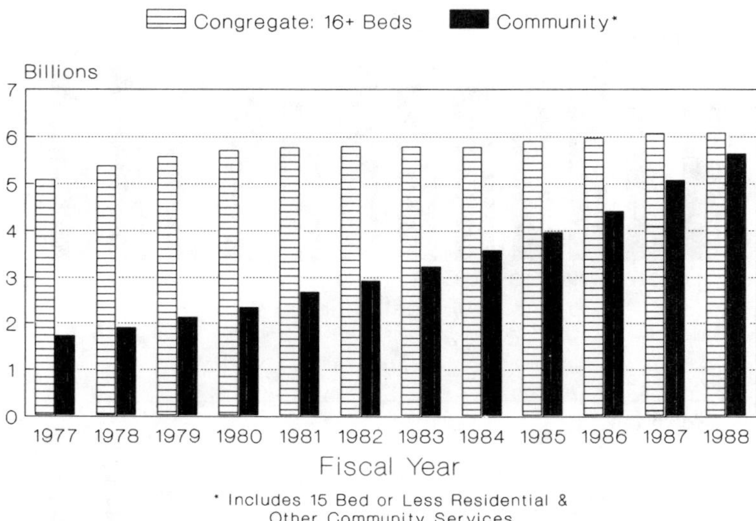

Figure 3.2. Aggregate United States spending for congregate and community services, adjusted for inflation, FY 1977–1988. (From Braddock, D., Hemp, R., Fujiura, G., Bachelder, L., & Mitchell, D. [1990]. *The state of the states in developmental disabilities*, p. 10. Baltimore: Paul H. Brookes Publishing Co. Reprinted by permission.)

The field of special education provides other examples. By the beginning of the twentieth century the constitutions of most states had clauses guaranteeing a free public education to all the children of the state at least between the ages of 6 and 14, and there were educators, such as J.E. Wallace Wallin (1955), who advocated public schools taking responsibility for children labeled "feebleminded" (including those referred to as "imbeciles") as well as children labeled "backward." Even Henry Goddard, who was very active between 1910 and 1930, and who saw "feeblemindedness" as most hereditary and always permanent, championed special classes in public schools (with no mention of exclusion), aimed at teaching practical skills and good habits. He and his colleague, Edward R. Johnstone, were advocates of positive reinforcement; they said teachers should create a climate in which children could succeed and achieve what we would today call a positive self image. He said, "We can show that praise increases energy and censure takes away energy" (Johnstone, 1918, p.25). As much as anyone today they saw productivity as a viable goal achievable by most, albeit usually with the support of social control along with segregation of selected adults sufficient to preclude procreation (Cobb, 1977; Gardner, 1993; Goddard, 1933; Johnstone, Goddard, & Nash, 1912; Wallin, 1955).

By 1930, professional consensus had advanced far enough to permit the 1930 White House Conference on Child Health and Protection to adopt the following goal as Point 13 of its Children's Charter: "For every child who is blind, deaf, or crippled or otherwise physically handicapped, and for the child who is mentally handicapped, appropriate measures to reduce his handicap, and training to become a useful member of society."

Thus, the goal of education for all was embraced publicly. In keeping with the ethos of the times, it was couched in benevolent terms. By 1978 it had become a matter of right, but not until the 1980s has the issue of "zero reject" been substantively addressed nationwide.

Benevolence toward adults was always harder to come by. It was in 1930 that Stanley P. Davies, a leader in the field of social work, wrote a book called *The Social Control of the Mentally Deficient*. The revised edition, published in 1959, was called *The Mentally Retarded in Society*.

PROGRESS DEFERRED: 1930–1945

The delay in implementing the consensus of 1930 was not exclusively due to the inertia of a long wave. The optimism of the 1920s about many things withered in the face of an all embracing catastrophe.

To understand the era of reconstruction (1945–1960) one must know that great damage was done to the social infrastructure during the extended period from 1930 to 1945 as the result of the Great Depression and World War II. The Depression badly eroded the tax bases for both state and local governments at a time when federal aid for direct health, education, and social services was not part of the fiscal pattern. The effect was particularly traumatic in the area of children's services because during the 1930s the United States had a particularly large cohort of school-age children. Several important earlier state and local programs for children and adults with mental retardation experienced retrenchment. Most dramatic was the destruction of much of the capacity for special education in the public schools that had been built up between 1912 and 1930, particularly in some of the northeastern and midwestern states and in California. Among the results of the economic disaster of the 1930s were, first, forced mainstreaming for many students identified as having mild mental retardation, but without the supports considered essential in the 1990s, and later, exclusion for almost all students with IQs below 50 who had been attending public day schools in many states during the 1920s. The exclusion of children from public schools increased the pressure for admission to the state training schools and hospitals.

The situation of both day and residential schools was further exacerbated by the shrinking job market. Whereas in the 1920s schools had been able to count on employment opportunities for their higher functioning special education graduates, the double digit unemployment rates of the 1930s closed many of these opportunities. Although most school systems still enrolled children labeled "educable," economic factors, along with lingering concerns about promiscuity, also brought many applications on behalf of adolescents identified as having mild mental retardation for admission or commitment to public institutions.

By the beginning of World War II, individuals labeled "morons" constituted half of the population of public residential institutions. In the absence of new construction, many existing facilities were forced to increase their census, thus producing untenable overcrowding, with a resultant deterioration of programming and demoralization of residents and personnel. Programs of research on the psychoeducational characteristics of children with mental retardation were largely abandoned. In all areas, recruitment and training of new professionals declined; a generation was largely lost. By the end of World War II few residents of these institutions had more than custodial care.

In addition to local schools, the community provisions for children with mental retardation in the 1920s included child guidance clinics in a number of states. At that time, these clinics focused on children with mental retardation and provided diagnosis of children and counseling for parents to enable them to care for their children at home. Later, those clinics that survived the Great Depression tended to shift their focus toward children with emotional disturbances, in response to conceptual changes in the new field of child psychiatry.

All this was feelingly deplored and vividly documented by George Stevenson (1947), the medical director of the National Committee on Mental Hygiene, in a ringing address at the convention of the American Association on Mental Deficiency. Considering the major adjustments needed to convert the war economy to peacetime and to cope with the unprecedented baby boom of the 1950s and 1960s, it is not surprising that reopening the special classes for children labeled "educable," reinstating children labeled trainable in the public schools, reviving the clinics, constructing new institutions, and generally reestablishing the status quo ante took more than 2 decades.

In his excellent book, *From Asylum to Welfare,* describing the development of mental retardation policy in Ontario, Canada, Harry Simmons (1982) noted that over a period of 150 years these policies had four major objectives:

> to provide asylum for mentally retarded people who could not physically survive in the community without government help; to educate mentally retarded people defined as being educable; to impose some kind of social control on mentally retarded people who were defined (or labeled) as delinquent or immoral, and to provide social welfare for mentally retarded people who would have been physically capable of surviving in the community but could not do so because of lack of employment, because they had personality or behavioral traits which led the community to reject them, or because of the absence of a social infrastructure appropriate to their needs. (p. xiii)

Any of these objectives may be pursued in or by way of special residential facilities or in the community. The original specialized institutions were definitely schools. Simmons goes on to point out that, for any of a variety of extraneous or intrinsic reasons, any one of these themes may be given special visibility at any given time and that all of them may be and often are pursued concurrently, partly because people we label as having mental retardation are so very heterogeneous. In the first 25 years of the twentieth century all the objectives mentioned by Simmons were being actively debated among the members of what is now the American Association on Mental Retardation, an example that illustrates the fallacy of assuming that only one paradigm can prevail at any one time.

As suggested above, the growth of the population of institutions in the United States after 1930 had been in no small measure the by-product of the displacements from the educational system. It was convenient for the public schools to redefine the problem as not educational for all students except those having the mildest mental retardation. Having been perceived in the nineteenth century largely as an educational problem for children and a welfare problem for adults, some time after the turn of the century mental retardation took on a dimension of social control, with stress placed on preventing delinquency and pregnancy. Several states constructed institutions for "feebleminded women of child bearing age."

Then, in the course of the second quarter of the twentieth century, in some but not all states, mental retardation took on the role of being an intractable, long-term "mental health problem" of secondary importance, formalized by an administrative placement in the emerging state departments of mental hygiene. It was in this context that some of the institutions took on the appellation of "hospital." During the organizational paradigm shift from "state school" to "hospital," and the corresponding transition from "training" to "treatment," an appreciable diminution of intensity appears to have occurred. How much of this should be attributed to the pessimism with which mental retardation was viewed within the hierarchy of mental disorders, and how much was due to the economic constraints of the 1930s is hard to say. Although many states had laws requiring institutional superintendents to be psychiatrists, those positions were not sought after by the more progressive members of that discipline. In the immediate post–World War II period, the institutions themselves were classed by the United States Public Health Service as "custodial," and, as such, generally not entitled to any federal aid that became available to "medical" facilities during the early days of post-war reconstruction.

THE SECOND HALF OF THE TWENTIETH CENTURY

Redefinition of Terms

How people perceive and define the terms they use tends to establish both the nature and scope of the agenda at any given time. Even within the field of mental retardation the scope of the agenda, as reflected in the numbers and characteristics of people included in it, has expanded and contracted over time. Interestingly enough, there have been parallels to this phenomenon in other fields, another example of the vesting of mental retardation within a larger social order.

Of particular importance historically has been the issue of how inclusive the classification of mental retardation (by whatever name) should be. The ambivalence on this subject goes back to the nineteenth century (Doll, 1962). Where is the line between normalcy and exceptionality, whether in relation to schooling, work, recreation, or state of health? Quantification became important in the early part of the twentieth century with the advent of the Binet test (Kite, 1915). With it Goddard "invented the moron" and began to estimate the prevalence of "feeblemindedness" among school children at 2% (Goddard, 1911). In discovering what we later came to call "mild mental retardation," Goddard confronted the problem of making the distinctions between "feeblemindedness," "backwardness," and "normality."

The phenomenon is not unique to mental retardation. In the field of aging where does normal aging give way to frailty, which in turn may give way to impairment or disability? Just as the age of 65 is an arbitrary, statistically useful but individually unreliable demarcation, so is an IQ score a point on a continuum that needs to be interpreted in the light of other factors. Among those whose intellectual functioning deviates conspicuously from the norm in some or many respects, the question also arises as to which atypical individuals represent the lower end of a "normal" distribution and which are qualitatively or clinically exceptional outside this continuum.

In an article entitled, *Comparison of Systems of Classifications Relating Degree of Mental Retardation to Measured Intelligence,* Gelof (1963) tabulated some 23 definitional documents written in English-speaking countries as far back as 1921, describing or defining and classifying mental retardation using IQ as an indicator, with or without other dimensions. Almost all were consistent in delineating IQs of 50 and 25 as the demarcation points for the two most limited categories (formerly "imbecile" and "idiot") but showed considerable variation between systems in specifying the upper limit in IQ, which ranged from 70 to 85.

Edgar A. Doll (1951), one of the most respected psychologists of his day, advocated a flexible 70 as the upper limit. However, the 1959/1961 revision of the American Association on Mental Deficiency's (AAMD) *Manual on Terminology and Classification* (Heber, 1959, 1961) for the first time went to the top of the range, which included individuals with IQs up to 85, some 16% of the population. This estimate is reduced by an indeterminate amount when those without significant impairment in "adaptive behavior" are removed from the count.

One of several effects of this change in the upper limit was to increase very substantially the number of individuals who could be labeled as having mental retardation if tested, but who had heretofore been able to pass as indistinguishable from other "underprivileged" people. Since most of these individuals were seen as "familial" (a term used ambiguously to refer to individuals whose parents also functioned marginally, rather than showing identifiable exogenous syndromes), this redefinition served to further shift the center of gravity of the targeted group away from those with a clinical identity and multiple impairments toward those showing "normal" variations.

Grave reservations were expressed from the field, not only by conservatives, but by the upcoming leaders such as Burton Blatt (1961), who was concerned about labeling, among other things. The AAMD expansion was rescinded in the 1973 edition of the classification manual, a fact duly noted by the Rehabilitation Services Administration. Concurrently, the World Health Organization's *International Classification of Diseases* (ICD), 8th Revision, dated 1968, included "borderline mental retardation," IQ 68–85, but this was eliminated in ICD-9 (1975) and ICD-10 (1992).

It is well known that, empirically, the numbers of people who score more than three standard deviations below the norm (below 50–55) far exceed the number predicted from the Gaussian curve. Dingman and Tarjan (1960) gave a visual representation to this idea in an attempt to quantify it, estimating an "excess" of nearly 300,000 people, mostly under age 30, for a total of 500,000 as compared to less than 200,000 predicted from the "normal" distribution curve. In contrast, all but 1% of those with scores between 50 and 70 can be accounted for in the Dingman-Tarjan paradigm as part of "normal" human variation. (See Kanner, 1949; Penrose, 1949; Zigler, 1967.) The excess or clinical group represented about 0.3% of the population in 1960, or 0.5% of the population under 35.

Concurrently, but independently, a broader, longer, and more profound but comparable tide was sweeping through the field of psychiatry in the United States. The international movement for "community mental health" was built around a psychosocial model that began to take hold in the United States soon after the end of World War II. It was the informing principle of the American Psychiatric Association's first *Diagnostic and Statistical Manual,* published in 1951. It was also the foundation for the community mental health center construction legislation that (although separately conceived) shared the congressional stage with the Kennedy mental retardation construction bills of 1963. According to Mitchell Wilson (1993), the psychosocial model in mental health, developed in the aftermath of World War II and favored by the leadership of the National Institute of Mental Health, moved away from recognition of any distinct syndromes toward a continuum "from neurosis to borderline conditions to psychosis," where "the boundary between the mentally well and the mentally ill is fluid," and also much encompassing (pp. 400–401). A new professional consensus developed around the revision of the American Psychiatric Association's DSM-III (*Diagnostic and Statistical Manual of Mental Disorders*), published in 1980. According to Wilson, DSM-III (to be succeeded by DSM-IV in 1994) has "remedicalized" psychiatry. Wilson summarizes by saying, "that while DSM-III, and the return to descriptive psychiatry it inaugurated, has had positive consequences for the profession, at the same time it represents a significant narrowing of psychiatry's clinical gaze."

In addition to the earlier example (in the section, The Propagation of Ideas) of how concealing the variable of people's age in a national aggregate of data can obscure important variations among children and adults, and among different states, there are many misleading summaries of institutional population trends. Looking into these details sheds light on, for example, the transitions that have taken place in the perception of mental retardation as "a mental health problem." Lakin and his colleagues at the University of Minnesota have presented annual reminders that in the 1950s and early 1960s many people with a primary or dual diagnosis of mental retardation were to be found in state psychiatric institutions and that, for a variety of reasons, the total has declined spectacularly and is only nominal at present (Boggs, 1987; Lakin et al., 1993). Still more revealing are the variations by age and state in the use of psychiatric facilities that can be found in the early records of the Biometrics Branch of the National Institute of Mental Health (United States Public Health Service, 1954). In the post–World War II period until Kennedy's time, mental retardation was, in many states, organizationally assigned to the mental health agency, whether that was a free standing department or part of a more inclusive health and social welfare umbrella agency. It was also viewed by many (e.g., social workers, educators, physicians, and the public) as primarily a problem of childhood. During that time more than 80% of individuals admitted to state institutions for people with mental retardation were under 20 years old.

Granted that mental retardation is by definition a problem that originates in childhood and that apparent prevalence declines after the school years, the extent of need among adults, although less than now, has never been negligible. Yet it was obscured in the post–World War II era by the practice of focusing on statistics about people in "institutions for the mentally defective and epileptic." These statistics omitted attention to the practice in some states of diverting adults with mental retardation who applied for residential care into state mental hospitals. Overall, more than half of those admitted to public residential care in the 1950s who were between the ages of 25 and 34, and two thirds of those admitted at age 35 or over were placed in mental hospitals (National Institute of Mental Health, 1969, Table 17). In 1950, of the number of residents with mental retardation ages 35 or over, in the population of public mental institutions, 40% were living in mental hospitals (National Institute of Mental Health, 1969, Tables 14a and 16a). The practice varied widely by state, however. The families of these older adults were not well represented in the early "parent movement" of the 1950s and their caregivers were not highly visible in the American Association on Mental Retardation.

Since 1970, people with mental retardation and other developmental disabilities, primarily adults, have been placed in the penumbra of nursing homes with the same kind of ambiguity experienced by adults with mental retardation placed in mental hospitals before 1970 (Lakin, Hill, & Anderson, 1991). Coincidentally the numbers are comparable, around 43,000 in mental hospitals in 1960 and 38,000 in nursing homes in 1991. Here, too, the national aggregate conceals great variation among states as illustrated by Lakin et al. (1993) (Table 3.10, p. 103).

The total nursing home population under 65 in 1993 is small compared to that over 65 (about 200,000 as compared to 2.5 million) and includes young adults who have disabilities acquired after age 22 as well as those with developmental disabilities whose mental retardation or cerebral palsy polio paralysis originated in childhood (Lair, 1992). The concerns of all adults with disabilities are increasingly becoming merged with those of old people with developmental disabilities as part of the complex of long-term health care issues being swept into the health care agenda of President Bill Clinton in 1993.

The Era of Reconstruction: 1946–1960

In the post–World War II years, renewal in the mental retardation field was abetted, even driven, by the impetus of the new and growing parent movement, evidenced by the founding at midcentury of the National Association of Parents and

Friends of Mentally Retarded Children, later the National Association for Retarded Children, and now The Arc, and of the United Cerebral Palsy Associations (UCPA). In one sense, these organizations were part of the post-war revival of the voluntary associations that have played such a prominent role in American life, and which, although they can survive war and depression, cannot flourish when gasoline is unavailable and personal time preempted. In another sense, they were the advance troops of a new consumer movement. Through organizations parents were able to regain some of the sense of control over their own and their children's lives that had been shattered for each of them by the news that there would be no medical miracles.

In the early years of the parent movement much progress was made against the early twentieth century public stereotype of "mental deficiency" as synonymous with delinquency and degeneracy, and a source of shame to parents. The notion that most mental retardation is inherited began to fade (Kanner, 1949; Reed & Reed, 1965) in favor of various kinds of social deprivation as a major cause of the milder forms of intellectual limitation, with external "insults" (e.g., prenatal or postnatal injury, disease, toxic exposure, or radiation) contributing over the full range of impairment but with less frequency. These revised images were not inconsistent with a certain compensating level of hope, based on pre-war models, hope which saw some redemption in special education, including preparation for unskilled work, and protection from harm, particularly from sexual exploitation.

To alleviate the stigma that had been experienced by parents and children alike, advocates promoted some fresh terminology. "Mental deficiency" became "mental retardation," "imbecile" and "idiot" became "moderate, severe, and profound retardation," "moron" became "mild" (or in school contexts "educable"), and "trainable" was used in school contexts for children who could tend to personal needs and understand simple commands but were not expected to progress in reading or arithmetic. The perceived need for such changes is recurrent, like the moves at the Mad Tea Party. Mental retardation is not a desired or desirable state or status, no matter what the terminology or the attitudes of society.

The primary thrusts in the early 1950s were to open the public schools to excluded children, to create humane conditions in the residential institutions, and to develop additional residential capacity to accommodate those children and adults found in soaring numbers on waiting lists. Many of the promoters of these changes had little knowledge of earlier developments and did not think of what was happening as reconstruction; rather they saw it as pioneering. In any case, for all three of these objectives the executive and legislative branches of state government were the primary targets. The National Association for Retarded Children (now The Arc) summarized the remarkable advances in a report to the 1960 White House Conference on Children and Youth (Boggs, 1959). They included state legislation to extend special education in almost every state; the construction, completed or underway, of 28 new institutions; the establishment of 70 special outpatient clinics; more than 100 sheltered workshops; and many summer camps.

Important groundwork for the future was laid in the 1950s when the Social Security Act was amended to provide for a federal role in income maintenance for people with mental and physical disabilities. Federal appropriations in selected areas, including research, were significantly enlarged (Boggs, 1971). The creation in 1953 of a new United States Department of Health, Education, and Welfare was of long term significance.

The National Association for Retarded Children (1958) began circulating a diagram entitled, "A Well Rounded Program." It depicted the individual with mental retardation at the center of concentric circles of support from families and neighbors and a variety of generic and specialized agencies. (See Figure 3.3.)

The Era of Habilitation: 1960–1985

The Kennedy Initiatives The transition from the reconstruction era to the next wave of innovation in the field of mental retardation coincided with the decline of the Progressive Era. It was marked by the unique excitement and constructive cacophony created by the President's Panel on Mental Retardation. The panel, set up by President Kennedy in 1961, reported in 1962 cogent recommendations on broad-based issues of health, education, employment, residential services, civil and criminal justice, prevention, coordination of services, information and referral, case management, research, training, and public information, thus setting an image of extensive private relevance and pervasive public responsibilities for many agencies, even including the armed forces. This was truly a comprehensive program predicated on the capacity of each individual to improve his or her level of functioning with intensive training and treatment.

The various federal legislative proposals that were eventually combined and passed as two bills were heavy on infrastructure and light on direct services to people with mental retardation and their families. The latter was left to the states, as it had been throughout the past except for what was affected by the direct income maintenance provisions that had been added to the Social Security Act in the 1950s.

Among the many short-term and long-term consequences, the following four are noted here:

- Federal funding was authorized for construction of university-based research centers and university affiliated clinical programs to provide students with hands-on experience with children with mental retardation. These programs later became broadly multidisciplinary and extended their activities to people of all ages and their families.
- Separation of mental retardation from mental health in both state and federal government structures was begun. A distinctive identity for mental retardation smoothed the entrance of children and adults with this now more respectable condition into the mainstream of political planning, if not yet into the "regular" life of the the community.

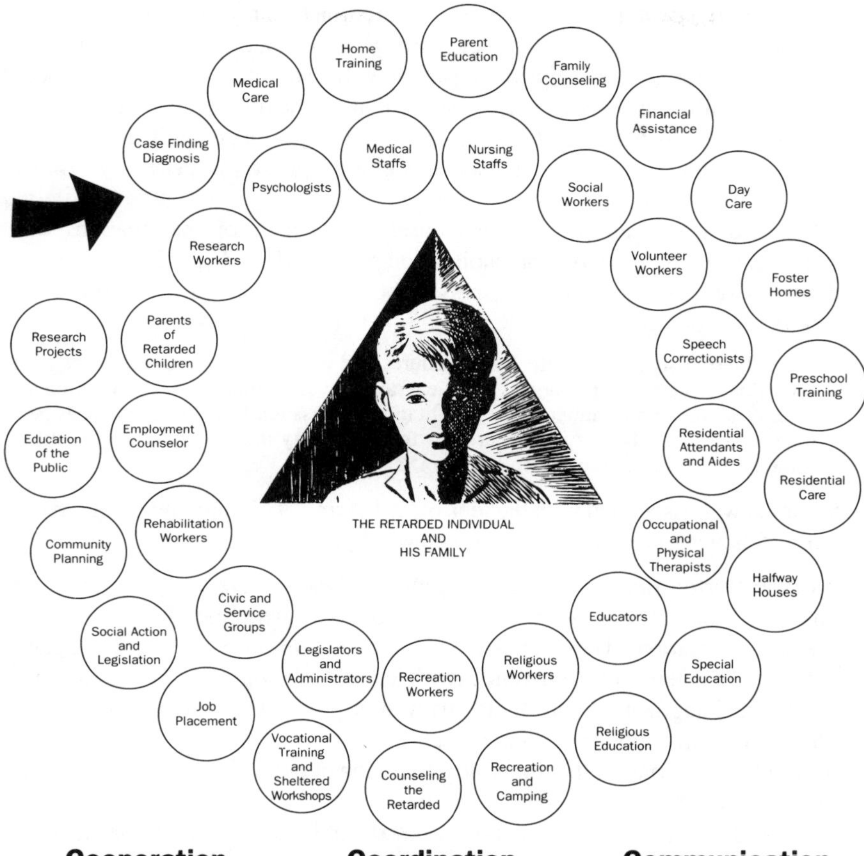

Figure 3.3. A Well Rounded Program for the Retarded—circulated by the National Association for Retarded Children, Inc., New York, 1958.

- Incentives were given to state governments to undertake "comprehensive mental retardation planning" across all relevant departments of state government and their private sectors.
- The Division of Handicapped Children and Youth was elevated conspicuously in the federal bureaucracy.

The professional and consumer communities were amply ready for all legislated programs and many other recommendations. One of five task forces was, however, ahead of its time. Little fanfare greeted a project on Mental Retardation and the Law, established at George Washington University. Its primary purpose was to increase the interest and expertise of young lawyers in fields of law relating to mental retardation, a field that came into its own in the early 1970s.

The Great Society: 1965–1970 In addition to carrying forward much of the Kennedy agenda, President Johnson, through his Great Society programs, laid the groundwork for greater inclusion of people with disabilities generally, and people with mental disabilities in particular, in generic health, education, employment, and human services systems. This set the stage for a significant 10-year escalation of federal support for "social welfare" programs generally (Bixby 1992).

In the area of disabilities of early onset, the concept of "habilitation" was born and legitimized in individual habilitation plans (IHPs). According to the Accreditation Council (1989), which stressed the concept from its inception in the late 1960s, habilitation is:

> a broad term used . . . to refer to procedures and interventions designed to help an individual achieve greater mental, physical, and social development. Habilitation includes training and treatment. The habilitation process teaches skills, enhances personal functional efficiency and increases the possibility that the individual will become progressively more self reliant. (p. 58)

Habilitation was associated with the idea of "achieving one's maximum potential."

The following specific events are noteworthy:

- In 1966 Burton Blatt and his photographer colleague, Fred Kaplan, made an unofficial tour of a number of public residential institutions for people with mental retardation. Their report, *Christmas in Purgatory* (Blatt & Kaplan, 1967) was extensively illustrated with candid photographs taken surreptitiously and augmented with Blatt's irreverent prose. Their urgent message of the need for institutional reform spread.
- In 1967, unobserved at the time, the population of public institutions for people with mental retardation began to decline.
- In 1969 the first edition of *Changing Patterns of Residential Care for the Mentally Retarded* (Kugel & Wolfensberger, 1969) was published; 20,000 copies were distributed worldwide. Among other stimuli this work introduced the Scandinavian concept of "normalization" to the American scene. It was further adapted into the American idiom by Wolfensberger (1972).
- In 1976 Burton Blatt and colleagues revisited the facilities described in *Christmas in Purgatory.* The sequel, *The Family Papers,* appeared in 1979. It documented considerable improvement in conditions within the traditional institutions but left Blatt with a conviction that repudiation rather than reform was called for, an opinion he shared with many receptive professional peers from his podium as president of the American Association on Mental Retardation.

The era of comprehensive planning, individualized habilitation, and process standards persists in somewhat attenuated form even as the twenty-first century approaches, but it has been overtaken and overshadowed first by the era of rights and next by the era of independence, integration, and productivity, which is now being replaced by choice and supports.

The Era of Rights, Litigation, and Advocacy: 1970–1985

Between 1969 and 1975 the rhetoric changed. Advocates for people with mental retardation and related disabilities began to use new strategies of litigation, in addition to, or in place of, prior strategies of legislation, executive action, and public information.

The early institutional court cases focused on the right of a confined individual to treatment or habilitation and to protection from harm, following the institutional reform paradigm. "Consensus" input standards were developed for both institutional and community programs. They were used by judges in early court cases and by bureaucrats to monitor the implementation of the so-called ICF/MR legislation passed in 1971. Under this legislation Congress extended the coverage of Medicaid to include, at state option, care (of an otherwise eligible person) in a specialized public "intermediate care facility for persons with mental retardation and related disorders," provided that certain population-specific federal standards were met, among them delivery of "active treatment" and protection of residents' rights (Boggs, Lakin, & Clauser, 1985). The law corrected a de facto form of discrimination against people with mental retardation arising from denial of Medicaid to otherwise eligible residents of public institutions.

Although the intent of the original ICF/MR legislation had been to give financial incentives to the states to improve conditions in their respective institutions, the new funding had several unintended consequences, some good, some bad. Initially (and through the early 1980s), reductions in populations were spurred by the requirement to bring occupancy of existing space down to the required level; in later years, however, the high level of federal financial participation (from 50% to approximately 78%) was a disincentive to the initiation of less costly alternatives that did not qualify for Medicaid funding (Lakin et al., 1993).

The 1970s and early 1980s witnessed an explosion of the following federal legislative activity:

- The Rehabilitation Act of 1973 (PL 93-112) included a brief section, Section 504, that broadly prohibited discrimination against "any otherwise qualified handicapped individual" by any program or activity receiving federal financial assistance. It also refocused the "basic" rehabilitation state program on those diagnosed as having the most severe disabilities and triggered the "independent living movement" (DeJong, 1979).
- The Developmental Disabilities Services and Facilities Construction Act of 1970 (PL 91-517) focused on a group of people diagnosed as having severe chronic disabilities, the majority of whom had intellectual impairments. In 1975 it became the Developmental Disabilities Assistance and Bill of Rights Act (PL 94-103); the 1975 amendments contained a hortatory statement declaring certain rights of people with developmental disabilities and called for the creation of state-based "systems for protection and advocacy" of these rights.

- In 1975 the first meeting of a new organization, The Association for Persons with Severe Handicaps (TASH), was convened in Kansas City, bringing together a congregation of highly motivated professional educators and parents of school-age children seeking a zero reject policy for the public schools. From its inception, the organization was adamant in its opposition to all forms of segregation of children with "severe intellectual handicaps." By 1979 the TASH mission was extended to all age groups (Brown, 1991).
- The enactment in 1975 of the Education for All Handicapped Children Act (PL 94-142) advanced the cause of "rights" by making federal funding available contingent on the support of a free appropriate public education in the "least restrictive environment" by state and local education authorities.
- In 1974, aid to people who are blind, aid to people with permanent and total disabilities, and aid to old people who are poor (under Titles I, X, XIV, and XVI of the Social Security Act) were federalized into a uniform income support program called Supplemental Security Income (SSI) (Title XVI). Although the income eligibility standard and federal benefit payable to an individual or couple is still well below the poverty level, it is on the whole more nearly adequate than in the previous program, is indexed to the cost of living, and covers children with disabilities.

A significant byproduct of the collaboration that achieved the 1970 developmental disabilities legislation and its subsequent amendments was the formation of a durable and effective "cross-disability" coalition. This coalition was long known as the Consortium for Citizens with Developmental Disabilities and changed in 1989 to CCD (dropping the limitation based on age at onset).

In addition to a monthly subsistence check, all SSI recipients are automatically eligible for social services and, except in a few states, for Medicaid coverage. The particular ideological significance of the SSI program lies in the fact that the individual (or his or her authorized personal representative) has discretion (autonomy) in spending the income. This provision offered *choice,* including choice of living arrangement (outside of medical institutions or public institutions) and therefore set the stage for community living alternatives that were to become popular in the 1980s. It facilitated the mix or match approach whereby the service package can be negotiated separately from the living arrangement. A significant provision ensured that no family members other than spouses and parents of minor children would be held liable for support of their relatives with disabilities when the income and assets tests were applied. Currently, more than a quarter of the 3 million recipients with disabilities have a primary diagnosis of mental retardation, and a third (more than a million children and adults) have had disabilities since childhood.

By the late 1970s the goal of institutional reform for people with mental retardation or related disorders was giving way to a paradigm based on the legal principle of "the least restrictive alternative," or the notion that any specific restraint placed on an individual in his or her own or the public interest must be minimized (Turnbull, 1981). It was then convincingly argued that anything therapeutic that can be done in an institution for long-term care can be done as well or better in an alternative setting, preferably a natural one. The new approach prompted a call for deinstitutionalization and the creation by the state of choices among alternative lifestyles and living arrangements.

The emphasis in the court decisions in cases brought on behalf of many people in various institutional settings moved away from improvements in conditions and basic civil rights in those institutions to the concept that no one should be expected to live there; that everyone, including people with disabilities, has a right to live in the community; and that the least restrictive alternative doctrine could not include institutions like (Pennsylvania's) Pennhurst as an alternative for anyone. This rationale was in distinct contrast to the litigative strategies previously used to depopulate mental hospitals. Through those strategies discharge of the patient also terminated the state's legal responsibility for care and protection. Though the focus on legal rights and the shift to community mandates improved the lives of many people, it also had a negative side that remains today, that is, the creation of a legally unequal classes of people with mental retardation: those with court-ordered benefits and those without.

Aside from this last consequence, these actions and their eventual success planted the seeds of personal and political empowerment of consumers and laid the groundwork for the massive grassroots movement that brought the Americans with Disabilities Act (ADA) (PL 101-336) to the president's desk in 1990.

The following trends achieved high visibility during the 1970s and 1980s:

- A sustained focus on issues of severe physical or mental disability, in both children and adults
- An increase in political activism by people with disabilities and their families, some of whom were able to affect the content and language of federal legislation in a way that altered the historical role of the executive branch in proposing legislation
- A leveling off of the expansion of federal programs and funding in human services generally, occasioned by economic circumstances, especially the escalating price of oil
- An acceleration of a strong trend toward privatization of components of the service system
- A spectacular decline in the use of large public residential institutions, accompanied by an accelerating diversification in options for lifestyle and living arrangements for many people with disabilities
- A new quantitative data based understanding in real time, of the acceleration of changes in the modalities of service delivery, as well as in lifestyles
- A reclamation by many people with disabilities of their right to take charge of their own lives, to be empowered, and to have choices

- Much talk about quality of life
- A coming together of people with diverse disabilities for mutual support and pursuit of common goals

CONCLUSION

The overview presented in this chapter provides a picture of the richness of events, trends, discoveries, and initiatives that form the backdrop for the discussions in this book. It also reflects the difficulty of marking any one moment in time as the birth of a new idea or paradigm, given the inevitable overlapping of ideas and movements and the impossibility of viewing the broad sweep of historical change from our limited vantage point. What is clear is that no idea is truly new nor can any shift be considered definitive or final. This recognition is both humbling and empowering because it suggests that the change that is apparent today is a product of multiple actions, large and small, that span many eras. However, it also suggests that the actions we take today will have an enduring impact on the shape of services and supports to people with mental retardation and other developmental disabilities in the future.

REFERENCES

Accreditation Council on Services for People with Developmental Disabilities. (1989). *Standards for services for people with developmental disabilities: National quality assurance program,* 1990 edition. Landover, MD: Author.

American Association on Mental Retardation. (1992). *Mental retardation: Definitions, classifications, and systems of supports.* Washington, DC: Author.

American Psychiatric Association. (1951). *Diagnostic and statistical manual.* Washington, DC: Author.

American Psychiatric Association. (1980). *The diagnostic and statistical manual of mental disorders: Third edition (DSM-III).* Washington, DC: Author.

Bixby, A.K. (1992). Public social welfare expenditures, fiscal year 1989. *Social Security Bulletin, 55,* 61–68.

Blatt, B. (1961). Toward a more acceptable terminology in mental retardation. *The Training School Bulletin, 58,* 47–51.

Blatt, B., & Kaplan, F. (1967). *Christmas in purgatory.* New York: Longman.

Blatt, B., Ozolins, A., & McNally, J. (1979). *The family papers: A return to purgatory.* New York: Longman.

Boggs, E.M. (1959). *Decade of decision.* Report prepared for the 1960 White House Conference on Children and Youth. New York: National Association for Retarded Children.

Boggs, E.M. (1971). Federal legislation (1955–1966). In J. Wortis (Ed.), *Mental retardation* (Vol. III, pp. 103–127). New York: Grune & Stratton.

Boggs, E.M. (1987). Two decades of change: Some programmatic trends for individuals with mental retardation 1966–1986. In President's Committee on Mental Retardation (Ed.), *Twentieth anniversary symposium: Maximizing the quality of life for individuals with mental retardation and other developmental disabilities* (pp. 16–29). Washington, DC: United States Department of Health and Human Services.

Boggs, E.M., Lakin, K.C., & Clauser, S. (1985). Medicaid coverage of residential services. In K.C. Lakin, B.K. Hill, & R.H. Bruininks (Eds.), *An analysis of Medicaid's intermediate care facility for the mentally retarded (ICF/MR) program.* Minneapolis: University of Minnesota, Department of Educational Psychology.

Braddock, D. (1987). *Federal policy toward mental retardation and developmental disabilities.* Baltimore: Paul H. Brookes Publishing Co.

Braddock, D., Hemp, R. Fujiura, G., Bachelder, L., & Mitchell, D. (1990). *The state of the states in developmental disabilities.* Baltimore: Paul H. Brookes Publishing Co.

Bronowski, J. (1973). *The ascent of man.* Boston: Little, Brown.

Brown, L. (1991). Who are they and what do they want: An essay on TASH. In L.H. Meyer, C.A. Peck, & L. Brown (Eds.), *Critical issues in the lives of people with severe disabilities* (pp. xxv–xxvii). Baltimore: Paul H. Brookes Publishing Co.

Butterfield, E. (1976). Some basic changes in residential facilities. In R.B. Kugel & A. Shearer (Eds.), *Changing patterns in residential services for the mentally retarded* (rev. ed., pp. 15–34). Washington, DC: President's Committee on Mental Retardation.

Cobb, H.V. (1977). *Mental retardation: Past and present* (Department of Health, Education, and Welfare Publication No. [OHD] 77-21016). Washington, DC: President's Committee on Mental Retardation.

Cornes, P. (1987). Vocational rehabilitation for tomorrow's world: A British view. In D.E. Woods & D. Vandergoot (Eds.), *The changing nature of work, society and disability: The impact on rehabilitation policy* (pp. 1–8). New York: World Rehabilitation Fund.

Davies, S.P. (1930). *The social control of the mentally deficient.* New York: Thomas Crowell.

Davies, S.P. (Ed.) (1959). *The mentally retarded in society.* New York: Columbia University Press.

Dejong, G. (1979). *The movement for independent living: Origins, ideology, and implications for disability research.* East Lansing, MI: University Centers for International Rehabilitation.

Dingman, H.F., & Tarjan, G. (1960). Mental retardation and the normal distribution curve. *American Journal of Mental Deficiency, 64,* 991–994.

Doll, E.A. (1951). *Encyclopaedia Britannica,* "mental deficiency."

Doll, E.E. (1962). A historical survey of research and management of mental retardation in the United States. In E.P. Trapp & P. Himelstein (Eds.), *Readings on the exceptional child* (pp. 21–68). New York: Appleton-Century-Crofts.

Drucker, P.F. (1989). *The new realities.* New York: Harper & Row.

Gardner, J.F. (1993). The era of optimism, 1850–1870: A preliminary reappraisal. *Mental Retardation, 31*(2), 89–95.

Gelof, M. (1963). Comparisons of systems of classifications relating the degree of retardation to measured intelligence. *American Journal of Mental Deficiency, 68,* 297–317.

Goddard, H.H. (1911). Causes of backwardness and mental deficiency in children and how to prevent them. *Proceedings from the National Education Association, July,* 1039–1046.

Heber, R. (1959). A manual on terminology and classification in mental retardation. *American Journal of Mental Deficiency,* Monograph supplement, *64* (No. 2).

Heber, R. (1961). Modifications in the manual on terminology and classification in mental retardation. *American Journal of Mental Deficiency,* Monograph supplement, *65* (No. 2).

Johnstone, E.R. (1918). Discipline. In C.N. Kendall (Ed.), *The teaching of children mentally three years or more below the normal* (pp. 25–27). Trenton: State of New Jersey Department of Public Instruction.

Kanner, L. (1949). *A miniature textbook of feeblemindedness* (Child Care Monographs, No. 1). New York: Child Care Publications.

Kirk, S.A. (1965). From public law 85-926 to public law 89-105. In T. Schuchat (Ed.), *Creative use of federal legislation for exceptional children: Proceedings from the CEC Conference on Creative Use of Federal Legislation for Exceptional Children* (pp. 10–13). Washington, DC: Council for Exceptional Children.

Kite, E.S. (1915). *The Binet-Simon Measuring Scale for Intelligence: What it is; what it does; how it does it; with a brief biography of its authors, Alfred Binet and Dr. Thomas Simon*. Philadelphia: The Committee on Provision for the Feeble-Minded.

Kugel, R.B., & Wolfensberger, W. (Eds.). (1969). *Changing patterns in residential services for the mentally retarded*. Washington, DC: President's Committee on Mental Retardation.

Lair, T. (1992). *A profile of nursing home users under age 65* (Publication no. 92–0060). National Medical Expenditure Survey Research Findings 13, Agency for Health Care Policy and Research. Rockville, MD: Public Health Service.

Lakin, K.C., Blake, E.M., Prouty, R.W., Mangan, T., & Bruininks, R.H. (1993). *Residential services for persons with developmental disabilities: Status and trends through 1991*. Minneapolis: University of Minnesota Center on Residential Services and Community Living, Institute on Community Integration/University Affiliated Program.

Lakin, K.C., Hill, B.K., & Anderson, D.J. (1991). Persons with mental retardation in nursing homes in 1977–1985. *Mental Retardation, 29*, 25–33.

Lerman, P. (1981). *Deinstitutionalization: A cross-problem analysis* (Department of Health and Human Services Publication No. [ADM] 81-987). Rockville, MD: United States Department of Health and Human Services.

Linstone, H.A. (1980). The postindustrial society and mental retardation. In S.C. Plog & M.B. Santamour (Eds.), *The year 2000 and mental retardation* (pp. 123–154). New York: Plenum.

Naisbitt, J. (1982). *Megatrends: Ten new directions transforming our lives*. New York: Warner.

National Association for Retarded Children. (1958). *A well-rounded program for the retarded*. New York: Author.

National Institute of Mental Health. (1964). *Patient movement data: State and county mental hospitals–1961* (United States Public Health Service Publication No. 1189). Washington, DC: United States Department of Health, Education, and Welfare.

National Institute of Mental Health. (1969). *Patients in public institutions for the mentally retarded 1967* (Public Health Service Publication No. 1860). Washington, DC: Department of Health, Education, and Welfare.

Penrose, L.S. (1949). *The biology of mental defect*. New York: Grune & Stratton.

President's Panel on Mental Retardation. (1962). *A proposed program for national action to combat mental retardation*. Washington, DC: United States Government Printing Office.

Pumphrey, R.E. (1980). Compassion and protection: Dual motivations in social welfare. In F.R. Breul & S.J. Diner (Eds.), *Compassion and responsibility* (pp. 5–13). Chicago: University of Chicago Press.

Purtilo, R. (1981). *Justice, liberty, compassion: Analysis of and implications for "humane" health care and rehabilitation in the United States*. New York: World Rehabilitation Fund.

Reed, E.W., & Reed, S.C. (1965). *Mental retardation: A family study*. Philadelphia: W.B. Saunders.

Rothman, D.J. (1978). The state as parent: Social policy in the progressive era. In W. Gaylin, I. Glasser, S. Marcus, & D. Rothman (Eds.), *Doing good: The limits of benevolence* (pp. 69–95). New York: Pantheon Books.

Rowitz, L. (1992). Predictions for the 1990's and beyond. In L. Rowitz (Ed.), *Mental retardation in the year 2000* (pp. 353–366). New York: Springer-Verlag.

Schwartz, D.B. (1992). *Crossing the river: Creating a conceptual revolution in community & disability*. Brookline, MA: Brookline.

Shakespeare, W. *Julius Caesar*, act IV, scene iii.

Simmons, H.G. (1982). *From asylum to welfare*. Canada: National Institute on Mental Retardation.

Smith, G.A., & Gettings, R.M. (1993). *Long term supports project series: Report no. 1: Medicaid-funded home and community-based waiver services for people with developmental disabilities.* Alexandria, VA: National Association of State Mental Retardation Program Directors.

Stevenson, G.S. (1947). Where and whither in mental deficiency. *American Journal of Mental Deficiency, 52,* 43–47.

Toffler, A. (1980). *The third wave.* New York: William Morrow.

Turnbull, H.R. (Ed.). (1991). *The least restrictive alternative: Principles and practices.* Washington, DC: American Association on Mental Retardation.

United States Public Health Service. (1954). *Patients in mental institutions, 1950 and 1951.* Washington, DC: Author.

Wallin, J.E.W. (1955). *Education of mentally handicapped children.* New York: Harper & Brothers.

White, C.C., Lakin, K.C., Bruininks, R.H., & Li, X. (1991). *Persons with mental retardation and related conditions in state-operated residential facilities: Year ending June 30, 1989 with longitudinal trends from 1950 to 1989.* Minneapolis: University of Minnesota, Department of Educational Psychology.

Wilson, M. (1993). DSM-III and the transformation of American psychiatry: A history. *American Journal of Psychiatry, 150,* 399–410.

Wolfensberger, W. (1972). *The principle of normalization in human services.* Toronto: National Institute on Mental Retardation.

World Health Organization. (1968). *The ICD-8 classification of mental and behavioural disorders: Clinical descriptions and diagnostic guidelines.* Geneva, Switzerland: Author.

World Health Organization. (1975). *The ICD-9 classification of mental and behavioural disorders: Clinical descriptions and diagnostic guidelines.* Geneva, Switzerland: Author.

World Health Organization. (1992). *The ICD-10 classification of mental and behavioural disorders: Clinical descriptions and diagnostic guidelines.* Geneva, Switzerland: Author.

Zigler, E. (1967). Familial mental retardation: A continuing dilemma. *Science, 155,* 292–298.

4

Increasing Quality while Reducing Costs

The Challenge of the 1990s

Michael W. Smull and
Agnesanne J. Danehey

In spite of efforts since the 1970s to bring individuals with disabilities into the community, provide new or expanded services, and reduce the number of people living together, many individuals with disabilities still do not enjoy full citizenship, full community participation (Taylor, 1987), and interdependence. The collective practices of the disability service system have made limited progress. The service system is operating on a program model that is neither flexible nor cost-effective. People with disabilities are not being offered the best services that are available with current resources. The only answer given to those who want to fix the system is that more money is needed. While more money will be needed, the system must refocus its efforts to increase quality, productivity, and efficiency. Changes to the system must address quality of life for individuals while reducing the average cost of services.

THE TRAP OF THE 1980S

The service system for individuals with disabilities has been trapped in a swirl of forces including the consequences of progressive underfunding of community services (Braddock, 1986; Krauss, 1986); the rising demands from those waiting for services (Davis, 1987); and the escalating costs of institutional services (White, Prouty, Lakin, & Blake, 1992). Even before the decline in state revenues, many managers felt trapped. The funding increases that the systems did receive were adequate to retain federal matching funds (Amado, Lakin, & Menke, 1990) but inadequate to reduce the unmet demand for services by those in the community (McDonald, Wilcox, Boles, & Bellamy, 1985). Those funds that were available were sufficient only to address emergency needs. Though catastrophic failures were avoided, the service systems began to drift in a sea of chronic crisis.

The strategy of shoring up an unsound structure is less and less possible if not unwise. State government funding has traditionally driven the tremendous growth of community services for individuals with disabilities (Braddock, Hemp, Fujiura, Bachelder, & Mitchell, 1990). With the economic downturn of the late 1980s, however, state revenues fell while federal resources only slowly increased (Mitchell, Bachman, Longhurst, & Braddock, 1990). Program managers in some states attempted to preserve their systems by spreading funding reductions across the community service system, while others developed living arrangements for larger groups of people. These strategies focus on surviving the economic downturn without positioning the system for the economic upturn.

As the economy recovers and state revenues increase, legislatures and executives will look to invest new funds where they will have the most pronounced and visible effect. The disability system is currently perceived by legislators and executives as a black hole that absorbs scarce resources without noticeable effect. They see large sums of money flowing into improving the quality of services provided in institutions, while the number of individuals living in institutions decreases (White et al., 1992). The expansion of community services from the late 1980s to the early 1990s has not met the demand for services from those individuals living in the community (Halloran, Engelke, Danehey, Lewis, & Walsh, 1986; McDonald et al., 1985). Without radical changes that will alter the theory, practice, and costs of program models, the future is one of chronic crises and eventual catastrophe.

Cost Containment Strategies

Within the current model of community services the primary mechanism to control per capita costs has been progressive underfunding. Each year the funding increase authorized for existing services is below the rate of inflation (Mitchell et al., 1990). Over the course of years, the shortfalls increase and the wages that make up 70% of the cost of services are reduced in terms of constant dollars (Mitchell et al., 1990). The result is entry level wages in community residential settings that average $5.26 per hour (Mitchell et al., 1990). When combined with the effects of current demographics, there is an average staff turnover rate of 68% (Mitchell et al., 1990). While the recession has given temporary respite to those affected by this turnover rate, the inevitable economic recovery will return staff turnover to unacceptable levels.

An alternative mechanism to controlling costs has been to return to past practices of increasing the number of people with disabilities who are supervised by each staff member. The logic is seductive since it would seem that costs should drop in proportion to the ratios. There are two problems, however, with this solution. First, the quality of life for most individuals declines as they are forced to live in larger groups. Second, research indicates that the savings from grouping more than four people are marginal (Conroy, 1992).

Increasing the number of people served by each staff person has been tried before and is a slippery slope. Warehousing people is cheaper. Institutions began in the mid-1800s as facilities that offered state-of-the-art segregated services (Wolfensberger, 1969). The pressure to serve more people for small increases in funding resulted in a rapid growth in institution census and trampled individual dignity (Wolfensberger, 1969). We must not forget that the appalling human warehouses we created are only 2 decades behind us.

Increasing Demands for Services

Any vision of the disability service system must accommodate the realities of the next decade. Requests for services will continue to increase. The policies of the past are contributing to the demands of the present. Community residential services have shown rapid growth over the past 2 decades but much of that growth has been the result of the priority given to people moving from institutions to community settings (Halloran et al., 1986; McDonald et al., 1985). While the absolute number of residential beds has increased by 8% over the last decade, the number of beds as a rate per 100,000 of the general population has decreased by nearly 13% (Amado et al., 1990). People who have been living at home have been asked to continue to live at home.

Increasing numbers of these individuals require immediate residential supports as caregivers age (Seltzer & Krauss, 1989; Suelzle & Keenan, 1981) and families experience crisis (Black, Cohn, Smull, & Crites, 1985; Smull, Sachs, & Black, 1990). They cannot wait any longer. For those who continue to wait, the service system's failure to offer alternatives to living in the family home decreases the quality of life of both families and individuals (Ward & Halloran, 1987). The service system's failure to support people who live with their families adds to the numbers of people in crisis (Black, Smull, Crites, & Sachs, 1987). Not addressing the needs of people in crisis will either increase the size of institutions or create a new group of vulnerable homeless people.

The entitlement environment of special education services has placed new and expanded demands on the adult service system. Children with special needs have made tremendous academic and vocational gains as a result of PL 94-142, the Education for All Handicapped Children Act of 1975 (McDonald et al., 1985; United States Department of Education, 1985). As students "age out" of the entitlement environment of the school system, they discover the absence of both entitlement and services from the adult system. Those making this transition also find a discrepancy between existing services and their increased capabilities (Halloran et al., 1986). Parents are bewildered and outraged. The prior public investment in the education of individuals is wasted as people lose academic and vocational skills because they sit idly at home (Ward & Halloran, 1987). The contribution that these individuals could make to society through employment is lost. Family stress increases markedly. There are numerous anecdotal reports of parents leaving their jobs in order to provide the support needed to ensure the safety of their sons or daughters.

CHALLENGE FOR THE 1990s

Quality of Life and Reducing Cost of Services

The quality of life for each individual must have priority over cost. In evaluating decisions, the first question must be, "Will it improve the quality of life of each of the individuals concerned?" However, there must be a balance; the resulting service system must be affordable. Only after the quality-of-life question is answered "Yes," may attention turn to the second question: "Will it help to create a more cost-effective service system?" In evaluating costs, the trap of simply asking if it is cheaper must be avoided.

There are real dangers in the search for more cost-effective services. There will be pressures to reduce the effort to a simple "cheaper is better" analysis. System managers need to ensure that any changes in the lives of individuals will result in improvement in quality as well as cost savings and not accept changes that are quality neutral at best. Changes that are being offered simply to lower costs or meet an administrative need without an analysis of impact on the lives of people with disabilities should be unacceptable.

People with disabilities need to become customers with the control that being a customer implies. The lessons of quality learned by industry need to be adapted to the disability service system. As Deming has said, "Inspection to improve quality is too late, costly and ineffective" (1986, p. 28). Quality must be designed in and supported throughout. Competition should be the norm within the system. Technology that reduces dependence on staff, increases independence, and does not increase social isolation must be developed.

The problem is that the service models "service" people rather than serving them. The disability service system is not flexible, has no incentives for efficiency, and funds programs rather than individuals. Control over the lives of the individuals served is not vested with the individuals or their representatives but with residential directors, social workers, case managers, psychologists, and other people who are often too distant from the individuals served. System-oriented managers narrowly define success as occurring when programs operate within budgets, expand according to schedule, and do not "discharge" participants. Program overseers add to this orientation by requiring licenses and accreditation based on program quality not quality of life (see Kimmich & Bradley, chap. 25, this volume). The practice of funding slots and capacity rather than funding actual individuals increases the difficulty of person-centered services. In sum, these collective practices cause us to lose sight of the individual and treat people as commodities.

In creating a system in which *individual* solutions are sought and innovative strategies are pursued, the costs of services for most people will go down, while the costs for some will go up. The test for cost-effectiveness must be a lower average cost, not a lower maximum cost. The search for more cost-effective services must not deny needed services for the expensive few. Maintaining these quality-of-life issues in the forefront requires a proactive stance on the part of managers and field professionals. Do not forget that the legislators and executive staff who have control over the distribution of funds know little about people with disabilities. Service professionals need to demonstrate that quality and cost issues can be dealt with simultaneously.

Balancing Quality, Choice, and Cost

Central to increasing the quality of life of people with disabilities is finding a new balance between freedom and protection. The disability system should:

- Assist people in discovering their choices
- Ensure that the opportunities needed to support those choices are present
- Rebalance the locus of control

Expressions of choice by individuals with disabilities have been suppressed and distorted (Biklen & Knoll, 1987; International League of Societies for Persons with Mental Handicap, 1984; Klein, 1992). Opportunities for individuals with disabilities have been severely limited (Kennedy, Killius, & Olson, 1987; Klein, 1992). Real control has been vested entirely within the disability system (Biklen & Knoll, 1987; Edgerton, 1990; Klein, 1992). All of this must change without exposing people with disabilities to undue risk. The disability system must ensure that people with disabilities have the resources needed to live ordinary lives at a cost that the public will support.

This cannot be achieved by increasing the number of people who live together or by simply reducing the supports offered. Affording people with disabilities a reasonable quality of life at a reduced average cost cannot be achieved using a "program model" of services. Anecdotal reports suggest that increasing choice and control tends to increase cost if it is simply superimposed on the current program model. This occurs because the program model relies on additional paid staff to support the divergent choices of the people who live together. Pervasive and comprehensive changes in the system of services are needed. There must be changes in: 1) how time and resources are invested in the system, 2) the structure of services and service providers, and 3) standards by which services are assessed. The remainder of this chapter focuses on the components of a person-driven support model and the investments that will be needed for a successful system of support for persons with disabilities.

ELEMENTS OF THE PERSON-DRIVEN SUPPORTS MODEL

Person-Centered Planning

A planning process that seeks to understand the person (rather than diagnosing or assessing the person) is referred to as being person-centered (see Mount, chap. 6, this volume). If people with disabilities are to achieve the lifestyle they desire, we need to understand them. Understanding requires insight, empathy, and time. The time that it takes to understand the person can be shortened by using the accumulated knowledge of people who know and care about the individual, but we cannot plan for someone we do not know. Unfortunately, this is the norm. People with disabilities are routinely "assigned" to programs by professionals who have spent more time with the records than with the person.

Understanding the Person The fundamental change in shifting from programs to supports is the emphasis on the individual rather than the program. For each individual, the core information needed is not the disability label but the preferences and desires of the individual with regard to:

- People to associate with
- Settings to spend time in
- Activities to engage in

For some individuals, these preferences have been expressed over and over again, but the service system has not listened. For others the effects of years of not being listened to has suppressed expressions of choice, and we need to learn together about real preferences and basic values. Some individuals are quite flexible and find a wide range of settings acceptable. Other individuals have a highly defined sense of what will work for them and will not settle for anything else.

There are a number of technologies that have been developed to assist in understanding people and in describing the supports they need to achieve their desired lifestyle. These include:

- Personal futures planning (Mount & Zwernik, 1988; O'Brien, 1987)
- Functional lifestyle planning (Green-McGowen, 1985)
- Individual service design (Yates, 1980)
- MAPS (McGill Action Planning System [Vandercook, York, & Forest, 1989])
- Essential lifestyle planning (Smull & Harrison, 1992)

While each process takes a somewhat different approach to understanding the person, they have some common characteristics. Each looks at the preferences and desires of the individual with the goal of determining the desired lifestyle of the individual. Each supports inclusion in the community and helps those who support learn what must be present (or absent) in the community setting in which the individual will live and work. All of these procedures help to lift us out of our habitual patterns of thinking and provide us with an alternative structure.

These procedures help to avoid the perversion already emerging in the provision of support services. The service system has been so seduced by labels that it relabels programs with support names and believes that it has achieved its goal. When people are simply assigned to supported employment (without choice), or when supported living only means that a lease is put in the name of someone with a disability who has not chosen where or with whom to live, then the way we think about people with disabilities has not changed at all.

Discovering the Person's Values and Hassles Unfortunately, efforts to help people live ordinary lives often begin when the "helpers" project their values onto the people supported. We seek to offer people with disabilities lives that would satisfy us. The positive aspects of this projection are that they rule out situations (e.g., abuse or substandard housing) that we would not tolerate for ourselves. Unfortunately, it also results in lifestyles that do not reflect the enormous variability among individuals and therefore are not always satisfying. Discovering the values and the hassles of each individual allows for the recognition of differences as well as similarities. It keeps the focus on the individual and not the label.

If what is highly valued and essential to an individual is known, its presence can be ensured. If the hassles that will not be tolerated are known, their absence can be ensured. When what is valued by each individual exceeds what that individual dislikes, he or she has a positive quality of life. While improvements may always be sought, the minor hassles that are always present can be tolerated. When the hassles outweigh what is valued, change is sought.

Unfortunately, people with disabilities have come to learn that merely complaining does little good. Dramatic behavior is required to change a setting. Reaction of service providers to this behavior is often a labor-intensive program designed to suppress an unusual means of communication. Doing a functional analysis to identify the purpose of the behavior may only identify what is wrong and not what changes are needed to achieve a positive balance of values to hassles.

Discovering the values and hassles of individuals with disabilities helps staff to understand that these individuals are not "different" from themselves. They are engaging in the human activity of seeking to have a positive balance between their individual values and hassles. When people who are not in the disability field find that the hassles in their lives outweigh the values, they make changes, like leaving a job or a relationship or moving. They do whatever they believe will result in a better balance between their values and hassles. The most significant difference between typical citizens and individuals with disabilities is a lack of control. When their hassles outweigh what they value, individuals with disabilities cannot make changes without support.

The process of discovering the values and hassles of individuals receiving support teaches us what was not known that should have been known and what our ignorance has done to people with disabilities. When the settings that the system has chosen for individuals are in contrast with their values and hassles, often it is the settings that need to be "fixed," and not the individual.

Creating a Shared Vision "Fixing" where people live or work requires a shared vision of a desirable future. Consensus must be achieved among the key stakeholders including the individual, the family, paid support provider(s), and the funding/regulating agency. The first effort should be to determine who the key stakeholders are. In many instances, only specific family members are key stakeholders, while in other instances no family member is a key stakeholder. In a number of instances there are public officials who are critical stakeholders. For each of the key stakeholders, the following needs to be determined:

- The essential elements/characteristics of a setting
- The negotiable elements or characteristics (those that are preferred but not essential or those that are disliked but not intolerable)

In looking at the essential and negotiable elements broad goals must be distinguished from essential elements. For example, while being safe is a universal goal, unless there is an operational set of characteristics that defines being safe for that individual, safety can become an excuse for overprotection. Once each stakeholder has operationally defined what being safe means, each element of the definition can be further determined to be either negotiable or essential. Negotiating over principles must be avoided (Fisher & Ury, 1983).

The service system also must look beneath the labels of living and working situations. A label for a living situation typically defines only the number of people who live together, not the critical issues for the people who live there, what the people are like, or the characteristics of the neighborhood in which the home is located. Service labels never provide the information needed for helping the individual determine where to live or work. Service labels often reinforce the perception that a person has to be "ready" to live or work in a particular setting (Taylor, 1987).

The process of discussing the elements of living and working situations and determining which are negotiable and which are not will clarify the positions of each of the stakeholders. Once initial positions have been clarified, the development of a shared vision becomes a process of negotiation among all of the stakeholders to reach a vision that meets the final essential elements of all the key stakeholders and a reasonable set of compromises for elements that are negotiable. The position of the individual with disabilities should be the starting place for all negotiations.

Assistance in Making Informed Choices Person-centered planning is not only needed to help compensate for the effects of cognitive disabilities, it is also required to compensate for the effects of the disability service system's practices. These efforts are necessary because of the effects of the program model on the expression of choice by people with disabilities. Many individuals with disabilities have experienced the disparity between our words and deeds. They realize that many requests for expression of choice are actually requests for them to tell us what we want to hear.

Many people with disabilities have been denied the life experience and opportunity needed to make informed choices. We have suppressed expressions of choice by consistently failing to honor the expressions of choice that are made. Where people have not been trained into passivity, they have been forced into rebellion and their expressions of choice have been distorted in the process. The effects of the disability have been used as an excuse to make choices *for* people. When considering choices, it is helpful to distinguish between two levels of choice: boundary choices and everyday choices. Boundary choices (i.e., whom to live with, where to live, and what to do with one's time) are made infrequently and set the parameters for day-to-day opportunities. Everyday choices (e.g., what to wear, what to eat, what time to go to bed) provide the richness in life. The effect of a disability may be an inability to articulate boundary or everyday choices.

Practice in making everyday choices is essential to making informed boundary choices. Life experiences that give people opportunities to try different experiences are essential to understanding the implications of choosing one setting over another. No single choice should become a life sentence. People with disabilities have the right to learn by making bad choices. We should not make them "live" with their choices because we "know better." It must be recognized also that everyone changes with time, both in the short range and in the long range. Choices that were made in the near or distant past may have been valid when they were made but not any longer.

For some people with disabilities, the job of the disability system is to get out of their way. They know what they want and their choices will be within the range of typical opportunities available to citizens in the community. The disability service system simply needs to ensure that the opportunities to exercise these reasonable choices are present. For other people with disabilities, the roles are more complex. Either a cognitive impairment or the effects of years of repression or a combination of both limits their expressions of boundary choices and everyday choices. With these individuals, efforts must focus on understanding the individual. Person-centered planning efforts simply provide a structured process by which this understanding can be achieved. However, doing a good person-centered plan only once is essential but insufficient. Continuous active treatment should be replaced with continuous active listening. Facilitating changes in whom the individual lives with, what the individual does during the day, or daily routines, and so forth, should be seen as the norm rather than the exception.

A Reliance Bias Community resources must be used with a "reliance bias." The concept of a reliance bias is simple. Supports that an individual needs should be provided by the person or persons closest to the individual (to the extent that is possible and reasonable). Each support identified (e.g., monitoring medication, housekeeping, or cooking) should be reviewed to find a person as close to the individual as possible to provide it. If the individual is thought of as a drop of water striking a still pond, with radiating concentric circles, the immediate circles represent the family, while subsequent circles represent friends, a community association, a generic agency, or a disability agency.

Bias is referred to rather than rules because rules carry the potential for abuse. Good sense must prevail, for example:

- Individuals should not be assigned tasks that they "could" or "should" do but will not.
- Families should not be asked to do what the individual would prefer they not do or what they are unlikely to do.
- Members of the community should not be asked to provide supports that an individual would prefer to receive from a disability professional.

Unbundling Services

Keeping choice and control within the fiscal reach of public funding requires "unbundling" services so that the service system:

- Makes effective use of community resources
- Is flexible and responsive
- Offers real choices with effective competition

All of these elements argue for a system that offers discrete services. Currently, services are delivered bundled in packages. Current community residential services supposedly provide all that an individual needs in one program. In a flexible system, services would be available discretely. How they are unbundled would vary from community to community.

The Community Supported Living Arrangements (CSLA) amendment (PL 101-508, 1990) to Section 1930[B] of the Social Security Act is an important step in this direction. It clearly separates housing from support and requires that people be supported in their own homes. The services it funds are broken into eight categories with a structure that will support individuals in receiving only those services that they want and need without their having to accept a package of services. CSLA also supports the concept that people need not obtain all of their paid supports from one source. For example, one provider could furnish an emergency response service, supervision to ensure health and safety could be provided by a second provider, and assistance with meals from a third provider. While other aspects of the CSLA amendment support old paradigm monitoring, and while CSLA funding flows through the Medicaid process, it still represents significant movement toward a system of support.

Unbundling the services will give the individual more options and alleviate some difficulties with staffing. Service providers can take advantage of the resources that communities and families offer and still ensure that individuals receive just the services they desire and need. For example, there are many more options for providing physical housing than are currently exercised (Laux & Moran-Laux, 1991; O'Connor & Racino, 1993). Providers do not need to be stopped from owning or leasing places to live, but the choice of where to live and whom to live with should rest with the individuals and their representatives. The permutations and combinations possible depend on the resources of the families and the community and the creativity of those coordinating the services.

Developing Natural Supports

Supports related to employment and community participation in general should also be unbundled. Behind the labels given to professional and paraprofessional staff are a set of roles that can be filled by a variety of nonpaid individuals. Among the results of filling roles this way would be an increase in the effective use of coworkers as mentors, facilitators, or job coaches. At the same time, there would continue to be circumstances in which paid agency staff would be used. Reviewing and rearranging the roles to be filled across all aspects of the lives of individuals with disabilities would result in reducing the distinction between day and residential staff.

Real power requires that an individual be able to bring about change. The individual needs to be able to change supports or settings without having to change both. For example, where housing is severed from services, the services can be changed without a change in where the individual lives. There are natural limits to the ability to control the effects of changes. Sometimes a change in with whom one lives does require a change in where one lives. Often, changing jobs requires changing employers. Everyone is limited by their financial resources. But these parameters are far broader for other people than for people with disabilities. The same breadth of opportunity for control must be sought for individuals with disabilities as are enjoyed by typical members of the community.

Using Public Dollars to Leverage Natural Supports

Achieving a system that reduces public costs while increasing quality requires looking beyond the use of public dollars simply for buying services. Public funds must be seen as a source of leverage for natural supports. Funding a community guide to link people with community resources is using public funds as leverage. In Maryland, Rev. David Denham spent several months helping a young woman leave a nursing home and achieve her desired lifestyle. The public funds that support Denham became the leverage for the development of a personal network and a system of support. A bright, gregarious woman now receives the extensive attendant care and other supports she needs without public funding beyond that provided through Title XIX (of PL 74-271, the Social Security Act of 1935, as amended). Otherwise, the typical cost of her support would have been measured in the tens of thousands of dollars annually. With an initial investment of less than $10,000 and ongoing financial assistance of less than $2,000 (in services coordination) she has the lifestyle that she desires. Leveraging natural supports with public dollars needs to be encouraged.

The use of natural supports is receiving increased attention in supported employment (Nisbet & Hagner, 1988). The efforts of people like Candace O'Neill and Jane Boone in the state of Washington are good examples of how natural supports can be recruited and used. They are developing supported employment without using provider agencies. Boone met with state officials and asked them what they would need to hire people with severe disabilities. After extensive discussions, they agreed upon funding for a personnel officer who would be an expert in supporting people with disabilities. In return for this investment of approximately $30,000, this personnel officer was able to leverage over 10 well-paying, career-oriented jobs. Such creative efforts need further expansion in the workplace and home.

Caution must be exercised. There is the distinct potential for these efforts to be turned into new ways of dumping people with disabilities. Leveraging natural supports is not the *only* answer; it is one answer. Some people will be supported with 100% natural supports; most people will receive a mix of paid and natural supports. Preventing those who are receiving more natural supports from being neglected will require ensuring that nonintrusive monitoring and coordination is part of their lives.

Public Funding and Limits to Opportunities

Choices that require public funding to implement are limited by public values. However, these limits are broad. These boundaries include not supporting criminal activities or ostentatious lifestyles. There is also an expectation that services supported by public funds will not put people at undue risk. These broad limits affect very few individuals. Public values will support almost any lifestyle that is reasonably available in the community. The public values expressed in the Individuals with Disabilities Education Act of 1990, PL 101-496, (independence, productivity, integration, and satisfaction) are congruent with a support model.

The real limits to the opportunities that are supported are rooted in the ways services are provided. While supported employment and supported living provide the structural flexibility that is required to offer a wide range of opportunities, the challenge is in the implementation. Program model thinking results in implementing support models without soliciting or honoring choice. While opportunities are naturally limited by the resources of the community and the funding available, opportunities should not be limited by the service system's patterns of thinking.

The control necessary to implement the choices should rest with the individual. Where the individual is not able to articulate a choice, the choices made on behalf of the individual should continue to reflect his or her values and preferences. Making choices for people should no longer be acceptable. We should strive to make choices with people. The more limited the individual's capacity to articulate choice, the greater the effort required of the service system to understand the choice that the individual has difficulty expressing.

As choice becomes more and more trendy an idea, the service system must guard against its perversions. The term *normalization* (Wolfensberger, 1972) lent itself to the perversion of "normal" consequences, including going to jail. The assertion that it is the individual's choice is already used to allow individuals to harm themselves, lose jobs, or become more isolated from the community. In most instances, this abuse of choice reflects the anger, ineptitude, or laziness of those who are paid to support the individual rather than the choice of the individual. Even when the individual makes choices with which service providers strongly disagree, the individual's power of choice is not a reason for him or her to be abandoned. Choice does not remove our responsibility to remain engaged (J. O'Brien, personal communication, May 1990).

CHANGING THE INVESTMENTS

To achieve a system of supports that is person-centered, investments need to be made in:

- Developing partnerships with families
- Developing partnerships with communities
- Preventing disabilities from becoming handicaps
- Utilizing technology

The lessons that industry is learning about quality and the importance of focusing on the long term apply to the disability service system. The system must stop seeking quick fix answers and look for real solutions. It must invest in solutions that maximize the flexibility of service responses to the needs expressed. Service system managers, advocates, and service providers must recognize, and then convince those who authorized funding, that real solutions require complex, interconnected efforts. This means no longer implementing only those efforts that generate a quick return, but, instead, working through consensus that developing investments that yield results over years are essential.

Partnership with Families

A fundamental flaw in the current service system is that it waits until people lose community before trying to build community. In times of scarce resources, only those services needed to resolve emergencies are funded. The service system waits until individuals have lost their families before offering out-of-home services. When a residential service is offered, it is rarely offered in the neighborhood where the individual grew up. The goals of full participation in community life and the use of community resources would be easier to achieve if a foundation were built on existing resources and linkages. Family-centered efforts (Dunst & Deal, 1992) must be supported and the transition to adult services seen as moving from being family-centered to being person-centered.

If people with disabilities are to have the opportunity to live in their home neighborhoods, family participation is critical. Many people want to be able to spend their adult years in the neighborhoods where they were children. Staying in their neighborhoods is more likely where families are involved in planning and transition. Some people would be able to stay in their own houses if the needed supports were available. Others would be able to move to nearby houses or apartments.

If families are supported, the requests for more costly, out-of-home services will be deferred. Supporting families will also improve their quality of life (Nisbet, Clark, & Covert, 1991). So long as neither the family nor the individual feels trapped by in-home support, then the goal of increasing quality of life while reducing the service system's costs is being met. Families who do not feel great stress are better able to support efforts to build community associations. When supports are adequate, family members can return to the work force and be tax payers as well as caregivers.

Additionally, community associations can be built on the foundation of those already present. Families who have spent years in a community have associations that can be used to develop and increase associations for their family members with disabilities. Some families have done this, and it is the job of the service system to support them and stay out of their way. Other families have the potential resources but need assistance in developing them.

The benefits of partnership with families are numerous. If families are adequately supported, requests for residential services resulting from family stress will be reduced. Good person-centered planning requires in-depth knowledge of the individual. Typically, parents and siblings have critical knowledge that professionals lack. Family members often know the values and hassles of each of the other family members and can provide this information in a very practical fashion. Whether through planning, assisting in community inclusion, or subsidizing rent, family members often want to participate in the support of relatives living outside the family home. Not the least of the benefits of involving families as partners in support is that they are often in the best position to know of community resources that may be used to support their relatives.

Partnership with the Community

Linkages with community associations must be sought as essential opportunities for those receiving support. These linkages are also part of the answer to staffing and cost problems. These are long-term answers. Community associations have to be created and nurtured. Members of the community offering support to people with disabilities needs to be part of the ethic of the community. Community associations linking with people with disabilities must be understood as the expectation rather than the exception. This challenge is increased in communities with few formal or informal structures on which to build. The magnitude of the challenge is significantly increased when not only are linkages with existing associations sought, but also community associations are being built.

This society looks for quick returns on its investments. Immediate relief from fiscal crisis is needed, but this relief must incorporate ensuring that the immediate responses help build long-term solutions. It is clear that the best protection that individuals with disabilities can have is a group of citizens in the community who care about what happens to them. It is also clear that to the degree that the community steps forward, the disability system can step back. Investment in building relationships between people with disabilities and the community is essential.

The cost of investing to develop these linkages will be reduced if they are seen in the context of all people with disabilities. Elders with disabilities, people with physical disabilities, people with long-term mental illnesses, and people with developmental disabilities all need community resources not only to live in the community but to participate in the community. In the past, the service system has used common "splinter" needs to group people in common settings. This "deviancy juxtaposition" (Wolfensberger, 1972) served no one well. It only isolated people and reinforced stereotypical perceptions of devalued people. Using common resources to support people in settings of their own choosing throughout the community eliminates the problems that arise from congregating devalued people.

A "circle of friends" (Perske, 1988) or "personal network" (G. Allan Roeher Institute, 1987) is the best safeguard. It is unlikely that everyone with a disability will be able to have a personal network. However, without the efforts of the service system, few people with disabilities will have them. In this area the boundaries of what is possible must be expanded. Even where a personal network cannot be developed, the efforts toward it will result in increased community associations.

Preventing Disabilities from Becoming Handicaps

Despite all of the time that is spent planning for services and developing programs, very little attention is devoted to preventing disabilities from becoming handicaps. A disability is a restriction of ability to perform an activity. A handicap is the disadvantage that results from not being able to fill a role or function (Hahn, 1989). Not being able to walk independently is a disability that becomes a handicap only to the degree that the environment is not accessible.

This concept is embedded in the Americans with Disabilities Act (ADA, PL 101-336, 1990). The ADA requires the resolution of many of the accessibility issues that have barred people with physical disabilities from full participation in community life. However, once accessibility has been addressed there remains the challenge of "reasonable accommodation." If viewed within the context of preventing disabilities from becoming handicaps, the idea of a reasonable accommodation captures the idea of the level of effort required to accommodate. However, these efforts must extend well beyond the requirements of the ADA.

Disabilities are made into handicaps by readiness tests and other practices of the disability service system. A simple example is the idea that one must have coin recognition skills to buy sodas from a machine. Dana Henning tells a delightful story of a man with a disability (who does not recognize coin denominations) who said that all you need to buy sodas is a handful of change. First you throw away the brown coins (because you cannot buy anything with them). Then you put coins in one at a time and push the button with the picture of the soda you want each time. Eventually, a soda appears, and sometimes you get money back (D. Henning, personal communication, 1990).

Instead of saying that someone is not ready for employment or community living, people must learn how to prevent disabilities from becoming handicaps. Disabilities are real, but the degrees to which disabilities become handicaps depend on the accommodation that can be made for individuals. A good match between the desired lifestyle and the setting typically reduces the degree to which a disability becomes a handicap. In approaching job development, first an individual's gifts and preferences should be understood, then these should be matched with jobs that make use of them. Service providers must understand that the absence of services that support someone in a desired lifestyle reflects the community's lack of capacity, rather than the individual's lack of readiness.

The Promise of Technology

The disability field is beginning to make use of technology in reducing the degree to which disabilities become handicaps. Simple adaptive technology is being used to make jobs accessible. Computers are beginning to make an impact on communication. But the promise of technology lies in the potential applications. Much of the quality of life is determined by control over everyday events. People establish routines and rhythms that are comfortable to them. They develop positive rituals that mark the transitions from one part of the day to another, as well as rituals of celebration and comfort. People seek to ensure that they have sufficient control not only to establish routines and rituals but to vary them at will. This control has been beyond the grasp of many people with disabilities because of their need to have others remind (or prompt) them through a host of activities. Impaired capacity to remember activities and sequence steps results in a handicap, which puts someone else in charge of the rhythm of their lives. Technology now holds the promise of changing this.

Technology is now being developed to free people with disabilities from much of their reliance on staff. Object-oriented programming and current hardware and software (e.g., touch screens, full motion video, and speech synthesizers) can be used to create an "orthotic/cognitive prosthesis." Conceptually, the system is simple. The individual's typical schedule, with common variations, is entered into the computer. Also entered are the domains or activities for which the individual will need assistance (e.g., food preparation). The computer could be programmed to assist at certain times without a request (e.g., it could wake someone and then prompt him or her through morning activities) and when requested at other times. For a person living with more than one user, the request could be initiated by voice or touching a picture of himself or herself on the screen. The computer would look at the date and time and then see what assistance is most typically requested by that individual at that time.

During a weekday evening the typical requests might be for preparing dinner and calling friends. The computer would bring up a picture of eating and talking on the telephone. If the person touched the screen where talking on the telephone was shown it would bring up pictures of friends (as well as pictures of the police, firefighters, and ambulance personnel). The individual would touch the picture of the friend to be called and the computer would make the telephone call. For individuals who need only reminders of activities and passive monitoring for safety, this system offers true independence. They would be able to live without staff. While they would continue to want and need human interactions, there is an enormous difference between a roommate who is there to talk to and a staff member who is there to supervise.

SUCCESS

Success requires a change in the way we think about people with disabilities, their service needs, and our responses to those needs. This is a daunting prospect. There are a host of entrenched stakeholders who do not want to give up current practices. Many community service providers and systems managers are overwhelmed by the current crisis and simply hope that it is resolved before the next crisis arrives. They are too embedded in the present to contemplate the future. Families have not been assisted in seeing what is possible and are often asked to make decisions when under great stress.

The old cost-containment strategies do not work. They do not offer people with disabilities a better quality of life. People with disabilities must stop being consumers and become customers. The new service system must ensure that:

- People with disabilities have the assistance necessary to make informed choices, opportunities to exercise those choices, and the control necessary to change those choices over time.
- Families are supported, their current contributions are recognized, and their potential contributions are developed.
- Natural supports are developed through linkages between people with disabilities and the community, personal networks are nurtured, and all supports are developed using a reliance bias.
- The disability system sees its role as preventing disabilities from becoming handicaps rather than "fixing" the individuals with disabilities.
- People own their jobs and live in their own homes so that they can change the supports without having to change their jobs or their homes.
- Programs are unbundled so that an efficient and flexible array of discrete services can be provided.
- The coordination needed to plan, provide, and modify the supports is present.

The service system must relinquish the bureaucratic tribalism of the "us versus them" mentality. System change will really start when people from all parts of the service system see themselves as allies. Partnerships need to be nourished.

Service providers must discover how to achieve the synergy of group efforts while respecting the different roles of all of the stakeholders. Partnerships should begin with person-centered plans, where the key stakeholders collectively seek to support individuals in their desired lifestyles.

REFERENCES

Amado, A.N., Lakin, K.C., & Menke, J.M. (1990). *1990 chartbook on services for people with developmental disabilities* (Report No. 32). Minneapolis: University of Minnesota, Center on Residential Services and Community Living.

Biklen, D., & Knoll, J. (1987). The disabled minority. In S.J. Taylor, D. Biklen, & J. Knoll (Eds.), *Community integration for people with severe disabilities* (pp. 3–24). New York: Teachers College Press.

Black, M.M., Cohn, J.F., Smull, M.W., & Crites, L.S. (1985). Individual and family factors associated with risk of institutionalization of mentally retarded adults. *American Journal of Mental Deficiency, 3,* 271–276.

Black, M.M., Smull, M.W., Crites, L.S., & Sachs, M.L. (1987). *Mentally retarded adults and their families: A model of stress and coping.* Unpublished manuscript, University of Maryland, Community Support & Access Unit, Baltimore.

Braddock, D. (1986). Federal assistance for mental retardation and developmental disabilities II: The modern era. *Mental Retardation, 24,* 209–218.

Braddock, D., Hemp, R., Fujiura, G., Bachelder, L., & Mitchell, D. (1990). *The state of the states in developmental disabilities.* Baltimore: Paul H. Brookes, Publishing Co.

Conroy, J. (1992). *Size and quality of residential programs for people with developmental disabilities.* Unpublished doctoral dissertation, Temple University, Philadelphia.

Davis, S. (1987). *A national status report on waiting lists of people with mental retardation for community services.* Arlington, TX: The Association for Retarded Citizens, United States.

Deming, W.E. (1986) *Out of the crisis.* Cambridge: Massachusetts Institute of Technology, Center for Advanced Engineering Study.

Dunst, C.J., & Deal, A.G. (1992). Early intervention practitioners to work effectively with families. *Family Involvement, 5(1),* 25–28.

Edgerton, R.B. (1990). Quality of life from a longitudinal research perspective. In R.L. Schalock (Ed.), *Quality of life: Perspectives and issues* (pp. 161–176). Washington, DC: American Association on Mental Retardation.

Fisher, R., & Ury, W. (1983). *Getting to yes: Negotiating agreement without giving in.* New York: Penguin Books.

G. Allan Roeher Institute. (1987). *Service brokerage: Individual empowerment and social service accountability.* Downsview, Ontario, Canada: Author.

Green-McGowen, K. (1985). *Functional life planning.* Peachtree City, Georgia: KMG Seminars.

Hahn, H. (1989). The politics of special education. In D.K. Lipsky & A. Gartner (Eds.), *Beyond separate education: Quality education for all* (pp. 225-242). Baltimore: Paul H. Brookes Publishing Co.

Halloran, W., Engelke, S., Danehey, A.J., Lewis, L., & Walsh, S. (1986). *Severely handicapped youth exiting public education: Issues and concerns.* Washington, DC: National Association of State Directors of Special Education.

International League of Societies for Persons with Mental Handicap. (1984). *Participation in family and community life.* Brussels: Author.

Kennedy, M., Killius, P., & Olson, D. (1987). Living in the community: Speaking for yourself. In S.J. Taylor, D. Biklen, & J. Knoll (Eds.), *Community integration for people with severe disabilities* (pp. 202–208). New York: Teachers College Press.

Klein, J. (1992). Get me the hell out of here. In National Association of Private Residential Resources (Ed.), *Supported living: Monograph volume II.* Annandale, VA: Author.

Krauss, M.W. (1986). Patterns and trends in public services to families with a mentally retarded member. In J.J. Gallagher & P.M. Vietze (Eds.), *Families of handicapped persons: Research, programs, and policy issues* (pp. 237–248). Baltimore: Paul H. Brookes Publishing Co.

Laux, B., & Moran-Laux, C. (1991). *"Your place or mine?" : A handbook for home ownership.* Chicago: Illinois Planning Council on Developmental Disabilities.

McDonald, J., Wilcox, B., Boles, S., & Bellamy, G. (1985). *Do we know enough to plan for transition? A national survey of state agencies responsible for services to persons with severe handicaps* (Grant No. G008302159023BH30028). Washington, DC: Superintendent of Documents, United States Government Printing Office.

Mitchell, D., Bachman, K., Longhurst, N., & Braddock, D. (1990). *Research on wages and turnover of direct care staff in residential facilities for people with developmental disabilities: An annotated bibliography.* Chicago: University Affiliated Programs in Developmental Disabilities.

Mount, B., & Zwernik, K. (1988). *It's never too early, it's never too late* (Publication No. 421-88-109). St. Paul, MN: Metropolitan Council.

Nisbet, J., & Hagner, D. (1988). Natural supports in the workplace: A reexamination of supported employment. *Journal of The Association for Persons with Severe Handicaps, 13,* 260–267.

Nisbet, J., Clark, M., & Covert, S. (1991). Living it up! An analysis of research on community living. In L.H. Meyer, C.A. Peck, & L. Brown (Eds.), *Critical issues in the lives of people with severe disabilities* (pp. 115–144). Baltimore: Paul H. Brookes Publishing Co.

O'Brien, J. (1987). A guide to life-style planning: Using The Activities Catalog to integrate services and natural support systems. In B. Wilcox & G.T. Bellamy, *A comprehensive guide to The Activities Catalog: An alternative curriculum for youth and adults with severe disabilities* (pp. 175–189). Baltimore: Paul H. Brookes Publishing Co.

O'Connor, S., & Racino, J.A. (1993). "A home of my own": Community housing options and strategies. In J.A. Racino, P. Walker, S. O'Connor, & S.J. Taylor (Eds.) *Housing, support, and community: Choices and strategies for adults with disabilities* (pp. 137–160). Baltimore: Paul H. Brookes Publishing Co.

Pedlar, A., Lord, J., & Van Loon, M. (1989). *The process of supported employment and quality of life.* Kitchener, Ontario, Canada: Centre for Research and Education in Human Services.

Perske, R. (1988). *Circles of friends: People with disabilities and their friends enrich the lives of one another.* Nashville: Abingdon Press.

Seltzer, M.M., & Krauss, M.W. (1989). Aging parents with adult mentally retarded children: Family risk factors and sources of support. *American Journal on Mental Retardation, 94,* 303–312.

Smull, M.W., & Harrison, S. (1992). *Supporting people with severe reputations in the community.* Alexandria, VA: National Association of State Mental Retardation Program Directors.

Smull, M.W., Sachs, M.L., & Black, M.M. (1990). *Developing a managed service system for persons with developmental disabilities: A state agency-university partnership.* Unpublished manuscript. University of Maryland at Baltimore, Applied Research and Evaluation Unit, Department of Pediatrics.

Suelzle, M., & Keenan, V. (1981). Changes in family support networks over the life cycle of mentally retarded persons. *American Journal of Mental Deficiency, 86,* 267–274.

Taylor, S.J. (1987). Continuum traps. In S.J. Taylor, D. Biklen, & J. Knoll (Eds.), *Community integration for people with severe disabilities* (pp. 25–35). New York: Teachers College Press.

United States Department of Education, Office of Special Education and Rehabilitative Services. (1985). *Seventh annual report to congress on the implementation of the Education of the Handicapped Act.* Washington, DC: United States Government Printing Office.

Vandercook, T., York, J., & Forest, M. (1989). The McGill Action Planning System (MAPS): A strategy for building the vision. *Journal of The Association for Persons with Severe Handicaps, 14,* 205–215.

Ward, M.J., & Halloran, W.D. (1987). *Transition to uncertainty: Status of many school leavers with severe disabilities.* Unpublished manuscript. Washington, DC: Office of Special Education Programs.

White, C.C., Prouty, R.W., Lakin, K.C., & Blake, E.M. (1992). *Persons with mental retardation and related conditions in state-operated residential facilities: Year ending June 30, 1990 with longitudinal trends from 1950 to 1990 and a directory of large state-operated residential facilities* (Report No. 36). Minneapolis: University of Minnesota, Center on Residential Services and Community Living/Institute on Community Integration (UAP).

Wolfensberger, W. (1969). The origin and nature of our institutional models. In R. Kugel & W. Wolfensberger (Eds.), *Changing patterns in residential services for the mentally retarded* (pp. 59–172). Washington, DC: President's Committee on Mental Retardation.

Wolfensberger, W. (1972). *The principle of normalization in human services.* Toronto, Canada: National Institute on Mental Retardation.

Yates, J. (1980). *Program design sessions.* Stoughton, MA: Author.

II

CONCEPTUAL CHANGE

Among those who aspire to quality in the lives of people with developmental disabilities, the current period resonates with feelings of anticipation, celebration, and the sense of growing opportunities for creativity and innovation. Within such a formative and emotionally charged period, the role played by the authors of this section is especially vital. They are attempting to conceptualize and, thereby, safeguard the paradigm shift, to root it in an analytic foundation capable of supporting in-depth change as opposed to the faddish renaming of existing patterns.

At the core of the new paradigm is a new way of perceiving and defining people with developmental disabilities. As Luckasson and Spitalnik note in Chapter 5, previous definitions have focused on deficiency and difference and, consequently, have created separate social and system environments for "them." These authors find within the new American Association on Mental Retardation definition of mental retardation the explicit assumption that people with mental retardation are people first, are "us." Indeed, the new definition contains an explication of personalized planning, a conceptualization of supports versus programs, and the imperative to think in terms of community values and opportunities not those of an isolating service system.

Mount, in Chapter 6, and O'Brien and O'Brien, in Chapter 7, are reconceptualizing planning and organizational formats in terms of their observations of both positive and misdirected notions of realizing the new paradigm. Mount is attempting to safeguard the person-centered core of personal futures planning to articulate certain nonnegotiable principles, such as choice, the role of a shared vision, and the necessity for personal (not just professional) commitment to the person with disabilities. Her admonitions occur against a backdrop of pervasive misconceptions of personal futures planning as a mere reform of the individualized service planning and the individualized habilitation planning processes. She is unequivocal in her conviction that the incorporation and routinization of personal futures planning in current system planning structures robs it of positive impact and merely creates the illusion of change.

Just as current system-focused planning may undermine person-centered approaches, O'Brien and O'Brien have observed that current organizational models, characterized by top-down and mechanistic thinking, cannot support people in enjoying real homes and rich lives in their communities. In a sense, they invite us to develop organizations that are more like communities than bureaucracies, where ambiguity and fallability are expected rather than punished and where egalitarian relationships are consciously nurtured by organizational formats. It may well be necessary to develop organizational communities in order to create the personal communities so utterly missing in the lives of people with disabilities. Community may be the most effective means to achieving community.

Blaney's Chapter 8 attests both to the persistence of the old paradigm as well as to the analytic power of the new paradigm thinking. The definition of people with developmental disabilities who are growing old has, he asserts, drawn upon stereotypes of the older adults as a biologically declining group who should be assisted in exiting from the mainstream into various forms of age segregation. In effect, this has led to the resurrection of patterns that the field has repudiated for other age groups, such as segregative and custodial programming, as well as institutionalization. The new paradigm needs to be applied to this newly devalued group with particular consciousness. Instead of defining a new population labeled "elder DDs" he urges that we adopt adult first language and thinking. Adults should be supported in entering valued roles and relationships in their communities, not marginalized in elder high rises and senior centers.

Blaney brings us full circle to the critical role of definition as emphasized by Luckasson and Spitalnik. He similarly echos Mount, and O'Brien and O'Brien in his admonition that the old paradigm is alive and well and must be addressed by in-depth and consistent adherence to the values and emerging knowledge base of the new paradigm.

5

Political and Programmatic Shifts of the 1992 AAMR Definition of Mental Retardation

Ruth Luckasson and Deborah Spitalnik

A trip to Australia in 1992 presented a rich opportunity to think about the relationship of native aboriginal people to the land of Australia, particularly the ways in which their language, stories, art, and oral history illuminate and define their world. The trip afforded a view of how the aboriginal people exemplify an important task of all human beings, that of making their territory by naming the things in it (Chatwin, 1987).

It may be useful to consider the periodic naming of mental retardation in light of this deeply human process. There are, however, important differences in the naming of mental retardation compared to the naming of the land or things in the land. If mental retardation were a thing, it could be named once, and defined once, for all time, like, for example, a thistle, or a rock formation, or an aboriginal songline.

Because mental retardation is not a thing, but a relationship, a status, it must continually be renamed and redefined. Societies are not static, and relationships in a nonstatic world evolve. This is the vitality of the understanding of mental retar-

The authors wish to acknowledge the contributions of the other members of the American Association on Mental Retardation (AAMR) Committee on Terminology and Classification: David Coulter, Edward Polloway, Steven Reiss, Robert Schalock, Martha Snell, and Jack Stark; the AAMR leadership, volunteers, and staff; and the assistance of Charlie Silva of the Special Education Program at The University of New Mexico. Although the authors are, respectively, the Chair and a member of the Committee on Terminology and Classification, this chapter does not necessarily represent the official position of the AAMR or a consensus view of the Committee.

dation and is the basis for the drive to understand it in this time and in this society. The current understanding of mental retardation evolves, of course, from the work and thought of all who came before. As Solzhenitsyn (1993) said of art when accepting the medal of honor for literature of the National Arts Club, "No new work of art comes into existence (whether consciously or unconsciously) without an organic link to what was created earlier" (p. 3).

This chapter attempts to consider the 1992 American Association on Mental Retardation (AAMR) definition of mental retardation (reprinted in Figure 5.1) as a part of the broader transformation from service systems to systems of support outlined by Bradley (chap. 2, this volume). The changing paradigm in mental retardation and the roles that the new definition will play in that shift will be described. Also, the new definition, assumptions, and classification system in light of the changing paradigm will be analyzed and the programmatic and political implications of the shift described.

A CHANGING PARADIGM

Among the gifts that people with mental retardation bring to their societies is the opportunity to reflect on important issues of citizenship. Personal independence, for example, is one area in which reflection about people with mental retardation has helped create a subtler understanding of this value for all members of society. It has become clear that "independence" is too simplistic a word for the desired relationship between people and their society. A more accurate word is "interdependence" (O'Brien & O'Brien, 1992), which acknowledges the countless ways in which we depend on others, and they in turn depend on us, to enable everyone to create satisfying lives.

This changed understanding, from independence to interdependence, reflects a general search for community and genuine community membership. As people with mental retardation and the field have moved from the idea of independence to interdependence and community, it should not be surprising that the concept of mental retardation increasingly has reflected these values, and that the supports paradigm has been incorporated into the official definition. The further challenge is to ensure that these changes become manifest in the lives of people with mental retardation, rather than being merely changes in name only (Smull & Harrison, 1992). This will be progress toward the vision of genuine justice, true inclusion, and real community membership.

History of the Paradigm Shift

In the authors' view, the paradigm shift and the new definition are part of the rhythm of change that has spanned the years from the 1950s to the 1990s. Three important strands converged in the early 1950s to generate the programmatic changes being contemplated in the 1990s. First, in the period that Dr. Elizabeth Boggs has referred to as the "era of reconstruction" (chap. 3, this volume), came

DEFINITION OF MENTAL RETARDATION

Mental Retardation refers to substantial limitations in present functioning. It is characterized by significantly subaverage intellectual functioning existing concurrently with related limitations in two or more of the following applicable adaptive skill areas: communication, self-care, home living, social skills, community use, self-direction, health and safety, functional academics, leisure, and work. Mental retardation manifests before age 18.

APPLICATION OF THE DEFINITION

The following four assumptions are essential to the application of the definition:

1. Valid assessment considers cultural and linguistic diversity as well as differences in communication and behavioral factors;
2. The existence of limitations in adaptive skills occurs within the context of community environments typical of the individual's age peers and is indexed to the person's individualized needs for supports;
3. Specific adaptive limitations often coexist with strengths in other adaptive skills or other personal capabilities; and
4. With appropriate supports over a sustained period, the life functioning of the person with mental retardation will generally improve. (Luckasson et al., 1992, p. 1)

Figure 5.1. The American Association on Mental Retardation's new definition of mental retardation, adopted in 1992.

the founding of The Arc (originally the National Association for Retarded Children), which provided an organizing focus for family members to advocate on behalf of sons and daughters with mental retardation and also stimulated research, teaching, and government attention to the needs of persons with mental retardation. Second, in 1953 the United States Department of Health, Education, and Welfare (HEW) was established, which provided a pioneering focus for the organization and funding of appropriate services for people with mental retardation. Third, was the widespread training of researchers and other professionals in the behavioral and teaching technologies, which, in turn, illustrated the benefits of more active and systematic services to people with mental retardation. This interaction of advocacy, public commitment, and technology, in turn, marks the beginning of the paradigm shift.

Impetus for a New Definition

Movements and currents leading to the new definition can be divided into three major themes: 1) thinking about what mental retardation is, 2) the interaction between mental retardation and environments, and 3) resulting changes in services and habilitation. Table 5.1 outlines some of the aspects of these themes, and they are discussed below.

Mental retardation has moved from being considered an absolute trait of the individual to the interaction between the individual who has limited intellectual functioning and his or her environments (see e.g., Gold, 1975). Compared to the earlier deficit model, this interactive conception entails a functional assessment and functional interpretation of a person's disabilities. From the notion of mental retardation as a statistical measure, the field has come to understand mental retardation as a functional interaction between the person and the environment. As a consequence, the field has begun to turn its attention to the ways in which environments can be changed and adapted and away from an earlier emphasis on the control and management of the individual with mental retardation (Wolfensberger, 1969).

With this change has come the end of the readiness model, in which people with mental retardation earned their right to community membership, and the beginning of an emphasis on self-determination and empowerment. The images of dependence have been transformed to calls for self-definition, personal autonomy, and choice (Mairs, 1986). Images of people with mental retardation as burdens to their families and society (e.g., Terman, 1919) are now replaced with images of people with special challenges and gifts who are members of their families, accepted by the families themselves and by people and institutions outside the family (e.g., Shriver, 1962; Turnbull & Turnbull, 1990). The view of helplessness and eternal childhood has changed to a commitment to facilitate the transition to adult

Table 5.1. Shifts leading to the new paradigm and the 1992 definition

What mental retardation is
- From trait to interaction between person and environments
- From deficit model to functional interpretation and assessment
- From a statistic to a functional interaction

Interaction between mental retardation and environments
- From control and coercion to empowerment
- From dependence to self-definition, personal autonomy, and choice
- From being a burden to being a person with challenges
- From an eternal child and helpless to transitions to adult status
- From fear of a person to understanding of a person's full humanness

Resulting changes in services and habilitation
- From ineffectual teaching to good teaching and learning
- From no schools to separate schools to inclusive schools
- From residential segregation to neighborhoods
- From custodial care and maintenance to teaching functional skills
- From institutions to group homes to supported living
- From risk to family to acceptance to affirmation and supports
- From denial of medical care to universal access to health care
- From idleness to adult day program to segregated workshop to jobs
- From job discrimination to antidiscrimination to supported employment
- From IQ = restrictiveness to individualized determination of supports

status (see e.g., Ludlow, Turnbull, & Luckasson, 1988; Nirje, 1969). Instead of being perceived as hopeless victims in need of charity, people with mental retardation are being assisted in pursuing their rights. There are protection and advocacy agencies in every state to support this effort. Finally, the fear of people with disabilities (see e.g., the popular film, *Freaks* [Browning, 1932]) is disappearing in favor of an acceptance of the full humanness of all people with mental retardation. All these factors suggest a growing appreciation for the complexity and multidimensionality of all people with mental retardation.

Listed below are resulting changes in practice and services, which have been equally dramatic.

- From scattered and often ineffectual attempts at teaching, the field has moved to widespread access to effective teaching and habilitation.
- The idea of exclusion of children with disabilities from schools has been replaced by instruction in regular schools.
- Custodial care has given way to teaching functional skills for community living.
- Segregation in geographically isolated residential institutions has been replaced by a presumption that individuals with mental retardation should live in their neighborhoods.
- The notion that a child with mental retardation is a risk to the family's health and integrity gradually has yielded to a celebration of all families and the provision of supportive services to enhance an entire family's well-being.
- It used to be that medical care, even life-saving medical care, was routinely denied people with mental retardation (see e.g., Amicus curiae brief, 1985), but now the push is for universal access to health care.
- Gradually, idleness and "make work" are being replaced by regular jobs.
- Job discrimination has yielded to broad legislation prohibiting discrimination (see e.g., Sections 503 and 504 of PL 93-112, the Rehabilitation Act of 1973, and PL 101-336, the Americans with Disabilities Act of 1990), to career training, and to job supports.
- The assumption that a particular IQ leads automatically to a comparable level of restrictiveness has given way to individualized determinations of supports (Smith & Luckasson, 1992).

These changes in practice and services have led logically to the current analysis and promotion of the concept of supports.

THE DEFINITION AND ASSUMPTIONS

This section analyzes the 1992 definition. (See Luckasson et al., 1992, for a full explication of this definition.) "Mental retardation refers to substantial limitations in present functioning"; this is the key phrase that captures the essence of the new definition and its focus on the effect of specific impairments on an individual's ability to function in given environments. "It is characterized by significantly subaverage intellectual functioning. . . ." The guideline for the IQ ceiling is approximately 70–75 and below, which exists "concurrently with related limitations in two or more of the following applicable adaptive skill areas: communication, self-care, home living, social skills, community use, self-direction, health and safety, functional academics, leisure, and work." The concept of adaptive skill areas here builds and extends previous work on adaptive behavior; it moves away from a conclusion about a supposed global deficit and attempts to measure the specific functioning of the individual in the 10 critical skill areas. "Mental retardation manifests before age 18," because age 18 is established as the end of the developmental period.

The definition does not stand alone. Four assumptions are essential to the application of the definition. Assumption 1 says: "Valid assessment considers cultural and linguistic diversity as well as differences in communication and behavioral factors." The definition assumes cultural competence and requires cultural competence in making determinations. It also shifts the burden in assessment from the person with mental retardation to examiners to find ways of assessing an individual's needs. It is no longer acceptable to conclude that someone is untestable; rather, different ways of assessing people need to be learned. (See also, Gold, 1975.)

Assumption 2 says: "The existence of limitations in adaptive skills occurs within the context of community environments typical of the individual's age peers and is indexed to the person's individualized needs for supports." (See the section, "Supports and Community," later in this chapter.)

Assumption 3 says: "Specific adaptive limitations often coexist with strengths in other adaptive skills or other personal capabilities." This assumption begins to shape the fuller view of personhood and makes specific the complexity of each individual with mental retardation. It also provides the opportunity for more precision in analyzing an individual's needs for supports. This is a radical departure from an earlier view that mental retardation always represents a complete depression of performance, with an individual's functioning in different areas at relatively homogeneous levels.

Assumption 4 says, "With appropriate supports over a sustained period, the life functioning of the person with mental retardation will generally improve." Here, the definition and the supports paradigm come together, making specific the fact that supports are a way of enabling a person to function in the community. The reference to a sustained period clarifies that mental retardation is a developmental disability that generally persists throughout the life span.

THE CLASSIFICATION SYSTEM

The classification system in the new definition is a three-step system of diagnosis, classification, and systems of support. *Step 1 is the diagnosis of mental retarda-*

tion. It is based on an IQ score of approximately 70–75 or below, concurrent limitations in two or more adaptive skill areas, and manifestation before age 18.

Step 2 is analysis of the individual in the four dimensions of: I) intellectual functioning and adaptive skills, II) psychological and emotional considerations, III) physical health and etiology, and IV) environmental considerations. If a diagnosis of mental retardation is made, further classification is indicated. This is a conceptual departure from the previous system of assessment, in which application of the label of mental retardation often signaled the end of the assessment process. The IQ-based levels of mental retardation—mild, moderate, severe, and profound—have been eliminated, suggesting that eligibility criteria based on such distinctions have to be revisited.

In *Step 3 each of the dimensions is analyzed in terms of the profile and intensities of needed supports* (i.e., intermittent, limited, extensive, or pervasive). Dimension IV, environmental considerations (e.g., where the person lives and works or goes to school), allows a more holistic view of the person and his or her life, and the latitude to imagine what the person's optimal environment would be. It is also at this point in the classification system that there is perhaps the greatest risk of repeating some of the practices of the past by simply identifying strengths and weaknesses in a professionally driven way. However, this may be the point of greatest opportunity to ascertain what the person genuinely desires, to explore the factors that will help the person satisfy those desires, and to determine what is likely to restrain the person or stand in the way of his or her vision being reached.

In focusing on the environmental considerations, the classification system affirms the shift to the environment as the variable that must be manipulated to support the person in the community, rather than the attempt being made to change some intrinsic condition within the person. This third part of the classification system really captures the shift in paradigm. It begins to call upon evaluators, facilitators, helpers, service providers, teachers, advocates, and others to look at the kinds of supports an individual needs as part and parcel of the whole diagnostic process, rather than as an afterthought.

SUPPORTS AND COMMUNITY

This section discusses Assumption 2: "The existence of limitations in adaptive skills occurs within the context of community environments typical of the individual's age peers and is indexed to the person's individualized needs for supports." This assumption represents a modern explication of the nature of supports and community. The focus on individualized supports that is embodied in this assumption guides away from a service delivery or program model perspective, to individual planning and functional supports. It moves away from approaches that ignore the preferences and wishes of people with mental retardation to a focus on the supports necessary to realize their desired futures.

The phrase "community environments typical of the individual's age peers" establishes the goal of full adult status for individuals with mental retardation and full inclusion and participation in community life. The phrase "community environments" refers to homes, neighborhoods, schools, businesses, and other environments in which individuals of a certain age ordinarily live, work, learn, and interact. The focus on community environments and the individual's functioning within a social context moves much closer to the notion of supports than to the notion of services. In this view, services, especially paid services, are a subset of supports.

With this part of the new definition, it is established that mental retardation as a description of individual functioning can only be ascribed in the context of community life. And, more important, community is not an alternative or a model for a particular kind of service delivery; rather, it is the environment for all. This affirmation of community as the naturally occurring environment affirms families first and foremost as an individual's most basic, natural, and typical environment. The concept of family supports immediately follows from this view of environment.

The commentary (Luckasson et al., 1992) to the new definition explains desirable environments as those that provide opportunities, foster well-being, and promote stability. It urges consideration of optimal environments in terms of independence/interdependence, productivity, and community inclusion. A word of caution, however, is that, unless environments are addressed in terms of the individual's desired choices, there is a high risk that the new definition will be merely new language for the same old power relationships. This is not to minimize the challenges of assessing the choices and competence of some individuals (see e.g., Burwell, Katz, & Allard, 1993; Lindsey & Luckasson, 1991).

O'Brien (1987) and O'Brien and Lyle (1987) suggested a framework of five essential accomplishments useful for determining desirable environments: 1) community presence, 2) choice, 3) competence, 4) respect, and 5) community participation. The framework of five valued accomplishments was used in *Mental Retardation: Definition, Classification and Systems of Supports* (Luckasson et al., 1992), in which the new definition was published, to describe desirable environments. These values are important for analyzing supports and services. Community presence concerns sharing the ordinary places that define community lives. Choice has to do with the experience of autonomy, decision-making, and control. Competence concerns the opportunity to learn and perform functional and meaningful activities and to have the opportunity to express one's gifts and capacities. Respect has to do with the reality of having a valued place in one's community. Community participation has to do with being part of a network of personal relationships.

Supports refer to an array, not a continuum, of services, individuals, and settings that match the person's needs. Again, these should be matched in the context of the person's desires. Supports are resources and strategies that promote the interests and causes of individuals with or without disabilities that enable them to secure access to resources, information, and relationships as part of inclusive work and living environments and that result in enhanced interdependence, productivity, community inclusion, and satisfaction. Support resources are individual resources, skills, and competencies and the ability and opportunity to make choices, manage money, manage information, and the like. These resources are also other people, whether family, friends, coworkers, people one lives with, mentors, or neighbors. Technology might also be a form of support resource and includes assistive devices, job or living accommodations, or even behavioral technology. Another support resource encompasses habilitation services that may be needed if the other naturally occurring resources are either not available or not sufficient to assist the person in a desired living, working, or school environment. Clearly, these services, whether provided by a specialized disability agency or a generic service agency, are a subset of supports.

The person is at the center of the constellation of supports. (See Figure 5.2.) Family and friends are closest to the person. Next are other nonpaid supports from people like coworkers, colleagues, and neighbors. Then are generic services, that everyone uses. Finally, there are the specialized services, typically provided by the specialized mental retardation service system. Inherent in this schema is the requirement of coordination or brokering to facilitate the blend of supports and services for people.

The orientation of the new definition toward the provision of systems of supports stresses personal growth, not merely maintenance of functioning. A variety of support functions are proposed including support in making friends, financial

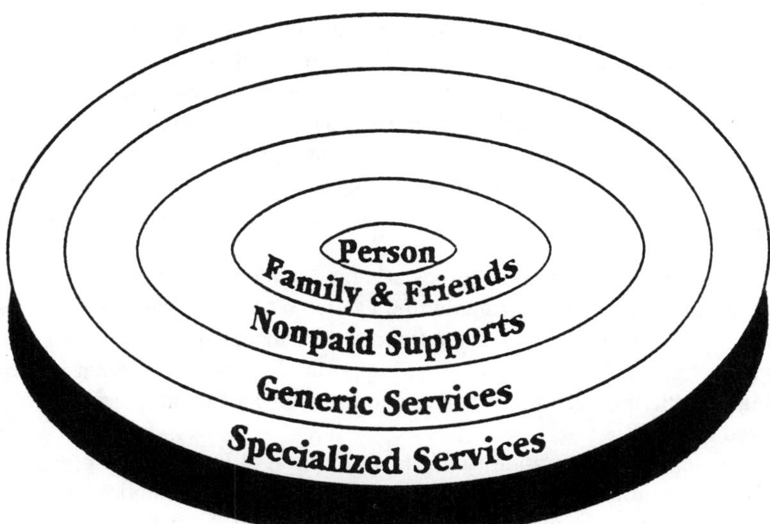

Figure 5.2. The constellation of supports. (From Luckasson et al. [1992]. *Mental retardation: Definition, classification, and systems of supports,* p. 144. Washington, DC: American Association on Mental Retardation. Reprinted by permission.)

planning, employee assistance, behavioral support, in-home living assistance, community access and use, and health assistance. The intent is to use ordinary terms that apply to everyone—such as financial planning rather than money management, employee assistance rather than job coaching—to indicate that the functions apply to everyone but that access is based on capabilities and supports.

One of the innovations in the definition and classification system is the classification by intensities of supports. Dr. Boggs has eloquently described the unfortunate result when services are offered in only one intensity, for example, when families who ask for some respite care are offered institutionalization or nothing at all (E. Boggs, personal communication, May, 1989). Systems have had an unfortunate tendency, in both planning and delivery, to deal with all services as if they were of equivalent magnitude and intensity. In the new definition and classification system, four intensities are specified: intermittent supports (I), provided on an as-needed basis; limited supports (L), those that are time limited but not intermittent, but may be characterized by consistency over time; extensive supports (E), those that are characterized by regular involvement, often daily, in at least some environments; and pervasive supports (P), those that are characterized by their constancy, high intensity, and need across environments, for example, life supports or even augmentative communication devices.

PROGRAMMATIC IMPLICATIONS OF THE SHIFT

This supports orientation is consistent with the contemporary thrust toward person-centered planning expressed elsewhere in this volume. (See Bradley, chap. 2, and Smull, chap. 4.) The focus is on the individual and his or her needs for supports and away from depersonalized, stereotypical views of what “EMRs” (“the educable mentally retarded”) need or what “TMRs” (“the trainable mentally retarded”) can do. It makes grouping by IQ level or by severity of disability less likely, creating opportunities to plan on the basis of individual preferences and needs.

This supports orientation comes at a time when new technologies and strategies are making enhanced functioning available to individuals of all levels and types of disability, making clear the trend toward increasingly available and effective means of teaching and providing supports. This is part of what is meant in saying that the new definition makes room for advancements that cannot yet be realized fully.

The supports orientation, with its description of individual preferences and needs, stands in strong contrast to the facilities-based orientation of most specialized delivery systems. Individual needs are now described in terms of the types, quantity, and intensity of supports needed. These needs for supports are separated from the location where the supports are or would be delivered, moving service delivery away from program approaches. Individual needs should no longer be described in terms of a particular type of service or placement but, instead, in terms of the types and constellations of supports that are to be addressed.

Funding and other practices that are based on the underlying concept of "program slots" or "beds" and that assume the uniform provision of a packaged service, need to be reconceptualized in terms of strategies to address individuals' preferences and needs for supports. As large service delivery systems struggle to redefine their roles in light of the supports orientation, there is likely to be a shift away from the direct provision of services and toward facilitation and brokering of supports (Sullivan & Spitalnik, 1988), which will need to be accompanied by an evolution of personnel roles (Knoll & Racino, chap. 17, this volume).

The enabling quality of supports is made explicit in Assumption 4 of the definition: "With appropriate supports over a sustained period, the life functioning of the person with mental retardation will generally improve." Although this assumption captures the promise and hopefulness inherent in the supports approach, it also augurs some potential risks if the approach is not implemented appropriately and if there are not controls within service delivery systems. Improvement in life functioning comes through an improvement in adaptive skills. This improvement in adaptive skills may be dependent on the continued provision of individual supports or be an opportunity to create an evolving blend of natural and service supports. Any policies or tendencies of large service delivery systems to arbitrarily allot or limit supports based on individual levels of functioning might put at risk the gains in life functioning made by the individual and would connote a system merely utilizing the language of the supports approach, not based on its full tenets.

Individuals must always have the choice to leave the embrace of the service system, but there must be easy and flexible access to return if life circumstances and choices warrant reconnection to the specialized delivery system. But, care must be taken to ensure that leaving is not a coercive attempt, however subtle, by a service system to avoid its responsibility to respond to people's individual needs.

Assessment and Clinical Decision-Making

The supports approach inherent in the new definition requires ongoing access to clinical decision-making, with the individual as a primary part of that process. The concerns raised above about the potential withdrawal or loss of access to supports can, to some extent, be mitigated by ongoing access to this type of decision-making. Clinical decision-making, as a component of the process of applying the definition, will parallel the emphasis of the supports approach. Data collection and planning will shift emphasis to the nature of environments and the nature of the supports needed, and away from narrow reliance on IQ measures and adaptive behavior scales. As the 10 adaptive skill areas replace the more unidimensional concept of adaptive behavior, the field is challenged to develop meaningful assessment strategies in each of these areas of life functioning. Identifying assessment resources to implement this more holistic approach, both in terms of personnel and financial resources, will present an additional challenge to most delivery systems.

Challenges for Research

The new definition will challenge the research community to develop more complete and accurate descriptions for the people who are the focus of research. The elimination of the four levels of mental retardation from the definition will eliminate convenient groupings of individuals and necessitate greater specificity and comprehensiveness in describing individuals and groupings of individuals. This should improve the generalizability of results. The emphasis in the definition on environments and supports will contribute to a movement away from the individuals' condition and level of functioning as the independent variable(s). The nature and structure of the environments and supports provided will begin to emerge as independent or intervening variables. Dependent variables will evolve to include such factors as level of satisfaction, level of functioning, and living or employment status. Also, the increased adoption of the supports orientation is likely to contribute to more consumer driven and consumer responsive research (Morris, 1991).

The supports model used in the new definition has implications for quality assurance and enhancement of services as well. Already, the field is moving toward outcome-based evaluations of quality services. (See e.g., The Accreditation Council, 1992.)

POLITICAL IMPLICATIONS OF THE SHIFT

A major political implication of the shift is a different view of citizenship. The political and legal history of people with mental retardation indicates over and over the fragility of their rights of citizenship (Scheerenberger, 1983, 1987). With the change of focus from personal deficits to needs for systems of supports in different areas, the burden should move from the individual, who is expected to "earn" rights or has rights jeopardized because of level of IQ, to society, which is striving to provide appropriate supports to all individuals. In individual cases, this different view of citizenship should translate to increasing attention to supporting people's independence, self-direction, and personal autonomy.

The improvements in helping individuals reach lifestyles they find personally satisfying have been possible, in great part, due to effective advocacy, by the individuals themselves (Williams & Shoultz, 1982) and others on their behalf. The changes made in definition should enhance the call for individualized determinations of systems of supports in conducting life with friends and family in community.

As the focus moves from individual deficits to needed supports, funding mechanisms will change, and these mechanisms will cause some reshaping of statutes and regulations. Activity began with, for example, the Social Security Administration's evolving definition of children with developmental disabilities. Continuing translation into federal and state laws and regulations is likely over the next decade (Lowitzer, Utley, & Baumeister, 1987).

States are integrating principles represented in the new definition into their statutes and regulations. For example, in 1992, Illinois mandated meaningful opportunities for people with disabilities and their families to contribute their perspectives and ensure their participation in the development of policies, supports, and services that affect them (Terrill, 1992). Movement toward changes reflected in the new definition has also been reported in Colorado, Massachusetts, and West Virginia.

Diagnosis and classification of mental retardation can also alert the civil and criminal justice systems to eligibility for certain services or certain legal protections. It is hoped that the clarification and extension of adaptive skill areas will assist courts in understanding the limitations of people with mental retardation and that the increased emphasis on supports will encourage development of appropriate accommodations and services in the justice system.

CONCLUSION

The avenues for accomplishing systems change are many and varied. This chapter has attempted to describe the rhythm of change behind the American Association on Mental Retardation's new definition of mental retardation and some of the programmatic and political implications of the shift. As with previous definitions of mental retardation, this one must be viewed within the unique philosophical, political, and professional context of this society and the current time. It reflects an evolution of thinking and assumptions and builds on a long, thoughtful tradition. However, unlike previous definitions, it uses the community as a reference point and the aspirations common to everyone as potential aims of intervention. This new perspective will have an impact on all aspects of the field and will add to the momentum of change toward a supports-based approach to assist people with mental retardation in realizing their dreams.

REFERENCES

The Accreditation Council. (1992). *Outcome based performance measures.* (Field review edition). Landover, MD: Author.

Amicus Curiae brief of the American Association on Mental Retardation, et al. (1985). *Heckler v. American Hospital Association*, 479 U.S. 610 (1986).

Browning, T. (director). (1932). *Freaks.*

Burwell, B., Katz, R., & Allard, M. (1993). *Supported living: A comparative analysis across four states.* Cambridge, MA: Systemetrics.

Chatwin, B. (1987). *The songlines.* New York: Viking.

Gold, M. (1975). *Try Another Way training manual.* Champaign-Urbana, IL: Marc Gold & Associates.

Lindsey, P., & Luckasson, R. (1991). Consent Screening Interview for community residential placement: Report on the initial pilot study data. *Mental Retardation, 29,* 119–124.

Lowitzer, A.C., Utley, C.A., & Baumeister, A.A. (1987). AAMD's 1983 Classification in

Mental Retardation as utilized by state mental retardation/developmental disabilities agencies. *Mental Retardation, 25,* 287–291.

Luckasson, R., Coulter, D.L., Polloway, E.A., Reiss, S., Schalock, R.L., Snell, M.E., Spitalnik, D.M., & Stark, J.A. (1992). *Mental retardation: Definition, classification, and systems of supports* (9th ed.). Washington, DC: American Association on Mental Retardation.

Ludlow, B.L., Turnbull, A.P., & Luckasson, R. (Eds.). (1988). *Transitions to adult life for people with mental retardation—Principles and practices.* Baltimore: Paul H. Brookes Publishing Co.

Mairs, N. (1986). *Plaintext.* Tucson: University of Arizona.

Morris, M. (1991, October). *The challenge of consumer responsiveness: Fifteen questions for a UAP or research center.* Presentation handout at American Association of University Affiliated Programs annual meeting, Austin.

Nirje, B. (1969). The normalization principle and its human management implications. In R. Kugel & W. Wolfensberger (Eds.), *Changing patterns in residential services for the mentally retarded* (pp. 179–195). Washington, DC: President's Committee on Mental Retardation. Reprinted in Nirje, B. (1992). *The normalization papers.* Sweden: Centre for Handicap Research, Uppsala University.

O'Brien, J. (1987). A guide to lifestyle planning: Using The Activities Catalog to integrate services and natural support systems. In B. Wilcox & G.T. Bellamy (Eds.), *A Comprehensive Guide to The Activities Catalog: An alternative curriculum for youth and adults with severe disabilities* (pp. 175–189). Baltimore: Paul H. Brookes Publishing Co.

O'Brien, J., & Lyle, C. (1987). *Framework for accomplishment.* Lithonia, GA: Responsive Systems Associates.

O'Brien, J., & O'Brien, C. (1992). Members of each other: Perspectives on social support for people with severe disabilities. In J. Nisbet (Ed.), *Natural supports in school, at work and in the community for people with severe disabilities* (pp. 17–63). Baltimore: Paul H. Brookes Publishing Co.

Scheerenberger, R.C. (1983). *A history of mental retardation.* Baltimore: Paul H. Brookes Publishing Co.

Scheerenberger, R.C. (1987). *A history of mental retardation: A quarter century of promise.* Baltimore: Paul H. Brookes Publishing Co.

Shriver, E.K. (1962, September 5). Hope for retarded children. Our retarded sister. *Saturday Evening Post,* pp. 71–75.

Smith, D.D., & Luckasson, R. (1992). *Introduction to special education: Teaching in an age of challenges.* Needham Heights, MA: Allyn & Bacon.

Smull, M.W., & Bellamy, G.T. (1991). Community services for adults with disabilities: Policy challenges in the emerging support paradigm. In L.H. Meyer, C.A. Peck, & L. Brown (Eds.), *Critical issues in the lives of people with severe disabilities* (pp. 527–536). Baltimore: Paul H. Brookes Publishing Co.

Smull, M.W., & Harrison, S.B. (1992, September/October). Person-centered planning and perversion prevention. *AAMR News & Notes,* p. 3.

Solzhenitsyn, A. (1993, February 7). The relentless cult of novelty and how it wrecked the century. *The New York Times Book Review,* pp. 3, 17.

Sullivan, M.E., & Spitalnik, D.M. (1988). *Case management services for persons with developmental disabilities in New Jersey: A systems analysis.* Piscataway, NJ: Robert Wood Johnson Medical School, University Affiliated Program of New Jersey.

Terman, L. (1919). *The intelligence of school children.* NY: Houghton Mifflin.

Terrill, C.F. (1992, November/December). Illinois passes legislation mandating consumer participation. *AAMR News & Notes,* p. 1.

Turnbull, A.P., & Turnbull, H.R. (1990). *Families, professionals, and exceptionality: A special partnership* (2nd ed.). Columbus, OH: Merrill.

Williams, P., & Shoultz, B. (1982). *We can speak for ourselves.* Bloomington: Indiana University Press.

Wolfensberger, W. (1969). The origin and nature of our institutional models. In R. Kugel & W. Wolfensberger (Eds.), *Changing patterns in residential services for the mentally retarded* (pp. 59–171). Washington, DC: President's Committee on Mental Retardation.

6

Benefits and Limitations of Personal Futures Planning

Beth Mount

Personal futures planning is an approach for learning about people with disabilities and creating a lifestyle that can help people contribute in community life. Personal futures planning is much more than a meeting; it is an ongoing process of social change. The effectiveness of a plan depends on a support group of concerned people who make a dream reality by learning to solve problems, build community, and change organizations together over time. The locus of change is moved away from the person with a disability toward change in social roles, responses, and existing organizational structures. As an ongoing process of innovation, it can help liberate people from oppressive environments and processes that are harmful.

Personal futures planning can be a helpful tool when it is used selectively to support long-range change in organizational cultures, and it can facilitate immediate changes in the quality of life experiences available to people. However, it can easily become another empty ritual if used as a quick fix without appreciation for the complex tasks of changing environments, enhancing respect and decision-making, and creating a context for friendships.

This chapter provides an overview of the basic assumptions and benefits of the personal futures planning approach. This overview is followed by a discussion of the breakdowns that begin when personal futures planning is implemented in a system-centered, rather than person-centered, way. Finally, an effective development project is outlined to provide a hopeful alternative to methods of implementation that fail.

AN ALTERNATIVE TO TRADITIONAL PLANNING

The way of describing people, thinking about their future, and solving problems together are among the many ways of expressing values, assumptions, and ideals. Personal futures planning is a way of planning together with people to express and live according to the values described in Section I of this volume. This form of planning is a powerful tool because it provides the capacity to develop new visions for people, reimagine what is possible for them, and reevaluate their own roles and investments in making these ideals livable.

In contrast, traditional forms of planning are based on the ideal of a developmental model, which negates this promise of renewal by emphasizing the deficits and needs of people, overwhelming people with endless program goals and objectives, and assigning responsibility for decision-making to professionals. Traditional planning often reinforces the status quo of organizations by focusing solely on accomplishments that are possible within existing programs and structures.

The underlying values of traditional planning communicate subtle messages, for example: The person is the problem and should be fixed but never will be. Learning to adapt to impossible situations is expected; the more a person protests, the more of a problem he or she is. Professionals know best, and the person must stay in segregated programs until he or she is ready for community. These messages undermine people's confidence and growth.

Many of the positive outcomes intended by well-meaning planners are sabotaged by these messages, the bias of others more interested in the control and maintenance of people under the rubric of care is strengthened. The message to people with disabilities and their families is that the planning process is to be used to clarify their needs and deficits, to identify how they need to change to fit existing programs, and to give professionals the opportunity to feel certain that they know what is best.

ANOTHER WAY OF THINKING

Personal futures planning reflects an alternative set of values and messages. It is based on the promise of community inclusion for everyone. The logic of personal futures planning amplifies the message that people with disabilities have important gifts and capacities that seek expression. Professionals need to learn to listen to, and take direction from, individuals and families. Many of the activities, people, and experiences they enjoy provide professionals with clues to their interests that professionals hope to expand and increase. Similarly, often when situations frustrate people it means that the setting, environment, activity, or people in the situation need to change.

Personal futures planning helps the professional to change from the superior role of expert to a more humble role as a partner whose motto is: Work so that people have many ways to be a part of community life. It is our job to work to negotiate needed organizational changes that may stand in the way. Caring, supportive friendships are central to well-being and professionals must work with individuals and families to learn how to develop community and friendships. The contrast between the focus of traditional program plans, and the alternative vision of positive futures plans is summarized in Table 6.1 (Mount, 1991b).

THE BENEFITS OF PERSONAL FUTURES PLANNING

Personal futures planning is most effective when it is used in conjunction with a number of other activities to question service practices and provide direction for innovation. Following are descriptions of five potential benefits of personal futures planning. Futures planning shares these benefits with planning approaches that have similar assumptions and ideals (Brost & Johnson, 1982; Forest & Snow, 1987; Green, 1984; O'Brien, 1987).

1. *A positive view of people* in personal futures planning helps professionals come to know people with disabilities and appreciate their capacities. This is a discovery process because the gifts, interests, and capacities of people with disabilities so often are buried under labels, poor reputations, and fragmentation of information. The personal profile process helps professionals see these individuals in a new light, by emphasizing their hidden gifts. The focus on capacity as a major aspect of futures planning is powerful because it can be liberating from the institutionalized process of detached criticism built into traditional diagnosis and assessment. In the author's experience, once this freedom is experienced, people with disabilities, their family members, and human service workers are eager to cast off the old descriptions that limit people and discover new ways to see people. The development of a positive view often generates constructive energy and optimism that people can channel into the process of change.

Table 6.1. Contrasts between traditional program planning and personal futures planning

Characteristics of traditional program plans	Characteristics of personal futures planning
Goals focus on *decreasing* specific negative behaviors.	Images of the future anticipate that positive change will occur and affirmative activities and experiences will *increase*.
Program categories and service options that are often *segregated* are identified.	Ideas and possibilities reflect specific *community* sites and settings and valued roles in those settings.
Many goals and objectives reflect potentially *minor accomplishments* that can be attained in existing programs without making any changes.	Some ideas will seem outlandish, unrealistic, and impractical and require *major* changes in existing patterns.

From Mount, B. (1991b). *Person-centered planning: A sourcebook of values, ideals and method to encourage person-centered development*. New York: Graphic Futures. Reprinted by permission.

2. *Motivation through inspiration* is the aspect of futures planning that develops the capacity to work for change on the basis of a common vision that feels more worthy than conventional practices. Often people feel drawn toward change when they create, invent, envision, and imagine a better life rich with community life and relationships. This motivation process offers a constructive alternative to the often boring and insulting process of traditional planning directed by endless lists of goals and objectives that lead nowhere.
3. *Personal empowerment* for people with disabilities, their families, and their friends is a goal of personal futures planning. An effective planning process can strengthen the voice and desires of the focus person in a way that enables others to respond. An effective planning process also includes people with disabilities in an ongoing process of problem-solving with the help of family and friends, thereby decreasing the control of paid professionals and, hopefully, increasing interdependence with informal support systems. When people have difficulty representing their own interests, the process seeks to inform and support those people who are most involved on a daily basis.
4. *Community involvement and development* are central to the personal futures planning process. An effective planning process seeks to widen, deepen, and strengthen relationships and the community life. The community-building focus of futures planning helps redirect attention, time, energy, and resources from building systems to building personal relationships.
5. *Organizational change* is an integral part of personal futures planning. Almost every personal futures plan that is true to the person challenges the existing organizational process and structure in some way. The personal futures planning process can illuminate the shortcomings of existing organizations and lead to clear, constructive alternatives that will truly support people's ideals and dreams. Organizations can benefit from the process by finding new directions for development, and learning new ways to respond to people.

WHAT DO WE KNOW ABOUT SUPPORTING POSITIVE OUTCOMES?

The most powerful outcomes of futures planning emerge through the stories that people themselves tell when they feel they are active in creating life experiences that reflect their own interests and when they have a growing support group of interested, committed, and effective people who provide both emotional and instrumental assistance. They report a growing sense of optimism and hope as the process of change unfolds. (Two powerful stories of change appear in Ducharme, Beeman, DeMarasse, and Ludlum [chap. 20, this volume].)

The stories of greatest change have shown that there are a number of conditions that strengthen the potential for positive outcomes. For example, personal and organizational support significantly increase the likelihood that a vision can be realized. Listed below are 10 conditions concerning a variety of factors that strengthen and nurture the power of a plan and the likelihood that it will result in positive change (Mount, 1991a).

1. Positive change is more likely when the person, parents, or committed advocates want it and the energy is focused by a clear set of values and assumptions. When at least one person feels stuck in the current situation, is aware of other options, and has the energy for change, there will probably be more effectiveness.
2. People need the opportunity to see themselves in light of their gifts and capacities. This view is more likely to be maintained when a group of people develop a shared appreciation of the capacities of the person, and work together over time to develop and support these capacities.
3. The individual needs a specific personal vision for a different life. This vision is more likely to lead to change when it is sensitive to individual interests and local community life.
4. A group of people should be willing to meet on a regular basis to solve problems over time on behalf of the focus person. This support group (also called circle of support or person-centered team) develops a shared appreciation of the capacities and desires of the focus person and works together to identify obstacles and solve problems.
5. A skilled facilitator should be available to support a group over time. Under ideal conditions, an effective facilitator not only supports individual circles of support, but also builds the conditions that lead to change.
6. The support group should include at least one person, unpaid or paid, with a strong commitment to act on behalf of the person. This person(s) takes a very active role in making emergent ideas reality and may be a parent, friend, community member, service provider, group facilitator, or the focus person.
7. The support network should include at least one person who builds connections and opens doors in the local community. This community builder is often deeply rooted in the local neighborhood and community and knows how to create opportunities and support there.
8. It is helpful for the focus person to be connected to other people facing similar obstacles or challenges. This network may be formal or informal, such as a group of parents concerned about inclusive education, residential options, and so forth.
9. At least one human service agency must be willing to change to support a person's dreams. Organizations providing flexible, individualized supports to help people realize their personal dreams are most effective. These individualized forms of support give control directly to those using the support.
10. The person should have access to people who make major decisions about resources at the local, regional, or state level. Influence with those in authority helps people express their issues and work constructively to find alternatives to existing limitations.

In keeping with the conditions listed above many of the agencies most interested in using a personal futures planning approach are innovative by nature. Staff in these agencies have a strong value base, a critical understanding of the nature of human services (Wolfensberger, 1983), and a powerful vision (O'Brien & Lyle, 1987). Many successful stories of change emerge from small agencies that use person-centered planning to support a radical conversion from segregated settings to individualized supports (Mount, 1987).

Other dramatic stories of change result from the intense advocacy efforts of a family member, the person with a disability, or a committed friend or ally (Mount & Caruso, 1989). Equally compelling outcomes occur when planners have access to substantial, flexible, individualized, packages of funding that can be used to finance the supports needed to realize a dream (Brost & Johnson, 1982; Mount, O'Brien, & Jacdo, 1991). Some of the most moving stories of change occur when community members take a leadership role in realizing a vision (Mount, Ducharme, & Beeman, 1991). The most powerful change comes through people, communities, and organizations that are pursuing a powerful vision, that value strengthening and building personal supports, and that offer a variety of organizational incentives to facilitate the planning process.

In contrast, many organizational environments lack the conditions that nourish the implementation of a plan. Efforts to replicate the positive benefits of personal futures planning in these settings may be far less successful and can even backfire, causing people to feel disappointed, powerless, and cynical about innovation. Potential planners should proceed with a great deal of caution to avoid the most common implementation problems. Potential futures planners must work at the organizational and community level to increase the activities and investments that strengthen the power of an individual plan. The following section presents an overview of typical implementation problems, followed by a model for effective implementation.

COMMON BREAKDOWNS IN IMPLEMENTATION

Personal futures planning is least effective when it is used in isolation from other complementary change activities. This fragmentation is most likely to occur if the futures planning process is standardized, implemented on a large scale, or otherwise molded to fit into existing structures of service instead of challenging them.

The usefulness of personal futures planning is most often undermined by its popularity. The power of the initial planning process is seductive and entices people to implement the process for as many people as possible and train a host of others to do so as well. The following sections show the most common problems that occur in interpretation and implementation.

Seduction of the Quick Fix

The most common breakdown in the futures planning process occurs when people place too much emphasis on the initial meetings and do not value, plan, and invest in the ongoing process of follow-up and renewal. The first several meetings are powerful, and people are energized by describing the capacities of people and creating a vision together. But then comes the hard work of making the ideas a reality and slogging through the details, obstacles, and frustrations of implementation. Planners can attend more to follow-up when they limit the number of plans they initiate and work to create an organizational climate that builds the capacity to respond.

Grandiosity

Often when people are investing in planning meetings without attention to follow-up, they are also indulging in another undermining practice, that is, doing too many plans for too many people. This error is quite common because it is natural to think that if something is helpful, offering it to everyone make sense. It goes against a sense of equity and justice to single out a few people who will benefit initially. But it is important to trust that an effective, small-scale effort ultimately will benefit many people.

Standardization and Efficiency

Another common breakdown in the futures planning process occurs when people seek to streamline, mandate, and/or standardize the process to meet the system's demand for compliance, control, accountability, and efficiency. When the system takes over the futures planning process, the activity immediately loses its power, flexibility, and responsiveness, quickly becoming one more intrusive, insensitive, and ineffective activity. When people lacking strong person-centered values are given the power to conduct a procedure that has no potential to change the system of which it is a part, then futures planning becomes one more way to process people through a series of empty and meaningless rituals. There is a long way to go before organizational cultures have the capacity to plan thoughtfully for many people. In the meantime, it makes sense to provide personal futures planning as a planning option, as part of an integrated set of innovation activities. It makes sense to train interested and committed people to lead innovative efforts. Effective implementation on a small scale truly can change the way of thinking about being effective in the lives of all people (Mount et al., 1991).

Fragmentation from Organizational Change

The most common problem of personal futures planning occurs when the individual planning process is detached from the effort to change existing organizational structures, processes, and cultures. In order for staff within an agency to have the time, energy, money, and flexibility to respond to people, organizations must change, and the process of change is complex. In order for community members to be invited to participate in a person's life, someone has to do the asking and provide the support. Increasing numbers of people need to be freed up, sheltered, and supported to do this work (Landis & Peeler, 1990).

People who plan for positive futures must be prepared to respond to the person, explore the community, and work to change the system to obtain free spaces in which people can respond and life can evolve. When futures planning is separated from the process of organizational change, ironically, it is harder to maintain the free spaces and flexibility in which the most lively change occurs. *Framework for Accomplishment*, by O'Brien and Lyle (1987), presents lessons and tools to help people develop some skills to bridge the gap between person-centered planning and organizational change.

There are some exceptions to the need for organizational support. For example, some people using the futures planning process are not dependent on human services systems and do not plan to be. They can avoid the challenge of organizational change by working exclusively to build informal supports, and this is an admirable effort. However, most people do not have the choice of working totally outside the boundaries of human services organizations.

CONSEQUENCES OF USING PERSONAL FUTURES PLANNING IN A SYSTEM-CENTERED WAY

Person-centered planning is least effective when it is implemented in a system-centered way. Systems rely on big numbers, magnify promises of change, and are driven by standardization and efficiency. System-centered change, likewise, is constrained by these qualities.

Fortunately, there are ways to safeguard the positive aspects of personal futures planning when it is integrated with a number of other renewing and innovative activities. These person-centered development projects create a safe haven from the demands of system-centered work and allow staff to learn how to think and respond in different ways. As people learn new ways of taking action, this knowledge begins to filter into larger systems and into the collective consciousness of possibility. This is a more effective way to spread the benefits of the futures planning approach. Some aspects of effective person-centered development are discussed in the following section.

A LEARNING PROCESS APPROACH

Learning about person-centered development comes from a variety of projects that integrate ongoing renewal activities with an implementation design that enables people to listen, test their ideals, learn new skills, make new investments, and measure success. These innovative projects are replacing a reliance on rules, regulations, and bureaucracy as the way to organize work. They create an alternative learning process that supports creativity, reflection, collaborative problem-solving, and personal learning that leads to change (Korten, 1983).

At the level of the individual, community, agency, region, or state, each project invests in five closely linked activities, each of which makes a contribution to helping people think and respond differently. If an organization cannot invest in each learning activity, personal futures planning alone is likely to become an empty ritual. Following are descriptions of these activities (O'Brien & Mount, 1988).

Personal futures planning provides an important opportunity for renewal within an agency. The process brings people together to develop images of desirable individual futures and collaborative strategies for realizing them. The process is adapted to fit the mission, the people, and the community. Four additional complementary activities that provide opportunities for learning and renewal are listed below:

1. *Interactive problem solving* involves small groups of people in creative management of the day-to-day problems of taking constructive action on personal futures planning and redesign efforts.
2. *Strategic redesign* entails investing a growing proportion of the organization's time and money in developing new community opportunities, creating new connections and roles for people, and supporting people's continuing participation.
3. *Systematic evaluation* ensures review of the effectiveness and efficiency of organizational changes.
4. *Structural reflection* provides occasions for those involved in changes to deepen their understanding of the ethical issues at stake in delivering responsible services to people who are socially devalued.

As individual support groups and/or organizations increase their investment in these activities, they are able to develop unique responses that increase the fit between the interests and gifts of people with disabilities on the one hand, and community opportunities and system resources on the other. These designs for support cannot simply be invented and imposed by hierarchical, standardized, bureaucratic processes. Direction for change must emerge from groups of people who listen to each other, respond, solve problems, reflect, and redesign services so they have more time, energy, and money to respond to people's needs.

The learning approach is different from standard operating procedure because it challenges people to develop and act on their own knowledge of the grassroots, which ultimately diminishes their reliance on the often meaningless demands of external authorities. It makes sense to build this learning capacity on a small scale and expand as people increase their ability to work in a completely different way. The following section outlines the key components of person-centered development projects that can shelter the free space needed for innovation.

PERSON-CENTERED DEVELOPMENT PROJECTS

Effective person-centered projects not only rely on a number of renewal activities for direction, they also include a process for learning about implementation, developing effective leadership, ensuring outcomes in people's lives, and changing organizations as needed. All of these activities are linked and integrated in an intentional design for learning. While these projects vary greatly in their scale, location, intent, leadership, and organizational environments, they share the following characteristics:

1. *Beginning with a focus question:* A focus is found by clarifying an issue or challenge that needs exploration, for example:
   - Providing more options for the transition out of high school
   - Dealing with behaviors that challenge existing environments
   - Owning a residence
   - Including children fully in neighborhood schools
2. *Convening a study group:* A small collective of people who have a stake in the focus question and want to be part of finding new solutions should be identified. This group often includes a facilitator, a change agent, the person with a disability, and a person from an executive area.
3. *Creating a listening body:* A place for innovation that is sheltered from the demands and requirements of the existing system should be designed. This listening body should have the four aspects listed below:
   - A limited number of people with disabilities whose lives will inform the focus question and who want to be involved in the process of exploration
   - Facilitators who take the lead in learning to conduct futures plans and provide follow-up
   - Support circles or groups to provide day-to-day and ongoing support to the focus person
   - The support of a representative from management who can respond with administrative flexibility and support
4. *Providing opportunities for renewal:* Ongoing occasions for people to obtain new ideas and reflect and deepen their values and commitment must be ensured.
5. *Planning regular forums/meetings with organizational stakeholders:* Members of the listening body should meet, as needed, to identify themes in the process of implementation and develop platforms for change that suggest concrete alternatives of what would be better. Members then meet in person with critical organizational stakeholders to discuss issues and work out solutions.

A person-centered development project draws some boundaries around a small number of people, facilitators, administrators, and community members so that they have the support to plan with people and see their ideas to fruition. As ideals are implemented, people grow in their sense of accomplishment and their personal and group authority and capacity to make good things happen. These positive approaches and outcomes then begin to spread to others, and new development projects are initiated. (See Mount et al. [1991] for further discussion.)

SUMMARY

The limits have been reached on the system-centered approach to people with disabilities and their families, which worked through rationality, efficiency, and equality. Person-centered development is a more organic approach. Personal futures planning is one of a number of person-centered planning approaches that strengthen the capacity to see people differently and to develop a vision that leads to powerful change. However, thinking differently is just the beginning of change. A wonderful personal futures plan is only one aspect of a number of innovative and renewing activities that help interested people learn new ways to respond. It is a helpful tool in the hands of committed people who work in a environment ripe for change. Planners interested in the futures planning approach must look beyond the lure of the quick fix of the initial planning meetings toward the long journey of learning to do things differently on personal, community, and organizational levels. The resources of the system can be used to support safe havens where people can learn the art of person-centered development. The continuing challenge is to create environments in which the nurturing needed for the concern, commitment, and caring that engenders true relationships can be given.

REFERENCES

Brost, M., & Johnson, T. (1982). *Getting to know you*. Madison: Wisconsin Coalition for Advocacy.

Forest, M., & Snow, J. (1987). *The MAPS process*. Toronto, Ontario, Canada: Frontier College.

Green, K. (1984). Twenty-four hour planning for persons with complex needs. *Canadian Journal on Mental Retardation, 34*(1), 3–11.

Korten, D. (1983). People-centered development: Toward a framework. In D. Korten & E. Klauss (Eds.), *People-centered development: Contributions toward theory and planning frameworks*. West Hartford: Kumarian Press.

Landis, S., & Peeler, J. (1990). *What have we noticed as we've tried to assist people one person at a time?* Chillicothe, OH: Ohio Safeguards.

Mount, B. (1987). *Personal futures planning: Finding directions for change*. University of Michigan Dissertation Service.

Mount, B. (1991a). *Dare to dream: An analysis of the conditions that lead to personal change for people with disabilities*. Manchester, CT: Communitas.

Mount, B. (1991b). *Person-centered planning: A sourcebook of values, ideals and method to encourage person-centered development*. New York: Graphic Futures.

Mount, B., & Caruso, G. (1989). *New dreams, new lives, new directions for alternative living, Inc*. Annapolis, MD: Alternative Living Inc.

Mount, B., Ducharme, G., & Beeman, P. (1991). *Person-centered development: A journey in learning to listen to people with disabilities*. Manchester, CT: Communitas.

Mount, B., O'Brien, L., & Jacdo, G. (1991). *New vision, new challenges: Reflections on the challenges of person-centered residential service development*. Annapolis, MD: Alternative Living, Inc.

O'Brien, J. (1987). A guide to life-style planning: Using The Activities Catalog to integrate services and natural support systems. In B. Wilcox & G. T. Bellamy (Eds.), *A comprehensive guide to The Activities Catalog: An alternative curriculum for youth and adults with severe disabilities* (pp. 175–189). Baltimore: Paul H. Brookes Publishing Co.

O'Brien, J., & Lyle, C. (1987). *Framework for accomplishment.* Lithonia, GA: Responsive Systems Associates.

O'Brien, J., & Mount, B. (1988). *Person-centered development: Thinking tool.* Atlanta: Responsive Systems Associates.

Wolfensberger, W. (1983). Social role valorization: A proposed new term for the principle of normalization. *Mental Retardation, 21*(6), 234–239.

7

More than Just a New Address

Images of Organization for Supported Living Agencies

John O'Brien and Connie Lyle O'Brien

The director of an agency that has moved from operating several group homes to providing supported living gave the following description of her experience:

> When we decided to change from group home to supported living, I thought it would be good for the people we serve. At first, I didn't think much about how our agency would have to change beyond figuring out how to find apartments and getting staff used to dealing with people in different locations. The change has been good, for all of us. But a lot more has had to change about the way we do things than I ever thought. *Doing supported living is more than just getting people a new address* [italics added].

This chapter is adapted from O'Brien, J. and O'Brien, C.L. (1991). *More than just a new address: Images of organization for supported living agencies. Perspectives on Community Building Series.* Lithonia, GA: Responsive Systems Associates, pp. 1–40. Reports in the *Perspectives on Community Building* series discuss issues of concern to those who are working to increase the presence and participation of people with developmental disabilities in the neighborhoods, workplaces, schools, and associations that constitute community life. These reports are based on visits to innovative human services programs and focus group discussions. Program visits include intensive interviews with program leaders and staff, and usually with some of the people they serve. Discussions include people with different interests and points of view: people with developmental disabilities, family members, people who provide and manage services, people who make policy and manage services systems, and others who work for stronger, more inclusive communities.

Preparation of the material in this chapter was supported through a subcontract from The Center on Human Policy, Syracuse University, for the Research & Training Center on Community Living. The Research & Training Center on Community Living is supported through a cooperative agreement (Number H133B80048) between the National Institute on Disability and Rehabilitation Research (NIDRR) and the University of Minnesota Institute on Community Integration. Members of the Center are encouraged to express their opinions; these do not necessarily represent the official position of NIDRR.

FROM RESIDENTIAL SERVICE TO SUPPORTED LIVING

People with developmental disabilities can live well in their own homes if service system and agency managers can implement significant change in the way the assistance they need is provided.[1] A growing number of innovators identify this change as a shift from residential service to supported living. Supported living entails providing people with disabilities the individualized help they need to live successfully in homes of their choice. It contrasts with residential service, which groups people with disabilities in residential facilities for the purpose of training, treating, or caring for them. Residential facilities may be large, like institutions or nursing homes, or small, like what some people call "family scale group homes" or "apartment living programs." Making the shift to supported living involves more than providing a different location or a different type of service. The shift requires organizing and managing systems and agencies in new ways that challenge common images of how organizations work and how they change.

The discussion and interviews at the base of this chapter asked people who are experienced in developing and managing supported living agencies to think about the following question: What is different about the way people organize their agency when the agency works to support people in their own homes and in community life instead of working to provide care and treatment in a residential program? Some new images of organization and agency management emerge from considering responses to this question.

This chapter has three main sections. The first section identifies some of the struggles in shaping an organizational culture that offers people with developmental disabilities good support for experiencing a life of inclusion in community. The second section focuses on issues of structure and power in supported living agencies. The third section describes the impact of different ways to organize and manage organizations on the effectiveness of supported living agencies.

Preparation of this chapter drew on the following:

- A series of working group meetings and interviews with members of the Washington State Residential Service Guidelines Task Force, which took place in March and May of 1991
- Interviews with staff and managers from Training Toward Self Reliance in Sacramento, California in December 1989 and April 1991
- Interviews with board members and managers of Residential, Inc., in New Lexington, Ohio, in 1988, 1989, 1990, and 1991
- Interviews with staff and managers of Renaissance House in Tiffin, Ohio, in February 1991
- Discussions with managers and staff of Options in Community Living, Madison, Wisconsin, in 1988, 1989, 1990, and 1991

---

[1]For good descriptions of several current approaches to supported living, see Taylor, Bogdan, and Racino (1991). Particularly relevant are Chapters 7–11, 14, and the editors' summary of responsive organizations in Chapter 18.

- A June 1991 working group meeting in South Onondaga, New York, with Kathy Bartholomew-Lorimer, Gail Jacob, Beth Mount, and Steve Taylor

The authors are grateful for the hospitality, openness, and thoughtfulness of all those above in identifying and discussing difficult and complex issues and the authors hope not to have distorted or oversimplified their concerns and insights. Also appreciated are the comments of the authors' colleagues Jack Pealer, Julie Racino, Mary Romer, and Steve Taylor on a draft of the report from which this chapter is adapted. Of course, the authors remain responsible for its content.

NEW VALUES CALL FOR A NEW ORGANIZATIONAL CULTURE

The Washington State Division of Developmental Disabilities has the goal of people who receive residential services experiencing the following benefits:

- Health and safety
- Power and choice
- Personal value and positive recognition by self and others
- A range of experiences that help people participate in the physical and social life of their communities
- Good relationships with friends and relatives
- Competence to manage daily activities and pursue personal goals

These benefits characterize good quality of life for all people, and people with developmental disabilities should not be deprived of them because they need particular services to meet their needs. Effective residential service providers learn to offer necessary assistance with housing and daily living in ways that increase an individual's experience of these benefits. Each person has unique preferences for using these benefits and makes unique decisions when facing conflicts among them. Dealing with this is a learning process that will challenge every program's capacity to offer individualized services. Because current regulations governing residential services focus on different requirements, implementing these requirements may require planned change in the organization of a program's resources.

Since 1983, the Washington State Division of Developmental Disabilities has supported a statewide learning process designed to build consensus on the desired outcomes of the state's residential services. Important activities in this process are:

- The Residential Service Guidelines Task Force has been established. This committee includes managers and direct service staff from residential service providers; representatives of People First, a statewide self-advocacy organization, many of whose members use residential services; the state ARC, an organization representing the interests of many families with members who have disabilities; the state Developmental Disabilities Planning Council; regional case management staff; and county and state officials with responsibility for the development, coordination, and operation of services. The task force acts as a focus for learning about residential services and has debated, drafted, disseminated, and revised several statements about service direction and regulation based on comments and criticisms from many people.

- An annual statewide conference is held in Ellensburg, Washington, to bring together a large number of service workers, service managers, and individuals and families who use services to share their experiences and to hear from innovators in community services and leaders in community building from outside the disability field from across North America. This conference provides an annual forum for discussion of progress and problems in understanding and implementing the service directions under consideration by the Residential Service Guidelines Task Force.
- Residential service providers are offered technical assistance that will allow them to hire people to assist their agencies. These activities focus on improving agency capacity to train staff and make organizational changes necessary to create the benefits identified as desirable by the Residential Service Guidelines Task Force. Some technical assistance is offered in workshops, and some is in the form of agency consultation.
- There is support for five residential service providers in implementing pilot projects under the guidance of the Residential Service Guidelines Task Force. Pilot agencies have engaged in planned organizational change projects in order to test different approaches to creating and measuring the benefits described in the task force's guidelines. Each pilot agency has received a small amount of money to free staff time for change activities and to allow agencies to hire consultants of their choice to assist them in their work. Members of the Residential Service Guidelines Task Force have monitored each pilot project, sponsored an external evaluation of changes resulting from the project, and held retreats to encourage exchange among pilot project participants. Representatives from each project have joined the task force.

Greater clarity about the benefits that supported living should offer people creates tension with agencies over current structures and procedures and the way staff jobs are organized. Out of this tension, new ways to organize can grow. The following section summarizes some of what members of the Residential Service Guidelines Task Force have learned about organizing to support people in community life. The images of change that the members shared in two retreats are depicted.

IMAGES OF CHANGE ENCOUNTERED BY THE RESIDENTIAL SERVICE GUIDELINES TASK FORCE

Ensuring that agencies support people with developmental disabilities to have valued experiences calls for long-term personal and organizational learning. The challenge is continuously to clarify the meaning of benefits through a process of developing practical ways to support a growing number of people in experiencing these benefits.

Agency focus on these benefits does not define a model or a set of answers. Awareness of the benefits works like a lens. By discussing the meaning of the benefits, developing ways to approximate measurements of the benefits, and continuously improving the effectiveness of their work, people who provide support learn to see in new ways. They learn to see the person who relies on them for assistance as an individual who belongs in the context of community life. This new way of seeing leads to better understanding of each person, more knowledge of local communities, and a growing understanding of what it takes to support people in taking and keeping their rightful place in the community. Each time people act on what they see, they refocus the lens.

Acting to support valued life experiences challenges all of the levels and relationships among participants in the existing system of services. People at each level have to strengthen their abilities to participate responsibly in equal relationships and decrease their dependence on top-down controls. Relationships have to become strong enough to allow people to figure out complex issues together. The levels of the service system are shown below:

1. Person to person
2. Staff member to agency
3. Agency to agency
4. Agency to funders and regulators

People who take residential support benefits seriously experience the following three levels of tensions.

1. Each benefit makes an important contribution to the quality of a person's life, but discovering the way to experience each benefit and achieving harmony among them is the project of a lifetime. People sometimes make choices that put their *safety* at risk; close relationships often constrain *choices*; moving out to participate and exercise new skills can threaten relationships. The more limited people's experiences have been and the less able people are to speak for themselves, the more complex these tensions will be.
2. Most stakeholders (from funders to family members) expect the residential service system to offer highly specified packages of *service* to people grouped by disability label, often in special buildings, and almost always in isolation from community life. Boundaries between day, residential, and case management systems are expected to be clear and distinct. But offering individual *support* on the basis of people's choices, abilities, and place in the community confounds these expectations.
3. The culture of most provider agencies expects and reinforces *certainty*: job descriptions and policies define clear staff roles and responsibilities; professional teams and human rights committees make individual plans that authoritatively guide everyone's behavior in difficult situations; objective in-

spection guarantees accountability. But *learning* how to identify and do what it takes to assist individuals calls for willingness to live constructively with ambiguity.

To avoid the discomfort of ambiguity, people retreat into false certainty or leap into abstraction. False certainty leads some people to reject the benefits as unrealistic. Abstraction lets people avoid what they need to learn about particular situations and specific individuals by debating about hypothetical examples and general questions. Because people do live in ambiguous situations, the best way to deal with ambiguity is to stay with it and work to learn how to manage particular situations involving real people.

Service providers who have worked to understand the benefits through action have often discovered that their existing structures and arrangements are shaped the wrong way. They eclipse the energy that flows from a clear focus on the benefits. Some providers have had to face obvious incompatibilities between group living arrangements and individual benefits; others, in apartment living programs, have had to redefine their jobs from a focus on training people in apartments to supporting people in community settings, roles, and relationships.

Most existing services are based on unequal, hierarchical relationships. Direct service workers, who are themselves at the bottom of the organization in status, salary, and influence over organizational resources, spend the most time with the people who rely on the agency. They are accountable to those above them for carrying out instructions. Often, their relationship with the people they support mirrors their relationship to their agencies; that is, they behave as if they were in charge of the people they assist and expect the people they assist to be accountable to them for following the instructions they pass on. Agencies that support valued life experiences strive to form and encourage equal relationships between the people who offer assistance and the people who rely on them. A person with a disability has the best chance to experience benefits in an equal relationship with someone who listens and who has influence over the way the support agency uses its resources. Of course, this means that agency administrators have to be willing and able to negotiate with funders and regulators for their own ability to influence the way their agency resources are used.

Many large and small changes in organizational systems and structures will be necessary to align available resources with the kind of staff activities that offer people real benefits. An agency supporting valued life experiences needs a management team committed to improving administrative, organizational, and supervisory skills while deepening understanding of the benefits.

Implementing services that support valued life experiences calls for a new way of defining opportunities, understanding issues, and solving problems. In short, it calls for a new way of thinking together. This new way of thinking begins with a shift of context.

In typical programs, action supposedly flows from state *policy and regulations* to local *program structure*. Regulation and program structure form the context for the *relationship* between the individuals assisted and the people who provide assistance. Administrators encourage staff to check their actions for conformity to individual plans, agency policies and procedures, and state regulations. Staff ask supervisors and technical assistants for cookbook approaches to problem-solving that will protect them from liability for mistakes.

To learn to implement guidelines for truly valuable assistance, administrators and staff shift the context of their work. They aim to make action flow from *relationships* with the people they assist. They work to merit people's trust by listening carefully and responding truthfully and consistently to what they hear. Better *understanding* of individuals' interests and needs grows from relationships and focuses problem-solving. Administrators encourage staff to think and act creatively to develop opportunities and overcome obstacles. *Creative problem-solving* has to do with figuring out ways to deal with regulations and take account of liability concerns. Staff ask administrators and technical assistants to join them in improving their problem-solving.

Seeing the contrast between these two contexts necessitates thinking about the practical difference between the following two questions: How do we comply? How do we build positive relationships and come to know and understand people in their communities better? Staff who consider the compliance question will see, act, and learn differently from staff who consider the relationship question.

Many repetitions of the learning process move people and agencies along the long wave of change toward greater capacity to offer people benefits. Working inside the boundaries defined by the guidelines, staff join the people they assist and other community members to learn by moving from action to reflection and back to action. This process means regularly taking time out from action to stop, look at what is working and what is not, think about what lessons the current situation offers, and plan for the next steps. Effective administrators encourage this process both around individuals and for the program as a whole. Most often reflection will be informal, a part of everyday work. More structured forms, like personal futures planning or retreats, offer opportunities to reflect on bigger chunks of experience.

Offering services that support valued life experiences means building an organizational culture that will sustain effective relationships and continuous learning. People who provide direct assistance build up an effective culture when they act more creatively in their everyday work. People in administrative roles build up an effective culture when they model the necessary qualities in their own lives and in interaction with the people and programs they supervise. The more funders and regulators understand and encourage the kinds of behavior that allow effective problem-solving, the less they will inhibit the development of effective organizational cultures in the agencies they depend on to serve people.

Characteristics of an organization that supports valued life experiences are listed below:

- Commitment to vision
- Ambiguity
- Questions
- Trying new ways to look at and do things
- Looking at yourself and your own life
- Asking for help
- Personal involvement with people being assisted
- Working outside usual program boundaries and routines
- Reaching out to involve new people in the work
- Negotiating for what people really want and need
- Taking time to reflect and to invest in learning something new

Administrators concerned with keeping learning alive will keep raising questions such as: "Are our values alive?" "Is our work satisfying?" "Have we mindlessly fallen into routine?" Effective administrators at every level of the system will make time to gather people together to deepen their understanding of the values and organizational qualities necessary to offer people real benefits. Budgets, job descriptions, supervision, and staff development processes will reflect growing understanding of the qualities that distinguish an effective organizational culture.

An important aspect of change is developing a new mindset: a different way to think about and evaluate situations. A mindset that focuses staff attention only on carrying out service procedures locks staff and the people they support into a narrow range of options. People experienced in implementing the guidelines call this "being in the box." What is needed is a mindset that "opens the box" and focuses attention on people in the context of their communities.

Staff who increase the benefits that people with disabilities experience do more than just behave differently from staff who deny or miss opportunities for greater benefits. They notice different aspects of situations and think differently about them. Their work requires them to be able to do the following:

- Think on the spot.
- Negotiate shared understanding of situations among people who often have conflicting views.
- Try something new and test whether or not it improves the benefits people experience.

Changing mindset is not easy. It involves letting go of the current boundaries that describe jobs and define priorities, and redefining boundaries to include more attention to differences in individual interests and circumstances, more attention to community opportunities, and more attention to negotiating better relationships. Experienced staff say that this change is like learning a new language. There is a movement away from the familiar; this feels uncomfortable because it involves loss of fluency, causes self-consciousness about choice of words, and causes frequent errors. As new patterns emerge, so do new opportunities for deepening understanding of people and their communities. Three kinds of actions help people make the shift to a more open, benefit-focused mindset. Following are discussions of them.

1. Bring together people who care about a person and other people with responsibilities to that person and strengthen their relationship with the person and the bonds between them. The purpose is to clarify and increase commitment to the person and to find common direction in varied ideas about the person.

2. Increase awareness of the ways current boundaries and rules are in the way of taking responsible action, and work to renegotiate these constraints. Crisis situations—situations that hold the threat of chaos—offer excellent opportunities to strengthen a new mindset. Acting constructively in crisis means moving into chaotic situations rather than trying to escape them. The challenge is to be part of an emotionally charged situation *and* think about how to redefine the situation so that the people involved can act in ways that will increase benefits. The process is simple; it is shown below:

- Notice that service providers are thinking and acting as if they were "in the box."
- Identify some of the specific ways people are thinking and acting that either make the crisis worse or frustrate the provision of some benefits for the people involved.
- Try new ways to think about the situation and new ways to act.
- Invite people from outside the local chaos to help see what is happening and what options exist.

3. Learn to discover and communicate visions that encompass the following approaches:

- Clarify answers to the basic question that defines the relationship between a person and those who provide service. That is: "Who is this person, and who are we in this person's life?"
- Make it obvious that the person and those who care about the person and those who provide service are in partnership to improve life together. The question is, "What do we want to be doing together in a better future?"
- Energize the hard work of changing the mindset by working to overcome barriers to change and acting responsibly in crisis situations.

Leaders of agencies that have worked to support valued life experiences say that they have had to invest time in building a shared understanding of the benefits.

People need an organized process to clarify their understanding of the benefits, debate their importance, and define ways to act that will increase the benefits people experience. This process of change can be organized around designing and testing ways to measure changes in the level of benefits people experience and by modifying policies and defining new procedures. But the written results of undertaking these tasks are a better record of what the agency has done than they are a recipe for a better future. One service provider noted that the investment in setting up new measures was well spent. It helped in making some important transitions. But after a while they were used less. The measures were still being used but had become less important because new ways to talk and work with the people being supported had been learned.

This discovery has important implications for the process of helping more agencies to implement the guidelines. Bureaucratic thinking would lead to the conclusion that the necessary changes could be effectively translated from innovating agencies to new implementors using only words. From this point of view, a new agency simply adopts policies, procedures, and measurement and planning systems from an effective pilot. Training and technical assistance focus on transmitting the products from pilot sites.

Experienced implementors of efforts to support valued life experiences fear that reliance on words alone as the translator to support organizational culture will create what has become their nightmare, that is, that the words will change but people's experiences will not. Even worse, more subtle measurements could lead to even greater control of people's daily lives.

Dissemination of what is learned in the pilot projects calls for the development of better translators of the pilot projects' experiences. Better translators help new implementors to become involved in the implementors' own pattern of learning through reflection on action. New implementors cannot be consumers of products developed by the pilots or passive recipients of teaching and technical assistance; they have to become producers of change in their own communities. New implementors cannot hold the people who assist them responsible for giving them sure-fire solutions to the problems that come along with implementing support for valued life experiences; they have to take responsibility for learning for themselves with the guidance and support of people who are more experienced.

Agencies that want to begin to support valued life experiences can accelerate their learning by doing the following:

- Listening carefully to descriptions of the processes other agencies have followed and thoughtfully designing their own change process based on what they have learned
- Studying the products of other agencies' change efforts and using them as stepping stones in the development of their own policies, procedures, and ways of gathering information about people's experiences
- Becoming involved in active learning experiences that give people a chance to

try some of the actions that can shape a new mindset; some pilot agencies have found the Framework for Accomplishment[2] workshop helpful for this kind of tryout

SUPPORTED LIVING CALLS FOR NEW STRUCTURES AND NEW USES OF POWER[3]

Effective supported living agencies are well structured and powerfully led, but they look and feel different from typical human services agencies. The structures and the forms of power that shape and guide them differ from the bureaucratic patterns of organization and management common in residential service agencies because the nature of a supported living agency's work differs fundamentally from the work of a residential service agency.

Reasonable people might wonder whether it makes sense to think about supported living agencies at all. A small and slowly growing number of people with severe disabilities do not rely on agencies to provide the support they need, nor do they depend completely on the help of family members. They, or their families and friends, raise and manage necessary funds and organize a support system for themselves. They resolve the question of structure without agency intervention.[4]

The notion of replacing agency–client relationships with consumer control in a personal assistance marketplace has many appealing features, especially to people worn out by the inflexible, costly clumsiness of bureaucratic systems. However, most people with developmental disabilities who live outside their family's homes or residential facilities now depend on a supported living agency because current public policy severely restricts people's option to control their share of available funds. And even when people with disabilities gain full control of available cash—as the authors believe they should—it is reasonable to assume that some people will probably choose the convenience of purchasing services from a supported living agency over the investment of time required to self-manage a personal support system.

Whether a supported living agency is legally organized as a nonprofit corporation or as a cooperative owned by those who use its services, whether board and

---

[2]Framework for Accomplishment (O'Brien & O'Brien, 1992) is a process for identifying the capacities a service program needs to develop in order to assist people in moving toward a desirable personal future. One support for change in Washington state has been a series of intensive workshops that give people experiences with using the Framework for Accomplishment process.

[3]This section is based on a working group discussion with Gail Jacob, Kathy Bartholemew-Lorimer, Beth Mount, and Steven Taylor, which focused many of the findings from our field visits to supported living agencies. We also acknowledge Jeff Taylor, Aaron Lemle, and Fiona Farrel for their contributions to our working group.

[4]For a description of a complex, personally managed support system, see Pearpoint (1990). The World Institute on Disability outlined the necessary policy foundation for a user-controlled personal assistance system in Litvak, Zukas, and Heumann (1987). McKnight (1989) makes the case for preferring income redistribution to service provision as a primary role of government.

staff members have disabilities or not, the way the agency resolves problems of structure and power determines the quality of life for those who rely on it for support.

Structure

It is difficult to write descriptively about structure without seeming to prescribe the one best kind. The descriptions here are of several different but effectively organized supported living agencies. Each agency has its own distinct and evolving ways of structuring itself.

Assistive Relationships The fundamental structure of a supported living agency is a set of relationships between a number of people with developmental disabilities and their assistants. Each person will have a unique and changing mix of personal assistance based on the person's preferences and needs as they emerge in the relationship.

Some assistance involves instrumental tasks such as dressing, eating, communicating, using the toilet, keeping house, shopping, going to appointments and activities, and managing money. This assistance may come from a person who lives with the person who has a disability or, more commonly, from a person who comes in to help according to a schedule and as needed. Many people will receive assistance from more than one person and some people will have additional helping relationships with tutors; counselors; or communication, physical, or occupational therapists. Sometimes, instrumental assistance will involve helping the person to develop or improve skills; often, the assistant will perform tasks that the person cannot efficiently do alone.

Some assistance involves helping a person to plan and coordinate activities and his or her come-in and live-in assistance. This help may involve determining the person's preferences and needs regarding type and location of housing; selection of roommates if they are desired; transportation arrangements; finding and scheduling activities that offer the person opportunities to pursue personally interesting goals; hiring, training, scheduling, supervising, and firing assistants; and personal problem-solving. For many people with developmental disabilities, this role will be like that of an executive assistant, who takes responsibility for carrying out the tasks that the person with a disability calls for according to that person's personal preferences. For a few people with substantial cognitive disabilities, the assistant will be much more active in interpreting the person's preferences based on involvement with and observation of the person. For some people, the assistant's role will be complex because the person will be able to assert clear preferences in some situations and will find other situations extremely challenging.

Instrumental assistance is different from assistance with planning and coordination, which entails some supervisory responsibility. However, it is very common for the person who provides planning assistance also to offer help with everyday tasks, and many people will have only one helper who combines both functions. Some people will have more than one live-in or come-in assistant.

Whatever the configuration, its emergence from the particular situation of the person with a disability involved is the hallmark of supported living.

Being a good assistant challenges each support worker's capacity to sustain a close working relationship. In the context of this relationship, depending on individual circumstances, support workers may be called on to do any of the following:

- Identify and help the person to respond to potential opportunities and potential dangers.
- Facilitate the person's problem-solving efforts.
- Help the person interpret and make sense of matters as diverse as apartment security deposits, the results of medical tests, or the possible reasons for a neighbor's hostility.
- Advise the person in matters of individual importance.
- Represent the person's interests when there are conflicts with landlords, bus drivers, police officers, other service providers, physicians, income maintenance workers, and so forth.
- Assist the person in identifying individual strengths and interests and the ways to pursue them.

Maintaining any good working relationship is difficult. Assistive relationships can be particularly complex because of the following:

- Sometimes the support worker has multiple responsibilities, for example: 1) to follow the instructions and respect the preferences of the person with a disability, 2) to help the person discover preferences, 3) to interpret the person's preferences when severe cognitive disability makes preferences uncertain, and 4) to protect the person who is vulnerable.
- The person with a disability depends on the support worker for vital assistance, and so, may try to please the support worker rather than asserting and negotiating his or her own needs and preferences, because of feeling vulnerable to the support worker's good will and threatened by the possibility of the support worker's disapproval.
- The person with a disability may have poor supervision skills and poor negotiating skills which may cause the support worker to feel mistreated and frustrated.
- Support workers share, often unthinkingly, in strong cultural prejudices that can easily lead them to treat people with disabilities as less valuable and less capable than themselves.
- Because of past experiences with services, the person with a disability may feel there is little reason to trust the support worker. The person with a disability may have been abused or ignored by support workers or may have had repeated experiences of losing good support workers to high turnover.
- In many ways, people with disabilities live in a hostile environment. Many of the people they meet will devalue them, a few will openly reject them because

of their disability, and a few will exploit their vulnerability. Therefore, the support worker has to assist the person in assessing and dealing with risks without either being naively optimistic or unrealistically pessimistic about other people's responses.

- The support worker has to be clear about the ways in which his or her personal preferences and values may differ from those of the person supported and keep re-creating ways to avoid imposing on that person without compromising his or her own integrity.

Support workers' jobs are complex because they are closely involved with socially devalued people who need their daily help with important matters. One of the complexities concerns individual freedom, which is, among other things, a matter of both choice and personal involvement or engagement. No one is free without choice, and no one is free unless what he or she chooses matters to someone else.

Policy and practice have routinely denied people with disabilities choice, thus trapping them in abusive or overprotective situations. Supported living agencies properly commit their workers to actively promoting people's choices. But policy and practice have also routinely discouraged committed, personal engagement with people with disabilities. Often this has extended to isolating people by breaking their relationships with their families and disrupting potential friendships among people with disabilities. Disengagement creates an abusive situation when people are also denied choice, and a potentially neglectful situation is set up when people can decide for themselves but no one is personally engaged with them. People who are isolated face a much increased risk of being exploited. Support staff who stand back and let isolated people sink into difficult or dangerous situations without comment or effort, saying that their agency gives people the right to make choices or that they believe in friendship and choice and the person picked an abusive friend, are actually neglectful. Support staff who work to strengthen their relationships with those they support by identifying and attempting to negotiate their differences with a person's choice may contribute to increasing the person's freedom, but the costs of such increased engagement often include confusion, emotional conflict with the person, self-questioning, and failure to influence the person's choice.

The Staff Team The team discussed here is not the multidisciplinary professional team whose control of the lives of people with disabilities is licensed by many current regulations. Rather, it comprises employees of an agency and supports them in their daily work.

Membership in an effective staff team helps support workers to be better participants in their assistive relationships. The team offers the support worker a place to figure out what is happening in complex situations. It provides colleagues who can offer empathy, suggestions, and resources while they pose questions and challenge apparently narrow or prejudiced perceptions or actions. An effective team serves as a focus for personal and organizational learning as team members reflect on their work and plan ways to improve their effectiveness.

The staff team provides a human link between the agency as a whole and the people the agency supports. In the team, people can come to know one another well enough to establish trust and to identify ways to help one another both one-to-one and as a group. Team members can, in time, come to know the people with disabilities whom the other members of the team support and, thus, provide informed back-up when a person's usual support worker is unavailable. Teams can self-manage the details of scheduling and much of the agency's day-to-day problem-solving. Team members can identify necessary agency or system changes based on their knowledge of particular people's lives and carefully evaluate the impact of agency-level decisions on them.

An effective staff team leader collaborates with team members to develop, renew, and deepen commitment to the values and direction the supported living agency stands for. Through individual coaching and group leadership, the team leader collaborates with members to improve each member's ability to realize the commitments in everyday relationships with the people he or she supports. The team leader serves as an active link between the decisions affecting the whole supported living agency and the work of the team. This involves representing the team to the whole agency and the agency to the team. The human desire to use groups as a place in which to flee from difficult issues to blaming or wishful thinking or unproductive fights makes effective team leadership a demanding role.

In view of the need that staff have for the support of a staff team, an important question arises concerning how people with disabilities will have independent opportunities to understand their situations and how those should improve. When people with developmental disabilities have friends and involved family members, they have the chance to develop an independent perspective on the assistance they receive. Services that isolate people and discourage them from reaching out to others cause them to have fewer options. Some people with disabilities have found independent support among other people with disabilities in advocacy groups. A few people have formed relationships through these advocacy groups. A few people have formed circles of support, usually with outside help. A community that lacks such independent, organized responses leaves people who need help to overcome isolation in a dilemma, so they rely on support workers to assist them in forming relationships independent of the support agency. Collaboration between people with disabilities and their support workers to overcome isolation is one of the most exciting and confusing areas of work in supported living.

The Management Team The management team orchestrates for the whole agency learning what the chosen values and direction mean and how best to realize them. The management team structures opportunities for people to invest their talents in developing the agency while they influence one another's appreciation of the agency's commitments. Some of the opportunities come in the form of training, but most arise from the work of managing the agency. Working groups take responsibility for such important tasks as evaluating agency performance; developing long-range strategies and plans for management and staff approval; designing necessary processes, policies, and procedures; and developing the agency's position with outside resources such as funders, regulators, housing associations, or community development groups. To bring together different talents and points of view, working groups purposely include people with developmental disabilities, support workers, management team members, agency board members, and other advisors.

The management team assists the work of teams in two ways. First, it coordinates the daily work of the agency in areas where teams may interfere with one another's work due to common dependence on the same resources, such as secretarial services or housing resources. Second, it provides team leaders with the opportunity to develop one another's abilities by offering support in understanding their team's work and challenging and expanding one another's ideas and skills. The agency director leads the management team and serves as the management team's primary link to the agency board.

The Director Most of the operational management of a supported living agency must come from those who have the information necessary to make operational decisions. The staff who provide planning and coordinating assistance need the judgment, problem-solving, and negotiation skills to deal with most plans and problems in collaboration with the person they assist. Of course, placing responsibility for most decisions with direct service staff and the people they support does not mean they are required to act alone. Indeed one of the staff's basic skills is knowing when and where to go for help. Teams members need the level of trust in one another, the level of commitment to the agency's direction and values, and the group problem-solving skills to serve as the main source of learning, support, and coordination for support workers. A variety of work groups, organized by the management team and the board, need the information and the skill to plan, evaluate, and design policies and procedures.

The director stays aware of the agency as a whole and exercises responsibility for maintaining the focus of the agency's values and direction. Awareness of the agency as a whole calls for the director's personal involvement with assistive relationships and team learning. This represents one of the effective limits on the size of a supported living agency. A supported living agency risks being undermanaged when the number of people it assists plus the number of staff becomes too large for the director to maintain personal contact. Responsibility for maintaining direction requires the director to attend carefully to the selection and development of team leaders and support staff and to the composition and preparation of work groups. The director needs more than the authority of position. The authority that comes from personal knowledge of people's situations and personal commitment to contributing to good solutions is essential when difficult problems threaten to compromise the agency's direction and values.

Environments The two different environments that provide the resources a supported living agency needs to do its work are the service system and the community. Because neither is accustomed to supporting people with severe disabilities in their own homes, an agency cannot passively adapt to what its environments expect of it. Otherwise, all but the most determined and capable people with disabilities would be in residential facilities. An effective agency works strategically to shape the service system and the community that contains it.

The Service System In most current instances, the service system provides the money to pay support workers and their managers and coordinates the supported living agency's work with other service providers (e.g., supported employment or day service providers). The service system typically coordinates both at the personal level, through some form of case management, and at the interagency level, through plans and contracts. The service environment can produce different kinds of conflicts, such as those listed below:

- Restrictions on the expenditure of available funds often limit the supported living agency's flexibility in matching individual needs and preferences with available resources. These restrictions increase the transaction cost of providing services in at least two ways: 1) they impose forms of meetings and paperwork that are unnecessary to support particular individuals and that effectively move decision-making power away from the person and those who assist for no reason other than to satisfy funding requirements; and 2) gaining waivers, permissions, and developing ways to work around holdups in order to do what seems necessary absorb substantial time. Widespread system dependence on Medicaid funds, which were intended to pay for people who are sick, compounds this problem.
- Most service systems simultaneously operate different types of services with incompatible assumptions about people with disabilities. Many people who live in and control their own homes with support spend their days in mindless, segregated activities designed to treat and cure or "habilitate" their disabilities. This creates conflicting and confusing experiences for the person. Although the staff of different agencies work within the same service system, they think about and do their work in different worlds. The fundamental differences in perception and relationship make conflicts across agencies hard to negotiate and greatly reduce the effectiveness of interagency coordination.
- Most current systems are built on the hierarchical assumption that people who provide direct service are less competent and should be paid less than the professionals who write plans. For example, most agencies assume that, because of their position, case managers have greater knowledge and far superior judgment about what makes sense for a person they meet formally and occasionally than the support workers who spend substantial time with the person every day. This leads service systems to the low expectations of direct service staff that

result in underpaying and undersupervising the people in the best position to learn about and act for the person. It also creates incentives for increase in agency size because larger agencies can pay more people as managers or specialists.

Failure to make these conflicts into opportunities for small steps toward reshaping the service system imposes the consequences of these conflicts on people with disabilities. Failure to succeed in particular attempts to change the service system can deepen support staff's understanding of the frustrating situation of people with disabilities and the commitment to making alliances with them to make systemic changes that will improve everyone's life.

The Community Communities provide people with disabilities with places in which to live, work, and learn; goods and services to buy; activities and associations to join; and people to make friends with.

Though some community members purposely exploit or behave with open hostility toward people with disabilities, most discrimination and exclusion arise thoughtlessly from ignorance. Developers see no way and no reason to ensure that they build accessible housing. Housing advocates create cooperatives and other new forms of housing on the mistaken assumption that people with developmental disabilities live happily in residential facilities. Landlords, neighbors, shopkeepers, dentists, pastors, and police officers worry about unusual demands on their abilities and tolerance or unusual threats to their property, prosperity, and safety. Leaders of associations and activities more often see people with disabilities as a potential project than as interested participants and members.

Supported living agencies most powerfully influence community environments when they assist individual people with developmental disabilities in establishing themselves in homes of their own and support them in developing community connections that allow them to discover and pursue their personal interests. Agencies can also support and challenge the people and organizations responsible for housing and improving the quality of neighborhood life to include people with developmental disabilities in their efforts, their memberships, and their agendas.

The supported living agency is linked bureaucratically to the service system. Most of the visible work of effectively positioning the agency in the service system is done in formal meetings and written plans, budgets, reports, and justifications. To deal with the service system, the supported living agency has to be able to look and act like a formal organization. The director or the director's official delegates deal with agency matters. Staff with professional titles represent the agency in multi-agency individual planning sessions. Budget revisions and reports are filed on the correct forms on time. When agencies do not meet these expectations it is for a purpose, otherwise the service system would be unable to hear the agency's communication. The less visible work necessary to keep bureaucracy from extinguishing purpose depends on agency leaders' ability to sustain good personal relationships with people who manage other parts of the system. These relationships allow the director to build trust and credibility and to make person-to-person requests for involvement in work on system changes.

The supported living agency is linked to the community in multiple, informal ways. Most of the work of effectively positioning the agency in the community is done through personal connections. Whom a person knows and what a person is willing to do are more important than a person's title in many areas of community action. Most contacts are casual and paperwork is infrequent. To deal with the community, the supported living agency has to act like a source of community action. The agency very seldom takes a formal, explicit position. Most actions are individual because they arise from individual interests. Support workers assist the people they support in matters such as satisfying a property owner's concerns about signing a lease, investigating the possibilities for membership in a community group of interest, preparing a covered dish for a neighborhood party, or negotiating appropriate restitution for an offense with the local courts. Agency staff and interested people with developmental disabilities may join a local housing action group to align their energy with the efforts of other citizens.

Building the capacity to assume two different characters to influence two different environments organizes a good deal of a supported living agency staff's learning. Different environments require shifts of mindset and even different clothing.

Power

Forms of Power Leaders of successful supported living agencies identify the use of power as one of the most important and difficult issues in their work. Several leaders have distinguished between three different types of power in their work.[5] These are discussed below.

Power over other people arises from the ability and willingness to make decisions for others and to enforce their compliance by authoritative control of rewards and punishments. Typical systems and agencies embody the assumption that people higher in a hierarchy will exercise power over the people beneath them. Professionals and staff unquestioningly expect that people with disabilities will do what they are told by those authorized to plan for them and see people who do not comply as having further and deeper disabilities. Power over others is the most common and familiar form of power. People expect its use, feel uncomfortable at its absence, fear the uncertain consequences of denying it, and easily fall back upon it in times of stress. Politicians, managers, and organizers rise and fall on their ability to manipulate power over others. But power over others poisons the relationships necessary to support people with disabilities in taking their rightful places in community life. This appears to be true even in structures that attempt change by

[5]A concise description of these different forms of power appears in Starhawk (1987). Also see French (1985), Chapter 7, in which the notion of power is similar to the approach to conflict management developed by Harvard Law School's Negotiation Project and described in Fisher and Brown (1988).

swapping the order in a hierarchy so that the people with disabilities assume power over their helpers.

Power with other people arises from people's ability and willingness to listen to and be influenced by the perceptions and suggestions of others and to offer theirs in turn. Power-with requires the kind of respect that grows with a willingness to be personally involved with one another and to share in a project that will shape and shift patterns of relationships among people. Differences provide information and occasions to clarify and strengthen relationships by negotiating creatively. Because power-with depends upon and reinforces cooperation, its exercise depends on people's mutual restraint and willingness to learn from their experience together. Not all exchanges of influence have positive motives or good consequences, so people need to assume responsibility for questioning and testing the fruits of their collaboration. Power-with defines a strong foundation for the kinds of relationships necessary to support people with disabilities in community life.

Power-from-within arises from a person's willingness and ability to discover and creatively express the abilities and concerns that he or she finds spiritually meaningful. In civic life and in the world of work power-from-within brings people beyond seeking a role to finding a vocation, a calling. Power-from-within gives a person courage to act when important values are threatened, even if the short-term prospects for success are poor. Several leaders in supported living identify power-from-within as the source of their own ability to overcome their fears and doubts in order to create and protect innovations in difficult circumstances. Because power-from-within expresses a person's deepest beliefs, conflicts can be painful and very difficult to resolve, so many people learn not to share their convictions. People acting on the basis of power-from-within need to exercise personal discipline to sharpen their discernment of what ultimately matters to them and to strengthen their abilities to express creatively what matters to them in everyday life with other people.

Power-with and power-from-within have particular relevance for supported living agencies. Assistive relationships cannot be based on the coercion and fear that come with the exercise of power-over. Support develops on the basis of mutual influence through the support worker listening and responding to the person with a developmental disability and, in turn, offering the person information, suggestions, and guidance and identifying and negotiating differences. Even when there is a definite element of control in the relationship—as when a person has been declared incompetent to make financial decisions or when a court makes some form of supervision a condition of release from jail—power-with provides the only constructive context for a support relationship. Either person's use of power-over marks trouble in an assistive relationship, which they can repair only by moving to the use of power-with. Team relationships cannot be based on coercion and fear. Learning and mutual support require trust and the ability to identify and negotiate differences.

Community relationships cannot be based on coercion and fear. The supported living agency strengthens necessary community relationships by looking for common ground and supporting people with disabilities in making clear requests for inclusion, assistance, or adaptation. Even in the relatively few instances in which these requests are backed by enforceable rights, outcomes depend more on creative negotiation and joint problem-solving than on giving orders. Even making simple changes, like making public buildings accessible, entails encountering many ways in which even well-meaning people can give the appearance of complying with rules. Assertion of rights gains the most ground when it leads people to establish power-with relationships.

Although the context is hierarchical, relationships within the service system cannot be based completely on power-over because the supported living agency is low in the hierarchy. Because of its position, the agency is expected to take and implement instructions from system managers and multi-disciplinary teams rather than be a source of action. By establishing power-with relationships in the network of people who manage the service system, supported living leaders multiply their ability to respond to the individual preferences and needs of the people with disabilities their agency supports.

Power-from-within gives the people involved with supported living agencies the energy and courage to stand up to unjust situations, to continue to face and learn from difficult problems day after day, and to find meaning in their lives despite slow progress or failure. Many effective supported living workers say that they are led and sustained by some individuals with disabilities whose power-from-within is very strong with those who take care to notice and listen to them.

Occasions of Power Assistive relationships form the daily testing ground for power-with and power-from-within. Each relationship encompasses many moments of truth in which people will either struggle for collaboration or fall back into coercion or withdrawal. Whether assistive relationships grow stronger from these tests depends partly on the people in the particular relationship and partly on the way the supported living agency develops as an organization.

The following five organizational issues test and strengthen the use of power in a supported living agency: 1) negotiating necessary resources, 2) building effective teams, 3) keeping balance between the work of the whole organization and the work of its teams, 4) setting and maintaining direction, and 5) maintaining the agency's integrity.

Together, these issues provide the agency with chances to build up alternatives to power-over. Each issue offers the opportunity to shape stronger collaborative relationships and deepen understanding of the links between work in supported living and what participants in supported living find personally meaningful. The way an agency manages these issues determines the amount of energy it can focus on realizing its values. The more practiced people become in organizing their efforts through the exercise of power-with and power-from-within, the less organizational relationships will be dominated by power-over.

Any member of a supported living organization can exercise power constructively in dealing with each of these issues. Power-with grows when people intentionally draw and redraw boundaries by moving toward some relationships and away from others. People strengthen the use of power-with in an agency when they do the following:

- Bring people together to focus on a common project, especially when this brings previously uninvolved people into the project.
- Encourage people to express clearly how they see and understand a situation and what they want from it.
- Inquire about the position of people who disagree or are unwilling to become involved in order to find out what it would take to gain their cooperation.
- Practice creative search for mutually beneficial actions.
- Advocate for suggestions that structure shared action.
- Cooperate with others' projects.
- Question limiting assumptions by inquiring why a desirable action appears impossible.
- Figure out ways to evaluate and learn from the effects of their actions.

People strengthen the exercise of power-from-within in an agency when they do the following:

- Invest time in strengthening and clarifying their awareness of what is personally meaningful to them.
- Look for ways in which the agency's work offers chances to express what is most important to them, especially in frightening or confusing or discouraging situations.
- Express clearly and strongly what matters to them as valuable and fundamental, especially when their agency's behavior seems to be negative or out of control.
- Listen respectfully and thoughtfully when others speak of what matters most to them.

1. Negotiating for Resources from the Service System Under current policies, supported living agencies need to establish a good supply of the following six resources from some part of the human services system:

- Permission to serve people is needed. Most service systems control eligibility, set service priorities, take the authority to decide or at least approve whom an agency can serve, and control access to people with disabilities, especially those who live in residential facilities
- Money to support people, and sometimes money to subsidize people's living expenses is essential. Most service systems allocate funds for services and money for living expenses above disability benefits to agencies rather than to people.
- Legitimacy is required. Most service systems take the authority to license or approve service providers, and most make this approval a condition of continuing operation.

- Flexibility is needed. Inability to respond to changing individual needs and preferences makes supported living impossible. Increasingly specific regulation and prescription of the details of agency relationships and behavior serve apparent rationality in public administration even as they destroy agency and system effectiveness. Supported living agencies survive or fold according to their ability to develop problem-solving relationships with service system managers who use instruments like waivers, new categories of program descriptions and regulations, pilot projects, and innovation funds to create flexibility.
- Knowledgeable and credible advisors on how the system works are essential.
- Information and influence on important issues are required. Service systems face uncertain pressures, and the ways in which they choose to respond will matter a great deal to the capacity for supported living. Service system managers may choose to listen more closely and be guided more by supported living providers than the size of their agencies or their apparent importance would suggest.

Two related strategic issues commonly arise in relationship to service systems. One poses the question of the scale and rate of growth of the agency. The other poses a tradeoff between flexibility and amount of available funds.

Service systems have a legitimate interest in offering good services to growing numbers of people. Successful supported living agencies provide an attractive service and are often uncommonly well-managed (even if the management style and the structure seem odd). So service system managers are likely to press successful supported living agencies to grow larger and to do so faster. Sometimes this pressure comes as an explicit proposal, such as, "We want you to double in size in the next 3 years," or "Another provider has lost its license; will you take over its agency and make it like yours?" Sometimes the pressure comes implicitly in the cumulative effects of individual requests, such as, "Won't you find room for just this one person who really needs you?" Supported living agency management has to maintain control of how large agencies become and how fast they grow. The difficulty of doing this can be compounded when board members or staff see requests for growth as a clear sign of success and uncritically conclude that the ability to offer good support to a small number of people is a clear sign of the ability to offer the same quality to as many people as the market will bear. Agencies that are well-managed when small often become uncontrolled when scale or rate of growth turns personal leadership into distant management. Growth inevitably will demand substantial leadership ability and time and will almost certainly lead to at least a short-term decline in the quality of support available. An agency that decides to grow needs to budget time and resources to learn how to grow bigger.

Money for services is scarce and many service systems predict that it will grow scarcer. This leads system managers to search for funds that have the advantage of availability and the disadvantage of bringing requirements that generate new levels of detail complexity for their system. Supported living agencies that want to sustain good assistive relationships by being able to offer support workers decent wages and benefits may be offered a deal that allows them a higher rate of reimbursement in return for much more intrusive and inflexible regulations. Supported living agencies that have carefully made a strategic decision to grow may well be offered the same deal. Flexibility is costly to achieve. Once achieved it is difficult to maintain and easy to lose. Tradeoffs between increased money and decreased flexibility need sober evaluation and time for people to explore and align with whatever position an agency finally takes.

2. Building Effective Teams Everyone in the agency contributes to team effectiveness. The agency strongly influences team effectiveness through its personnel and staff development activities. Whom to hire as team members and whom to identify as team leaders are the most important operational decisions the agency makes. Creating ways to develop competence and leadership in team members and team leaders are the most important operational investments the agency makes.

Common assumptions that shape service systems can constrain effectiveness in hiring and developing people. Though the supportive living agencies studied here had relatively low turnover, most systems assume that the people who offer direct service will do so for very short periods. This assumption makes investments in developing people look like a waste of time and money, so systems generate a vicious circle of underinvestment and adjustment to built in incompetence.

Every team faces two predictable stresses that have agency-wide impact: 1) making decisions in situations in which people's safety is threatened, and 2) complying with requirements necessary to agency survival but irrelevant to people's sense of what matters in their work. It is important for the agency to support teams systematically in each of these areas.

Support workers occasionally have to make decisions when a person's safety, health, or continued freedom to live in the community is at stake. The agency needs to support its workers in these situations by ensuring that they identify these situations, recognize these situations as occasions to obtain help, and have a well-organized process for thinking through these situations with others and in terms of the agency's values. The agency owes the people it supports and its support workers a framework for making these difficult decisions that is publicly and widely debated, endorsed by the agency board, and regularly reviewed and revised. This framework cannot be in the form of simple instructions like, "If this, then do exactly that." It must encompass enough that people will need personal and team support to understand, apply, and learn from the framework. The issue of response to threat to health or safety can never be finally resolved. In each assistive relationship in which such threats arise, the agency has to keep balance; otherwise the situation could easily fall to neglect or bring overprotection.

As long as a supported living agency has to function part time as a bureaucracy, support workers will have to meet requirements that have no clear relationship to what matters to them in their jobs. The agency can support teams to deal with this in at least four ways: 1) minimizing the agency's reliance on intrusive funding sources and providing staff with opportunities to explore and debate the implications of the tradeoffs the agency makes (e.g., "We'll be able to serve five more people and raise your pay. But these are the requirements you will have to meet."); 2) continuously looking for ways to decrease the cost of compliance, probably under the coordination of a work group composed of people who enjoy looking for ways to simplify and streamline routine work; 3) regularly reviewing the actual costs of compliance with regulations and actively negotiating with the service system for release from damaging requirements; and 4) recognizing support staff who find ways to comply with requirements without compromising the quality of the assistance they provide.

3. Keeping Balance Between the Whole Organization and Its Teams

Teams carry most of the day-to-day responsibility for supporting assistive relationships, and an effective team will be a cohesive group. This has advantages for making good decisions and promoting learning. But team closeness can become a screen for moving away from the agency's values and direction or even a cover for poor performance of support work. Strong teams could mean a weak agency if there are not explicit investments in maintaining a balance between teams and the agency as a whole.

To manage this issue well the agency needs to adopt and apply the principle that any decision that can be made effectively by the person with a disability or those close to the person should be made this way. No decision will be made at a point in the organization farther from the person with a disability than necessary. This means that any requirements for uniformity across teams need careful discussion and regular review.

Staff team leaders play an important role in maintaining balance. If they work actively to link the management team with the team they lead, they will help each group understand the whole organization better. Being an active link involves work that is more stressful than simply identifying with one group or the other. It is easier on the staff team leader to define the job as obtaining what the leader's team needs from the management team or telling the leader's team what the management team has decided for them. The director's leadership in the management team has an important effect on the way team leaders play their role. The director needs to ensure that each management team member takes responsibility for keeping a view of the whole organization, which includes each team. Work groups on agency issues give team members the opportunity to develop a perspective on the whole organization while they influence its direction and practice.

Team members help maintain the balance between the whole agency and its teams by proudly showing the organization signs of what makes the team distinctive as a group. Inevitable feelings of competition between teams can be ritualized in agency customs, jokes, and folklore. Social occasions and agency ceremonies strengthen both people's sense of distinctiveness and their unity when these events include people with disabilities, support workers, and others involved with the whole agency.

4. Setting and Maintaining Direction People involved in supported living need to be proud of what they do. And people involved in supported living need to recognize how easy it is to lose track of direction and compromise values in order to deal with the stress of daily relationships or to deal with environmental barriers. To develop personal and organizational competencies, the agency needs to schedule a balance of activities to affirm and question its practices. These activities should include the following:

- Small and large celebrations of the victories of people with disabilities
- Regular times for retreat and reflection
- Encouraging people to visit and form relationships with people who do similar work in other agencies
- Supporting participation in training and development activities outside the agency
- Regular agency evaluation, designed in collaboration with agency staff
- Encouraging people to balance their commitments to work with other important personal, family, and civic activities

Each activity offers a scheduled chance to affirm what is working well, check direction, question established practice, deepen understanding of values and of tensions the agency's commitments create, and define the agenda of issues important to the agency's next stage of development.

Daily interactions are as important as scheduled activities in maintaining direction. Effective teams encourage routine discussion to question how well people are listening in assistive relationships and to test the fit between staff activity and what people with disabilities say is most important. In times of crisis and confusion, agency leaders ensure that someone actively advocates for the agency's values as people search for solutions.

5. Maintaining Integrity Many people develop new skills and deepen their maturity through their struggles to provide people with disabilities with good support. No one does the job without confusion, problems, and errors, but people who are capable of doing the job learn from their experiences. When times are difficult for them, they may put other issues before their responsibility to the people they support. It is important for colleagues, team leaders, and the agency director to be aware of these times in one another's lives so that they can confront the person involved, offer extra support, or make arrangements for the person to take a break.

Sometimes support work or team leadership simply does not suit a person's abilities and gifts. A person who recognizes the mismatch and moves on to other work does relatively little harm. People who keep working despite this mismatch threaten the supported living agency's integrity by putting their own needs and convenience before the needs and preferences of the people they support. Those in this situation will find it as difficult to listen to the people they support and act on their behalf as to honestly share in identifying difficulties and problem-solving with team members.

Sometimes a person who offers good support to a particular individual lacks the personal integrity to be a constructive part of an agency. Such a person exploits team colleagues and undermines the trust necessary in effective working relationships.

The person whose own needs and interests do not match the demands of supported living work should find other work. Usually such a person will accept counseling but, occasionally, it may be necessary for the supported living agency to act formally to terminate someone's employment. Because the agency needs to function on trust, it often takes additional time to satisfy an employee's right to written evaluations that document performance problems, formal warnings, hearings, and so forth. Sometimes these more formal procedures do allow a person to accept responsibility for his or her work, but often they do not.

Sometimes teams develop an agenda at cross-purposes with agency values. Usually this is less a conscious plan than a kind of an unconscious conspiracy. Instead of openly advocating for agency change, a team in this situation hoards its concerns and conflicts as a source of its own cohesion and sense of superiority. Effectively confronting the negative energy of such a group will call on all of the power within the other people in the agency, especially the director.

The Director's Responsibility The director has a particular responsibility to ensure that the agency, through its assistive relationships, teams, and working groups, focuses enough power on the five recurring issues that the organization keeps developing its capacity to support its values. In a sense, the director acts as a trustee of the agency's direction and struggle for the ability to carry out its work without resorting to coercion.

This seems odd from the point of view of a hierarchical organization. Theoretically, in such organizations the board acts as trustee and the director implements the board's policies. The director delegates responsibility and takes care not to scramble proper channels by becoming involved in matters that belong to subordinate personnel. In reality, however, the workings of successful supported living agencies are less neat and clear cut. Board members have vital roles to play, but they do not simply dictate policy, because that would mean imposing unilaterally on assistive relationships and organizing the agency around power-over relationships. Team leaders have crucial roles to play, but the director will from time to time be an active participant in team work and in assistive relationships. In these instances, the director will participate as a collaborator even though this may cause some confusion among workers who instinctively identify the boss only in terms of power-over. As with any other member of the agency, when the director resorts to power-over signals, there is a personal and organizational problem.

REALIZING THE PROMISE OF SUPPORTED LIVING CALLS FOR NEW IDEAS ABOUT ORGANIZATION AND MANAGEMENT

Supported living arises from a reversal of socially devaluing assumptions. Increasing numbers of people believe that congregating and segregating people for care and treatment is unjust and unnecessary. They are convinced that it is desirable and possible for people with developmental disabilities to face the challenges and enjoy the benefits of living in homes of their own. From this point of view, the mission of publicly supported human services turns from a primary concern for treatment, protection, and control to a focus on assisting people in living successfully in homes of their choice.

Realizing the mission of supported living calls for new ways to organize and manage work. The images of organization that emerge from innovators' experiences call for big changes in common assumptions about how to design and manage agencies. Supported living challenges both common ideas about people with disabilities and common ideas about organizations.

Viewing Organizations as Machines Leads to Poor Understanding of Necessary Changes

Some of the problems with working in supported living are easy to see. Much of the discussion among organizations considering it concerns important, obvious questions such as those related to safety, funds, finding real estate, new job roles, and more complicated schedules. A growing number of agencies have successfully tackled these and other difficult problems and demonstrated that supported living can be done successfully and over periods as long as 10 years.

As they have solved the apparent problems, supported living innovators have run into additional problems that lie submerged in a common sense mental picture of how organizations function. Many people presume that organizations are like machines; this limits understanding of what it takes to make and sustain important changes. Managers, workers, and outside advocates frequently picture their organization as a thing outside themselves. In this view, an organization is staff and buildings configured to produce a valuable product. Necessary work is specified, delegated, and coordinated by strategic plans, organizational charts, procedure manuals, and schedules. In this apparently rational picture, change means reconfiguring the machinery by changing schedules, job descriptions, and procedure manuals, often with the help of technical assistants. Staff training adjusts workers to new arrangements. Resistance to change results from poor communication or under use of authority and is met by authorities sending the message again, more clearly and louder.[6]

[6]For helpful contrasts between the machine image and a number of other possible images of organization, see Morgan (1986). Morgan summarizes the machine image in Chapter 2 and then explores seven other contrasting images of organization. For a useful discussion of the negative consequences of having only a machine image of organization to manage corporate life, see Mitroff and Kilmann (1984).

The mental picture of agencies as machines oversimplifies the change process in the transition from residential services to supported living. It suggests that if system managers want a new form of service, like supported living, they can simply change what they buy through contracts or direct expenditure. If system managers want more of some valuable quality, like choice or personal relationships, they can change product specifications by changing laws and regulations. According to the machine image, advocates may prevail simply by persuading a court or a legislative body to tell system managers to tell providers to make a change. When managers who see their agencies as machines receive the signal that group homes are no longer a valued product, they try to redirect the organization to produce supported living by changing plans, job descriptions, and procedures. They look to technical assistants to provide models that answer their new questions about how to find real estate, how to design jobs, how to keep people safe, how to give people more choices and a better chance at forming relationships, and so forth. They rely on staff trainers to give staff the values, motivate them, and tell them how to make the change work. They speak of marketing the concept of supported living to funding agencies and family members.

This oversimplification accumulates negative effects because it leaves out much of what has to change if people with developmental disabilities are to have good support. Organizations are not just entities to rearrange; people belong to organizations and feel the effects of organizational life and change emotionally. Supported living challenges more than schedules, procedures, and job descriptions. It challenges people's basic understanding of their work and themselves.

Supported living advocates attest to the depth of necessary change when they describe the change from residential service to supported living as a paradigm shift. This means a fundamental change in the way people understand and respond to situations. This could be a helpful image for guiding complex change, but the machine image of organization abets a misconception that paradigms can be shifted easily. Everything from the introduction of New Coke and the buttons on the fly of Levi's 501 Jeans to the general theory of relativity has been enthusiastically publicized as a paradigm shift. This overworks the term so that its meaning is exhausted, and people are misdirected to underestimate the difficulty of the basic change. Dana Meadows (1991) gave the reminder:

> A paradigm is not only an assumption about how things are; it is also a commitment to their being that way. There is an emotional investment in a paradigm because it defines one's world and oneself. A paradigm shapes language, thought, and perceptions—and systems. In social interactions, slogans, common sayings, the reigning paradigm . . . is repeated and reinforced over and over, many times a day. . . . (p. 3)

This suggests that shifting a paradigm involves more than an individual conceptual makeover. It means social activity, that is, building a community of meaning around different emotional commitments, different ways of seeing, and different ways of acting. When the machine image of organization dominates thinking, people simply try to reprogram the old organization with a new concept. The result is more of the same, just with new labels.

New Images of Organization Fit the Reality of Providing Supported Living Better than Machine Images Do

The machine image of organization is popular because it has worked as a way to efficiently program many human tasks. When its tasks can be analyzed and sequenced in a routine that permits easy external measurement, an organization is set up as a simple machine. When the repertoire of standard solutions is extensive and when deciding which solution matches what problem requires expert judgment, an organization is set up as a professional machine.

Most existing residential services operate with a mix of simple machine and professional machine structures. Direct service work is organized as simple machine work; that is jobs are specified by procedures and individual program plans. Individualization supposedly results from the activities of professionally organized teams established by policy to decide which procedures staff should carry out to yield progress toward objectives that the team selects as meaningful. Team judgments and management's effectiveness in ensuring compliance with planned schedules are regularly monitored by outside inspectors who decide whether or not agency performance is providing appropriate care and treatment.

The status, pay, and working conditions of workers who carry out small steps at the direction of others is different from that of professionals who exercise discretion in the solutions they apply. But both the counterperson at a fast food restaurant and the physician member of an interdisciplinary team work in organizations structured to develop and consistently deliver standardized solutions to a predefined set of problems. Whether the product is tacos or modern health care, the organization run like a machine invests in and rewards ways of thinking that converge toward routine solutions. Proper diagnosis and prescription here mean correctly identifying a defect and matching it with an approved remedy.[7]

The machine image of organization fits poorly when an agency has to solve diverse and novel problems in a rapidly changing environment. One big, unobvious challenge facing managers who implement supported living is creating and sustaining a problem-seeking organization in a system that expects, monitors, and values standard performance. This challenge does not arise from management books; it arises from the nature of the work that must be done to support people with significant disabilities.

[7]For a helpful discussion of important similarities between professional human services work and assembly line work and a discussion of the ironic effects of trying to redefine the outcomes of the special education system while still under the spell of the machine picture of organization, see Skrtic (1991). Thomas (1983) describes the changes that have taken place as technological advances have organized the practice of medicine as a professional machine. Mintzberg (1989) discusses the benefits, limitations, and costs of managing as if organizations were machines and describes several other organizational configurations that make a better fit with different technical and environmental conditions.

If supported living is going to work for people with developmental disabilities, workers in supported living agencies have to create good and lasting relationships with a variety of individuals. Through their relationships, staff collaborate with the people they support to identify new problems and opportunities as they come up and to create new solutions as people need them. The fact that the person with a developmental disability usually depends on the supported living worker for essential assistance complicates their relationship. So does the fact that important people outside their relationship legitimately hold the supported living worker accountable for what happens to the person with a developmental disability.

The stakes in discovering new images of organization are high. When a person meets a professional worker or a direct service worker who represents an agency organized around matching people to existing solutions, only the part of that person that fits the menu of available solutions will make sense to the worker. The parts that do not fit into the agency's solutions will be ignored. A person whose desires cannot be made to fit will be sent elsewhere. But most services for people with developmental disabilities are already the other places to which other systems send those whose needs and desires do not fit their preferred set of solutions. So a growing number of people end up with no alternative. Those who cannot leave and persist in resisting the organization's preferred solutions risk being rejected by those they must continue to rely on for the most basic daily assistance. The mutual frustration produced by this interpersonal bind pushes people to withdrawal, burnout, and violence.

Working in a residential facility, even a very small one, can be like working on an assembly line. Working effectively in supported living must be more like inventing and negotiating solutions to political problems. When an ongoing fight between a person and her roommate leads neighbors to complain to the landlord or when a person decides to stop taking medication, procedures and past experience may provide a guide for negotiating a balance among competing interests in a way that preserves important values, but there are no prescriptions.

E.F. Schumacher (1973) contrasts convergent problems, which have one best answer, with divergent problems, which call for a widening variety of responses and usually involve dealing creatively with conflicts over values. Providing for supported living means organizing to support people in dealing with divergent problems. Schumacher describes the everyday art of dealing with divergent problems:

> Through all our lives we are faced with the task of reconciling opposites which, in logical thought, cannot be reconciled. . . . How can one reconcile the demand for freedom and discipline in education? Countless mothers and teachers, in fact, do it everyday, but no one can write down a solution. They do it by bringing into the situation a force that belongs to a higher level where opposites are transcended—the power of love.
>
> Divergent problems force people to strain themselves to a level above themselves; divergent problems demand, and thus provide the supply of, forces from a higher level, thus bringing love, beauty, goodness, and truth into our lives. It is only with the help of these higher forces that opposites can be reconciled in the living situation. (p. 76)

The work of supporting people with developmental disabilities does not demand extraordinary creativity; it calls for the sort of ordinary creativity that organizations in the machine image program out. The important abilities have to do with forming and sustaining relationships; listening, looking, and thinking carefully; and inventing solutions to everyday problems.

Experience shows that many ordinary people have the skills and talent to master the art of assisting people with disabilities in making and keeping their places in community. All that is necessary for ordinary creativity to flower is that organizations develop ways to enlist and expand their workers' commitment to better lives for the individuals they serve and discipline in learning to collaborate better with these individuals to assist them.

REFERENCES

Fisher, R., & Brown, S. (1988). *Getting together: Building a relationship that gets to yes.* Boston: Houghton Mifflin.

French, M. (1985). *Beyond power*. New York: Summit.

Litvak, S., Zukas, H., & Heumann, J. (1987). *Attending to America: Personal assistance for independent living*. Berkeley: World Institute on Disability.

McKnight, J. (1989). *Do no harm: A policymaker's guide to evaluating human services and their alternatives*. Evanston: Center for Urban Affairs and Policy Research.

Meadows, D. (1991). *The global citizen*. Washington, DC: Island Press.

Mintzberg, H. (1989). *On management: Inside our strange world of organizations*. New York: Free Press.

Mitroff, I., & Kilmann R, (1984). *Corporate tragedies*. New York: Praeger.

Morgan, G. (1986). *Images of organization*. Beverly Hills: Sage.

O'Brien, J., & O'Brien, C.L. (1991). *More than just a new address: Images of organization for supported living agencies. Perspectives on Community Building Series*. Lithonia, GA: Responsive Systems Associates.

O'Brien, J., & O'Brien, C.L. (1992). *Framework for accomplishment*. Lithonia, GA: Responsive Systems Associates.

Pearpoint, J. (1990). *From behind the piano*. Toronto: Inclusion Press.

Schumacher, E. (1973). *Small is beautiful: Economics as if people mattered*. London: Blond & Briggs.

Skrtic, T. (1991). *Behind special education: A critical analysis of professional culture and school organization*. Denver: Love Publishing.

Starhawk. (1987). *Truth or dare: Encounters with power, authority, and mystery*. San Francisco: Harper & Row.

Taylor, S.J., Bogdan, R., & Racino, J.A. (Eds.). (1991). *Life in the community: Case studies of organizations supporting people with disabilities*. Baltimore: Paul H. Brookes Publishing Co.

Thomas, L. (1983). *The youngest science: Notes of a medicine watcher*. New York: Viking Press.

8

Adulthood or Oldness

In Search of a Vision

Bruce C. Blaney

In the early 1980s the field of developmental disabilities began to react to people with developmental disabilities growing old with a sense of discovery. Research studies, conferences, and even textbooks announced the emergence of a new field. Conventional wisdom accounts for these activities as a response to demographic changes. The same medical advances affecting the longevity of the general population underlay the emergence of a growing population of older adults with lifelong disabilities. The appearance of an aging focus within the field of disabilities was, therefore, a predictable response to an increasingly visible "new population."

This chapter departs from this account in suggesting that the apparent discovery of older adults with developmental disabilities has in reality been a process of definition, which has led to construing a new and devalued categorical group. As Walter Lippmann observed of the similar process of labeling people "feeble-minded" in the 1920s, "We do not see and then define. We define first, then we see" (Schur, 1980, p. 132). This chapter is an attempt both to critique this process of definition and to introduce a vision and conceptual framework more adaptive and responsive to adults with disabilities who are growing old. Such a framework derives from a synthesis of "social role valorization" as conceived by Wolfensberger and Tullman (1982) and an assessment of old age as a socially constructed role.

LESSONS FROM THE FIELD OF DEVELOPMENTAL DISABILITIES

Perhaps no field has enjoyed such a broad mandate in attempting to compensate the victims of social devaluation as the field of developmental disabilities. From the 1970s into the 1990s that mandate has been epitomized by the principles of normalization and social role valorization, which exhort human services to support "life conditions and social roles at least as good as the average citizen" (Wolfensberger, 1982, p. 133).

Since the 1980s various professionals in the field have attempted to extend that mandate, including normalization and social role valorization, to older adults with developmental disabilities. In the main, this effort has suffered from a failure to recognize that being old means being given a devalued role. Therefore, operating under the normalizing rubric of "old age-appropriate options" has had the perverse result of primarily replicating devalued patterns and roles.

A critical analysis and alternative to this devaluing approach has also emerged as a parallel trend during the same period. This critique represents the first attempt to unite the theory of social role valorization with an analysis of old age as a socially constructed, devalued role (Blaney, 1989, 1991). The section below discusses the possibility that the effort to articulate a positive vision of supports to older adults will draw important lessons from this ongoing contest between visions and paradigms within the field of developmental disabilities.

A REGRESSIVE VISION OF OLD AGE

At the core of the modern experience of aging is the assumption that a certain chronological age is synonymous with biological decline (Achenbaum, 1979). Old people have been defined as a biologically bonded peer group who have naturally congregated in their shared situation. The impact of these norms is the nearly universal belief that it is acceptable for a person to lose most of his or her valued roles and to be socially segregated upon reaching a certain age.

One may assess the power and content of these stereotypes by examining their capacity to undermine and reverse as comprehensive and widely shared a vision as that informing the field of developmental disabilities. As framed by Wolfensberger (1991), the principal theoretician of social role valorization, this core vision may be summarized as, the enablement, establishment, enhancement, maintenance, and/or defense of valued social roles—particularly for those at value risk—by using, as much as possible, culturally valued means (p. 21). In this formulation, Wolfensberger substantially evolves the guiding conceptual framework of the field. The clear focus on entry into respected social roles represents a much more specific explanation and vision of the goal of human services supports than was available in the earlier principle of normalization. The goal is not attaining normalcy; it is becoming a *valued* member of the community.

The comparatively radical nature of this vision is clear when one realizes that most people with developmental disabilities have been excluded from valued roles, many suffering the unconditional isolation of institutionalization. Since the 1980s this vision has become reality more and more as even those people with developmental disabilities who are most stigmatized have become workers, tenants, owners, friends, neighbors, and other members of the community. Such transformations are possible because of the emergence of formal support systems that assist communities in becoming more hospitable to people with disabilities and their families and that provide the resources and knowledge required to include them fully. Proponents of this new paradigm hold up the latter situation in sharp contrast to the historical and still predominant segregated continuum of service programs (Bradley & Knoll, 1990).

Since the late 1980s, many in the field of developmental disabilities have searched for ways to support and enhance the lives of older adults with developmental disabilities by attempting to help them emulate older adults without disabilities in the roles typically available to them. Now that the dust has begun to settle, it is clear that this path has not led to more valued roles for older adults with disabilities. What has occurred instead is the construction and imposition of a powerful new devalued role for people with developmental disabilities, which is often referred to as the "elderly developmentally disabled." A look at some of the specifics of this process discloses three core patterns: 1) retirement/role exclusion; 2) age segregation in virtually all service contexts; and 3) institutionalism, that is, reformulation of institutionalization as a relevant service form.

Retirement/Role Exclusion

Retirement programming is an emerging means of addressing the needs of older people with disabilities (Hawkins & Eklund, 1987). Retirement in this context seldom refers to an actual exit from a work role because most people with mental disabilities have never been employed. On the contrary, one could describe such programming as facilitating an *exit from role expectations* or, in effect, eliminating individuals from any consideration for a job role. The more global presumption, introduced by this use of the term retirement, may be described as the *withdrawal of the expectation that one will ever enter any adult roles,* such as owner, friend, spouse, community member, or employee (Matthews, 1979). The resulting role is apparent from its label, "retired client."

The program model frequently adopted by retirement programming is the *day-care model,* first introduced by parent organizations in the 1950s and later rejected in favor of an educational model and then a vocational model. Programming comprises games, often very childlike, such as plastic bowling or kickball, some arts and crafts, group outings, and so forth. Often there is a group discussion format patterned after reality orientation, an intervention that presumes the presence of some dementia. The model is custodial, age-segregated, and resembles the activities programming in many nursing homes.

Clearly, such programming can be characterized as "retired clienthood," or the final rejection of the possibility of adult roles and community membership, and the definitive entry into a stereotypical old-age role, for which the day-care model, now eschewed by the field of developmental disabilities, again is considered appropriate. The reintroduction of such service patterns into the field of developmental disabilities is dramatic testimony to the power of age stereotypes, the power, in effect, to undermine the social developmental model.

Age Segregation

The tendency of society to create age-segregated groups is almost irresistible. Defining people as old in the stereotypical sense entails using age as the major criterion in defining their peer group. Indeed, this tendency derives from the very core of social policy toward people over 60: "America's social policies for the aged are structurally segregated, particularistic policies that tend to separate the old from others in society" (Estes, 1979, p. 228). Within services to people with developmental disabilities, this predisposition frequently takes the form of the development of an age-segregated subsystem of services for those labeled the "elderly developmentally disabled." Or it may be a kind of pseudo-integration that places older adults with developmental disabilities in age-segregated spaces for older adults without disabilities.[1] In either event, individuals remain isolated from the valued mainstream of their community and in separate social spaces that daily reinforce the perception that *they* are very different from the rest of *us*.

Institutionalism

A survey of residential settings for adults with developmental disabilities over the age of 60 in New York, California, and Massachusetts revealed that 58% were living in public institutions, not including nursing homes (Janicki & Wisniewski, 1985). A later study in Massachusetts found that more than half of *all* people with mental retardation, based on prevalence estimates, were in either nursing homes or state schools, a rate of institutionalization three times greater than that for younger adults (Knoll & Blaney, 1990). The pattern revealed in these studies may be described as institutionalism. This norm, that institutions are appropriate for older adults, has, at best, been weakly challenged and is largely condoned by professionals. Indeed, as discussed below, an unbroken historical connection exists between stereotypes of older adults and the total institution.

In the twentieth century, there have been at least two major deinstitutionalization movements. The first, in the period during and after World War I, replaced the scandal-ridden poor house with a system of so-called outdoor relief or welfare payments. It is important to note that, although every other category of poor-house inmate was provided an alternative, older adults were left to languish in these institutions. Old people were not deinstitutionalized because, alone among the classes of poor people, they were viewed as having no rehabilitative potential

[1]It is interesting to note the use of language in the description of these practices: Janicki (1986), for example, uses the phrase, "integration into generic services for the elderly." Here, "integration" refers to services that are thoroughly *segregated* by age, while "generic" describes the *categorical* services of the aging network. Neither works toward the intended meaning, that is, services utilized by all valued members of the community.

(Haber, 1985). Beginning in the 1920s, the functions of the poor house devolved to the state mental hospital, which by the mid-1930s, predominantly housed people over 60 who lacked both income and family support.

In the second major deinstitutionalization movement, beginning in the late 1960s, both mental institutions and institutions for people with developmental disabilities were decried as anti-habilitative. For older adults, however, the institution continued to be viewed as an appropriate setting. As the Janicki and Wisniewski (1985) and Knoll and Blaney (1990) surveys illustrated, they remained in the state school. Many older adults were also "transinstitutionalized" to nursing homes, and the size of the nursing home population more than doubled during the high tide of deinstitutionalization in the late 1960s and early 1970s.

During the 1980s there were attempts to give institutions for people with developmental disabilities a new lease on life as high technology hospitals and hospices for older adults.[2] This trend reflects a kind of organizational preservation instinct at work. Proponents of institutionalization for people with developmental disabilities (an approach in which institutionalism has been more thoroughly challenged than perhaps any other) are focusing on the one area of ideology and social policy in which institutionalism is alive and well, that is, services to older adults.

POST-ADULTHOOD

The field of developmental disabilities brings out in bold relief the primary social patterns generated by age-based stereotypes. Perhaps because the field has confronted issues of aging only since the 1980s, or because people with developmental disabilities had never before been thought of in terms of their needs as older adults, the events since the 1980s constitute a kind of natural laboratory in which one may see the impact of a relatively pure culture of age-based stereotypes and patterns on a field whose governing ideology sees stereotypes as anathema. The core patterns of retirement, segregation, and institutionalism make revelations about the contemporary paradigm of the old-age stereotype.

At the heart of the paradigm of the old-age stereotype is the construction of a role new to the twentieth century, post-adulthood.

> The process that began in the 1930s when retirement and a retirement age were instituted on a broad scale has finally culminated in the institutionalization of a post-adult period in the life cycle in which persons past retirement age are officially considered incapable of dealing effectively with their own lives. . . . The old, simply because of

[2]Currently, three state schools in Massachusetts have substituted geriatric units or cottages as the only specialization and grouping; these are for residents over 55. Wrentham State School in Massachusetts has become a national center for the reformulation of these state institutions as a valid service form for older adults with mental retardation. This process of "geriatrizing" the state institution is visible throughout the United States, especially in the Midwest, New England, and the mid-Atlantic states.

their age, are deemed incapable. In essence they are assumed to be "post-adults." (Matthews, 1979, p. 132)

Evidence for this insight can be seen in the impact of age-based stereotyping upon people with developmental disabilities. What most has imposed definition on people with developmental disabilities is their exclusion from adulthood both ideologically and socially. People with developmental disabilities have been not only physically separated from the community by brick walls, as might happen to people who break the law, but defined as outside of adulthood, incapable of being adults. People with real or alleged intellectual impairments were defined as pre-adults, that is, above all, never possessing the abilities to enter and perform adult roles (Blaney, 1985). As people were freed from institutions, they were not at the same time freed from this pre-adult role. They were still expected to live outside the adult world of jobs, relationships, and other active community membership roles. A whole separate world was structured for these pre-adults, with sheltered day programs, separate residences, and separate spaces for recreation in which they would be cared for by adult staff.

The attention to the aging of people with developmental disabilities since the 1980s may at first seem contradictory. Much of this time has been consumed with convincing the field and the public that people with developmental disabilities do leave childhood, grow up, and become adults. But still, people with developmental disabilities are pushed into the old-age stereotype when they cross over some magical chronological divide.

The movement from the stereotype of people with disabilities to the old-age stereotype turns out to be not much of a transformation at all. At the root of both stereotypes is the expectation that people are incapable of performing adult roles. People are moved from one stereotype to the other so easily because this transition occurs at the intersection of pre-adulthood and post-adulthood. Indeed, people who have never been allowed to enter adulthood are entering a new role that likewise precludes adult roles and relationships. In effect, people with developmental disabilities are going from pre-adulthood to post-adulthood without passing through adulthood.

The core service patterns of retirement/role exclusion, age segregation, and institutionalism embraced and promoted in the field of developmental disabilities, are rooted in the presumption that the typical older person is incapable of occupying adult roles or coping with the social spaces frequented by adults. Furthermore, post-adults are perceived as belonging with their own kind where they can be cared for more efficiently while they engage in a variety of nonproductive and generally trivial routines. The imposition of "retired clienthood" upon adults with developmental disabilities ensures their ongoing dependency upon human services and professionals. Their clienthood is, indeed, doubly affirmed. The presumptions of the core service patterns reveal the depth and extent of dependency inducement, the core dynamic of the paradigm of the old-age stereotype.

A CREATIVE VISION OF ADULTHOOD

Behind these patterns is a unique predicament, obvious in the field of developmental disabilities and the field of aging. It concerns defining the role of human services in a situation in which the replication of social norms is, in essence, also a process of devaluation and age segregation.

Social role valorization as a theory of policy and service design has always distinguished what is culturally valued from what is typical or normative. This distinction bears directly on the predicament just described in that, when social norms are themselves devaluing, human services actors must reject what is typical and seek instead to support valued processes and outcomes.

The field of aging, especially since the late 1980s, has embarked on a major paradigm shift toward a values base more congruent with social role valorization, as articulated in the following words by Robert Binstock (1983) in his Kent Memorial Lecture to the American Gerontological Society:

> Ultimately one would need to have public policy framed within a *non-ageist political context* [italics added] in which the *heterogeneity* [italics added] of older persons is recognized. I can see no reason why our organization cannot refocus to be more self-consciously concerned with *age-relations* [italics added] rather than the aged. (p. 139)

Binstock, Neugarten, Estes, and other influential policy analysts are urging the field of aging to abandon its notions of old people as a homogeneous group to be congregated and, instead, to view citizens over 60 as the most internally diverse and heterogeneous of any age group (Neugarten, 1982). At the same time, the field, in accord with Binstock, is stressing that aging policy should be focused on support to intergenerational relationships, rather than on age-segregation.

The approach to older adults through the principle of social role valorization has made it apparent that the role in the old-age stereotype simply is not valued and that duplicating that role and its accompanying service patterns leads to devaluing outcomes. The authors recommend a widely shared and deeply internalized vision of people over 60 as first and foremost *adults*. Just as People-First language has assisted society in experiencing the essential commonalities among people with and without disabilities, adopting "adult-first" language will support a comparable social experience of intergenerational commonality and continuity.

Holding human services and, indeed, the broader society accountable to the standard of valued adult roles for older adults represents a crucial addition to the critique offered by policy analysts such as Binstock. Without specifying such a goal, mere refinements of post-adult roles are likely to persist as valid goals. The invitation by the fast food industry to "senior citizens" to enter dead-end service jobs is an example of one such pernicious refinement of post-adulthood.

After more than 2 decades of use as a critical tool to debunk pre-adult roles, social role valorization now poses the challenge to make a qualitative break with post-adult roles and service patterns. The values base and configuration of the current service system will not be touched by superficial reforms; the system must be transformed fundamentally with a focus on the key constituent parts: role exclusion, segregation, and custodial/institutional models.

BRINGING THE VISION OF ADULTHOOD TO REALITY

From Role Exclusion to Role Continuity and Entry

Life areas that adult involvements and interests encompass include family, employment, worship, education, personal relationships, volunteer roles, recreation/leisure, and involvement in clubs and civic organizations. Following are several questions that must be answered regarding any support systems designed to move from a system that generates devalued roles to a system that supports valued social roles:

- Within each life area, what post-adult roles and relationships does this person experience?
- Within each life area, what adult roles and relationships does this person experience? Is he or she at risk of losing any of these roles? How can he or she be supported in maintaining these roles and relationships?
- How often does this person participate in these roles and relationships?
- How would the quality of these roles and relationships be described, for example, how much of a contributing role in a community association, or how much of a decision-making role in his or her family, does the person have?
- What are the current roles of human services in promoting or preventing this person's maintenance of, or entry into, adult roles and relationships?
- What other roles should formal or informal supports play in promoting adult roles and relationships for this person?

It will be useful to answer these questions for persons not defined in the old-age stereotype and persons who are defined in this stereotype. Closing the gap between the two sets of responses would illustrate what should become the driving mission of supports to adults who are growing old.

From Segregation to Personal Community Relationship and Membership

Binstock's call for concern with age-relations or intergenerational relationships occurs within the context of a system of supports that now exemplifies age segregation. The presumption that older adults are essentially different from other people and all the same among themselves has led to the extensive "seniorization" of social space since the 1970s. Senior centers are adjacent to community centers, and virtually every human activity has now been age-segregated, including sports and college classes.

The challenge for the aging services system is to make a commitment to social inclusion that focuses on a plan to become desegregated. In what surely will be an agonizingly difficult process of redirection, social role valorization offers the aging services system a penetrating analysis of social inclusion with guidelines for accomplishing such broad-based desegregation.

The key insight offered by social role valorization and missing in the vision of the aging services network is the distinction between physical and social inclusion. Currently, the aging services network has made a commitment to physical inclusion, that is, the physical presence of older adults in the community. Through the home care system, senior housing, adult day care, and other supports, aging services are attempting to prevent the physical removal of older adults to institutions.

However, each of these service forms is still mainly socially segregated, erecting substantial barriers to the social participation and relationships of older adults in the mainstream community. In effect, the aging services system uses socially segregated service forms to accomplish physical presence. One of the key insights of social role valorization has been to redefine physical inclusion not as a goal, but as a precondition, a means to the goal of social inclusion, that is, personal membership, participation, and relationship in the community.

Social inclusion would mean the inclusion of older adults in the social spaces and organizations utilized by valued members of the community, such as housing, community centers, clubs, and valued paid and volunteer job roles. At the heart of the matter must also be a visible demonstration by the aging services system that it is desegregating, that is, ceasing to promote senior centers, senior housing, and age-segregated supports such as adult day care. At the same time the aging services network must allocate resources to intergenerational housing and social opportunities that bring the generations together as adults contributing to their shared communities.

Judy Heumann (1986) of the World Institute on Disability cogently articulated this issue in the following words:

> The same type of segregated service delivery system has been created for the elderly that younger disabled people and their supporters have been fighting for years to disassemble. I do not want to see myself or other disabled people who have fought so hard for integration being relegated back into segregated programs when they grow old. (pp. 9–10)

The challenge for the field of developmental disabilities is to look to its social role valorization paradigm for guidance and inspiration rather than to the paradigm of the old-age stereotype. Reduced to its essentials, the latter paradigm is the same bio-eugenics ideology that was decisively rejected by the major reformers in the field of developmental disabilities, such as Blatt (1966), Dybwad (1969), and Wolfensberger (1972). They discarded the notion that mental retardation was the result of some reified biological essence that necessitated the social removal of people with mental retardation. The field must now affirm its paradigm by similarly rejecting the bio-medicalization and segregation of adults with developmental disabilities who are growing old.

Unlike the field of aging, the field of developmental disabilities possesses in its history a powerful knowledge base with which to combat this new incarnation of eugenic thinking. Since the 1960s, it has accomplished a profound paradigm shift. All that holds back a similar effort regarding older adults, with and without disabilities, was perhaps best captured in the reflections of Henri Nouwen (1982) who said: As long as the old remain strangers, caring can hardly be meaningful. The old stranger must first become part of our inner self and a welcome friend (p. 89).

From Institution to Community

As explained earlier, there is an unbroken historical connection between people defined in the stereotype of old age and institutionalization. There has never been deinstitutionalization of nursing homes. The continuing presence of the institution as a relevant service form in the vision of the aging services network may be the major obstacle to creating a vision of older people as adults. Whether characterized as "houses of death" or as the social space for the delivery of "unloving care," nursing homes are periodically revealed as scandalously anti-habilitative. Yet they remain on the service continuum in the aging services system with no initiative forthcoming in the aging services network for deinstitutionalization.[3] The continuing validation of institutionalization for older adults is evidence of the extent to which the aging services network has embraced the image of post-adulthood for older adults. Consigning people to the accompanying social space, which no one would truly desire, works from a view of people as virtually post-human.

Social role valorization has grown out of a 20-year effort to create an institution-free society. People with cognitive impairments at least as severe as those in late-stage Alzheimer's disease and people with physical impairments comparable to any encountered in people in nursing homes have left institutions and are living in the community in their houses and apartments. This 20-year experience provides the knowledge and skills to accomplish a similar community inclusion of older people who are now in nursing homes.

However, knowledge is not the central issue. Society knows how to support people outside of institutions. The issue is how society, including human services, has chosen to define older people, that is, as post-adults living in institutions or as adults living in homes. The role of the human services system must become a key support for an interdependent community in which the gifts and desires of all individuals, including those over 60, are affirmed, and the stereotypical thinking behind categorization and segregation is rejected.

[3]The Nursing Home Reform Act of the Omnibus Budget Reconciliation Act of 1987 (OBRA-87) has occurred as an initiative of the developmental disabilities network. In its interpretation by the states and the Health Care Financing Administration, OBRA seems to constitute as much a validation of nursing homes as an appropriate service form as it does a very modest first step toward deinstitutionalization.

REFERENCES

Achenbaum, W.A. (1979). *Old age in the new land.* Baltimore: Johns Hopkins University Press.

Binstock, R.H. (1983). The aged as scapegoat. *Gerontologist, 23*(2), 133–139.

Blaney, B.C. (1985). *The mismeasure of us all: IQ and the social creation of the "mentally retarded."* Boston: Department of Mental Health and Retardation.

Blaney, B.C. (1989). *Planning our vision: A planning guide on issues of aging and developmental disabilities.* Cambridge, MA: Human Services Research Institute.

Blaney, B.C. (1991). Aging and mental retardation: A conceptual framework for policy and program design. In M. Howell (Ed.), *Serving the underserved* (pp. 315–322). Brookline, MA: Exceptional Parent Press.

Bradley, V.J., & Knoll, J. (1990). *Shifting paradigms in services to people with developmental disabilities.* Cambridge, MA: Human Services Research Institute.

Blatt, B., & Kaplan, F. (1966). *Christmas in purgatory: A photographic essay on mental retardation.* Boston: Allyn & Bacon.

Dybwad, G. (1964). *Challenges in mental retardation.* New York: Columbia.

Estes, C.R. (1979). *The aging enterprise: A critical examination of social policies and services for the aged.* San Francisco: Jossey-Bass.

Haber, C. (1985). *Beyond sixty-five: The dilemma of old age in America's past.* New York: Cambridge University.

Hawkins, B.A., & Eklund, S.J. (1987). *A national profile on projects and studies on aging/aged persons with developmental disabilities.* Bloomington: Indiana Developmental Center.

Heumann, J. (1986). The relevance of the independent living model. In C. Mahoney, C. Estes, & J. Heumann (Eds.), *Toward a unified agenda: Proceedings of a National Conference on Aging and Disability.* San Francisco: Institute for Health and Aging.

Janicki, M.P., & Wisniewski, H.M. (Eds.). (1985). *Aging and developmental disabilities: Issues and approaches.* Baltimore: Paul H. Brookes Publishing Co.

Janicki, M. (1986, September). *Issues in aging and developmental disabilities.* Address to Conference on Aging and Developmental Disabilities, Baltimore.

Knoll, J., & Blaney, B.C. (1990). *A fact sheet in support of legislation entitling persons with mental retardation who are over 50 to services in the community.* Cambridge, MA: Human Services Research Institute.

Matthews, S.H. (1979). *The social world of old women: A study in the management of identity.* Beverly Hills: Sage.

Neugarten, B.L. (1982). Policy for the 1980's: Age or need entitlement. In B.L. Neugarten (Ed.), *Age or need.* Beverly Hills: Sage.

Nouwen, H. (1982). *Aging.* New York: Image Books.

Schur, E.M. (1980). *The politics of deviance.* New Jersey: Prentice-Hall.

Vladick, B. (1980). *Unloving care.* Washington, DC: Brookings Institution.

Wolfensberger, W. (1991). *A brief introduction to social role valorization as a high order concept for structuring human services.* Syracuse: Training Institute.

Wolfensberger, W. (1972). *The principle of normalization in human services.* Toronto: National Institute on Mental Retardation.

Wolfensberger, W., & Tullman, S.A. (1982). A brief outline of the principle of normalization. *Rehabilitation Psychology, 27,* 131–145.

III

CHANGE THROUGHOUT THE SYSTEM

In order to bring about the transformations envisioned in this book, changes will have to take place at multiple levels and in multiple contexts. These changes must begin at the federal level where, as Gettings argues in Chapter 9, centralized regulatory policies in Medicaid have constrained the ability of states and localities to design individualized programs, to mount more responsive quality assurance mechanisms, and to decentralize decision-making. In Chapter 10, Racino picks up these themes and points out the importance of building change around the specific culture and competencies of states. Covert, MacIntosh, and Shumway, in Chapter 11, show how various interests within a state can achieve dramatic change when those interests are mobilized around a common end—the closure of a state institution.

There will also be a need for change at the local level. As Nisbet, Jorgensen, and Powers point out in Chapter 12, the inclusion of children in regular classrooms is no longer an experimental exercise but an aim that should be embraced in every school district. Those districts that have sought to change their schools to become more inclusive have multiple lessons to teach other educators and administrators. In addition to schools, local recreational opportunities must also be inclusive and welcoming to children and adults with developmental disabilities. In Chapter 13, Blaney and Freud recount the ways in which individuals have been assisted in participating in recreational opportunities in communities around the United States, and they highlight the importance of respecting the individual's preferences and seeking inclusion one individual at a time. Building competency at the local level also extends to the community system of agencies and providers, both residential and vocational. Magis-Agosta, in Chapter 14; Dufresne and Laux, in Chapter 15; and Kiracofe, in Chapter 16; all provide valuable insights into organizational transformations based on personal experiences with specific agencies. They all underscore the importance of creating change at the heart of an organization through a reorientation in staff attitudes about people with developmental disabilities, and changes in organizational values and mission. These three chapters provide frank depictions of the difficulties encountered in bringing about change, as well as the sense of triumph and accomplishment that accompanies change. These authors also point out the dynamic character of organizational transformation and the importance of a continuing process of re-examination.

Chapter 17, the final chapter in this section, by Knoll and Racino, discusses the changes that must take place in the formal training of people entering the field as professionals and paraprofessionals. These authors speculate on the nature of a new community support curriculum as well as the appropriate academic "home" for this emerging and somewhat hybrid vocation.

9

The Link Between Public Financing and Systemic Change

Robert M. Gettings

The earlier chapters of this book reviewed the changes that are taking place in the field of developmental disabilities. These changes have been underway since the 1970s but have been unfolding at an accelerating pace since the mid-1980s. They are grounded in the belief that the fundamental goal of a service delivery system should be to assist people with lifelong disabilities to live more independent, productive lives as fully participating members of their local communities. As policy-makers, professionals, family members, and other involved citizens have come to accept this new way of thinking, it has become increasingly evident that many deeply entrenched service delivery philosophies and practices must be abandoned in favor of radically new approaches. However, it is proving to be much easier to embrace the rhetoric of what Bradley and Knoll (1990) have referred to as the "community membership paradigm" and identify the flaws in existing service delivery practices than it is to solve the practical dilemmas associated with building a service delivery system that is fully reflective of this new approach to assisting people with developmental disabilities.

Clearly, state governments are playing and will continue to play a pivotal role in the process of developing service delivery policies and practices that are consistent with the new person-centered approach to delivering services. Cooperation among the federal government, local jurisdictions, private provider agencies, and consumer organizations will be essential to the success of this far-reaching enterprise. But, as the principal source of financial support as well as the chief purveyors of public policy, the states must take the lead in translating the aims of this reform agenda into everyday practice.

Quality assurance and quality enhancement are two of the most complex yet least understood challenges that the states face in developing service delivery systems that embody these new values. The overriding objective is to assist individuals and their families to make their own life choices within the framework of a person-centered approach to delivery of needed services and supports. However, it is quite evident that traditional methods of assuring the quality of service programs and facilities are incompatible with this framework. What is not clear at present are the precise features of an alternative approach that emphasize the achievement of professionally valued outcomes for the consumer without the loss of individual autonomy.

The purpose of this chapter is to highlight some of the key challenges that the states face in their attempts to design and implement service delivery systems that are consistent with the underlying values of the new service paradigm that is rapidly assuming preeminence in the developmental disabilities field. Particular attention is given to the ways in which this shift toward person-centered services and supports is influenced by the financing options and incentives that are currently available to the states. Attention is also given to the dilemmas states face in devising reasonable and responsible measures to assure the quality of consumer-centered support services. The principal features of a new model for organizing state and local quality assurance and enhancement activities is discussed along with the ways in which the adoption of this model is likely to be affected—positively or negatively—by future changes in federal and state policies.

Before discussing the barriers to change, however, a few general observations concerning the establishment and maintenance of high quality human services programs seem to be in order.

THE IMPACT OF MEDICAID FINANCING

As is the case with any major social reform movement, the ultimate success of current efforts to reconfigure the delivery of developmental disabilities services along lines that are consistent with the community supports paradigm will rest on the ability of leaders in the field to overcome many imposing barriers. Recognizing the nature and complexity of these barriers is, of course, a prerequisite to identifying workable solutions.

One such barrier is the service system's heavy reliance on the federal–state Medicaid program as a source of financing. During fiscal year (FY) 1992, the states collectively spent over $12 billion on institutional and community-based services for people with developmental disabilities through their Medicaid programs. Three out of every 5 dollars that the states spend on specialized developmental disabilities services now flow through Medicaid (Title XIX of PL 89-97, the Social Security Act Amendments of 1965)—and these figures do not include the acute health care payments made on behalf of Title XIX-eligible individuals with developmental disabilities.

Unquestionably, Medicaid payments have played an essential role in underwriting improvements in developmental disabilities services nationwide from 1972 to the present. Yet, despite the increasing, often precedent-setting attempts by the states and local service providers to use Title XIX dollars in ways that allow consumers to live richer, more rewarding lives in the community, Medicaid support for developmental disabilities services continues to be deeply rooted in a "care and treatment" model of delivering services.

In the area of services to people with developmental disabilities, the clearest example of this model is the intermediate care facilities for persons with mental retardation (ICF/MR) coverage option. The enactment of the ICF/MR funding authority in 1971 marked an important turning point in the contemporary history of services to people with mental retardation and related developmental disabilities. The legislation provided the states with the federal financial support necessary to eliminate the often deplorable conditions that existed in many public residential treatment centers for persons with mental retardation, plus a method of equalizing the financial incentives affecting the establishment of community-based residences for these individuals. Because adherence to federally prescribed operating standards was a statutory quid pro quo for the receipt of federal Medicaid payments, states were forced to take steps to upgrade the physical plants and staffing configurations of ICF/MR–certified facilities in order to ensure the continued flow of federal financial assistance.

In retrospect, it is clear that the field of developmental disabilities has paid a steep price for the advances achieved through the ICF/MR coverage option. To qualify for this funding, states (as well as private agencies operating as state-certified vendors of ICF/MR services) have been forced to adhere to a facility-based, 24-hour programming model that is unnecessary and inappropriate for the vast majority of people with developmental disabilities who require ongoing assistance.

No one would argue with the proposition that 24-hour care is essential for a relatively small subpopulation of people with developmental disabilities, although the composition and dimensions of this subpopulation, as well as the most effective means of serving these individuals, remain the subject of sharp debate. Regardless of one's views, however, most state officials, service providers, and consumer advocates would readily agree that the ability to shift 50%–80% of the cost of services to the federal Medicaid budget has been the principal motivating factor behind the growth in ICF/MR utilization from 1972 to the present. Given the choice of an alternative method of financing residential services and supports for people with developmental disabilities that assures a roughly equivalent level of federal financial participation, most state policy-makers and local practitioners would not elect to use the ICF/MR model. The one size fits all approach to financing services that is embodied in the ICF/MR coverage model places many constraints on the provider agency's ability to tailor services and supports to the individual needs of each program participant. It also imposes many restrictions on the capacity of individuals to achieve greater independence and control over their own lives and involves excessively high costs for activities that often are of marginal utility to facility residents and, in some instances, actually are counterproductive.

The best evidence that the ICF/MR model is out of step with current exemplary practice in the field is the rapid growth in the utilization of the Medicaid Home and Community-Based (HCB) waiver authority as an alternative means of financing daytime and residential support services for people with developmental disabilities. Currently, 49 states operate over 80 separate waiver programs for people with mental retardation/developmental disabilities (MR/DD). It is important to recognize that the decision to initiate each of these waiver programs represented a conscious choice on the part of state policy-makers to contain the future growth of ICF/MR services; federal waiver policies require a state to prove that the individuals to be served through the proposed waiver program otherwise would be residents of ICF/MR facilities.

As illustrated in Figure 9.1 participation in HCB waiver programs has been growing at a rate of approximately 15% per year and is expected to involve roughly 65,000 participants by the end of FY 1992 (or over 90% more than for FY 1989).

By contrast, the total number of ICF/MR residents nationally has remained relatively static since 1982 (fluctuating from roughly 140,000 to 147,000 residents). As shown in Figure 9.2, virtually all of the growth in the number of recipients of Medicaid-financed long-term care services for people with developmental

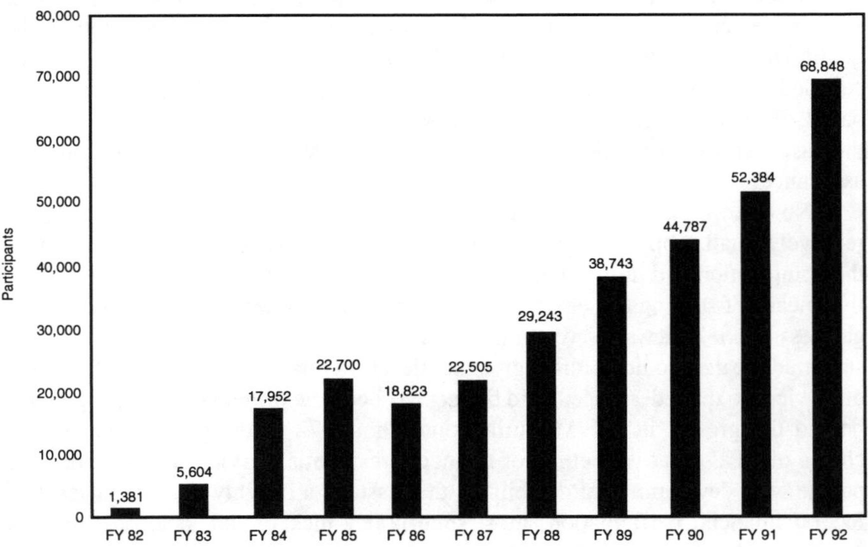

Figure 9.1. Persons with developmental disabilities participating in the HCB waiver program from FY 1982 to FY 1992.

disabilities from 1981 to 1991 is attributable to the increased participation in HCB waiver-financed services. In other words, given the clear choice of financing the expansion of long-term care services through the ICF/MR program or the HCB waiver authority, states have opted for the latter.

HCB waiver expenditures have been increasing even faster than program utilization (in excess of 25% per year) and are expected to top $1.6 billion during FY 1992. The average per capita cost of HCB waivers is less than half the average cost of ICF/MR services (e.g., $24,042 versus an estimated $61,000). While HCB waiver costs have been increasing at a rate in excess of the general rate of inflation, they have not risen as rapidly as average ICF/MR per diems (Smith & Gettings, in press).

Despite the rapidly expanding use of the HCB waiver as a vehicle for supporting community developmental disabilities services and the states' clear preference for this method of Medicaid financing, federal–state payments to ICF/MR facilities still constitute roughly three quarters of all Medicaid expenditures for long-term care services provided to people with developmental disabilities. The continuing upward spiral in ICF/MR outlays (from $3.3 billion in FY 1982 to an estimated $9.3 billion in FY 1992) is the major reason for which the proportion of total state expenditures devoted to ICF/MR services remains so high despite the rapid expansion in waiver utilization and outlays. Lakin, White, Prouty, Bruininks, and Kimm (1991) for example, reported that the total number of ICF/MR recipients increased at an average annual rate of only 0.6% between FY 1982 and FY 1989 (or from 140,752 to 147,148). In sharp contrast, total ICF/MR outlays grew from $5.5

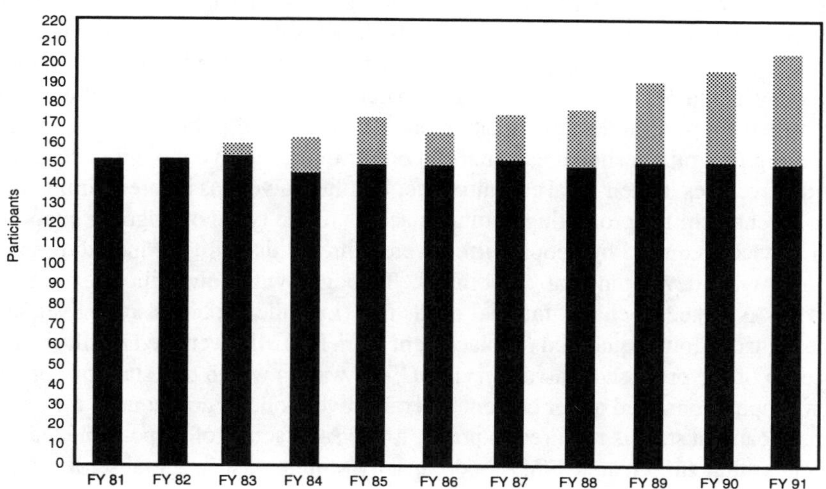

Figure 9.2. Persons with developmental disabilities participating in ICF/MR programs and HCB waiver programs from FY 1981 to FY 1991. (Solid bar = ICF/MR programs; shaded bar = HCB waiver programs.)

billion to $8.2 billion between FY 1987 and FY 1991, or at an average annual rate of 10.4% (Burwell, 1992).

This escalation of ICF/MR costs is one of the factors that has limited the capacity of the states to address the burgeoning demand for community-based services, which has been fueled by the growing number of young adults who have graduated from the public schools and now need adult training and support services. In many states the result has been much longer waiting lists for adult day and residential services and a growing level of dissatisfaction among consumers and their families whose needs go unserved.

For example, Lakin reported that the total number of people with developmental disabilities receiving publicly funded residential services of any type increased by only 8% in the 21 years between 1967 and 1988 (i.e., from 304,000 to 330,500 individuals) (Amado, Lakin, & Manke, 1990). In other word-, the sizable increases in public spending that have been recorded (from $3.4 billion in FY 1977 to $11.7 billion in FY 1988 [Braddock, Hemp, Fujiura, & Bachelder, 1990]) have occurred largely because of the reconfiguration of existing services (i.e., from an emphasis on large, congregate residential settings to smaller, community-based services), rather than the expansion of services to the unserved or underserved population. One of the fundamental challenges to be faced in the 1990s, therefore, is finding ways of making more efficient use of available resources so that the overall number of service recipients can be increased significantly. If history is any guide, it will be virtually impossible to achieve this objective as long as the lion's share of Medicaid expenditures are tied to a model of service delivery that mandates, as a basic condition of continued federal funding, the provision of aggressive, continuous active treatment services to all participants in a specialized facility setting—regardless of the costs or the benefits derived by facility residents.

Primarily through more aggressive utilization of the Medicaid HCB waiver authority, a number of states have begun to demonstrate the feasibility of creating individual support models that make more efficient use of public resources while affording program participants enhanced opportunities to live more independent, productive lives in their local communities. But the waiver has inherent limitations as a mechanism for promoting equitable access to the types of ongoing supports and services required by people with severe, chronic disabilities, including individuals with developmental disabilities. To begin with, eligibility for waiver services is linked to an institutional needs test (i.e., the applicant for waiver services must be found qualified for placement in an ICF/MR–certified facility in the absence of the proposed waiver services). The way in which this statutory provision is operationalized under current federal waiver policies compounds the problem, because a state is required to prove, to the satisfaction of responsible federal officials, that sufficient ICF/MR bed capacity would exist in the absence of the requested waiver services to serve the number of individuals projected to receive waiver-financed services. Within certain boundaries, therefore, this so-called "cold bed" approach to regulating waiver utilization turns federal–state negotiations into a zero sums game. In other words, by employing the waiver authority, a state can trade off current and projected ICF/MR beds for waiver "slots"; however, it can expect to achieve only marginal real growth in the total number of recipients of Medicaid-funded long-term care services.

As a permanent mechanism for promoting greater efficiency and effectiveness in the use of scarce resources, the waiver has other drawbacks. First, in order to maximize federal financial participation on behalf of the limited number of people they are authorized to serve, states face a powerful inducement to select recipients who need a comprehensive array of services. There is a strong temptation to refinance traditional facility-based day and residential services, where the bulk of state-only community service dollars historically has been directed, rather than promoting the development of new, more individualized service delivery models through the waiver program. Indeed, despite the expansion and diversification of waiver-financed services which have occurred over the past 5 years, traditional facility-based models still form the backbone of waiver-financed services in most states.

Second, although the HCB waiver authority provides states with a ready vehicle to expand significantly the range and scope of Medicaid-reimbursable community services, it does not allow a state to circumvent a variety of basic statutory and regulatory requirements that fit poorly with the concepts and values that undergird the community supports paradigm. One example is that Medicaid is basically a mechanism for reimbursing health care providers after the fact for services rendered to an eligible recipient. Consequently, a basic tenet of Medicaid policy is that federal funds may not be used to provide cash assistance to recipients. Given the increasing emphasis on the use of cash subsidies and other devices to empower individuals and their families to make their own choices about how public funds can be deployed most effectively, this fundamental, long-standing principle of Medicaid policy is an impediment to using the community supports paradigm to assist individuals with developmental disabilities and their families. It is always possible to pursue modifications in the statutory provisions of Medicaid law that prohibit cash payments; however, in view of the fact that funding for long-term care services to people with developmental disabilities constitutes only a small portion of overall Medicaid outlays, it is doubtful that federal law-makers would be willing to redirect program funding in this manner.

The dilemma is as follows: states (and, by extension, local service providers and consumers) are heavily reliant on the Medicaid program as a funding source for ongoing services/supports that are required by people with developmental disabilities, but existing Medicaid policies are ill-suited to supporting emerging state-of-the-art methods of organizing and delivering such services. Furthermore, the prospects for restructuring existing program policies in ways that are fully compatible with the community supports paradigm are, at best, highly problematic.

There is growing disenchantment with the Medicaid program as a general mechanism for funding long-term care services. Numerous proposals have been advanced to replace Medicaid with a federal statutory authority that would put a stronger emphasis on home and community-based alternatives to institutional care. The problem is that most of these proposals virtually ignore the special needs of persons with developmental disabilities (as well as other persons with severe, chronic disabilities, besides senior citizens) and often include provisions that are incompatible with emerging service delivery trends in the field of developmental disabilities (e.g., the establishment of cost-effectiveness thresholds for the provision of reimbursable home and community-based care services) (The Pepper Commission, 1990).

Demographic trends and public opinion polls suggest to the author that Congress is likely to enact long-term care reform legislation in the foreseeable future. The question is whether this legislation will take into account the distinctive needs and aspirations of people with developmental disabilities. At present, there is every reason to believe that these interests will be overlooked or given short shrift unless leaders in the field of developmental disabilities begin to take a far more active part in the dialogue that will determine the contents of future legislation in this critical policy area.

OTHER STATE/LOCAL BARRIERS TO CHANGE

The development of appropriate financing strategies is not the only impediment to the organization and delivery of person-centered community services for people with developmental disabilities. There are a variety of interrelated forces at work that will have to be addressed to achieve a smooth transition to the community supports paradigm. Among these forces are the interests of organized labor and the literally thousands of private agencies that presently operate facility-based day and residential service programs in the community for people with developmental disabilities.

Labor leaders are likely to see the shift toward more individualized service models as a threat to the already declining union membership base. The ongoing depopulation of public facilities for people with mental retardation and the accompanying dramatic shift of responsibility to nonunionized, private community vendor agencies has eroded the ranks of organized labor in many states, and there is every indication that this process will continue. In some states, the loss of institutional jobs has been offset largely by the establishment of state-operated group homes and, in some cases, daytime habilitation centers. These congregate care programs, however, are incompatible with the fundamental aims of person-centered services, and, consequently, the continuation and certainly the further expansion of these programs represents a potential source of friction as states increase the number and range of non–facility-based service options. A few states have begun to experiment with using public employees as family caretakers, as case managers, and in other support roles within the community service system. Most of these efforts, however, are still too new and small in scope to permit a realistic appraisal of their value as a method of avoiding strong labor union opposition to the expanded use of the community supports paradigm.

Similarly, staff and volunteer leaders of private agencies that currently operate group homes, sheltered workshops, and other facility-based programs have ambivalent views regarding the shift toward person-centered service models. On the one hand, they often express support for the aims of this approach to organizing and delivering services. On the other hand, they are worried about the potential consequences this shift in funding priorities may have for the long-term financial and organizational viability of their agencies. Typically, such agencies are heavily invested, both financially and psychically, in real property and capital equipment. Indeed, the capacity of many agencies to meet their payments on this property and equipment is directly tied to continued public support for existing service programs and facilities. Quite understandably, they ask, "If public funding for our agency's facility-based programs were to be shifted elsewhere, how would we continue to meet our mortgage payments?"

Most fair-minded observers would agree that the states have a moral obligation to assist existing community service providers to convert to a person-centered programming format. The extent of this obligation and how it can best be fulfilled has not yet been settled in many states.

Several states have begun to develop creative methods of converting existing facilities to new uses so that local service agencies can make the transition to person-centered programming formats. However, such conversion options are limited by bleak state budgets now and probably for several years to come.

A continuation of the status quo would simply exacerbate the backlog of unmet demand that has accumulated. States have little choice but to adopt policies that foster the transition to the community supports paradigm if they expect to respond to the burgeoning demand for community-based services. Provider agencies, likewise, must be sensitive to this dramatic shift in service philosophy and be prepared to make the necessary accommodations in their agencies' programs and activities.

QUALITY: AN ILLUSIVE CONCEPT

The provision of high quality services is, of course, a goal of all parties who have a role in assisting people with developmental disabilities. Yet, serious discussions of the operational meaning of the term "quality" in this context are still rare. It is true that there has been a continuous, often intense, dialogue concerning appropriate standards of program/facility performance as well as the proper methods of measuring compliance with such standards; however, the underlying premise in this dialogue typically has been that standards compliance equates with the provision of quality services, when in fact there is scant evidence to support this proposition.

It is important, therefore, to recognize at the outset that quality is not a fixed concept; rather it is a constantly evolving set of performance aspirations. As Peter

Tropman so aptly pointed out, "Quality is a journey not a destination" (Tropman, 1990, p. 8). From this perspective, the provision of quality services, by its very nature, cannot be standardized, quantified, or objectively measured.

Unfortunately, in the public policy-making arena, there is an overwhelming tendency to ignore the distinction between attempts to enhance program quality and efforts to ensure that service providers adhere to minimally acceptable standards of performance. The taxpaying public has a right to expect that public funds will be managed prudently and effectively. In carrying out their fiduciary obligations, public managers must employ methods of assessing compliance with service expectations that both conform to acceptable standards of performance and hold tax-supported providers accountable for meeting such standards. Too often, however, the process of formulating and enforcing quality assurance standards has tended to reinforce mediocre performance and discourage providers from striving to move beyond minimal compliance toward true program excellence. In part this is a reflection of the tendency of slow moving public bureaucracies to apply standards that trail behind current progressive thinking and to gravitate toward requirements that represent the least common denominator of performance. But, perhaps more important, it reflects the fundamental incompatibility between quality control, as a legitimate and essential governmental function, and fostering an environment that promotes excellence.

If, in fact, the true measure of quality lies in the eye of the beholder, the question to be answered is, "Whose views should prevail?" Advocates of the community supports paradigm answer this question by pointing out that the recipient of services and his or her family have an overriding stake in achieving favorable service outcomes and, therefore, should determine when existing or proposed services are appropriate and effectively furnished. This emphasis on the role of "the customer" in shaping service decisions and assessing program outcomes represents a refreshing departure from typical practice, in which consumers and their families are largely left out of the decision-making process. Reconciling this customer-driven model of service planning and delivery with the need for government to ensure public accountability poses numerous, as yet unresolved, issues. However, creative ways of addressing this dilemma are currently being piloted in a number of states and local communities across the United States.

FASHIONING A NEW APPROACH TO QUALITY ASSURANCE AND ENHANCEMENT

One of the most serious obstacles to the expanded use of the community supports paradigm is the lack of consensus regarding an acceptable approach to quality assurance and enhancement that is compatible with a person-centered model of organizing and delivering needed services and supports to people with developmental disabilities. The central question to be answered in formulating a strategy to reach this consensus is: How does one ensure that the rights and interests of program participants are adequately safeguarded without violating the fundamental goal of allowing such individuals to control their own lives and take their rightful places as participating members of the community? Clearly, the traditional methods used to regulate the quality of community developmental disabilities services and the principal aims and values of the community supports paradigm work at cross-purposes. A uniform set of statutory or regulatory protections that are applicable to all program participants in a state are based on a set of generalizable assumptions about the persons to be served. In actual practice the needs of each program participant are different, and standardized assumptions will tend to undermine the principle of tailoring program protections to the particular circumstances of each individual.

The task of designing an alternative model of quality assurance is far from simple, especially when one takes into account the overlapping levels of public accountability that inevitably are associated with programs in which federal, state, and local agencies have interlocking roles to play. The philosophy underlying the community supports paradigm emphasizes the importance of decentralizing decision-making in order to involve the program participant and his or her family. The basic function of the service provider/agency is to assist the participant, with the help of those who are closest to him or her, to reach his or her personal goals and to act as the vital link between the individual and the local, state, and/or federal agencies that are providing funding to assist in reaching these goals. Public policy-makers at the federal, state, and local levels, however, have an overriding obligation to ensure that government funds are used prudently and in accordance with all applicable legal requirements. Unfortunately, in fulfilling this legitimate and necessary oversight role, it is quite possible for government agencies to impose statutory or regulatory requirements that have the effect of restricting the flexibility of response at the point of service delivery, a principle that lies at the heart of the community supports paradigm.

Specific approaches to assuring public accountability while still allowing consumers to make their own life choices are just beginning to emerge. The following are common principles governing the design of a quality assurance system that can be derived from these approaches:

- Quality assurance and enhancement activities should be sensitive to the main goals of the community supports model—that is, to promote, on an individualized basis, expanded opportunities for independence, productivity, and community inclusion on behalf of each program participant.
- Consumers should be empowered to make their own life choices and assisted in pursuing their goals. Consequently, the systematic assessment of the extent to which program participants are satisfied with the quality of their own lives should be an integral part of any comprehensive quality assurance program.

- In those instances in which the federal government contributes funding for providing community services and supports to people with developmental disabilities, applicable laws and/or regulations should specify minimum safeguards to protect the health, safety, and well-being of all participants and require each state to submit a comprehensive quality assurance/enhancement plan. The steps that are needed to ensure that such protections are in place and are being observed for each program participant should be spelled out by responsible state officials in the state's quality assurance plan. State officials, in turn, should grant the local governing structure and provider agencies the latitude to determine the best means of meeting the specifications of the state quality assurance plan in the case of each program participant.
- Quality assurance/enhancement plans should be an integral component of each program participant's individual service/support plan and should be tailored to the particular needs and circumstances of the individual.
- Federal and state policies should emphasize the use of multifaceted strategies for monitoring the quality and appropriateness of the services and supports that are furnished to participants of community developmental disabilities programs, rather than relying entirely on a single, uni-dimensional compliance monitoring process.
- The objective of a state or local quality assurance/enhancement plan should be to promote the provision of superior services, instead of simply achieving minimum compliance. To reach this objective, it will be necessary to include in the plan explicit provisions for assisting local provider agencies to strive for excellence, including ways of assisting them to improve their performance in areas that reach beyond compliance with minimum statutory and regulatory requirements.

The quality assurance requirements that are built into the statutory authority governing Medicaid coverage of Community Supported Living Arrangements (CSLA) for persons with developmental disabilities represent an initial attempt to follow the above principles. Section 1930(d) of the Social Security Act, as added by Section 4712 of the Omnibus Budget Reconciliation Act of 1990 (OBRA-90) (PL 101-508), spells out the essential elements of the quality assurance program that a state must establish in order to cover CSLA services under its Medicaid plan. Some of these requirements are standard elements in any quality assurance program (e.g., procedures for surveying and certifying CSLA provider agencies based on state standards, which include at least the following provisions: 1) minimum qualifications and training requirements applicable to provider staff, 2) financial operating standards, and 3) a consumer grievance process). But the law also directs states to build several unique elements into its quality assurance plan, including a system of monitoring boards made up of "providers, family members, consumers and neighbors," and a method for the "ongoing monitoring of the health and well-being of each [CSLA] recipient" (Section 4712). Another noteworthy feature of the CSLA quality assurance requirements is the emphasis that is placed on involving the public in the planning and provision of such services. A state is required to hold public hearings on its quality assurance plan before it can be approved by the Secretary of the Department of Health and Human Services (HHS). In addition, a state must make available to the public information about the operation of its CSLA program on an ongoing basis.

The provisions of Medicaid law that authorize the CSLA coverage option seek to carve out a fundamentally different relationship between the federal government and the states in the area of quality assurance. Instead of empowering the secretary of HHS to promulgate detailed operating standards that provider agencies must adhere to in order to qualify for federal reimbursement (as presently is the case for Medicaid-certified nursing facilities and ICFs/MR), Section 1930 of OBRA-90 sets forth only the basic elements that must be included in a comprehensive statewide quality assurance plan. It leaves to the states the determination of how these elements should be addressed within the context of the overall plan. Secretarial approval of the plan is a prerequisite for covering CSLA services under the state's Medicaid plan.

In recognition of the differing circumstances that apply in each state that may elect to cover CSLA services, OBRA allows state officials considerable latitude in developing a quality assurance program that is tailored to the resources and needs of particular jurisdictions. The expectation is that states, in turn, will permit responsible local jurisdictions (e.g., county boards, regional centers) and ultimately service providers a good deal of flexibility in constructing quality assurance strategies that are molded to the particular strengths, needs, and aspirations of each program participant.

Section 1930 of the Social Security Act, however, also contains evidence of the continuing lack of consensus about the most appropriate role for the federal government to play in overseeing the delivery of federally assisted services. In addition to the provisions discussed above, the legislation contains separate authority for the secretary of HHS to publish federal regulations governing certain specified measures "to protect the health, safety and welfare of individuals receiving community supported living arrangement services" (Section 1930[h][1][A]). Federal rules implementing these "minimum protections" must assure compliance "through methods other than reliance on State licensure processes or the State quality assurance programs" (Section 1930[h][1][B]). The following safeguards are delineated in the statute: 1) protection from neglect, physical and sexual abuse, and financial exploitation; 2) prohibition of employing workers with a history of child or client abuse, neglect, or mistreatment; 3) prohibition of abusive financial arrangements; and 4) protection from unethical insurance practices.

House conferees on the 1990 legislation that added Section 1930 to the Social Security Act, led by Rep. Henry Waxman (D-CA), insisted that these minimum protections be incorporated in the final legislation. They were motivated by a concern that participants in CSLA-funded programs would be vulnerable to abuse and neglect unless the legislation carved out a specific, pro-active role for the federal government in looking out for their interests.

The views of Rep. Waxman, as well as many of his congressional colleagues, are influenced by the repeated reports of substandard, often scandalous conditions in nursing homes and board-and-care facilities of various types over the years. The only way to prevent such abuse, they argue, is to enact explicit federal statutory and regulatory requirements, tighten enforcement mechanisms as well as penalties for noncompliance, and expand federal oversight, as was done in the case of Medicare- and Medicaid-certified nursing homes in 1987 through the passage of comprehensive reform legislation (PL 100-203, the Omnibus Budget Reconciliation Act of 1987). Proponents of this approach, not surprisingly, are skeptical of proposals to further delegate quality assurance responsibilities to the state and local levels.

It is still too early to reach even tentative conclusions about the prospects for reconciling these divergent views of the respective roles of the federal government and the states in overseeing the appropriateness and quality of CSLA services. As of this writing, the eight states that were selected to cover CSLA services in October 1991, are just beginning their programs. It will take at least a year or 2 of operating experience to gain a clear sense of the strengths and weaknesses of these eight programs in the area of quality assurance and the possible ramifications for future federal policy.

One point seems clear: the debate that surrounded the formulation of the CSLA quality assurance provisions highlights a key issue, which will have to be resolved before further legislative steps can be taken to expand federal aid for community-based developmental disabilities services. On the one hand, it is difficult to conceive of a scenario in which the use of the community supports model could flourish in the face of a uniform, proscriptive set of federal quality assurance standards that, almost inevitably, would be applied through a traditional survey/certification model. Not only would such an approach contradict the underlying objective of creating a person-centered service environment, but it also would stifle further innovation in a rapidly evolving area of program practice, thus choking off opportunities to identify new and better ways of assisting people with severe, lifelong disabilities to live fuller and richer lives in the community.

On the other hand, sharp disagreements over the distribution of intergovernmental responsibilities date back to the founding fathers. Under the circumstances, it would be unrealistic to assume that the tensions historically associated with the relationships between federal, state, and local governments could be removed entirely. Instead, efforts should be directed toward identifying specific ways of accommodating the legitimate interests of the federal government without restricting the capacity of: 1) state officials to develop quality assurance policies that are tailored to the needs and resources of the particular jurisdiction and centered on helping each program participant to achieve his or her own aspirations, and 2) local officials and service providers to build specific quality assurance strategies into the individualized service/support plan of each person they serve. In establishing the CSLA coverage option, OBRA-90 provides a framework for achieving such a balance. However, further work will be necessary to flesh out the components of this approach to quality assurance. In particular, more thought needs to be given to integrating the notion of minimum protections into the general quality assurance framework.

Furthermore, additional attention needs to be given to examining the experiences of other states and localities that are attempting to employ the community supports paradigm. As illustrated in other chapters of this book, a veritable explosion of creative new programs premised on the community supports paradigm have been launched. There is a need to review systematically the experiences of these programs and glean from them the lessons that can be learned. Unfortunately, both the federal government and the states currently invest little money in critically evaluating the impact of promising new programmatic strategies; as a consequence, past mistakes are repeated while worthwhile new approaches are not. This situation must be reversed if the transition to a person-centered service delivery system is to be achieved.

Finally, better mechanisms for collecting, analyzing, and disseminating information about new strategies for organizing and delivering services in accordance with the community supports paradigm must be developed. Much of the information that is currently available focuses primarily on the ideology and values that undergird this approach to programming. What is needed now is more insightful nuts and bolts information on translating these concepts into day-to-day practice, including proven methods of circumventing the practical problems that are often encountered in attempting to apply the supports model in a variety of program situations and settings. Also, policy-makers, practitioners, and theorists need to have a regular forum in which they can exchange ideas, information, and materials about innovative practices.

CONCLUSION

The field of developmental disabilities is on the threshold of a promising new era in which people with disabilities will be able to exercise greater control over their destinies and have more opportunities to live in, work in, and become integral parts of their local communities. The key to crossing this threshold and entering the new era is to restructure existing methods of organizing, delivering, and financing services so that the consumer becomes the hub, rather than the hubcap, of the service delivery process. The task of restructuring service delivery along more individualized, person-centered lines poses enormous challenges for the field. It will be necessary not only to rethink existing methods of financing community developmental disabilities services, but also to find ways of accommodating the legitimate interests of powerful forces within the field that currently have a vested interest in the continuation of the status quo. The precise ways in which these actual and potential roadblocks might be removed remain unclear at this point. Nonetheless, the enormous burst of energy and enthusiasm that has been unleashed in the field over the past few years offers considerable hope that workable solutions to these problems can and will be found.

REFERENCES

Amado, A.N., Lakin, K.C., & Manke, J.M. (1990). *Chartbook on services for people with developmental disabilities.* Minneapolis: University of Minnesota, Center for Residential and Community Services.

Braddock, D., Hemp, R., Fujiura, G., & Bachelder, L. (1990). *The state of the states in developmental disabilities.* Chicago: The University of Illinois at Chicago, University Affiliated Program in Developmental Disabilities, Institute for the Study of Developmental Disabilities.

Bradley, V.J., & Knoll, J. (1990). *Shifting paradigms in services to people with developmental disabilities.* Unpublished manuscript, Administration on Developmental Disabilities, United States Department of Health and Human Services.

Burwell B. (1992, January 10). Memorandum on *Medicaid long term care expenditures for FY 1991.* Unpublished manuscript.

Lakin, K.C., White, C.C., Prouty, R.W., Bruininks, R.H., & Kimm, C. (1991). *Medicaid institutional (ICF/MR) and home and community-based services for persons with mental retardation and related conditions* (Report No. 35). Minneapolis: University of Minnesota, Center on Residential Services and Community Living.

The Pepper Commission (United States Bipartisan Commission on Comprehensive Health Care). (1990). *A call for action: Final report.* Washington, DC: United States Government Printing Office.

Smith, G., & Gettings, R.M. (in press). *Medicaid in the community: The HCB waiver and CSLA programs.* Alexandria, VA: National Association of State Mental Retardation Program Directors, Inc.

Tropman, P. (1990). *The quality initiative: Community-based long term care for the elderly and disabled.* (Distributed by The Management Group, Madison.)

10

Creating Change in States, Agencies, and Communities

Julie Ann Racino

The field of disability is on the brink of an era that demands new concepts to guide it into the future. Working together with people with disabilities, this society can develop schools, communities, neighborhoods, health care systems, recreation, and workplaces where everyone belongs and is valued (Bogdan & Taylor, 1987; Biklen & Knoll, 1987; Lakin, 1988; Stainback & Stainback, 1990; Taylor, Racino, & Walker, 1992). Since the 1980s, social justice issues have revolved around the move from institutional to community life, with an emphasis on the community presence of women, men, and children with disabilities. However, the next decade will pose a challenge to address the attitudinal, political, social, economic, and administrative barriers that stand in the way of the full participation and freedom of all citizens.

The support/empowerment framework (see Table 10.1) is an attempt to reframe the major theoretical and practical guides in the field of developmental disabilities to reflect an alliance among people with disabilities, professionals, friends and families, and others who would participate in such alliances if given an opportunity to do so (Racino, 1992; Racino, Walker, O'Connor, & Taylor, 1993). While retaining the independent living movement's features of personal control of

---

This chapter was prepared with partial support from the Research and Training Center on Community Integration, Center on Human Policy, Division of Special Education and Rehabilitation, School of Education, Syracuse University, through Cooperative Agreement H133B00003-90, funded by the United States Department of Education, Office of Special Education and Rehabilitative Services, National Institute on Disability and Rehabilitation Research (NIDRR). No official endorsement by the United States Department of Education or Syracuse University of the opinions expressed herein should be inferred.

Table 10.1. A comparison of the rehabilitation, independent living, and support/empowerment paradigms

Focus	Rehabilitation paradigm[a]	Independent living paradigm[a]	Support/empowerment paradigm[b]
Definition of problem	Physical impairment, lack of vocational skill, psychological maladjustment, lack of motivation and cooperation	Dependence on professionals, relatives, and others; inadequate support services; architectural barriers; economic barriers	Attitudinal, political, economic, and administrative barriers to societal participation; inadequate supports within society
Locus of problem	In individual	In environment; in rehabilitation process	In society/environment; in rehabilitation process
Social role(s)	Patient–client	Consumer	Coworker, community member, student, neighbor, so forth
Solution to problem	Professional intervention by physician, physical therapist, occupational therapist, vocational counselor, and others	Peer counseling; advocacy; self-help; consumer control; removal of barriers and disincentives	Redesign of schools, homes, work places, health-care systems, transportation, and social environments to include everyone
Who is in control	Professional	Consumer	People in alliance with each other
Desired outcomes	Maximum activities of daily living (ADL), gainful employment, psychological adjustment, improved motivation, completed treatment	Self-direction, least restrictive environment, social and economic productivity	Pluralistic society inclusive of all people; quality lives as defined by people themselves; self-direction embedded in collaborative decision making and problem solving.

[a]Adapted from DeJong, G. (1978, 1983).

[b]From Racino, J.A. (1992). Living in the community: Independence, support, and transition. In F. R. Rusch, L. DeStefano, J. Chadsey-Rusch, L. A. Phelps, & E. Szymanski (Eds.), *Transition from school to adult life: Models, linkages, and policy.* Sycamore, IL: Sycamore Press. Copyright © 1991 by Sycamore Publishing. Reprinted by permission of Brooks/Cole Publishing Company, Pacific Grove, CA 93950.

one's own life (DeJong, 1978), the support/empowerment paradigm has as its vision an inclusive society where power is shared (O'Brien, 1989).

Through a support/empowerment paradigm, the perspectives of individuals with disabilities and families are raised from their current unequal power positions to allow an opportunity for genuine alliances to form. This is not done solely to benefit people with disabilities, since addressing the interests of this "minority" is viewed to benefit all. Applying this new way of thinking (Governor's Planning Council on Developmental Disabilities, 1987) to disability issues raises questions about how things work, whether these beliefs are society-wide or exist primarily within a social segment of society or within a field.

The current movement of offering greater choices to individuals with disabilities and their families (Bradley & Knoll, 1990; Hibbard, Ferguson, Leinen, & Schaff, 1989; Nisbet, 1992; Smull & Bellamy, 1991; Taylor, Racino, Knoll, & Lutfiyya, 1987) has, in practice, maintained the power structure largely as it exists, while increasing the "market" options available to people with disabilities. The assumptions on which service systems are based, including the nature of the person–agency interaction, have remained substantially untouched. Ultimately, discussions will be needed about who will control fiscal resources, define what the problem is, and determine how people with disabilities and others will live together (Racino, 1992).

The concept of support can be viewed most basically as an act or set of actions, an attitude or set of values, a feeling or personal experience, a set of standards or expectations, a relationship descriptor, and an expected goal or accomplishment (Racino & O'Connor, 1994). From the service perspective, the word "support" has attained popular usage, often becoming equated with paid (formal) or unpaid (informal) services. (In practice, the word "formal" is often used synonymously with paid services and "informal" with unpaid services. For a theoretical description of characteristics of formal and informal supports, see Bulmer [1987].) Today, the disability field is moving toward supported education, recreation, work, and living (e.g., Hibbard et al., 1989), while still retaining many of the program and professional origins of these concepts.

While research and writing about the nature of support and the relationship between formal and informal supports have proliferated (Dunst, Trivette, Gordon, & Pletcher, 1989; Hagner, Rogan, & Murphy, 1992; King's Fund Centre, 1988; O'Brien & O'Brien, 1992a; O'Connor, 1993b; Traustadottir, 1991; Walker, 1987), the distinctions between how support is perceived by individuals with disabilities and how workers understand the concept is just becoming clear (Racino & O'Connor, 1994). These distinctions are proving critical in understanding the nature of potential alliances that are a must for substantive change.

This chapter considers directions and issues, particularly related to change at the agency, state systems, community, and societal levels, using a support/empowerment paradigm. It combines four different kinds of information (e.g., training and technical assistance experience across the United States, qualitative policy, organizational and community research studies, and literature reviews) to contribute to the emerging discussion on what can, is, and should be done to create these changes in day-to-day life.

DISABILITY AGENCY CHANGE[1]

A variety of disability agencies at the local level have tremendous impact on, and control over, the lives of individuals with disabilities and their families. Some agencies have started a process of change based on a vision founded on principles such as community presence, participation, competence, choice, and respect (O'Brien, 1987b). This process involves coming to know people and listening to what they want, such as good jobs, homes, friends, opportunities for learning and contribution, and self-esteem.

Once the decision to change has been made, agencies face all of the challenges inherent in any change endeavor and must resolve the critical questions of what needs to change and how in order to better respond to people with disabilities. As part of a national research and training center effort conducted in over 35 states, the author identified four major target areas for change in local disability agencies (Racino, 1986). They are listed below:

1. *Attitudes*—those of professionals, policy-makers, administrators, human service groups, parents, people with disabilities, neighbors, and coworkers
2. *Service design*—quality of life standards, flexible and individualized supports, individual needs assessments and plans, consumer-direction, and case management
3. *Staff*—roles, recruitment, training and support, organization of staffing, and evaluation
4. *Management*—role definition, dispersed service management, agency structure and design, creative scheduling, quality assurance, and financing

These continue to be common interest areas for change at the local disability agency level, as evidenced by the current popularity of life planning (McGowan, 1987; Mount & Zwernik, 1988; O'Brien, 1987b; Vandercook, York, & Forest, 1989), assessment strategies (Brost & Johnson, 1982); case management and service brokerage approaches (Beardshaw & Towell, 1990; Lippert, 1987; Salisbury, Dickey, & Crawford, 1987); support services (Karan & Granfield, 1990; Nosek, 1990); staff roles (Hagner, 1989; Mount, Beeman, & Ducharme, 1988; O'Brien & O'Brien, 1992); staff training (Baumgart & Ferguson, 1991; Kaiser & McWhorter, 1990; Wallace, Larson, & Hewitt, 1992); and quality assurance (Bradley & Bersani, 1990; Options in Community Living, 1987; Schalock, 1990).

However, a national study of organizations supporting people with disabilities in the community (Racino, 1991c; Taylor, Bogdan, & Racino, 1991) indicated that

[1]Many of the ideas shared in this section were developed in conjunction with Pat Rogan for the graduate seminar on Community Services and Systems Change taught at Syracuse University.

the most critical aspects of these organizations were not specific staff, management, or design mechanisms; they were the following aspects: 1) a philosophy, belief system, or world view that guides the parts and whole of the organization; 2) a spirit of self-reflection and learning (O'Brien, 1987a); 3) placing the quality of lives of people ahead of policies, regulations, financing, and technology; 4) empowering, valuing, and supporting staff (Provencal, 1987); and 5) developing an atmosphere of mutual collaboration and personal autonomy. Since specific mechanisms (e.g., financing and staff design) tended to vary from organization to organization, most important was how these agency characteristics were developed and maintained.

Several constructs are helpful (see Table 10.2) in forming an understanding of how to guide disability agency change toward supporting the full participation of individuals with disabilities and families in community life: disability service frameworks focusing on a shift from facility-based to non–facility-based services; service frameworks reflecting a movement toward community (disability) services; personal perspectives describing change from an individual standpoint; and

Table 10.2. Service and personal perspectives on agency change

	Agency-level change: Service perspectives	
Facility-based	Non–facility-based	Community/categorical
Sheltered workshops	Supported work -Job coach -Natural supports	Work with employer and community supports
Community residences	Supported living Supported housing	Housing and supports
	Family support services	Supporting families and their children Permanency planning
Day habilitation programs	Inclusive day/leisure activities	Support in community places and sites
	Agency-level change: Community/disability agency	
Community agency/ disability agency	Community agency/ separate disability program Community agency/ community supports	Community agency/ disability support services
	Agency-level change: Personal perspectives	
Worker–family member or individual relationship as affected by: Agency structure and resources Worker–worker relationships Agency–agency relationships System–agency–family relationships Community–agency–family relationships		

community perspectives starting from a basic understanding of the nature of associations, community agencies, and relationships.

From Facility-Based to Non–Facility-Based Services

Most work nationwide on local disability agency change revolves around the movement from facility-based to non–facility-based disability services, for example, from sheltered to supported work (Hagner & Murphy, 1989) or from group home to supported living (Racino & Knoll, 1986). Undergirding this change is a set of values that includes the belief that people can be supported in regular work places, homes, and community sites if given the resources needed to do so.

Facility-based services, which are the primary vehicle for service delivery today, tend to involve: agency-owned or agency-rented facilities; licensed or certified facilities; agency staffing; staffing ratios based on groups instead of individuals; linkage of work; home, or recreation site with services; core funding tied to a facility; and a weak relationship between funding and individual planning (Taylor, Racino, & Rothenberg, 1988). Facility-based services include not only large congregate settings, but small group homes as well.

In contrast, non–facility-based services, such as family support services or supported living, tend to focus on service availability in a variety of community sites (e.g., homes, work, or recreation); promote greater choice for people with disabilities in dealing with support services and all other aspects of life; provide for the availability of individualized and flexible supports; and develop a closer tie among planning, assessment, and funding.

From Non–Facility-Based Services to Community Services

Generally, non–facility-based services include family support services, supported work, and supported living. While resulting in a change in service characteristics, they often retain the underlying features and assumptions that reflect a traditional Weberian approach to organizations (Atsely, 1985) and a service model approach to the lives of people with disabilities (Paine, Bellamy, & Wilcox, 1988).

In contrast, as disability services become more community- and person-centered, they move away from model approaches toward changed relationships among members of the organization and among people at the outer and inner interfaces of the agencies. Tools such as personal futures planning are often used to assist organizations in making these kinds of changes. (The definition of "organization" here is broad and can include formalized circles of support.) However, these organizations still retain their disability roots and tend to make the person with a disability the center of attention instead of starting from a community focus where it is recognized that everyone needs support (Kennedy, 1993) and has roles in relationship to each other.

One example of an approach that starts from this disability service basis but begins to expand and challenge standard constructions is a housing and support approach in which adults with disabilities are supported to live in their own homes no matter what their level of ability. The following states some of the key concepts that underlie a housing and support approach:

> It's not a new program model, but is an attempt to help people think, and consequently act, in ways that are more responsive to the needs and preferences of individuals with disabilities and their families. It does not imply a change only, or even primarily, in services or that these are the most critical ones in the lives of individuals with disabilities and families. It is about new relationships among people in different sectors, and about a change in how people are viewed and approached. (Adapted from Racino & Taylor, 1993, pp. 46–47)

These concepts go beyond a program change orientation and entail changing the nature of agencies and systems themselves and the role of community in relationship to people. These approaches are less tied to specific program structures and more to the quality of life.

Community Perspectives and Agency Change

In contrast to disability-based approaches, change can also begin with examination of how other community agencies, organizations, and associations work (Biklen, 1992; Bogdan, 1992a, 1992b, 1992c; Lutfiyya, 1991; Racino, 1991a; Stainback, Stainback, & Jackson, 1992; Walker & Edinger, 1988) and how they already do include different kinds of people.

From a service perspective, the tendency on the part of disability agencies is to try to integrate their clients in community organizations and associations. In contrast, understanding how community agencies and associations view their roles and mission (Gretz, 1992; McKnight, 1989) and starting from their view or, even better, a view developed with them, can result in new ways of defining the problems and seeking desired changes for how people with and without disabilities can live together and support one another.

Personal Perspectives of Agency Change

Agencies and people with disabilities come together at the level of the worker–consumer interchange, though larger structures influence this interchange. Changing the nature of the relationship between agencies and people with disabilities will require a dialogue based on an open exchange among people in many different positions. Following are examples of qualitative research findings (Racino, O'Connor, & Walker, 1993) that can help to highlight the voices of people with disabilities, which are not currently prevalent or powerful enough in the field's discourse.

- *Implicit and explicit worker roles* Workers have both implicit and explicit roles that affect their relationships with people with disabilities and families. It is not enough simply to change the roles and functions of workers and expect that to result in a fundamental shift in the nature of the worker–consumer relationship (Racino, O'Connor, Walker, & Taylor, 1991).

- *Personal constructions of how systems work* Human services workers view the system differently than do individuals with disabilities and families. People in "client" roles construct their own view of how systems work based on how these systems can be used actively to meet their own purposes (Wiseman, 1979).
- *Effects of human services* Human services can be neutral or harmful as well as helpful to people with disabilities and their families (McKnight, 1989). People are often enveloped in a cocoon of services that disrupts their personal connections and limits their opportunities for relationships and to make contributions.
- *Social control* Social control, including the ability to define what is good, is a central feature in the interaction between agencies and individuals with disabilities and their families. When agencies are involved in defining the relationship between formal services and informal supports, especially related to people of various ethnic, cultural, and income groups, the agencies may effectively widen the life areas over which they have control and dominance.
- *Transcending role boundaries* On a positive note, individual workers can and do transcend their strict role boundaries. Sometimes at personal cost, they develop relationships with people with disabilities, move toward alliances to address the negative effect of formal systems, and offer the personal support that systems do not.

These views of helping relationships contrast sharply with the views commonly held by service agencies. They represent perspectives that are seldom shared. Yet they can form the basis for a real dialogue about change in the nature of the relationship between agencies and the people they were created to serve.

Current Issues in the Agency Change Process

Each of the previous four perspectives are viable ways to begin to move toward more personalized, responsive approaches at the local disability agency level. Each approach addresses different aspects of the broader changes that are necessary in the relationship between individuals with disabilities and services. The following are a few examples of the issues emerging in the area of change at the local agency level, based on a support/empowerment paradigm.

The Need for Leadership in Agency Change While there is a tremendous amount of information available on organizational change (Goldberg, 1980; Hedberg, Nystrom, & Starbuck, 1976; Martin, 1990; Peters, 1987), more people are needed who both understand the organizational development process and are familiar with individualized supports from the personal perspective.

From Agency to Personal Perspectives In creating change from a personal perspective, one common problem that agencies face is the perceived threat of acknowledging the legitimacy of the viewpoints of individuals with disabilities and families. Workers in disability agencies have played the role of white knight, and it is often difficult to accept that good intentions have not always translated into good experiences in the lives of the people supported.

Change in Language Versus Substantive Change When staff members and organizations are faced with huge waiting lists and tremendous demands on their personal and professional resources, it is understandably easy to rely on techniques or quick fixes instead of working toward substantive change. Despite expressed interest in moving from a "model" approach to one of supports (e.g., Hagner et al., 1992; Klein, 1992), often it is only a language shift that is occurring, or new models (e.g., the natural supports model) are replacing or supplementing other models (e.g., the job coach model).

The Starting Basis for Change How people in an organization view agency change depends partially on the starting point for this change, which is influenced by the way in which members of the organization view the world. For example, although there is a trend toward blurring boundaries among disciplines and across services categories, whether an organization's focus is primarily on residential support, education, vocational support, family support, or independent living will influence how it frames problems and their solutions in the lives of people with disabilities.

Appreciating the Contributions Different fields (e.g., work, community living, recreation, education) are making a variety of unique contributions to the knowledge about change and the change processes. For instance, the literature on change from sheltered work to supported work can be a useful introduction to basic principles of change (Bellamy, Rhodes, Mank, & Albin, 1988; Gardner, Chapman, Donaldson, & Jacobson, 1988; Hagner & Murphy, 1989). The emerging change literature in the residential field (e.g., Mount & Caruso, 1989; O'Brien & O'Brien, 1991; Racino, 1993c; Traustadottir, 1987; Walker, 1993) points up the key importance of values; questions assumptions about staff-controlled models; and describes approaches based on shared leadership, personal commitment, and collaboration.

From Categorical Services to Personal Lives Change across service categories is just beginning to occur; for example, instead of a person moving into either a work or day activity program, he or she may elect to participate in a wide variety of community options. In similar fashion, personal assistance can vary in form across residential, vocational, and leisure areas depending upon the preferences of the individual involved.

There are many challenges that lie ahead as disability-based organizations explore ways of reframing their roles and relationships, and as community organizations begin to accept people with disabilities once again.

STATE LEVEL DISABILITY SYSTEMS CHANGE[2]

Since the late 1980s, attention has shifted from the debate about institutional service versus community services to how people with disabilities can be part of community life (Bogdan & Taylor, 1987; Wolfensberger & Thomas, 1983). As re-

[2]This section draws on policy research conducted in New Hampshire from 1990 to 1991 and policy analyses in states from 1985 to 1990.

flected in the 1990 report prepared by the National Association of Developmental Disabilities Councils (1990), people with developmental disabilities want to live, work, and go to school in the community, even as many need supports to do so. This means more opportunities to form relationships with people with and without disabilities, to develop lifestyles that express people's own preferences, and to assume a variety of valued social roles.

On the state disability service level, in 1989 the field witnessed what Lakin (1991) called the "milestone of the community majority" (p. xiii). The balance changed so that more people with developmental disabilities were living in community residential settings than were living in residential institutions with 16 or more people (Lakin, 1991). Following are other developments in the service system that occurred:

- Growth in family support services (Fujiura, Garza, & Braddock, 1990; Knoll et al., 1990) and the development of cash subsidy programs (Herman, 1991)
- Increase in supported work (Wehman, Kregel, & Shafer, 1989); movement toward coworker and other regular supports in the workplace (Nisbet & Callahan, 1987); and the development of inclusive day activities
- Efforts to explore creating housing financing (Housing Technical Assistance Project, n.d.; Randolph, Laux, & Carling, 1987; Skarnulis & Lakin, 1990) and other finance options (Braddock, Hemp, Fujiura, Bachelder, & Mitchell, 1990; Lakin et al., 1989)
- Increased interest in support service options (Taylor et al., 1991; Taylor, Racino, Knoll, & Lutfiyya, 1987), including personal assistance (Litvak, 1991; Nosek, 1990) and supported living (National Association of Private Residential Resources, 1991; Smith, 1990)
- The expansion of assistive technology (Hemp, Youngwerth, Haasen, & Braddock, 1992), including introduction of facilitated communication (Biklen, Morton, Gold, Berrigan, & Swaminathan, 1992; Donnellan, Sabin, & Majure, 1992); and attention to environmental accessibility (Adaptive Environments Center, 1991)
- The emerging movement to return children home from out-of-state placements; the expansion of early intervention and support (Dunst, 1989); attention to permanency planning (Taylor, Lakin, & Hill, 1987); adoption (Taylor, Racino, Walker, Lutfiyya, & Shoultz, 1992); and family life for all children (Center on Human Policy, 1987; Rosenau, 1990)
- Increasing the inclusion of children with disabilities in neighborhood schools (Biklen, Ferguson, & Ford, 1989; Lipsky & Gartner, 1989)
- Supporting the transition of children from schools to adult lives (Ludlow, Turnbull, & Luckasson, 1988; Rogan, 1992; Rusch, DeStefano, Chadsey-Rusch, Phelps, & Szymanski, 1992; Wehman, Moon, Everson, Wood, & Barcus, 1988)

However, these developments proceeded within the same general framework for planning, quality assurance, program development, and financing that had guided the evolution and construction of the current facility-based system of community services. In moving toward systems of support, how to think about the nature of change and about how systems work will need to be re-examined.

Nature of State Systems Change

When change comes to complex human services systems, especially on the state level, it is impossible to predict with precision the outcomes of any new initiative (Taylor & Racino, 1991). Every advance reveals new challenges. Every solution creates its own set of problems. Every plan encounters unanticipated obstacles in implementation. This is not to question attempts to change service systems. It is to suggest that there are no simple solutions to complex problems.

Fundamental change, as defined here, is change that improves the life quality of people with disabilities. Service systems, particularly those related to disability, cannot and should not provide everything that people want and need. When people with developmental disabilities rely exclusively on service systems, they cannot become part of their communities.

Variations Among States

No two state disability systems are alike and political environments vary greatly. In the disability field, states vary in terms of their degree of centralization and decentralization, their commitment to community versus institutional services, financing and structure of the community service system, legislation and court cases on deinstitutionalization and inclusion, presence and strength of advocacy and parent groups, and so forth. For these and other reasons, change strategies in each state must be approached differently.

Many of the changes necessary for moving toward quality lives for people with disabilities extend beyond the developmental disabilities field and will require radical political change in some states in terms of how citizens who are poor, older, or in other disadvantaged groups are treated, and how all citizens within a state have input into state government. These are difficult issues that could easily involve a decade or more of work to address.

Top-Down or Bottom-Up Approaches

Efforts to change systems tend to be top-down approaches, which include developing shared values among key stakeholders, creating state legislation and policies in support of community life, changing financial structures and incentives, shifting power among state departments, and developing new state programs. More local approaches include efforts such as demonstration projects funded through disability planning councils and attempts to educate and organize at the grassroots level. Even these approaches often adopt a state-systems perspective of the issues and problems involved.

Because systems are usually constructed on models reflecting old assumptions about people with disabilities, layers of barriers to the full participation of people with disabilities in community life are often in place. Given the complexity of today's state service systems, it is becoming more important to begin to examine state systems change from a bottom-up approach. This means to start from the point of view of the person with a disability and from his or her perspective of the system.

Through planning with a small number of people about their futures, it is possible to identify a series of state-specific, regulative, legislative, financing, and training changes that are needed to facilitate inclusion in community life. This bottom-up approach does not imply that every problem must be worked through on a person-by-person basis, nor does it relieve state and federal officials of their responsibilities. It represents a practical approach for understanding how each separate system must be adapted to facilitate fundamental change in the lives of people with disabilities.

Strategies for Creating Systems Change

Some states are trying to balance three systems: 1) an institutional system, 2) a traditional community system, and 3) an emerging supports system. Each reflects a different constituent base, with the latter currently evolving toward a greater role on the part of families. Following is one state disability system administrator's explanation of the movement toward the creation of a support system:

> If families don't feel like they are being supported by our systems, they will not be there to advocate for the budgets when we need them to be. That's how the state employees used to be . . . The people who now vote are people with disabilities and their families and they are now the people who need to be satisfied . . . . It is a real power shift from the institution, state employees, state services to individuals. (Racino, 1991b, pp. 31–32)

Table 10.3 illustrates how (in the area of housing and support) the roles of state departments are continuing to change to better respond to the needs of people with disabilities (Pederson, Chaikin, Koehler, Campbell, & Arcand, 1993; Kennedy, 1993; Worth, 1989) and how new state initiatives are being undertaken to incorporate this "support" philosophy into practice. Most of these efforts parallel on the state level the movement from agency to non–facility-based services.

Based on collective experience in trying to create change in state systems, many of the standard organizing techniques for change both within and outside the system continue to be used effectively in many states (Biklen, 1974; Racino, 1993b; Zirpoli, Hancox, Wieck, & Skarnulis, 1989). The greatest challenges lie with states where the changes envisioned must be part of, or preceded by, changes outside the disability area, with states that have very large bureaucracies, and with states confronting overriding large-scale urban issues. While there is common wisdom about how systems change occurs, it is still unclear, for example, if, and particularly how, system changes result in change in quality of life for individual people with disabilities. For example, for some families, particularly from different cultural groups, family support services become an entree into out-of-home placement rather than a way to strengthen the family.

Table 10.3. State response to change

New roles of state disability departments: Housing and support

- To separate housing services from support services and to explore new ways to work with state housing departments
- To identify and address impediments in their own systems that stand in the way of full community participation, including adults living in their own homes
- To become more familiar with generic services in their state and to explore ways to coordinate across disability groups
- To support service provider experience in developing individualization and flexible supports
- To promote decision-making on the part of people with disabilities and to take direction from this constituency

State initiatives: Housing and support

- Promoting choice in where and with whom one lives
- Moving to a closer tie between family, assessment, and planning
- Creating state policies in support of community life
- Promoting flexibility and individualization in systems
- Promoting supportive living as a feasible systems strategy
- Developing state supported living programs
- Changing state policies to support people in their own homes
- Encouraging agency and systems change
- Promoting choice in case management
- Supporting community for all
- Using a people first approach in quality assurance

In a study in New Hampshire (Covert, MacIntosh, & Shumway, chap. 11, this volume; Racino, 1993b), key factors in systems change included specific characteristics of the state, such as formal and informal talk networks, shared leadership among people in different roles and organizations, small state size, and a sense of shared values and direction. Also important were structures such as the area agencies that build community support, develop local ties, and have flexibility that the state system cannot.

On another level, individual people's personal commitments to change also appear critical where they persevered with a vision even during times of personal hardship and persisted in building a base of support with other people. Many different people, including administrators, parents, people with disabilities, and university personnel, working from different directions, contributed to the move from institutional to community services.

Among the lessons from New Hampshire's experience in the closure of the Laconia State School and Training Center (see Covert, MacIntosh, & Shumway, chap. 11, this volume), the state's only public institution for people with developmental disabilities, are that it is possible to accomplish major changes with attention to the individuality and dignity of each person, whether staff or consumer, that different types of leadership are needed at different times in the system, and that systems change may not be separable from the personal commitments and leadership of the people who make up the system. These lessons lend support to the theoretical perspective that large-scale change begins with a change in personal beliefs.

Issues in Disability Systems Change

A support/empowerment framework implies change in all aspects of how systems work. The disability field is at the initial stages of understanding the kinds of systems change processes that can result in the radical changes that will be necessary in moving toward more inclusive and supportive service structures. Following are descriptions of a few examples of the kinds of state systems issues that are arising as the disability field explores the development of support systems.

The State-by-State Approach Changes that are occurring generally in the disability field are not necessarily occurring in each state, and the field tends to overlook this. For example, basic information on normalization principles is still not available today in some states. As national change efforts occur, attention must be given to such basics to ensure that people in all states are part of the change process, that their specific state issues are addressed, and that harm is not done by the assumption that a foundation is already in place to make further changes toward support systems.

Systems Management In terms of management systems, critical mechanistic issues include how states will approach quality assurance, financing, case management, and cross-departmental relationships. Failure to examine the interaction between the federal, state, regional, county, and personal levels is one of the most common problems when "progressive integration" policies are implemented at the state level. For example, trying to individualize financing of specific services on the state level may actually result in a decrease in individualization on the agency and personal levels. Such attempts fail to take into account how multi-level systems actually work in practice, thus resulting in an increased rigidity in local and personal decision-making.

Systems and Communities The developmental disabilities service system is only one of many systems that affect the lives of people with developmental disabilities. Often this system has a minor role in resolving some of the relevant issues concerned. Issues today must be addressed inside and outside the narrow developmental disabilities field, with greater attention to cross-system strategies.

People involved with systems tend to approach communities as if they are another system and attempt to make them abide by bureaucratic rules and expectations that conflict with the associational life of communities. One of the problems with service system approaches to communities is that typical citizens may come to see and define issues as the system does (e.g., families have been taught to think in terms of concepts such as respite instead of the typical routines and structures that provide natural relief in parent–child relationships).

COMMUNITY AND SOCIETAL CHANGE[3]

Fundamental change in people's lives does not appear to occur simply because legislation is passed, a new program is financed, or policy is changed. This means that changes are necessary not only in the formal support systems upon which people rely, but also in informal relationships, communities, and the social mores that define how people should live together.

Societal change is broader and more basic than disability system change. It means, for instance, addressing the disability-based assumptions that permeate people's daily lives. Nora Groce's book, *Everyone Here Spoke Sign Language* (1985), describes a wonderful example of how a disability, such as deafness, can be taken for granted in a society and not treated as a negative difference. Every change needs to be examined on the basis of whether it brings people closer to the kind of society in which disability is accepted as a matter of routine, not as a cause for stigmatization. Strategies with short-term effectiveness, which do not bring people closer to this goal, should not be pursued. The strong argument against "reverse integration" is that, in the long run, it is based on an approach that assumes that service agencies own people with disabilities.

The cross system nature of the changes that are needed will require people working at many different levels, such as systems, personal, or community, and along many different avenues, such as housing, community regeneration, legislative and policy analyses, program evaluation and research, advocacy, and training. Societal change can and does begin from a variety of different bases, some of which appear to be in conflict with each other.

Community Integration and Independent Living: The Agency Perspective on Community and Change

People involved in change endeavors often work from different conceptual bases in defining what they are trying to achieve (the ends) and how they go about it (the means). This can result in people undermining each other's efforts instead of seeking the common ground that is necessary for substantive community and societal change to occur.

While there are many ways to examine community change, one approach is to understand how service organizations are presently attempting to achieve community integration or independent living. In a forthcoming study (Racino, 1993a) of five agencies located in Wisconsin, California, New Hampshire, Minnesota, and North Dakota, and known for their support of people with disabilities, the goal of community integration was typically defined in practice as the achievement of a lifestyle and routine similar to others (i.e., the service workers) and involving

---

[3]The author acknowledges with gratitude the ideas of Diane Murphy on family policy, Susan O'Connor and Jan Goings on multicultural issues, Judy Heumann on cross-disability issues, and Steve Taylor on poverty.

physical presence and participation in the community (i.e., anything outside the service setting).

To some extent, community integration in practice was something that people without disabilities do to people with disabilities, though this may be through offering opportunities. Relatively little recognition was paid to the role that people with disabilities play in being on the forefront of social change.

In contrast, the major themes in independent living revolved around the centrality of freedom, personal control, and a variety of different lifestyles. The direction tended to move away from service agency dependency and control. While access to the community (i.e., the political, economic, social, and other structures) was considered a right, whether or not one participated or how was viewed as a personal choice.

In discussing what it means to achieve community integration or independent living, the research participants talked about the need for changes on a personal basis, for individuals in relation to one another, in systems and agencies, and in the community. Specifically, these changes included accepting and appreciating who people are; listening better to each other; getting along; respect; trust building; support from others, whether family, friends, paid staff, or people with similar experiences; community acceptance, exposure, and coexistence; service and financing changes; and control of services, housing, and one's own life.

This study identified several critical areas that organizations need to attend to, with only a few being the service and finance changes that often consume the majority of an organization's energy and other resources. It also indicated the need to seek out people involved in other change endeavors, people working through diverse avenues and fields toward a society based on acceptance and trust.

Critical Issues

As the next decade begins, many of the critical change issues that affect the lives of people with disabilities will be grounded in broader societal issues and social concerns. With the support of the Americans with Disabilities Act of 1990 (PL 101-336), the issues and concerns of the 43 million Americans with disabilities have gained the attention of the general public. This provides a key opportunity to address society's barriers to the inclusion and participation of people with disabilities.

Achieving societal change necessitates better understanding of the perspectives of typical citizens and their view of community, and the way in which community change efforts of people coming together at the local level intersect with legislation that may reflect and/or support local grassroots efforts. Following are explanations of a few examples of issues that society must address in order to further the full inclusion of people with disabilities.

Personal to Societal Change In the field of disabilities, as in other areas, people have a tendency to talk in abstract terms that depersonalize, objectify, and distance the issues from their personal values and beliefs. Many arguments about change are grounded in different beliefs about the capacities of people, about hope for the future, about the relationship of personal change to larger societal change, and about people's own experience of mutual relationships and freedom in the society. Taking the cloaks off these hidden issues has the potential to lead to increased dialogue that recognizes and respects the diversity of views of the people involved.

Neighborhood Revitalization and Community Regeneration On the local level, efforts to create functioning neighborhoods and communities offer opportunities to form stronger local support networks for all, including people with disabilities (Lehman, 1988; McKnight, 1987). Neighborhoods already provide a sense of identity, a sense of movement, a sense of familiarity, ownership and belonging, environmental control and choice, safety and security, preservation of traditions and culture, social exchange opportunities, personal and social identity, a sense of place and roots, and a sense of history for many people with disabilities (Racino & O'Connor, 1994). Yet, service systems have tended to disrupt people's local relationships and connections and the identification that people may feel with certain neighborhoods.

Health Care for All In the United States, the availability of health care depends upon income, insurability, and physician discretion (O'Brien, 1989). People who are poor or are viewed as being unprofitable patients face the public perception that they are seeking charity in trying to obtain decent health care. Since "one-fourth of all Americans now experience what people with disabilities have always known—that coverage can be unavailable, unaffordable, or inadequate in times of medical need" (Ohio Developmental Disabilities Planning Council, 1990), politically the time seems right for the development of a health care system accessible to all citizens.

The Definition of Person as a Burden One of the major attitudinal change issues that must be overcome is the process of defining someone as a burden to society (Racino & Heumann, 1992). For example, family support programs are typically based on the concept of relieving family stress considered to be caused by the person with a disability. As long as the field continues to understand and define the problem in this way, people with disabilities will continue to face devaluation. Personal assistance for children is an attractive alternative concept to explore because it is based on the belief that if adequate support services were provided as a matter of course, the child might not be perceived or experienced as a burden.

Family and Other Social Policy Another way to reflect the growing reality of family life in America, inclusive of people with disabilities, is to examine national family policy (Turnbull, Garlow, & Barber, 1991). Instead of a band-aid approach to these issues, the total approach to the support of family life, in all its diversity, must be used. Disability issues are exacerbated in environments where flexibility is not available, where resources such as child care and family leave are not a matter of course, and where rigid expectations exist for career progressions.

Citizens and Democracy The United States has reached a crisis in democracy in that the majority of Americans no longer believe that they influence their government, that the government takes direction from its citizens. This crisis affects the least influential citizens the most giving them the least voice for their interests, which are instead often overshadowed by paid lobbying blocks or by people who represent their own interests.

Poverty Given that people with disabilities are often poor, they are disproportionately affected by social policies and community stereotypes about people who have low incomes. Many of the issues regarding the inclusion of people with disabilities in recreation, health care, education, work, and home living cannot be addressed without changes in the way in which people who are poor are treated, the way welfare policies are developed and implemented, and attitudes about the role of society in relationship to all of its citizens.

Cross-Disability and Age The major issues facing people with disabilities are often the same regardless of disability type or age. A comprehensive review of the literature related to community integration for all disability groups (Carling, Randolph, Blanch, & Ridgway, 1988) concluded that: 1) housing needs were similar for all these groups; 2) the availability of supports was a critical factor that determined whether people could stay in housing of their choice; 3) housing problems were less closely related to disability than they were to economic and social factors; 4) regardless of disability group, strong differences existed between professionals and people with disabilities about specific needs for housing and support; and 5) choices and control were critical elements of concern for all community integration efforts.

Culture and Ethnicity Community integration has generally been implemented using a framework of assimilation, where the goal at times seems to be for people with disabilities to blend in with the dominant, white middle-class culture. In the 1990s, efforts to highlight the richness of various cultures and to bring this awareness into the human service field have received increased attention in the literature (Baxter, Poonia, Ward, & Nadirshaw, 1990; Harry, 1992; O'Connor, 1993a; Traustadottir, Lutfiyya, & Shoultz, 1994). To achieve a society that fully includes people with disabilities, diversity and the richness of personal identities must not only be accepted, but actively fostered.

New Concepts Because the concepts of normalization (Nirje, 1969; Wolfensberger, 1972) and social role valorization (Wolfensberger, 1991) have become subject to so many different interpretations, they are no longer as powerful as they once were as guiding forces in intervention for people with disabilities. Even though most states and human services agencies endorse normalization, they operate under different definitions and interpretations of it. There is a need for new concepts for guidance into the future.

The new concepts need to develop from an understanding more strongly based on such principles as self-determination, mutual decision-making, and social justice. While Nirje's formulation of the normalization principle is grounded in a more egalitarian base, Wolfensberger's construction (which is most known in the United States) tends to emphasize culturally valued roles and has tones of protectionism and societal conformity (Perrin & Nirje, 1985). Both are primarily disability-based formulations, though with a vision of community life for all. Today's issues call for theoretical concepts and practical applications that lead to community efforts to find solutions that improve individual lives, society, and the world, and that include people with disabilities.

CONCLUSION

The support/empowerment paradigm provides an opportunity to re-examine the ways in which professionals and community members have thought about and acted toward people with disabilities and their families. Moving toward a view of people's lives reflecting their personal richness, diversity, and identities can help people to better understand how everyone can live together and share this world. Whether change stems from agencies, systems, or communities, creating change needs to continue the process of discovery and to support people's diverse contributions. The current ways of thinking about these multifaceted problems must be unraveled.

The disability field is making these changes at a critical time in the world. Central world issues such as the interplay between mutuality and self-determination, diversity and unity, and those who are powerful and those who are powerless are playing out daily, whether through the ethnic and cultural rivalries in Eastern Europe or on the city streets in the United States. In this context, the disability field has an opportunity to contribute to these historic movements, leading the way past the minor and inconsequential differences that divide people, toward the commonalities that unite and provide the basis for joint endeavor.

REFERENCES

Adaptive Environments Center. (1991). *A consumer's guide to home adaptation*. Boston: Author.

Atsely, G. (1985). Organizational size and bureaucratic structure. *Organization Studies*, *63*, 201–228.

Baumgart, D., & Ferguson, D.L. (1991). Personnel preparation: Directions for the next decade. In L.H. Meyer, C.A. Peck, & L. Brown (Eds.), *Critical issues in the lives of people with severe disabilities* (pp. 313–352). Baltimore: Paul H. Brookes Publishing Co.

Baxter, C., Poonia, K., Ward, L., & Nadirshaw, Z. (1990). *Double discrimination: Issues and services for people with learning difficulties from black and ethnic minority communities*. London: King Edward's Hospital Fund.

Beardshaw, V., & Towell, D. (1990). *Assessment and case management: Implications for the implementation of "caring people."* London: King's Fund Institute.

Bellamy, G.T., Rhodes, L.E., Mank, D.M., & Albin, J.M. (1988). *Supported employment: A community implementation guide*. Baltimore: Paul H. Brookes Publishing Co.

Biklen, D. (1974). *Let our children go: An organizing manual for advocates and parents*. Syracuse: Human Policy Press.

Biklen, D. (1992). *Schooling without labels: Parents, educators, and inclusive education*. New York: Teachers College Press.

Biklen, D., Ferguson, D.L., & Ford, A. (1989). *Schooling and disability: Eighty-eighth yearbook of the National Society for the Study of Education, Part II*. Chicago: University of Chicago Press.

Biklen, D., & Knoll, J. (1987). The disabled minority. In S.J. Taylor, D. Biklen, & J. Knoll (Eds.), *Community integration for people with severe disabilities* (pp. 3–24). New York: Teachers College Press.

Biklen, D., Morton, M.W., Gold, D., Berrigan, C., & Swaminathan, S. (1992). Facilitated communication: Implications for individuals with autism. In D. Biklen & R. Crossley (Eds.), Facilitated communication: Implications for people with autism and other developmental disabilities [Feature issue]. *Topics in Language Disorders*, *12*(4), 1–28.

Bogdan, R. (1992a). The community choir: Singing for an inclusive society. *The Association for Persons with Severe Handicaps Newsletter*, *18*(4), 11–12.

Bogdan, R. (1992b). The community choir: Singing for an inclusive society. *The Association for Persons with Severe Handicaps Newsletter*, *18*(5), 14–15.

Bogdan, R. (1992c). The community choir: Singing for an inclusive society. *The Association for Persons with Severe Handicaps Newsletter*, *18*(6), 6–7.

Bogdan, R., & Taylor, S.J. (1987). Toward a sociology of acceptance: The other side of the study of deviance. *Social Policy*, *18*(2), 34–39.

Braddock, D., Hemp, R., Fujiura, G., Bachelder, L., & Mitchell, D. (1990). *The state of the states in developmental disabilities*. Baltimore: Paul H. Brookes Publishing Co.

Bradley, V.J., & Bersani, H.A. (Eds.). (1990). *Quality assurance for individuals with developmental disabilities: It's everybody's business*. Baltimore: Paul H. Brookes Publishing Co.

Bradley, V., & Knoll, J. (1990). *Shifting paradigms in services to people with developmental disabilities*. Cambridge, MA: Human Services Research Institute.

Brost, M.M., & Johnson, T.Z. (1982). *Getting to know you: One approach to service assessment and planning for individuals with disabilities*. Madison: Department of Health and Human Services-Division of Community Services.

Bulmer, M. (1987). *The social basis of community care*. Winchester, MA: Allen & Unwin, Inc.

Carling, P.J., Randolph, F.L., Blanch, A.K., & Ridgway, P. (1988). A review of the research on housing and community integration for people with psychiatric disabilities. *NARIC Quarterly*, *1*(3), 1, 6–18.

Center on Human Policy. (1987). *Families for all children*. Syracuse: Author.

DeJong, G. (1978). *The movement for independent living: Origins, ideology, and implications for disability research*. Boston: Tufts-New England Medical Center, Medical Rehabilitation Institute.

DeJong, G. (1983). Defining and implementing the independent living concept. In N. Crewe & I. Zola (Eds.), *Independent living for physically disabled people*. San Francisco: Jossey-Bass.

Donnellan, A.M., Sabin, L.A., & Majure, L.A. (1992). Facilitated communication: Beyond the quandary to the questions. In D. Biklen & R. Crossley (Eds.), Facilitated communication: Implications for people with autism and other developmental disabilities [Feature issue]. *Topics in Language Disorders*, *12*(4), 69–82.

Dunst, C.J., Trivette, C.M., Gordon, N.J., & Pletcher, L.L. (1989). Building and mobilizing informal family support networks. In G.H.S. Singer & L.K. Irvin (Eds.), *Support for caregiving families: Enabling positive adaptation to disability* (pp. 121–141). Baltimore: Paul H. Brookes Publishing Co.

Fujiura, G., Garza, J., & Braddock, D. (1990). *National survey of family support services in developmental disabilities*. Chicago: Institute on the Study of Developmental Disabilities, University of Illinois-Chicago.

Gardner, J.F., Chapman, M.S., Donaldson, G., & Jacobson, S.G. (1988). *Toward supported employment: A process guide for planned change*. Baltimore: Paul H. Brookes Publishing Co.

Goldberg, G.S. (1980). New directions for the Community Service Society of New York: A study of organizational change. *Social Service Review, June*, 184–219.

Governor's Planning Council on Developmental Disabilities. (1987). *A new way of thinking*. St. Paul: Author.

Gretz, S. (1992). Citizen participation: Connecting people to associational life. In D. Schwartz (Ed.), *Crossing the river: Creating a conceptual revolution in community and disability* (pp. 11–30). Cambridge, MA: Brookline Books.

Groce, N. (1985). *Everyone here spoke sign language: Hereditary deafness on Martha's Vineyard*. Cambridge, MA: Harvard University Press.

Hagner, D., & Murphy, S. (1989). Closing the shop on sheltered work: Case studies of organizational change. *Journal of Rehabilitation*, July, August, September, 83–89.

Hagner, D., Rogan, P., & Murphy, S. (1992). Facilitating natural supports in the workplace: Strategies for support consultants. *Journal of Rehabilitation, 58*(1), 29–34.

Harry, B. (1992). *Cultural diversity, families, and the special education system: Communication and empowerment*. New York: Teachers College Press.

Hedberg, B.L.T., Nystrom, P.D., & Starbuck, W.H. (1976). Camping on seesaws: Prescriptions for a self-designing organization. *Administrative Science Quarterly, 21*, 41–65.

Hemp, R., Youngwerth, C., Haasen, K., & Braddock, D. (1992). *Financing assistive technology: An annotated bibliography*. Chicago: University of Chicago at Illinois.

Herman, S.E. (1991). Use and impact of a cash subsidy program. *Mental Retardation, 29*(5), 253–258.

Hibbard, M., Ferguson, P., Leinen, J., & Schaff, S. (1989). Supported community life and mediating structures: Joining theory to practice in disability policy reform. In P. Ferguson & D. Olson (Eds.), *Supported community life: Community policy to practice in disability research*. Portland: Specialized Training Program, University of Oregon.

Housing Technical Assistance Project. (n.d.). *Volume I. The development process, Volume II. The financing mechanisms*. Washington, DC: The Arc and National Association of Home Builders National Research Center.

Kaiser, A., & McWhorter, C. (Eds.). (1990). *Preparing personnel to work with persons with severe disabilities*. Baltimore: Paul H. Brookes Publishing Co.

Karan, O.C., & Granfield, J.M. (1990). *Engaging people in life: A report on one supported living program in Connecticut*. Connecticut: University Affiliated Program.

Kennedy, M.J. (1993). Turning the pages of life. In J.A. Racino, P. Walker, S. O'Connor, & S.J. Taylor (Eds.), *Housing, support, and community: Choices and strategies for adults with disabilities* (pp. 205–216). Baltimore: Paul H. Brookes Publishing Co.

King's Fund Centre. (1988). *Ties and connections: An ordinary community life for people with learning difficulties*. London: Author.

Klein, J. (1992). Get me the hell out of here: Supporting people with disabilities to live in their own homes. In J. Nisbet (Ed.), *Natural supports in school, at work, and in the community for people with severe disabilities* (pp. 277–339). Baltimore: Paul H. Brookes Publishing Co.

Knoll, J., Covert, S., Osuch, R., O'Connor, S., Agosta, J., & Blaney, B. (1990). *Family support services in the United States: An end of the decade status report*. Cambridge, MA: Human Services Research Institute.

Lakin, K.C. (1988, November). *An overview of the concept and research on community living*. Paper presented at the Leadership Institute on Community Integration for People with Developmental Disabilities, Washington, DC.

Lakin, K.C. (1991). Foreword. In S.J. Taylor, R. Bogdan, & J.A. Racino (Eds.), *Life in the community: Case studies of organizations supporting people with disabilities* (pp. xiii–xv). Baltimore: Paul H. Brookes Publishing Co.

Lakin, K.C., Jaskulski, T.M., Hill, B.K., Bruininks, R.H., Menke, J.M., White, C.C., & Wright, E.A. (1989). *Medicaid services for persons with mental retardation and related conditions* (Project Report No. 27). Minneapolis: Center for Residential and Community Services, Institute on Community Integration, University of Minnesota.

Lehman, K. (1988). Beyond Oz: The path to regeneration. *Social Policy, 18*(4), 56–58.

Lippert, T. (1987). *The case management team: Building community connections*. St. Paul: Developmental Disabilities Program of The Metropolitan Council.

Lipsky, D.K., & Gartner, A. (1989). Building the future. In D.K. Lipsky & A. Gartner (Eds.), *Beyond separate education: Quality education for all* (pp. 255–290). Baltimore: Paul H. Brookes Publishing Co.

Litvak, S. (1991). State and federal funding sources for PAS. In Research and Training Center on Public Policy in Independent Living, InfoUse, & Western Consortium for Public Health. *Personal assistance services: A guide to policy and action*. Oakland: World Institute on Disability.

Ludlow, B.L., Turnbull, A.P., & Luckasson, R. (Eds.). (1988). *Transitions to adult life for people with mental retardation—Principles and practices*. Baltimore: Paul H. Brookes Publishing Co.

Lutfiyya, Z.M. (1991, April). Tony Santi and the bakery. In Z.M. Lutfiyya (Ed.), *Personal relationships and social networks: Facilitating the participation of individuals with disabilities in community life*. Syracuse: Center on Human Policy, Syracuse University.

Martin, P.Y. (1990). Rethinking feminist organizations. *Gender & Society, 4*(2), 182–206.

McGowan, K.G. (1987). *Functional life planning for persons with complex needs*. Peachtree City, GA: KMG Seminars.

McKnight, J.L. (1987). Regenerating community. *Social Policy, 18*(3), 54–58.

McKnight, J.L. (1989). *Do no harm: A policymaker's guide to evaluating human services and their alternatives*. Evanston, IL: Northwestern University.

Mount, B., Beeman, P., & Ducharme, G. (1988). *What are we learning about bridge-building? A summary of dialogue between people seeking to build community for people with disabilities*. Manchester, CT: Communitas.

Mount, B., & Caruso, G. (1989). *New dreams, new lives, new directions for Alternative Living, Inc.: A report on the initial outcomes, findings, and implications of the Citizenship Project*. Annapolis, MD: Alternative Living, Inc.

Mount, B., & Zwernik, K. (1988). *It's never too early, it's never too late: A booklet about personal futures planning*. St. Paul: Developmental Disabilities Case Mangement Project, Metropolitan Council.

National Association of Developmental Disabilities Councils. (1990). Forging a new era: The 1990 reports on people with developmental disabilities. *Journal of Disability Policy Studies, 1*(4), 15–42.

National Association of Private Residential Resources. (1991, November). *Supported living monograph*. Annandale, VA: Author.

Nirje, B. (1969). The normalization principle and its human management implications. In R. Kugel & W. Wolfensberger (Eds.), *Changing patterns in residential services for the mentally retarded*. Washington, DC: President's Committee on Mental Retardation.

Nisbet, J. (Ed.). (1992). *Natural supports in school, at work, and in the community for people with severe disabilities*. Baltimore: Paul H. Brookes Publishing Co.

Nisbet, J., & Callahan, M. (1987). Achieving success in integrated workplaces: Critical elements in assisting persons with severe disabilities. In S.J. Taylor, D. Biklen, & J. Knoll (Eds.), *Community integration for people with severe disabilities* (pp. 184–201). New York: Teachers College Press.

Nosek, M.A. (1990). *Personal assistance services for persons with mental disabilities.* Houston: Baylor College of Medicine.

O'Brien, J. (1987a). Embracing ignorance, error, and fallibility: Competencies for leadership of effective services. In S.J. Taylor, D. Biklen, & J. Knoll (Eds.), *Community integration for people with severe disabilities* (pp. 85–108). New York: Teachers College Press.

O'Brien, J. (1987b). A guide to life-style planning: Using *The Activities Catalog* to integrate services and natural support systems. In B. Wilcox & G.T. Bellamy, *A comprehensive guide to The Activities Catalog: An alternative curriculum for youth and adults with severe disabilities* (pp. 175–189). Baltimore: Paul H. Brookes Publishing Co.

O'Brien, C. (1989a, December). Power. In Center on Human Policy, *Policy Institute 1989: Community living for adults summary*. Syracuse: Center on Human Policy, Syracuse University.

O'Brien, J. (1989b, December). *Common interests among people concerned with changing societal responses to elders, people with physical disabilities, and people with cognitive disabilities*. Summary of a Working Group sponsored by the World Institute on Disability and the Center on Human policy, Berkeley.

O'Brien, J., & O'Brien, C. (1991). Sustaining positive changes: The future development of the Residential Support Program. In S.J. Taylor, R. Bogdan, & J.A. Racino (Eds.), *Life in the community: Case studies of organizations supporting people with disabilities* (pp. 153–168). Baltimore: Paul H. Brookes Publishing Co.

O'Brien, J., & O'Brien, C. (1992a). Members of each other: Perspectives on social support for people with severe disabilities. In J. Nisbet (Ed.), *Natural supports in school, at work, and in the community for people with severe disabilities* (pp. 17–63). Baltimore: Paul H. Brookes Publishing Co.

O'Brien, J., & O'Brien, C. (Eds.). (1992b). *Remembering the soul of our work: Stories by the staff of Options in Community Living, Madison, Wisconsin*. Madison: Options in Community Living.

O'Connor, S. (1993a). "I'm not Indian anymore": The challenge of providing culturally sensitive services to American Indians (pp. 313–331). In J.A. Racino, P. Walker, S. O'Connor, & S.J. Taylor (Eds.), *Housing, support, and community: Choices and strategies for adults with disabilities*. Baltimore: Paul H. Brookes Publishing Co.

O'Connor, S. (1993b). Supporting families: What they need versus what they get. *OSERS News in Print*.

Ohio Developmental Disabilities Planning Council. (1990). *Insuring health care for people with developmental disabilities*. Columbus: Author.

Options in Community Living. (1987). *Options policy on quality of life*. Madison: Author.

Paine, S.C., Bellamy, G.T., & Wilcox, B. (Eds.). (1988). *Human services that work: From innovation to standard practice*. Baltimore: Paul H. Brookes Publishing Co.

Pederson, E.L., Chaikin, M., Koehler, D., Campbell, A., & Arcand, M. (1993). Strategies that close the gap between research, planning, and self-advocacy. In S. Sutton, A.R. Factor, B.A. Hawkins, T. Heller, & G.B. Seltzer (Eds.), *Older adults with developmental disabilities: Optimizing choice and change* (pp. 277–327). Baltimore: Paul H. Brookes Publishing Co.

Perrin, B., & Nirje, B. (1985). Setting the record straight: A critique of some frequent misconceptions of the normalization principle. *Australia and New Zealand Journal of Developmental Disabilities*, *11*(2), 69–74.

Provencal, G. (1987). Culturing commitment. In S.J Taylor, D. Biklen, & J. Knoll (Eds.), *Community integration for people with severe disabilities* (pp. 67–84). New York: Teachers College Press.

Racino, J.A. (1986, June). *Resources and research in community integration*. Presentation at statewide community integration conference, Hartford, CT.

Racino, J.A. (1991a). *Madison Mutual Housing Association and Cooperative: "People and Housing Building Communities."* Syracuse: Center on Human Policy, Syracuse University.

Racino, J.A. (1991b). [New Hampshire policy research field notes]. Unpublished raw data.

Racino, J.A. (1991c). Organizations in community living: Supporting people with disabilities. *Journal of Mental Health Association, 18*(1), 51–59.

Racino, J.A. (1992). Living in the community: Independence, support, and transition. In F.R. Rusch, L. DeStefano, J. Chadsey-Rusch, L.A. Phelps, & E. Szymanski (Eds.), *Transition from school to adult life: Models, linkages, and policy* (pp. 131–148). Sycamore, IL: Sycamore Publishing Co.

Racino, J.A. (1993a). *Housing and support: Perspectives on creating change.* Manuscript submitted for publication.

Racino, J.A. (1993b). *Policy analysis of state systems change and community integration in New Hampshire.* Unpublished manuscript, Community and Policy Studies, Syracuse.

Racino, J.A. (1993c). "There if you need and want them": Changing roles of support organizations. In J.A. Racino, P. Walker, S. O'Connor, & S.J. Taylor (Eds.), *Housing, support, and community: Choices and strategies for adults with disabilities* (pp. 107–135). Baltimore: Paul H. Brookes Publishing Co.

Racino, J.A., & Heumann, J.E. (1992). Independent living and community life: Building coalitions among elders, people with disabilities and our allies. *Generations, XI*(I), 43–47.

Racino, J.A., & Knoll, J.A. (1986, September). Life in the community: Developing non-facility-based services. *The Association for Persons with Severe Handicaps Newsletter, 12*(9), 6.

Racino, J.A., & O'Connor, S. (1994). "A home of our own": Homes, neighborhoods, and personal connections. In M.F. Hayden & B.H. Abery (Eds.), *Challenges for a service system in transition: Ensuring quality community experiences for persons with developmental disabilities* (pp. 381–403). Baltimore: Paul H. Brookes Publishing Co.

Racino, J.A., O'Connor, S., & Walker, P. (1993). Conclusion. In J.A. Racino, P. Walker, S. O'Connor, & S.J. Taylor (Eds.), *Housing, support, and community: Choices and strategies for adults with disabilities* (pp. 355–366). Baltimore: Paul H. Brookes Publishing Co.

Racino, J.A., O'Connor, S., Walker, P., & Taylor, S.J. (1991). *Innovations in family supports.* Unpublished confidential research report.

Racino, J.A., & Taylor, S.J. (1993). "People first": Approaches to housing and support. In J.A. Racino, P. Walker, S. O'Connor, & S.J. Taylor (Eds.), *Housing, support, and community: Choices and strategies for adults with disabilities* (pp. 2–56). Baltimore: Paul H. Brookes Publishing Co.

Racino, J.A., Walker, P., O'Connor, S., & Taylor, S.J. (Eds.). (1993). *Housing, support, and community: Choices and strategies for adults with disabilities.* Baltimore: Paul H. Brookes Publishing Co.

Randolph, F.L., Laux, R., & Carling, P.J. (1987). *In search of housing: Creative approaches to financing integrated housing.* Monograph Series on Housing and Rehabilitation in Mental Health. Boston: Boston University, Center for Psychiatric Rehabilitation.

Rogan, P. (1992). Preparing students with severe disabilities for integrated employment. *The Forum, 18*(1), 15–17.

Rosenau, N. (Ed.). (1990). *A child's birthright: To live in a family.* Mt. Clemens, MI: Macomb-Oakland Regional Center.

Rusch, F.R., DeStefano, L., Chadsey-Rusch, J., Phelps, L.A., & Szymanski, E. (Eds.). (1992). *Transition from school to adult life: Models, linkages, and policy.* Sycamore, IL: Sycamore Publishing Co.

Salisbury, S., Dickey, J., & Crawford, C. (1987). *Individual empowerment and social service accountability.* Downsview, Ontario, Canada: The G. Allan Roeher Institute.

Schalock, R.L. (Ed.). (1990). *Quality of life: Perspectives and issues*. Washington, DC: American Association on Mental Retardation.

Skarnulis, E., & Lakin, C. (Eds.). (1990). Consumer controlled housing [Feature issue]. *IMPACT*, *3*(1).

Smith, G.A. (1990). *Supported living: New directions in services to people with developmental disabilities*. Alexandria, VA: National Association of State Mental Retardation Program Directors.

Smull, M.W., & Bellamy, G.T. (1991). Community services for adults with disabilities: Policy challenges in the emerging support paradigm. In L.H. Meyer, C.A. Peck, & L. Brown (Eds.), *Critical issues in the lives of people with severe disabilities* (pp. 527–536). Baltimore: Paul H. Brookes Publishing Co.

Stainback, S., & Stainback, W. (1990). Facilitating support networks. In W. Stainback & S. Stainback (Eds.), *Support networks for inclusive schooling: Interdependent integrated education* (pp. 25–36). Baltimore: Paul H. Brookes Publishing Co.

Stainback, S., Stainback, W., & Jackson, H.J. (1992). Toward inclusive classrooms. In S. Stainback & W. Stainback (Eds.), *Curriculum considerations for inclusive classrooms: Facilitating learning for all students* (pp. 3–17). Baltimore: Paul H. Brookes Publishing Co.

Taylor, S.J., Bogdan, R., & Racino, J.A. (Eds.). (1991). *Life in the community: Case studies of organizations supporting people with disabilities*. Baltimore: Paul H. Brookes Publishing Co.

Taylor, S.J., Lakin, K.C., & Hill, B.K. (1987). Permanency planning for children and youth: Out-of-home placement decisions. *Exceptional Children*, *55*(6), 541–549.

Taylor, S.J., Racino, J.A., & Walker, P. (1992). Inclusive community. In W. Stainback & S. Stainback (Eds.), *Controversial issues confronting special education: Divergent perspectives* (pp. 299–312). Boston: Allyn & Bacon.

Taylor, S.J., Racino, J.A., Knoll, J.A., & Lutfiyya, Z. (1987). *The nonrestrictive environment: On community integration for people with the most severe disabilities*. Syracuse: Human Policy Press.

Taylor, S.J., Racino, J.A., & Rothenberg, K. (1988). *A policy analysis of private community living arrangements in Connecticut*. Syracuse: Center on Human Policy, Syracuse University.

Taylor, S.J., Racino, J.A., & Walker, P. (1992). Inclusive community. In W. Stainback & S. Stainback (Eds.), *Controversial issues confronting special education: Divergent perspectives* (pp. 299–312). Boston: Allyn & Bacon.

Taylor, S.J., Racino, J.A., Walker, P., Lutfiyya, Z.M., & Shoultz, B. (1992). *Permanency planning for children with developmental disabilities in Pennsylvania: The lessons of Project STAR*. Syracuse: Center on Human Policy, Syracuse University.

Traustadottir, R. (1987). *"The answer to my prayers": A case study of the CITE Family Support Program, Cincinnati, Ohio*. Syracuse: Center on Human Policy, Syracuse University.

Traustadottir, R. (1991). *Supports for community living: A case study*. Syracuse, NY: Center on Human Policy, Syracuse University.

Traustadottir, R., Lutfiyya, Z.M., & Shoultz, B. (1994). Community living: A multicultural perspective. In M.F. Hayden & B.H. Abery (Eds.), *Challenges for a service system in transition: Ensuring quality community experiences for persons with developmental disabilities* (pp. 405–426). Baltimore: Paul H. Brookes Publishing Co.

Turnbull, H.R., Garlow, J., & Barber, P. (1991). A policy analysis of family support for families with members with disabilities. *The University of Kansas Law Review*, *39*(3).

Vandercook, T., York, J., & Forest, M. (1989). The McGill Action Planning System (MAPS): A strategy for building the vision. *Journal of The Association for Persons with Severe Handicaps*, *14*(3), 205–215.

Wallace, T., Larson, S.A., & Hewitt, A. (Eds.). (1992). Training of direct service staff [Feature issue]. *IMPACT*, *5*(1).

Walker, A. (1987). Enlarging the caring capacity of the community: Informal support networks and the welfare state. *International Journal of Health Services*, *17*(3), 369–383.

Walker, P., & Edinger, B. (1988). The kid from Cabin 17. *Camping Magazine*, *May*, 18–21.

Wehman, P., Kregel, J., & Shafer, M.S. (1989). *Emerging trends in the national supported employment initiative: A preliminary analysis of twenty-seven states*. Richmond: Rehabilitation Research and Training Center on Supported Employment, Virginia Commonwealth University.

Wehman, P., Moon, M.S., Everson, J.M., Wood, W., & Barcus, J.M. (1988). *Transition from school to work: New challenges for youth with severe disabilities*. Baltimore: Paul H. Brookes Publishing Co.

Wiseman, J.P. (1979). *Stations of the lost: The treatment of skid row alcoholics*. Chicago: University of Chicago Press.

Wolfensberger, W. (1972). *The principle of normalization in human services*. Toronto: National Institute on Mental Retardation.

Wolfensberger, W. (1991). *A brief introduction to Social Role Valorization as a high-order concept for structuring human services*. Syracuse: Training Institute for Human Service Planning, Leadership and Change Agentry, Syracuse University.

Wolfensberger, W., & Thomas, S. (1983). *PASSING: Program analysis of service systems' implementation of normalization goals*. Toronto: National Institute on Mental Retardation.

Worth, P. (1989). You've got a friend. In *The pursuit of leisure: Enriching the lives of people who have a disability* (pp. 73–78). Downsview, Ontario, Canada: The G. Allan Roeher Institute.

Zirpoli, T.J., Hancox, D., Wieck, C., & Skarnulis, E. (1989). Partners in policymaking: Empowering people. *Journal of The Association for Persons with Severe Handicaps*, *14*(2), 163–167.

11

Closing the Laconia State School and Training Center

A Case Study in Systems Change

Susan B. Covert, John D. MacIntosh, and Donald L. Shumway

On January 31, 1992, nearly 14 years after the New Hampshire Association for Retarded Citizens brought suit against the state because of conditions at the Laconia State School and Training Center, New Hampshire closed the doors to its only institution for people with developmental disabilities. New Hampshire became the first state in the country whose developmental disabilities service system did not include a state-run institution. While other states had responded to similar lawsuits with massive infusions of public dollars into their institutions, New Hampshire chose to direct its creativity and resources to the development of a community-based system of support and services.

On the face of it New Hampshire would appear to be an unlikely leader in service innovations and system change. This tiny New England state, with a population of just over 1 million, is fiscally and politically one of the nation's most conservative. The Granite State is tight fisted, tradition bound, and fiercely independent. Yet, from 1983 to 1993, New Hampshire has been a pioneer in promoting and achieving community inclusion for its citizens with disabilities. The development of a comprehensive community developmental service system and the subsequent closing of the Laconia State School were possible only through the combined efforts of advocates, state administrators, service providers, and persons with disabilities and their families. In a unique and not always comfortable collaboration, these players created a shared vision of what life could be like for individuals with developmental disabilities. New Hampshire expanded the notion of what was possible; expectations that state residents with developmental disabilities could be participating and contributing community members were raised. Guided by this vision and blessed with a certain amount of serendipity, New Hampshire seized opportunities to bring about a new reality for its citizens with developmental disabilities.

THE ROAD TO TRIAL

When Sandra Garrity walked into Laconia State School and Training Center at the age of 8 it was an alternative of last resort for her parents. Told by their school district that Sandra was too challenging and finding no community resources to offer support, her parents were left with no choice but to commit their daughter to the state institution by order of the probate court. Sandra's admission to Laconia was approached more with apprehension than relief by her parents. They were told not to expect to see Sandra for at least a month, or until she "adjusted" to her new surroundings. Not long afterward, the Garritys' neighbors also placed their son, Mark, at Laconia. Several months earlier, Mark's parents had been told by their local school district that Mark no longer could be handled at school. His abusive behaviors had his parents at their wits' end. Again, the Laconia State School and Training Center was this family's only alternative.

Over the course of the next 10 years, Mark, Sandra, and their parents suffered the pain, anguish, and indignities that are the unfortunate hallmarks of institutional care. Sandra, who could talk, told her parents on their weekend visits about cold showers, beatings by staff, and being locked in her room for days at a time. Mark's self-abusive behaviors were thought to be caused by a neurological disorder. After two unsuccessful lobotomies, Mark's behavior problems still were present, but he no longer could walk independently.

Sandra and Mark's parents, along with families of other Laconia residents, time and again brought these and other injustices to the attention of state officials. Administrators at the institution and in the state's developmental disabilities services office in Concord, while sympathetic, essentially were powerless to bring about any change. The parents began to organize themselves; they formed a Laconia State School branch of the state's Association for Retarded Citizens. More parents became politically active; several were elected to the state legislature. In the mid-1970s parents lobbied the legislature and secured passage of RSA 171-A, a bill guaranteeing certain treatment rights and services for individuals with developmental disabilities. While the law "guaranteed" rights and promised the creation of certain services, the appropriations to put these services in place amounted to the paltry sum of $400,000.

The population at the institution continued to grow; Laconia State School and Training Center now housed nearly 800 children and adults and was run by a staff who were demoralized and overwhelmed. Frustrations for parents of Laconia State School residents increased, and with the Association for Retarded Citizens they moved closer to bringing their concerns to federal court. Politicians and state officials in the executive branch attempted to dissuade parents from filing a lawsuit. (It is worth noting that, while the state's public stance was against the lawsuit, there were administrators at the state school and in the Division of Developmental Services who quietly worked with parent groups to help them prepare for litigation.) The state advised parents that long-term reforms could best be achieved through patience and legislative change. Bringing lawyers into the picture would only draw battle lines and deter meaningful reform. Parents also were told, in not so subtle ways, that they should be thankful for Laconia's existence since they obviously were unable to care for their children at home. Conditions at Laconia continued to deteriorate. When Governor Meldrin Thompson imposed a hiring freeze in 1977, the result was an alarming rise in resident deaths (primarily from aspiration) and repeated outbreaks of infectious hepatitis.

Finally, in 1978, the Association for Retarded Citizens, together with several parents, brought a class action suit in federal court challenging conditions at Laconia. Although lawsuits of this kind were not novel, the legal "relief" sought by New Hampshire parents and their advocates was unusual. The lawsuit stated that the Laconia State School and Training Center, no matter how improved, amounted to an unconstitutional deprivation of the liberties of its residents. In simple terms, parents sought through the lawsuit to close the institution and replace it with a "comprehensive system of community-based services."

The decision to forsake the institution and replace it with a community-based system was reached with much difficulty. Most parents loathed Laconia but struggled with the idea that their children ultimately might return to their home schools and neighborhoods. After all, doctors and other professionals historically had told parents that living outside an institution was an impossibility for people with disabilities, implying that it even might be life threatening. The parents' attorneys were also aware of the risks in this strategy but were persuaded by members of The Association for the Severely Handicapped and other progressive professionals around the country that any attempts to "fix" institutions were futile.

The state's official response to the parents' demand to close Laconia State School was nothing short of outrage. The plaintiffs' attorneys were assailed by elected officials, the lawyers from the Attorney General's Office, and the press as radicals who were more interested in social engineering than finding a practical solution to problems at the institution (Loeb, 1980). Parents of Laconia residents and the Association for Retarded Citizens were accused of being manipulative, vindictive, and ungrateful.

As the trial date approached in 1980, the prospects for the parents did not look encouraging. The political climate in the country had grown increasingly conservative; Ronald Reagan recently had been elected president and promised to replace the federal judiciary with judges who would apply the constitution rather than interpret it. Chief Judge Shane Devine, who would hear the Laconia case, privately acknowledged some changes were necessary, but expressed concerns about the parents' legal claims. State attorneys offered appealing settlements which promised to create some community alternatives, but which insisted the institution was necessary for people who were medically fragile and behaviorally involved, and as an undefined backup resource for communities. Enormous pressure was brought to bear on parents and their attorneys to settle the case by way of a consent decree. The parents, their attorneys, and even the court knew full well that the promise of "best efforts" could not guarantee reforms that would require at least 5–10 years of hard work and millions of public dollars. The stage was set for a classic confrontation between states' rights and the role of the federal court.

THE TRIAL: *GARRITY v. GALLEN*

The Laconia State School and Training Center trial dramatically illustrated the process of social change. The courtroom trial of *Garrity v. Gallen* (1984), at the time the longest civil suit in New Hampshire's history, lasted for nearly 40 days over the course of 3 months. The real drama, however, was played out in the media and in the public consciousness. Extensive testimony about abuses, shortages of staff, physicians performing surgery without anesthesia, and unnecessary deaths was covered daily by both the written and electronic media. Although the parents' decision to go to trial was motivated in large part by a hope that they could obtain a court order (as opposed to a more amorphous consent decree), the impact of the widespread press coverage, both upon the elected officials and New Hampshire citizens, was grossly underestimated. At the time the trial concluded in the summer of 1980, all parties involved, including the court, were exhausted. However, a curious change had occurred in how the press, politicians, and the public perceived the conflict. In large part, due to the compelling testimony of their parents and professionals like Lou Brown, Marc Gold, and Gunnar Dybwad, residents of the Laconia State School and Training Center were no longer perceived as dangerous or subhuman; instead they came to be perceived as victims of a political and educational system that saw them as valueless. When the court issued its order in 1981 requiring sweeping changes in the care of persons with developmental disabilities, an editorial in the *Manchester Union Leader* (a newspaper not known for its liberal leanings) lambasted public officials for failing to deal forthrightly with legitimate needs of persons with disabilities and their families (Finnegan, 1981). This was a far cry from pretrial editorials, which adopted the state's party line that the parents' concerns were exaggerated, bordering on the histrionic. Elected state officials dramatically predicted, even before the court order was issued, that the state would need to spend in excess of $100 million to remedy the problems at the institution.

In the meantime, the court struggled with whether the federal constitution required, as the plaintiffs claimed, that *all* persons at Laconia had a right to live in the community. The court ultimately found that there was no such right under the constitution. Nevertheless, it ordered massive reforms *both* at the institution and in the community, which clearly obligated the state to overhaul its system of services to persons with developmental disabilities. More significantly, the federal court indicated it would retain jurisdiction (i.e., control) of the case until all of its orders were implemented. Any intransigence on the part of the state would be met with the appointment of a court monitor or special master. This potential intrusion on states' rights by the federal court was anathema to state officials. While the threat of bringing in a court master was an important stick, not having a master appointed at the outset allowed New Hampshire to assume ownership of the implementation of the court order, and later a pride in its accomplishments. The court's willingness to grant this degree of flexibility and authority was extremely important to the ultimate ability of the state to reform its system of services.

In response to the court's order for reform, the state offered three proposals. The first proposed to fix up the institution, the second called for closing the institution within 2 years, and the third—the one recommended by the state's Division of Developmental Services—was a combination of both institutional reform and community placements. This last proposal was developed behind the scenes in a collaborative planning effort involving the Division of Developmental Services, advocates, and parents. This option left open the possibility that Laconia would be phased out but did not guarantee its closure. Attorneys for the state argued that the state at any time could deviate from any of these options depending upon the availability of funds or changes in public policy. The court and the parents disagreed.

The recommended implementation plan by the Division of Developmental Services relied heavily on community resources, but over an extended period of time. The decision on this approach was made for two reasons. First, the state had no community service model to speak of, and to create one would require time. Second, state officials and the parents knew that long-term court supervision was essential in order to implement any lasting change. The concept of gradual movement to a community-based system over a period of 5 or more years meant that the court would continue to be involved should the state's commitment waiver. This was a *key factor* in the ultimate closure of Laconia because, while the state retained broad discretion and had time to change the service system fundamentally, parents and the court held the trump card (i.e., the appointment of a court monitor) throughout the process. Above all, during the course of the 12-week trial, the court had been educated about the value of community placement. The court could ensure that the state stayed on course. Finally, while a court order was dependent upon legislative funding, state officials and legislators knew that any backsliding would result in the takeover of the system by a judicially ordered monitor or master. These dynamics provided the necessary tension to move decisively toward a community-based system.

In 1981 the federal court in New Hampshire issued a detailed plan that provided specific relief to residents of the Laconia State School and Training Center. Among other provisions, the institution was required to meet certain minimum standards and 235 individuals (a little less than half of Laconia's population at the time) were to be placed in the community in order to allow the institution to be reduced to a size that would be more manageable. The New Hampshire Department of Education, also enjoined in the suit, was required to provide educational services to individuals with severe disabilities under state law RSA 186-C. Most important, the court ordered the development and maintenance of a statewide service delivery system that would include a comprehensive array of services for the diagnosis, evaluation, habilitation, and rehabilitation of people with developmental disabilities. The court did not require the closure of the Laconia State School and Training Center.

IMPLEMENTING THE COURT ORDER: BUILDING A COMMUNITY-BASED SYSTEM OF SERVICES

In responding to the court order, New Hampshire found itself in the unique position of creating from scratch a community-based service system. The state was able to take advantage of opportunities in ways that would not have been possible in most other states. As late as 1978 there were virtually no organized community alternatives to institutional care. The few group homes that existed were started and supported by parents or were small nonprofit organizations. New Hampshire was a clean slate. New Hampshire's Division of Developmental Services was able to develop a community system based on the most recent thinking, rather than (as had other states faced with similar litigation) adopting the corrupted approach of relying on regional centers (institutions by any other name) and "small" 8- to 10-bed intermediate care facilities for persons with mental retardation (ICFs/MR). In addition, the state already had a statutory model, RSA 171-A, for a community service system. This law, enacted by the state legislature in 1975 with strong support from parents, called for the creation of regional area agencies to administer services for New Hampshire citizens with developmental disabilities. It was a promising concept, but no public funds had been appropriated to implement even one of these area agencies.

Developing the Area Agency System

The state's 12 area agencies became the cornerstone on which the regional community service system was built. It is critical to mention that, while area agencies were supported primarily with state dollars, they were not state agencies. This independence meant that the communities and not the state "owned" the area agencies. The area agencies were private nonprofit organizations governed by independent community boards of directors. By law an area agency board was required to have at least one third consumer and/or family representation. Area agencies were part of the fabric of their communities, and their boards were representative of the same. Now persons with developmental disabilities not only had service providers as allies, but merchants, bankers, lawyers, realtors, and legislators as well. Furthermore, the area agencies generally were insulated from manipulation at the state level and from the political pressures that could be brought to bear on state employees. By limiting the role of state bureaucracy, the area agency system maintained an important New Hampshire tradition of home rule and local control.

The state's Division of Developmental Services with the directors of the area agencies developed a joint mission statement, which outlined their commitment to integration, interdependence, and the support required to maintain individuals with disabilities in their home communities. While allowing for a good deal of regional autonomy, all area agencies initially were responsible for administering case management, residential, and day program services. As time passed the area agencies also became responsible for developing programs in the areas of supported employment, early intervention, and family support. By the end of the decade, the Laconia State School and Training Center had a little over 100 residents, and the area agencies served in excess of 4,000 individuals with developmental disabilities.

The community housing options included supervised apartments, group homes, enhanced family care (an expanded foster care arrangement), and a handful of eight-bed ICFs/MR. The ICFs/MR had been developed by some area agencies that felt they were necessary in order to reduce the population at Laconia quickly. While the ICFs/MR were not in keeping with the state's move toward smaller, more personalized housing, they have served an important function in the system's fiscal planning. New Hampshire's community developmental disabilities service system is primarily dependent on monies obtained through the state's Home and Community-Based (HCB) waiver to the federal Medicaid program. The presence of a small number of ICF/MR beds in the state enabled the Division of Developmental Services to leverage federal funds and obtain a favorable rate structure for their waiver. Without the existence of these ICFs/MR, it is doubtful the state would have achieved the same degree of success in its pursuit of HCB waiver dollars. Later, housing efforts in New Hampshire came to include the development of individual housing supports and subsidized home ownership. These initiatives have helped to expand flexibility and consumer control but have also responded to the very real problems of staff burnout and the isolation created by group home living. Today, over 1,100 individuals live in family homes or residences supported by the state. The average number of individuals with disabilities who share a residence is three.

The creation of a state-wide system of comprehensive early intervention for infants and toddlers gave New Hampshire a first line of support for families with children who had developmental disabilities or delays. These programs served and supported families who, in earlier days, might have sought institutional placements for their children. In bringing about the closure of Laconia, it was crucial for New Hampshire parents to have access to support and services at the very outset of having their child's disability diagnosed. In the 5 years prior to its closing, no admissions were made to Laconia, and it had ceased to be an option for New Hampshire families and their children.

As area agencies matured, program development focused more and more on community integration and inclusion. Supported employment became the day program of choice for adults with developmental disabilities. Many former state school residents, along with individuals with disabilities who had never lived in an institution, began to join the state's work force. Today, over 1,200 adults with disabilities are supported employees in New Hampshire businesses. The state ranks first in the country in the percentage of adults with disabilities working in supported employment programs; over 40% of all adults in developmental disabilities services day programs are working at real jobs for real pay in their communities.

It would be remiss to imply that the creation of New Hampshire's community service system occurred without incident. System change does not happen without periodic tension and confrontation. Between 1981 and 1989 the state of New Hampshire, under three different governors, challenged the implementation of the court order. A series of heated exchanges occurred between the federal court and the state's executive branch of government. At each of these critical stages the court remained stalwart in ensuring that the state would not renege on its promise. Curiously, these skirmishes tended to reinforce, rather than undermine, the public (media) and legislative support for community reform. In many ways the confrontations between the state and court were necessary in order to keep the momentum of service development and reform. The value of proceeding to trial and obtaining a court order, rather than accepting a consent decree, have been borne out.

The Evolving Role of Families

In developing the area agency system, New Hampshire gained a new family constituency that had its own visions and strategies. The demands made by these community parents were different. Their children had always lived in their home communities and that is where they wanted their children to remain. These families were not vulnerable to the accusations of public officials that parents of children in institutions were being ungrateful. They, after all, were doing their best to maintain their children in the community, but resources and support were inadequate. In 1989, it was community parents who introduced and successfully fought for the passage of a bill that allocated $2.5 million to address the area agency waiting lists for community developmental disabilities services.

While New Hampshire families had historically played an important role in advocating for and helping to create needed services, they began in the mid-1980s to demand a role in state policy-making. In 1987, the state legislature appointed a Task Force to Study Support Services for Families of Developmentally Disabled

Children. For 16 months the Task Force, in collaboration with the Division of Developmental Services and other state agencies and with assistance from the Institute on Disability at The University of New Hampshire, made an extensive study of the needs of families caring for children with disabilities. The final report of the Task Force, *For the Love of Our Families, for the Sake of Us All* (1988), contained detailed recommendations on how New Hampshire could better support families, enabling them to provide quality care at home for their family members with disabilities.

The Task Force's first and most important recommendation called for the passage of legislation, with adequate appropriations, to establish a comprehensive statewide family support network. New Hampshire families rallied behind the Task Force, and, with one of the best grassroots lobbying efforts the state had ever seen, parents convinced the legislature that supporting families was necessary. In 1989, the state's Family Support bill was signed into law. Money for family support services was appropriated to all of the state's area agencies, which determined how family support dollars would be spent. The developmental services system experienced a subtle but real shift in power from the bureaucracy to the families and individuals with disabilities.

Special Education Services

Simultaneous to the development of the community services network, New Hampshire's Bureau of Special Education worked to achieve the inclusion of students with disabilities into regular classes in their neighborhood schools. In addition, the Bureau of Special Education, in collaboration with the Division of Developmental Services, secured legislation to support the return of New Hampshire children needing significant levels of support who were being educated out of state. The resources provided by this special legislation, along with technical assistance funded through a federal systems change grant from the United States Department of Education and provided by the Bureau and the Institute on Disability, supported local school districts in their efforts to educate *all* their students within the local district and in regular classrooms. Furthermore, the Division of Developmental Services established a Medicaid funding plan to assist school districts in financing needed therapeutic and educationally related services. These factors along with the decision not to operate a separate school on the Laconia campus, increased the community's capacity to provide appropriate educational services to students with a wide range of disabilities and eliminated institutional placement for even those needing the most significant levels of support.

The Institute on Disability, an Additional Resource

The Institute on Disability at The University of New Hampshire was established through the combined vision and efforts of New Hampshire's Council of State Planning Agencies. The council was composed of the directors of the state's Developmental Disabilities Council, the Division of Mental Health and Developmental Services, the Department of Education, and the Job Training Council. With leadership from the Developmental Disabilities Council, blueprints for the institute were drawn up and support obtained from the governor's office and The University of New Hampshire. In 1987, the institute opened its doors at the main campus of the university at Durham.

In 1989 the Institute on Disability, in collaboration with the Clinical Genetics and Child Development Center at Dartmouth College, was awarded University Affiliated Program (UAP) status by the United States Administration on Developmental Disabilities. As a sanctioned UAP, the institute became eligible for federal funds to conduct training and research, promote exemplary services, and disseminate information about disability issues. Since its inception, the Institute on Disability has brought substantial federal dollars into the state. The UAP has developed extensive preservice training and internship opportunities for graduate and undergraduate students at the state's university and technical colleges. The UAP also works closely with the medical school at Dartmouth and with Franklin Pierce Law Center, the state's only law school, to ensure disability issues are included in each school's curriculum. In addition, the Institute on Disability has become an important technical assistance resource for community service providers and public educators. Through its leadership series, the institute has worked to empower individuals with disabilities and their families to be effective change agents. (Parents who were graduates from the institute's first leadership series organized the grassroots lobbying effort that resulted in passage of the Family Support bill.) In all of its endeavors, the Institute on Disability has worked to further full community inclusion for New Hampshire citizens with disabilities.

Funding Is Important

The state's commitment to small, community-based services, along with the significant cost of creating and maintaining a comprehensive community system, led New Hampshire to develop extensive HCB Medicaid waiver programs, rather than utilizing residential programs based upon the ICF/MR model. Using the HCB waiver as the primary method of funding developmental services enabled the state to tap the monies it needed to build its community system. With its HCB waiver, New Hampshire was able to reduce significantly the state's per capita cost of operating the developmental services system. By 1989, New Hampshire, by a wide margin, led the nation in capturing Medicaid dollars. In addition, the HCB waiver allowed New Hampshire to develop its community system based on a competency enhancement model, rather than on the ICF/MR medical model, which dictated provision of specific therapies and treatments. Using the competency model, New Hampshire's area agencies were expected to assist individuals with developmental disabilities in developing skills that would enable them to live, work, and, in all other ways, participate in the life of their communities.

In addition to use of the HCB waiver, the other financial decision that hastened the closing of the Laconia State School and Training Center concerned the transfer of institutional funds to the community. With each building closure at Laconia, state dollars were transferred to the community. Additional dollars in the community meant an increase in matching money for Medicaid waiver programs and enabled New Hampshire to leverage a significant amount of federal funds.

QUIETLY CLOSING THE DOORS

A number of factors helped to bring about the final closure of Laconia State School and Training Center. Ironically, New Hampshire officials expedited the closing of their institution by never announcing a closure plan. As late as 6 months before closure, New Hampshire officials still had not said that Laconia would close. Instead, in the decade following the lawsuit, officials continued to articulate the state's commitment to developing a comprehensive community system that would allow individuals with developmental disabilities, regardless of the level of support they needed, to be served in their home communities. By focusing on the positive: service development, rather than on the negative: institutional closure, New Hampshire avoided the polarization of families, legislators, state employees, and state departments over the philosophy of deinstitutionalization.

The New Hampshire officials simply and incrementally went about the business of developing opportunities for citizens with disabilities, one by one, within their respective communities. As area agencies developed community services, parents and guardians of Laconia residents were offered the option of having their family members or wards return to their communities and receive services there. Sandra and Mark returned to their home town, although not without some initial community opposition and parental concerns. The changes in their lives were dramatic. Sandra, once considered the worst behavior problem in an institution of 800 residents, lost 30 pounds, bought her first pair of designer jeans, and began attending weekly dances at the local VFW. Mark moved into a home just a few miles away from his parents and developed a close and trusting relationship with the staff who supported him. Not until only 30 residents remained at Laconia and the economies of institutional support and community support became so disproportionate that closure was inevitable, were individual families beseeched to make placements.

The additional institutional support and staff mandated by the court order increased the average cost per resident from $20,000 a year at the time of the lawsuit to in excess of $100,000 by 1988. The cost of Laconia had obvious economic implications. Legislators who had become accustomed to funding the court-ordered improvements without question now wondered why it cost twice as much to support someone in the institution as in the community. Although economic savings were never used as the primary argument for creating community alternatives, cost increasingly became an issue and weighted the argument in favor of the community system. As the New Hampshire economy sank deeper into the recession, policy-makers at all levels began to question the need for a dual system of care.

Finally, in closing Laconia, state officials worked closely with institutional staff to gain their support and assistance in community placements. A wide variety of activities were undertaken to ensure closure was accomplished in a supportive and positive manner. Staff at Laconia were urged to attend training for PASSING (Program Analysis of Service Systems' Implementation of Normalization Goals). Through this experience, the majority of staff developed a strong commitment to community placements. In addition, every effort was made to offer institutional staff job opportunities within state-operated services or in community-contracted programs. Layoffs and other terminations for state school employees were minimized. There was no organized opposition to the institution's closure by Laconia staff. (It should also be noted, however, that institutional staff were not unionized.)

LOOKING AHEAD

In the years since the Laconia State School and Training Center lawsuit was filed, New Hampshire has made great, some might say unbelievable, strides in how it cares for and supports its citizens with developmental disabilities. The state's evolution from a service model that relied almost totally on institutional care to one that is completely community-centered has had difficulties. Its success can be credited to a variety of factors. For one thing, the political culture of New Hampshire itself is based on values consistent with community-based services, including the belief that small is better, a healthy distrust of government and large bureaucracies, the reliance on home rule and local control, and the notion that each individual makes a difference. In addition, New Hampshire's small size made it easier for people to work together. These factors meant that the state was able to create and pursue a shared vision of full citizenship for New Hampshire residents with disabilities.

Throughout this evolutionary process, New Hampshire families have been a strong and cohesive voice; they have consistently been the state's conscience, demanding that New Hampshire do the right thing. As a group they never became visibly fragmented into opposing camps. Their solidarity made collaboration between families and state regional administrators possible. And to the credit of the state, family participation and decision-making—through the area agency boards and Family Support Councils—has been built into the community service system. Through the Institute on Disability's leadership trainings, New Hampshire has developed a strong and growing core of informed and politically active families who recently saved the Developmental Services budget from the deep cuts that affected all other state agencies.

In addition, New Hampshire has been fortunate to have had, on the whole, effective leadership within its developmental disabilities service system, at both the state and regional levels. It also has had a continuity of leadership in key positions that has ensured a continuing vision for a decade. While not perfect, the alliance between the state Division of Developmental Services and the area agencies has allowed New Hampshire to work toward the same goals in establishing a statewide comprehensive system of services. In 1987, the state office, in collaboration with its 12 area agencies, rewrote the mission statement for the Division of Developmental Services. New Hampshire became the only state in the country to put forward a statewide mandate for the community inclusion of people with developmental disabilities. The following is New Hampshire's vision, embodied in the mission statement:

> Our mission is to create new opportunities for Granite State citizens with developmental disabilities. We shall work hard to promote the independence and integration of our neighbors with developmental disabilities so they can participate—right along side of non-handicapped people—in all facets of community life.
>
> We'll know we've been successful when there is evidence that people with disabilities are participating in their community, working at meaningful jobs, involved in integrated employment situations, and enjoying the simple opportunities for life and recreation that the rest of the world takes for granted. (New Hampshire Department of Health and Human Services, Division of Mental Health and Developmental Services, 1991, p. 1)

New Hampshire's job is not yet done. If history is a predictor of the future, then the 1990s will see changes in the service delivery system as dramatic as in the 1980s, following the Laconia State School and Training Center suit. Guided by the desires of individuals with disabilities and their families, services and supports should become increasingly individualized and consumer-directed. For this to occur, New Hampshire, both in policy and practice, must regard Medicaid and state dollars as belonging to the individual and not to the developmental disabilities service system. More and more, decisions about how public dollars are spent to support and care for the individual should be made by the individual, his or her family, and trusted friends. Over time, the area agencies should function less as administrators of specialized services and more as brokers for individuals and their families, helping them to find and utilize both specialized and community resources. On a limited basis this is already happening in some area agencies; relinquishing or even sharing control of service dollars may present the most significant challenge to date for area agencies.

In addition, the state will need to find the resources and the will to serve those individuals who are currently on waiting lists for services. Parents whose children were never placed at Laconia are demanding community living arrangements and employment options as their children reach adulthood. Families whose children have grown up in the era of PL 94-142, the Education for All Handicapped Children Act of 1975, which guaranteed *all* students the right to a free, appropriate public education, have come to expect the provision of adequate services and support. It is possible that PL 101-336, the Americans with Disabilities Act of 1990 will begin to expand opportunities, especially in the area of employment, that previously have not existed for individuals with disabilities. In the years to come, the impetus for achieving social change will likely include both political and legal strategies.

New Hampshire is making a concerted effort to realize full community inclusion for its citizens with disabilities. A Home of Your Own, a federally funded project developed by the Institute on Disability, will assist individuals to become homeowners. A strong People First movement has been forming in the state. Individuals with disabilities have themselves become politically active and vocal. Roberta Gallant, a former Laconia State School and Training Center resident and long-time advocate, received the Martin Luther King, Jr. Award in 1991 for her work to advance the civil rights of people with disabilities. There is continued and increased work needed at the local level to bring children with disabilities back to their neighborhood schools and into regular classrooms. All across the state, families and providers are struggling to find ways to increase opportunities for individuals with disabilities to form real and reciprocal friendships with others in their communities.

While it indeed has come a long way, it is important that New Hampshire remember where it came from. In the spring of 1991, a ceremony was held on what had once been the grounds of the Laconia State School and Training Center to commemorate its closing. With great emotion, parents whose children once had resided at this institution reminded those present not to forget what life had been like for the residents who lived there. Freda Smith, whose daughter had lived at Laconia had these parting thoughts.

> It took a lot of courage on the part of the parents of residents at the Laconia State School to support the closing of this institution. Many feared the possibility of state and federal funds drying up, and of day programs and residential services ending. Those fears are still very real. These parents are the pioneers who blazed the trail and made it easier for the parents of today whose children are developmentally disabled. I hope they never experience the devastation that we did, when instead of entering preschool, our Janet entered this institution. I hope they hear and understand how far we have come and all we went through.
>
> We must never forget there was once a place called Laconia State School and Training Center. For those who know of our pain let us take turns reminding ourselves of what it was like in Murphy, Powell, Keyes, Blood, Baker and Floyd [institutional residences]. For those who don't know, we must keep this alive to remind everyone that institutions must never again be a way of life for anyone. (Smith, 1991, p. 2)

REFERENCES

Finnegan, J. (1981, August 20). Why not the best? *Manchester Union Leader*, p. 14.

Garrity v. Gallen, 522 F. Supp. 171 (D.N.H. 1981) aff'd sub. nom. Garrity v. Sununu, 697 F 2d 452 (1st Cir. 1983) and 752 F. 2d 272 (1st Cir. 1984)

Loeb, W. (1980, June 24). The Laconia tragedy—Attempting to reverse progress. *Manchester Union Leader*.

New Hampshire Department of Health and Human Services, Division of Mental Health and Developmental Services. (1991). *New decade, new decisions,* Concord, NH: Author.

Smith, F. (1991). *Speech commemorating the closing of the Laconia State School and Training Center.* Laconia, NH.

Task Force to Study Support Services for Families of Developmentally Disabled Children. (1988). *For the love of our families, for the sake of us all.* Concord, NH: Author.

12

Systems Change Directed at Inclusive Education

Jane A. Nisbet, Cheryl Jorgensen, and Stephanie Powers

Facilitating change in the systems and support structures that affect public education requires a clear vision, a tolerance for chaos, a willingness to work with multiple players, and the means to move from vision to implementation. The systems change process for students with severe disabilities in New Hampshire has been supported since 1988 through a 5-year systems change project grant from the Department of Special Education and Rehabilitative Services. New Hampshire, known for its large citizen legislature, has a very distinct political and social culture that values local and community control, strong family orientation, individual rights, and policy-making by the general public. This constellation of values contributed to New Hampshire's status as the first state to close its residential institution for individuals with developmental disabilities, and one of the first to create a state-wide family support network focusing on family empowerment and control. These same positions also govern the systems change process described in this chapter to bring about the full inclusion of students with disabilities into their neighborhood schools.

RATIONALE FOR INCLUSION

The initial process of creating the vision of inclusion is aided by data to support inclusion. This does not mean that data are required to justify inclusion or limit its scope; rather, data can support the value of inclusion. Inclusion of students with disabilities into regular schools has long been justified on the basis of several rationales including civil rights, belief that schools should reflect a pluralistic society, potential for the development of social relationships, benefits to typical children, and preparation for optimum functioning in inclusive adult communities

(Biklen, 1985; Brinker & Thorpe, 1984; *Brown v. Board of Education,* 1954; Brown et al., 1987; Brown et al., 1989; Brown, Nietupski, & Hamre-Nietupski, 1976; Halvorsen & Sailor, 1990; *PARC v. Commonwealth of Pennsylvania,* 1971; Voeltz, Johnson, & McQuarter, 1983). Much of the research does not, however, concern the full regular classroom membership for students who have severe disabilities known as "inclusive education."

The inclusive education model is based upon the beliefs that: 1) children who have disabilities are full human beings whose presence enriches our schools; 2) people with severe disabilities do not need to be "fixed" before being allowed to participate in the mainstream of school and community life; 3) support systems should be provided by the most natural, available person in the environment; and 4) changes in the educational system that will facilitate the inclusion of children with the most challenges coincide with changes that will benefit all children (Gartner & Lipsky, 1987; Rowe, 1989; Strully & Strully, 1985; Thousand & Villa, 1989). In inclusive schools all children are welcomed into their neighborhood schools, and instructional groupings and curricular decisions are guided by the overriding value that heterogeneity is necessary for all children to learn. Classroom teachers are supported by specialists in content areas (e.g., reading, communication, cooperative education, math) rather than specialists who know about "types" of students. And the goals of public education are expanded to include developing personal relationships as well as building a public service and community support ethic. Some individuals who support these new goals for education contend that the continuation of two separate systems is antithetical to the values and desired outcomes that characterize this new system. They recommend the merger of special and regular education into a unitary system of quality education for all students (Gartner & Lipsky, 1987; Stainback, Stainback, & Bunch, 1989; Wang, Reynolds, & Walberg, 1986).

DEVELOPING THE VISION

There is strong support for the inclusion of individuals with severe disabilities in all aspects of community life (Biklen, 1985; Brown et al., 1989; Lipsky & Gartner, 1989; Stainback, Stainback, & Forest, 1989; Taylor, Biklen, & Knoll, 1987; Taylor, Racino, Knoll, & Lutfiyya, 1987). The movement to expand community integration and school inclusion is now national in scope and has been fueled by the growing prevalence of litigation; by professionals, families, and consumers nationwide; and through increased awareness on the part of the general public of the rights of people with disabilities.

The literature on education of children and young adults with disabilities offers important reasons why inclusion of these students in the public schools benefits society as well as the students:

- Students with severe disabilities learn better in inclusive environments (Brinker & Thorpe, 1984; Voeltz, 1982).

- Friendships between people with disabilities and people without disabilities occur more often in integrated environments (Strully & Strully, 1985).
- Inclusion may be more cost-effective (Voeltz et al., 1983).
- Inclusion in mainstream school activities provides better preparation for a more independent, self-sufficient adult life (Brown et al., 1989).
- Inclusion is a civil right (Voeltz et al., 1983).

Stainback et al. (1989) suggested that, while education is

> "technically a sub-system of regular education, . . . the United States has in effect created a separate system for educating students with disabilities. The operation of separate systems has a number of disadvantages, including: a) the instructional needs of students do not warrant the operation of a dual system; b) maintaining a dual system is inefficient; and c) the dual system fosters an inappropriate and unfair attitude about the education of students classified as having disabilities" (p. 15).

This separate system has come under increasing scrutiny. Several reasons for this emerge. First, the cost of maintaining a second system is increasingly a concern for budget conscious policy-makers. Second, the effectiveness of the specialist approach is being reassessed as the earliest beneficiaries of PL 94-142, the Education for All Handicapped Children Act of 1975, are now graduating from the system and their outcomes are being studied. Third, for many parents and advocates, separateness for students with disabilities has become a stark reminder of a haunting past in American education when segregation of students based on race, and/or socioeconomic status was tolerated. A negative historical parallel for both the American education system, as well as the rest of society, begins to emerge:

> As Chief Justice Earl Warren ruled in the 1954 *Brown v. Board of Education* decision, separateness in education is inherently unequal. By assigning some students to "special" education, we physically separate them from their peers. Others, although mainstreamed, carry with them the label "special" and are psychologically separated both in their own minds and in the minds of their teachers from their regular peers. (Stainback et al., 1989, p. 15)

Research conducted on the effectiveness of special education has contributed to a growing body of evidence against the efficacy of separate educational environments, instructional groupings by disability or severity of disability, and the specialist approach. Results of these studies similarly indicate the need for retooling existing practices in favor of strategies geared to the acquisition of functional skills and information that enable students to perform competently in the community once they leave the school environment (Brown et al., 1987; Edgar, Levine, & Maddox, 1985; Hasazi, Gordon, & Roe, 1985; Wehman, Kregel, & Zollers, 1984; Zollers, Conroy, Hess, & Newman, 1984).

THE FEDERAL INITIATIVE

The Office of Special Education and Rehabilitative Services (OSERS) in the United States Department of Education has provided significant research and demonstration funds for program development aimed at the improvement of outcomes for students with severe disabilities. Throughout the 1980s, OSERS promoted the inclusion of students with severe disabilities into mainstream school programs, focusing its funding priorities on critical areas such as teacher preparation at the post-secondary level, the school-to-work transition process for students aging out of school, and innovations in instruction that emphasize greater interaction for students with severe disabilities in their natural environments and with peers without disabilities.

Leading research centers for the OSERS priorities have been identifying effective educational strategies and developing program models to assist local education agencies (LEAs) in redefining their program outcomes for students with severe disabilities. Exemplary practice strategies have included adaptation of regular classroom curricula (rather than design of special curricula), secondary school programs utilizing vocational education and vocational rehabilitation services, inclusive classroom instructional practices, related services delivery within regular classrooms, utilizing local education inservice models, innovative parent involvement practices, collaborative teamwork among teachers and those providing support in related services disciplines, and utilizing cooperative learning models. The knowledge gained from these activities is leading to a progressive acceptance of more effective approaches of educating students with severe disabilities.

For example, in the area of program effectiveness, The University of Vermont has developed a list of indicators that provide educators and parents with a framework for developing and evaluating services for students with intensive needs. The use of these guidelines at the local level "will optimize the participation of students in integrated school and community settings and prepare them for adult life" (Fox et al., 1987, p. 1). The guidelines fall into the following nine areas:

- Age-appropriate placement in local public schools
- Integrated delivery of educational and related services
- Social integration
- Transition planning
- Community-based instruction
- Curricular expectations
- Systematic, data-based instruction
- Home–school partnership
- Systematic evaluation of educational and related services

In New Hampshire, the Special Education Bureau has been implementing its own comprehensive evaluation program for assessing the effectiveness of special education programs since 1985. These New Hampshire indicators are not designed specifically for students with severe disabilities; however, they are broad enough to accommodate the educational measures for these students. This system of program evaluation is called "Profiling Effectiveness in Special Education" and it has identified nine indicators of program effectiveness for New Hampshire special education programs. These indicators, while not mandated, have been accepted by 107 school districts. Program evaluation teams in these districts have been examining their special education programs using these indicators and are improving their programs based on the information gleaned from the district-wide review. The New Hampshire indicators fall into the following nine areas:

- Student and program outcomes
- Philosophies, policies, and procedures
- Resources
- School programs
- Instructional practices
- Staff competencies, attitudes, and relationships
- Parent participation
- School and classroom climates
- Leadership (Center for Resource Management, 1986)

CRITICAL EDUCATION PRACTICES AND CONCEPTS

In order to better assess the effectiveness of New Hampshire's existing systems change approach in light of the emerging exemplary practices research, a brief presentation of some of the important components associated with effective education for students with disabilities is germane. The concepts of inclusive schools, comprehensive educational programs, and parental involvement are three areas of inquiry that the systems change project in New Hampshire has included in its 5-year plan. Following is a brief overview of each area.

Inclusive Schools

An inclusive school is one that serves the needs of all the children in a given geographic area. Children in inclusive programs go to the neighborhood or home school that they would normally attend if they were not labeled as needing educational support. Children with severe disabilities who attend inclusive schools participate in regular education programs, while receiving individualized programming through adaptive instructional practices and/or cooperative learning activities.

Comprehensive Educational Programs

A comprehensive school program utilizes the zero reject concept to accommodate all children without regard to the severity of their disability or the extent of their educational needs. A quality program includes the following characteristics:

1. It is chronologically age-appropriate for all of its students.
2. Transportation to and from the school is accomplished in a reasonable time period and is integrated to the maximum extent possible.

3. Procedures are carried out regularly to promote interactions between students with disabilities and non-disabled students throughout the whole school.
4. The school reflects, at all times, the natural proportion of students with disabilities in the school district at large.
5. The school program will at all times promote the inclusion of each student in all school activities, including social, recreational, and administrative activities in which non-disabled students of comparable ages are included. (Sailor, 1989, p. 57)

Parent Involvement

Schools that respect the diversity of students also recognize the important role that parents play in defining the vision of the future for their children. It is with this vision in mind that the educational program can be planned and executed. Schools must also recognize the knowledge and expertise that parents have regarding their child's abilities and history.

Lipsky and Gartner (1989) contended that the involvement of parents in the educational process has changed since the passage of PL 94-142 and that ongoing improvements in professional–parent collaboration must be emphasized. Recommending that schools exhibit a greater understanding of the wider range of family needs, she reinforced the notion that school programs must be planned with family support in mind. In fact, a reconceptualization of the parent–professional relationship is necessary to reflect the greater understanding of what is possible for children with severe disabilities. Lipsky and Gartner believe, ultimately, "they [parents and professionals] will be equal partners with differing strengths in addressing a shared task, that is, the education and growth of children" (p. 175).

BARRIERS AND SUPPORTS TO INCLUSIVE EDUCATION

Problem Areas and Barriers

While there is an increased level of activity concerning inclusive education in New Hampshire, there are still many perceived barriers and problem areas that will require attention and solutions before systemic changes can be achieved. In interviews with special education directors throughout the state, the following issues emerged as the most challenging in making changes in existing programs.

Fear of Change Changes in programs and traditional approaches to services create discomfort for teachers, administrators, and parents, mostly due to fear of the unknown.

Fear of Incompetence Regular classroom teachers feel inadequate to teach and deal with students they perceive to be special or difficult. Feelings of inadequacy are accompanied by concerns that appropriate supports will not be available when these new students enter their classrooms, particularly students with challenging behaviors.

Lack of Qualified Personnel The availability of regular classroom educators with training in working with students with special needs is almost nonexistent, and special education personnel with training relevant to inclusion are limited. Personnel shortages across all disciplines relating to special education is particularly acute in the northern rural tier of New Hampshire. Teacher preparation programs need to incorporate the exemplary practices literature immediately so that the teaching pool can provide teachers with the needed competencies in the near future in order to meet the critical labor shortage in the profession.

Lack of Space Availability of classroom space is not an uncommon concern in most parts of the state. There is the perception that reintegrating students will require new or additional space, which is not always available.

Accessibility Issues Many schools are inaccessible to students with physical disabilities, and to make them accessible is a major expense for some local educational agencies.

Attitudes Attitudes in line with stereotypes about people with disabilities hinder the acceptance of students by regular education personnel. Added to this are negative attitudes about specific students in some districts, particularly toward students known as having behavior problems in classrooms.

Adherence to Traditional Approaches The regional collaborative is an educational concept firmly rooted in the rurality of New Hampshire and is widely believed to provide an economical approach to educating students perceived as high cost and in need of exceptionally specialized services. Concerns abound regarding the return of students from these separate, cost-shared classrooms to their home schools. Generally, the perception is that greater dollar allocations will be required to educate these students individually, at a time when increases in local school budgets are unlikely and no new funds are expected from state or federal sources.

Variables that Predict Successful Inclusion

The California Research Institute has conducted interviews with principals in schools throughout the country that are implementing successful inclusive programs. At least eight variables emerged as critical aspects of those successful programs:

1. A clear philosophy
2. Proactive, committed leadership
3. A stable school environment
4. Strong support from central administration
5. Parent involvement
6. Use of instructional strategies with demonstrated effectiveness for heterogeneous groups of students
7. An emphasis on preparation and planning
8. Collaborative teamwork between regular education classroom teachers and special education support staff (California Research Institute, 1991)

Collaborative Consultation Many people believe that the foundation upon which successful inclusive school programs are developed is collaboration between regular education classroom teachers and other support staff (Thousand & Villa, 1988; West & Brown, 1987; West & Cannon, 1988). Consultation among educators is recognized as a promising exemplary practice in achieving maximally effective instruction in regular education classroom settings for students with disabilities (Conoley & Conoley, 1988; Robinson, 1990; West & Brown, 1987; West & Cannon, 1988; West, Idol, & Cannon, 1989; Zins, Greden, Curtis, Ponti, 1988). The proven benefits of adult cooperation in enhancing problem-solving outcomes support the logic of collaborative versus unilateral functioning (Johnson & Johnson, 1987; Thousand & Villa, 1988).

Successful consultation outcomes in educational programming for students with severe disabilities depend on the existence of shared ownership, shared responsibility, cooperation, and mutual support that characterize healthy and effective educational team functioning (Ford, 1989; Johnson & Johnson, 1987; Thousand & Villa, 1988). "Collaborative consultation" was developed by Tharp and Wetzel (1969) and adapted for educational settings by Idol, Paolucci-Whitcomb, and Nevin (1986). It assumes a parity of skills among all educational team members in a cooperative, problem-solving dynamic relationship rather than relying on a model of expert, unilateral consultation. Students whose educational teams consult collaboratively reap the benefits of individually designed, quality instructional interventions that synthesize the skills of a variety of professional, paraprofessional, parent, and community experts (Idol et al., 1986). Teachers benefit from the pool of expertise available to them through such a cooperative approach to instructional problem-solving in responding to students' diverse needs (Thousand & Villa, 1988).

The importance of specific interpersonal collaborative skills, in addition to technical educational skills, for effective consultation among educational team members is well-documented (Carter, 1989; Idol et al., 1986; Pugach & Johnson, 1988; Zins et al., 1988). Idol and West describe consultation as an "artful science, with training required in both the technical skills of effective teaching . . . as well as in communicative/interactive and problem solving skills" (West et al., 1989, p. viii). West and Cannon (1988) identified 47 interactive communication and problem-solving skills deemed essential to the effective collaborative consultation in addition to technical teaching skills such as curriculum-based assessment, curricular modification, classroom and behavior management, and data-based instruction. These technical teaching skills define one component of the collaborative consultation model and are also considered to be among a set of exemplary practice quality indicators for students who have severe disabilities.

Schools that value and strive for effective instruction within an inclusive model must also adopt and apply several additional exemplary practices specific to the educational needs of students with severe disabilities, including: 1) use of functional, community referenced curricula; 2) age-appropriate placement and activities; 3) integrated delivery of related services; and 4) comprehensive, coordinated transition to adult life (Fox et al., 1987; Meyer, Eichinger, & Park Lee, 1987).

Supportive School Climate and Structure While West and Brown (1987) found that consultation is frequently a job expectation for special education support teachers, few schools delineate that function in job descriptions, and rarely are skills specific to accomplishing effective collaborative consultation included in teacher preparation programs. Likewise, school structures that support collaboration (e.g., time to meet, school climate condusive to cooperation among colleagues, flexible scheduling options for service provision, essential funding) are rarely in place. Difficulty in implementing the collaborative consultative model may be traced to a lack of effective communication or problem-solving skills and/or inadequate systemic and organizational support (Carter, 1989; Johnson & Johnson, 1987). Problematic, misplaced attributions by regular education classroom teachers may incorrectly blame student characteristics or lack of skill in the support teacher for the difficulty; this would reflect a weak sense of teacher ownership for the instruction of all students and result in decreased receptivity to the collaborative consultative problem-solving process (San-Nicholas & Moore, 1989).

IMPETUS FOR SCHOOL RESTRUCTURING

While the inclusive education movement is guided by parent and professional concerns about the quality of life for students with severe disabilities, the restructuring or effective schools movement has its foundation in concerns about the educational and post-educational performance of typical students, students who are at risk because of their race or culture, and students with mild disabilities (Brookover et al., 1982; Gartner & Lipsky, 1987). Educational restructuring has been characterized by teacher empowerment; site based management; involvement of students in having some control over the learning process; increased reliance on collaboration between classroom teachers and support staff; and a total reexamination of how public education is structured, managed, evaluated, and, in some cases, funded (Pugach & Johnson, 1989; Villa & Thousand, 1993; West, 1990). Not coincidentally, the same variables that have been shown to be indicators of successful inclusive schools are also strongly correlated with successful restructuring efforts (Harris, 1990; Villa & Thousand, 1993). These efforts require an understanding of the change process itself. Change results from systematic and calculating efforts, not casual adherence to a set of principles.

Change: A Misunderstood Process

Years of failed educational reform have resulted in the need to assess present knowledge more critically and to describe it. According to Fullan and Miles (1992), the following seven major barriers impede progress toward an educational system that includes all students:

1. Faulty maps of change
2. Complex problems that are treated simplistically, with little appreciation of their interrelationships
3. The adoption of external innovations for opportunistic reasons rather than to solve a particular problem
4. Impatient and superficial solutions introduced too quickly in an atmosphere of crisis
5. Misunderstanding that resistance is a process that reflects natural responses to transitions and normally slows down the process of change
6. Attrition of pockets of success due to failure to institutionalize an innovation by building into it the normal structures and practices of the organization
7. Misuse of knowledge about the change process

These barriers must be integrated into a systems change effort focused on reform and inclusion. Beyond these barriers, Fullan and Miles (1992) have generated a *proposition for success,* some of the themes of which has been utilized in the New Hampshire systems change process. The proposition uses the following seven themes:

1. *Understand that all change involves learning.* Furthermore, all learning involves coming to understand in order to be good at something new. Thus, systems change both conceptually and financially must support frequent in-service training time for collaborative planning and an understanding that learning will be gradual.
2. *Change is a journey, not a blueprint.* The message is not the traditional "plan, then do" but "do, then plan . . . and do and plan some more" (Fullan & Miles, 1992, p. 749). Even the development of a shared vision that is central to reform is better thought of as a journey in which people's sense of purpose is identified, considered, and continuously shaped and reshaped (Fullan & Miles, 1992). The systems change project has built in the role of educational consultant—one who is prepared to work through the long haul with a district and help that district to record its journey and realize the strengths and weaknesses of the planning.
3. *Problems are our friends.* Effective responses to complex situations cannot be developed unless we actively seek and confront real problems that are difficult to solve. By initially focusing on individual students and resolving the issues surrounding them, a district can learn valuable lessons, identify barriers, and discover leaders and those who are more hesitant. Often, system problems appear too large and unwieldy; however, these same problems associated with an individual student are solvable and, hence, become lessons for larger systems change.
4. *Change is resource hungry.* Change involves additional resources for training, for substitutes, for new materials, for new space, and above all, for time. This notion presents a particular dilemma for externally funded projects. New Hampshire's systems change project has chosen not to provide any direct fi-

nancial support to school districts involved in the change process. Instead the project finances technical assistance, substitute teachers, ongoing consultation, materials, and so forth. Participants in the project have learned that funding a new inclusion facilitator, for example, can result in dependency and, ultimately, the change process will fail when the funding is terminated. Therefore, funding is focused on learning and reorganization rather than additional personnel and offsetting expenses associated with change.

5. *Change requires the power to manage it.* Initiatives require that substantial effort be devoted to such tasks as monitoring implementation, keeping everyone informed of activities and progress, linking multiple change projects, identifying unsolved problems, and taking clear coping action. Each school district associated with effective systemic change has a strong leader and a strong task force dedicated to the change process. Districts identify their own goals, identify their own leadership teams, and monitor their own progress. Change can be facilitated from the outside, but it cannot be managed from the outside.
6. *Change is systemic.* Reform must focus on the development and interrelationships of all the main components of the system simultaneously, including curriculum, teaching and teacher development, community, and student support systems. Also reform must focus not just on structure, policy, and regulations but also on the culture of the system. Again, it is clear that policy forums and task forces independent of action at the local level do not capitalize on the potential for change.
7. *All large-scale change is implemented locally and cannot be accomplished from afar.* Outside agencies such as universities and alliances have critical—though decidedly nontraditional—roles to play (Fullan & Miles, 1992, pp. 751–752). Too often universities and external researchers have been the impetus for change in schools, rather than the reform being generated from the school and community. Obviously, this is a problem and must be overcome. One method of doing so used by New Hampshire's project was first to provide general education on the topic of school inclusion and then to solicit requests for technical assistance and training. In fact, each year the project selected four sites from a pool of over 15. This permitted the project to choose schools that had the strongest chance for success and demonstrated the most commitment. Some of the early systems change sites that had success provided demonstrations for other school districts. Additionally, successful districts became mentors for other districts in the process of change. The process of mentorship facilitates the process of ownership and the removal of the locus of change from the university.

Federal Initiatives

School reform is a popular and necessary concept given the less than favorable outcomes for young people in the United States. Most of the rhetoric revolves around regular education. However, the overwhelming concepts associated with the Alliance for Effective Schools, for example, reflect the kind of changes and strategies necessary to change the ways in which this country educates children with challenges and disabilities. The essence of a new educational philosophy translated into practice calls for a major change in focus from students as passive recipients of knowledge to students as actively engaged workers ultimately responsible for not only education but also their lives. In *Schools for the 21st Century,* Philip Shlechty (1990) argued that educators need to recognize that their business is not simply to teach students but to create "knowledge-workers," young people who develop successful abilities to acquire knowledge and use it in purposeful ways. The principles presented in the next section reflect the assumption by Ted Sizer (*Horace's School: Redesigning the American High School,* 1992) and are essential to the foundations of systems change at the school level. These principles have been articulated by Robert Mackin, Ph.D., at Souhegan High School in Amherst, New Hampshire.

A Community of Learners

At the heart of New Hampshire's belief system is the philosophy that the public schools must strive to be a community of learners in which intellectual development and adaptability to change become driving forces for everyone—students and staff alike—but in which the climate is humane and caring, promoting respect for diversity. The following principles, then, are the fabric of this emerging philosophy.

1. *An intellectual focus* As Ted Sizer asserted, "The school should focus on helping adolescents to learn to use their minds well" (1992, p. 22). The overriding belief must be that every student can and will learn to read, to write, to compute, and to think, and that every student will be academically successful. Educators must strive to establish high standards and expectations as they promote those habits of mind that embrace inquiry and critical reasoning.
2. *Interdisciplinary learning* Knowledge is as interrelated as human experience. From this perspective, the traditional academic disciplines can be arbitrary divisions that fragment knowledge and understanding. The development of connections between kinds of knowledge helps to crystalize understanding and enable problem-solving. New Hampshire is developing interdisciplinary approaches to learning while simultaneously developing curricula that add to student skills, knowledge, and appreciation within the varied academic disciplines.
3. *A few simple, but clear goals* The emphasis must become a *depth* of understanding of those concepts, skills, and attitudes that will be important to lifelong learning, rather than simply breadth of content knowledge. This dominant theme is reflected in the Coalition of Essential Schools' principle "Less is More" meaning that curriculum decisions should be directed at "thorough student mastery and achievement rather than by an effort merely to cover content."

4. *A just community that reflects democratic principles* Schools must become a democracy based upon the rights and responsibilities of individuals to make choices, to share in decisions, to accept consequences, and to expect justice. Clear expectations for behavior must be established that include explicit consequences and fair judicial procedures. Students cannot truly learn to become citizens without opportunities to practice decision-making within a just and democratic school community.
5. *Personalization and interdependence* Schools must strive to be positive, caring places where people share a common pride but where individuals feel a sense of identity, power, and connectedness as well. The culture of the school should reflect trust and confidence, open and honest communication, celebration and humor, caring, and empathy. Students and staff should feel rewarded and recognized. Concern for the development of ethics, values, and character must be made explicit.
6. *An ethic of growth, development, and inquiry* Schools must become communities of learners in which a spirit of inquiry, reflection, and risk-taking prevails. A commitment to mutual support for learning, experimentation, and self-renewal, first and foremost, should exist among teachers, and, in turn, be reflected in the classroom.
7. *Student as worker* Learning must be an active rather than a passive experience. Students need to be responsible for their own learning, engaged in purposeful work rather than simply receiving services from teachers. There are various means of giving students an active role in their education that in turn will allow teachers a role as coach or advisor in addition to the role of presenter of knowledge. As students grow, the greater maturity and experience of older students should lead to greater independence and responsibility culminating in a series of senior portfolios that exhibit synthesis and mastery of knowledge.
8. *Student as giver* Contributions in the way of service to the school or the community must be promoted as an experiential opportunity for students to learn about themselves as well as to gain poise and confidence in dealing with others. Furthermore, community service will foster both an exposure and a responsibility to a larger society. In this context, school should be viewed by students as a privilege and not an obligation.
9. *Home, school, and community partnerships* Given the significant change in family structures and working patterns, the need for creative cooperation between the home and the school has become even greater. Diminished contact by the school with parents and guardians has led to reduced student accountability both at home and at school. Research shows that greater parent involvement in school work increases student achievement. Significant efforts on the part of educators are required to ensure that relationships among students, family, and school are strengthened. At the same time, educators need to recognize that the business community benefits directly from the quality of

the public schools. Local companies and corporations must be invited to serve as resources and as partners in the effort to redefine programs for the twenty-first century.

The principles in this list are not dissimilar from those associated with inclusive education for students with disabilities. The principles and premises are outlined in Table 12.1.

Implementing Inclusion in Restructured Schools

While there are few highly visible schools in the United States that have combined inclusive education initiatives with total school restructuring (e.g., Johnson City, New York and several schools in Vermont), not all aspects of the inclusive education model have had comprehensive descriptions developed, and replication of the model has not been systematically implemented and evaluated (Pugach & Sapon-Shevin, 1987). Answers to the following questions are not apparent from reading the broad array of literature dealing with inclusive education issues. However, they are essential questions in any systems change process.

- What are the relative roles of the principal and special education director if a site-based management model for inclusion is followed?
- What are the new roles of categorically trained and certified special education support teachers?
- What are the relative merits of the inclusion facilitator model versus the noncategorical grade level support teacher model?
- How are state program approval and certification regulations addressed when all students are in the regular education classroom and support staff are working to assist teachers with students who have a wide variety of educational needs?
- How do the building-based support team members support one another through role release, cross-disciplinary training, and collaboration?
- What systems of accountability must be utilized when responsibilities of specialists blur in a noncategorical support model?
- How must the school schedule and staffing patterns change to allow time for collaboration between regular education classroom teachers and support staff.
- How do schools provide community-based training without segregating students with severe disabilities?
- What are some specific examples of how academic curricula or instructional methods can be modified so that the individualized learning objectives of all students are met (especially those of students with the most severe disabilities)?

NEW EDUCATIONAL DIRECTIONS OF LOCAL SCHOOLS IN NEW HAMPSHIRE

New directions are being taken by schools committed to including all of their students in regular education programs. For example, in the 1989–1990 school year,

Table 12.1. Principles of the new philosophy of Souhegan High School as a community of learners

Principles of essential schools	Emerging Souhegan beliefs and practices	Corresponding exemplary practices relative to students with disabilities	Project focus areas that support alignment of essential school principles and inclusion exemplary practices	Project research and evaluation questions (See evaluation section.)
General principles and concepts	Souhegan High School must model a community of learners in which a spirit of inquiry, reflection, and risk-taking prevails.	Students with disabilities should be allowed to participate in activities that provide them with an opportunity to fail as well as an opportunity to succeed.	Provide students and staff with outdoor education experiences at UNHs award-winning Ropes Course to develop interdependence, trust, and enthusiasm for new ideas and experiences.	Are students with disabilities included in the same variety of activities (e.g., senior week, environmental camp, field trips, proms, sporting events) as typical students?
	Students are expected to provide service to the school and community.	Students with disabilities should not always be the recipients of help and support. They should have opportunities to provide assistance and service to others.	Provide technical assistance to staff relative to identifying opportunities for all students, including those with significant disabilities, to participate in community service projects.	Do all students with disabilities have community service on their resumés prior to leaving school?
	Significant efforts on our part are required to ensure that relationships among students, family, and the school are strengthened.	Families should be active partners with the school in the development, implementation, and evaluation of students' educational programs.	Provide staff opportunities for training in productive family–school partnerships.	Are parents satisfied with their role in their child's educational program?
Essential schools are for all students.	The school has adopted a policy of full inclusion of all students with disabilities. There will be no special education and supports will be provided in the regular education class to enable all students to learn.	All students should be fully participating members of regular education classes in their home schools.	Provide opportunities for staff and community members to develop positive attitudes toward and support for full inclusion.	Do a significant majority of students, staff, administrators, and community members actively support full inclusion?

(*continued*)

Table 12.1. *(continued)*

Principles of essential schools	Emerging Souhegan beliefs and practices	Corresponding exemplary practices relative to students with disabilities	Project focus areas that support alignment of essential school principles and inclusion exemplary practices	Project research and evaluation questions (See evaluation section.)
Teaching style and time allotted to achieve mastery will be individualized.		Teachers should use methods and materials that are appropriate for heterogeneous groups of learners. The goal of instruction should be to reach "all of the students some of the time."	Provide opportunities for training of all teachers in multi-level instruction.	Do teachers utilize multi-level instruction and other adaptive teaching approaches?
	Souhegan High School must become a democratic school based upon the rights and responsibilities of individuals to make choices, share in decisions, accept consequences, and expect justice.	Students with disabilities should have the opportunity to make choices similar to those afforded typical students. Students with disabilities should be active in school governance, such as Student Council or Conduct Boards.	Provide training to staff in strategies for teaching students self-determination, communication, self-advocacy, and choice-making skills.	Do students with disabilities have ample opportunities to make choices and express preferences? Are they involved in school governance?
	Clear expectations for behavior must be established that include explicit consequences and fair judicial procedures.	Students with disabilities should have conduct and behavioral expectations that are similar to those of typical students, but modified according to their individual challenges.	Provide training to staff in classroom and individual student behavior management, including strategies for helping students communicate effectively and develop self-control.	Do staff utilize positive, nonaversive, educative behavior management strategies? Do students monitor their own behavior and demonstrate self-control?
Principal and staff must control decisions about curriculum, pedagogy, materials, and time.				

The governing image of the school should be "student as worker."	Learning must be an active rather than a passive experience. Students need to be responsible for their own learning.	Students with disabilities should be involved in the development of their educational plans, selection of courses, and schedule, and they should participate actively in guidance and career planning activities. They should be active participants in classes, not just physically present.	Train staff to use IEP development procedures that are student- and family-centered. Provide training to teachers in the identification of regular education class learning opportunities for students with disabilities.	Are students active participants in the development of their educational programs? Do they enthusiastically participate in classroom lessons and other school activities?
	Knowledge is as interrelated as human experiences. We are developing interdisciplinary approaches to learning.	Students with disabilities need to learn and practice skills across a broad spectrum of environments, with many different people, and in varied situations in order to generalize those skills to novel situations. An interdisciplinary curriculum makes learning of discipline-specific skills more relevant and interesting.	Work collaboratively with staff and administrators to assist them in expanding the curriculum to include knowledge and skills relevant for all students, including those with disabilities.	Does the regular education curriculum accommodate a wide spectrum of students, including those with advanced skills as well as those with few skills in the area?
The dominant pedagogy should be coaching.	There are various means of giving students an active role in their education that in turn will allow teachers a role as coaches or advisors.	Support teachers and staff should be skilled in multi-level instruction, activity-based instruction, cooperative learning, and other student-centered teaching approaches.	Provide opportunities for staff training in adaptive, student-centered teaching, including visitations to and peer support from master teachers from other school districts.	Do teachers use adaptive instructional techniques in their classes?

(*continued*)

Table 12.1. *(continued)*

Principles of essential schools	Emerging Souhegan beliefs and practices	Corresponding exemplary practices relative to students with disabilities	Project focus areas that support alignment of essential school principles and inclusion exemplary practices	Project research and evaluation questions (See evaluation section.)
Students entering secondary school should have demonstrated competence in language arts and elementary mathematics.		Students entering secondary school should have at least 8 years of prior quality education focused on knowledge and skills that will enable them to be fully participating members of their high school community, as well as provide them with a foundation for post-school life (e.g., work, college, technical training).	Collaborate with teachers and administrators to develop guidelines for accommodating high school–age students with disabilities who do not demonstrate competence in language arts and elementary mathematics.	Does the Essential Schools principle of a "set of standards for all" apply to students with disabilities?
Teachers should be directly responsible for no more than 80 students.				
Students who are high school–age who do not demonstrate competence in language arts and elementary mathematics will be given time and support to improve.		All students including those with disabilities should be given the time and support to learn skills and develop knowledge that have been determined as educational priorities for them.	Collaborate with school staff to develop a structure within the school for tutoring and/or remedial assistance that can be utilized by all students, not just those with disabilities.	Are support and remedial services available to all students, not just those with identified disabilities?

School culture should value unanxious expectations, trust, and decency.	Souhegan High School must strive to be a positive, caring place where people share a common pride but where an individual feels a sense of identity, power, and connectedness as well.	Schools should demonstrate respect for each student's gifts and talents. Friendships between students should be intentionally facilitated, when necessary.	Provide training to staff in strategies for infusing diversity issues across the curriculum. Provide training for staff in strategies for developing students' "circles of friends" and sense of belonging to a community.	Do students with disabilities have social networks (e.g., friends, acquaintances) that are as varied and rich as those of typical students?
Staff should be generalists first and specialists second.		Staff supporting classroom teachers should be skilled in the subject area, curriculum modification, classroom and individual behavior management, evaluation and assessment, and facilitation of friendships between students; they must also possess a highly developed level of collaborative skills.	Provide technical assistance to staff and administrators in the development of job descriptions and a staffing support model that is consistent with the values and desired outcomes of a fully inclusive high school.	Do all staff feel comfortable with and demonstrate competence in teaching students with diverse learning styles? Do classroom teachers feel positive about the support given them by other staff?
There should be time for teaming among staff.		Collaboration is a key to successful inclusion, and support teachers should be present at all cluster/house/team meetings.	Provide technical assistance to staff and administrators relative to collaborative teaming.	Do staff demonstrate effective collaborative skills, including communication, efficient use of planning time, conflict resolution, and so forth?

at least 15 SAUs were in various stages of systematic planning to increase the placement of students with severe disabilities in their home schools, including reorganizing their resources to meet this goal. These schools are changing policies that previously contributed to: 1) the segregation of students with severe disabilities, 2) the grouping of students by disability or severity of disability, and/or 3) the out-of-district placement of these students based on the same factors.

The role of the special educator is changing. In six districts, inclusion facilitators are assisting both regular and special educators to modify existing curricula for the regular education classroom to include all students in daily activities and routines. These facilitators consult with regular education classroom teachers on strategies that merge regular education instructional activities with a student's individualized education program goals. Job descriptions for these staff are being revised to reflect the emerging duties associated with facilitating inclusion.

At least five school districts are reviewing the way in which related services, such as occupational, physical, and speech therapies, are being delivered. Through inservice training implementation of classroom-based techniques, and site specific technical assistance, these schools are decreasing their reliance on the traditional pull-out approaches to providing these ancillary services, in favor of teaching the needed skills in regular education school environments and the community.

Other issues being addressed by schools relate to administrative leadership needs, information dissemination to their community, extended year programs, paraprofessional recruitment and training, home–school collaboration, budget reallocation, transportation patterns, and student grading policies. One of the more complex issues surrounds the need for alternative home care for students who are able to receive their educational program in their district, but are unable to live with their families. There is growing evidence that this problem must be solved through multi-agency collaboration within the local community.

Two SAUs have each been working with their area agency for developmental services to develop cooperatively funded programs for students with multiple disabilities. One 16-year-old student is returning from an in-state residential facility to her local school and requires an alternative living situation in her home community due to family circumstances. Another adolescent is no longer able to be maintained in the family home, but can receive his educational services locally. As a result of collaborative planning and resource sharing, more costly placements in out-of-district residential facilities are being avoided in both cases.

In addition to these carefully planned and implemented institutional changes around the state, noteworthy changes for children are occurring daily in local schools. For example:

- James is an 8-year-old 2nd grader with multiple disabilities in a small rural community in central New Hampshire. Last year, he rode a bus to a school located 45 minutes from his home to a classroom for eight students with severe disabilities, none of whom could walk or talk. This year an inclusive school program began. James has been included in all aspects of his 2nd-grade class, in which he is educated with children without disabilities. His teacher, with the help of the special education teacher, has identified appropriate learning goals for James and has merged those goals with daily class activities. James' life has changed dramatically. He rides the regular education school bus with his brother and other friends. He is a member of the art club and is a big supporter of the soccer team.

- In a southern New Hampshire high school, Karen, a 16-year-old freshman, takes regular education courses in word processing, painting, and culinary arts during her morning schedule, similarly to her peers without disabilities, and in the afternoon alternates between community-based instruction and an in-school library job. Karen is the first student with Down syndrome in the history of this school to maintain a regular education high school schedule, with appropriate curriculum modifications geared toward preparation for employment and independent living in the community after graduation. Karen's success has demonstrated to the district that it can provide a more effective and meaningful education for Karen in her home school.
- George has autism, because of which he was previously educated in self-contained classes in special schools and spent 2 years in a residential school for students with severe behavior challenges. Last year, George became a member of the 4th-grade class in his home school. He moved up this year with his class to 5th-grade. He is 12 years old and is learning to write his name and match numbers, words, and letters and is performing classroom jobs along with his peers. George's behavior has become more appropriate. His educational team is pleased at his ability to cope with and to participate in a learning environment not previously made available to him.

The success derived from bold new steps with students previously considered too challenging for participation in the mainstream will ultimately lay the foundation for permanent change in institutional responses and personal attitudes about the learning capabilities of children with severe disabilities. Ongoing program demonstration, encouragement of meaningful parent involvement, and commitments to ongoing statewide inservice training for educators are worthwhile endeavors for the New Hampshire Department of Education and local school districts to pursue in this process. Through the change brought about, the likelihood that students with severe disabilities will become productive, contributing members of their communities upon graduation will increase dramatically.

REFERENCES

Biklen, D. (1985). *Achieving the complete school: Strategies for effective mainstreaming.* New York: Teachers College Press.

Brinker, R.P., & Thorpe, M.E. (1984). Integration of severely handicapped students and the proportion of IEP objectives achieved. *Exceptional Children, 51*(2), 168–175.

Brookover, W., Beamer, L., Efthim, H., Hathaway, L., Miller, J., & Tornatsky, L. (1982).

Creating effective schools: An in-service program for enhancing school learning climate and achievement. Holmes Beach, FL: Learning Publications, Inc.
Brown v. Board of Education, 347 US 483 (1954).
Brown, L., Long, E., Udvari, A., Davis, L., VanDeventer, P., Ahlgren, C., Johnson, F., Gruenewald, L., & Jorgensen, J. (1989). The home school: Why students with severe intellectual disabilities must attend the schools of their brothers, sisters, friends and neighbors. *Journal of The Association for Persons with Severe Handicaps, 14*, 1–7.
Brown, L., Nietupski, J., & Hamre-Nietupski, S. (1976). The criterion of ultimate functioning. In M. Thomas (Ed.), *Hey! Don't forget about me* (pp. 2–15). Reston, VA: Council for Exceptional Children.
Brown, L., Rogan, P., Shiraga, B., Albright, K., Kessler, K., Bryson, F., VanDeventer, P., & Loomis, R. (1987). *A vocational follow up evaluation of the 1984–1986 Madison Metropolitan School District graduates with severe intellectual disabilities*. Madison: University of Wisconsin and Madison Metropolitan School District.
California Research Institute. (1991). Bridging the gap: critical systems change activities. *The Association for Persons with Severe Handicaps Newsletter, 2*(2), 7–10.
Carter, J. (1989). The fact and fiction of consultation. *Academic Therapy, 25*, 231–242.
Center for Resource Management, Inc. (1986). *Effectiveness indicators for special education*. Hampton, NH: Author.
Conoley, J.C., & Conoley, C.W. (1988). Useful theories in school-based consultation. *Remedial and Special Education (RASE), 9*, 14–20.
Edgar, E., Levine, P., & Maddox, M. (1985). *Washington State follow-up data of postsecondary special education students*. Seattle: Networking and Evaluation Team, University of Washington.
Elksnin, L.L., & Elksnin, N. (1989). Collaborative consultation: Improving parent-teacher communication. *Academic Therapy, January*, 261–269.
Ford, A. (1989). *You can't do it alone: Using a team approach*. Unpublished manuscript.
Fox, W., Thousand, J., Williams, W., Fox, T., Towne, P., Reid, R., Conn-Powers, C., & Calcagni, L. (1987). *Best educational practices '87: Educating learners with severe handicaps*. Burlington: University of Vermont, Center for Developmental Disabilities.
Fullan, M.G., & Miles, M.B. (1992). Getting reform right: What works and what doesn't. *Phi Delta Kappan, June*, 745–752.
Gartner, A., & Lipsky, D. (1987). Beyond special education: Toward a quality system for all students. *Harvard Educational Review, 57*, 367–395.
Halvorsen, A., & Sailor, W. (1990). Integration of students with severe and profound disabilities: A review of research. In R. Gaylord-Ross (Ed.), *Issues and research in special education* (pp. 110–172). New York: Teachers College Press.
Harris, K. (1990). Meeting diverse needs through collaborative consultation. In S. Stainback & W. Stainback (Eds.), *Support networks for inclusive schooling: Interdependent integrated education* (pp. 139–150). Baltimore: Paul H. Brookes Publishing Co.
Hasazi, S., Gordon, L., & Roe, C. (1985). Factors associated with the employment status of handicapped youth exiting high school from 1979 to 1983. *Exceptional Children, 51*(6), 455–469.
Idol, L., Paolucci-Whitcomb, P., & Nevin, A. (1986). *Collaborative consultation*. Rockville, MD: Aspen Publishers.
Johnson, D.W., & Johnson, R.T. (1987). Research shows the benefits of adult cooperation. *Educational Leadership, 45*, 27–30.
Jorgensen, C. (1990). Inclusive education in New Hampshire: The challenge for the 1990's. *The New Hampshire Challenge, Winter*, 1–3.
Long, J.W. (1987). The wilderness lab comes of age. *Training and Development Journal, March*, 30–39.
Meyer, L.H., Eichinger, J., & Park-Lee, S. (1987). A validation of quality indicators in

educational programs for students with severe handicaps. *Journal of The Association for Persons with Severe Handicaps, 12*(4), 251–263.

New Hampshire Special Education Information System. (1989, November). *Monthly census reports.*

New York State Association for Retarded Children v. Carey (612 F.2d 644, 2d Cir. 1979).

Nisbet, J. (1989). *Annual Report of the Institute on Disability.* Durham, New Hampshire.

PARC II (C.A. No. 71-42, 3d Cir. June 14, 1983).

PARC v. Commonwealth of Pennsylvania, 334 F. Supp. 1257 (E.D. Penn. 1971).

Powers, S., Schuh, M.C., Tashie, C., Sgambati, F.A., Nisbet, J.A., & Kennedy, R.T. (in press). *The status of integrated educational services for students with severe disabilities in New Hampshire.* Durham: University of New Hampshire, Institute on Disability.

Pugach, M.C., & Johnson, L.J. (1988). Rethinking the relationship between consultation and collaborative problem-solving. *Focus on Exceptional Children, 21,* 4–8.

Pugach, M.C., & Johnson, L.J. (1989). The challenge of implementing collaboration between general and special education. *Exceptional Children, 56,* 232–235.

Pugach, M., & Sapon-Shevin, M. (1987). New agendas for special education policy: What the national reports haven't said. *Exceptional Children, 53*(4), 295–299.

Robinson, V. (1990). Regular education initiative: Debate on the current state and future promise of a new approach to educating children with disabilities. *Counterpoint, Fall,* 5.

Roncker v. Walter (700 F 2d 1058, 6th Cir. 1983).

Rowe, L. (1989, May). *A description of the Johnson City, New York, School District.* Paper presented at the meeting of the New Hampshire Special Education Administrators, Concord, New Hampshire.

Sailor, W. (1989). The educational, social, and vocational integration of students with the most severe disabilities. In D.K. Lipsky & A. Gartner (Eds.), *Beyond separate education: Quality education for all* (pp. 53–74) Baltimore: Paul H. Brookes Publishing Co.

San-Nicholas, G., & Moore, M. (1989). *Attributions about consultation outcomes by special and regular educators.* Monograph.

Schlechty, P. (1990). Schools for the 21st century: *Leadership imperative for educational reform.* San Francisco: Jossey-Bass.

Sizer, T. (1992). *Horace's school: Redesigning the American high school.* Boston: Houghton Mifflin.

Stainback, W., & Stainback, S. (1984). A rationale for the merger of special and regular education. *Exceptional Children, 51*(2), 102–111.

Stainback, W., Stainback, S., & Bunch, G. (1989). A rationale for the merger of regular and special education. In S. Stainback, W. Stainback, & M. Forest (Eds.), *Educating all students in the mainstream of regular education* (pp. 15–26). Baltimore: Paul H. Brookes Publishing Co.

Stainback, S., Stainback, W., & Forest, M. (Eds.). (1989). *Educating all children in the mainstream of regular education.* Baltimore: Paul H. Brookes Publishing Co.

Strully, J., & Strully, C. (1987). Friendship and our children. *Journal of The Association for Persons with Severe Handicaps, 10*(4), 224–227.

Taylor, S.J., Biklen, D., & Knoll, J. (1987). *Community integration for people with severe disabilities.* New York: Teachers College Press, Columbia University.

Taylor, S.J., Racino, J., Knoll, J., & Lutfiyya, Z. (1987). *The nonrestrictive environment: Community integration for people with the most severe disabilities.* Syracuse: Human Policy Press.

Tharp, R., & Wetzel, R. (1969). *Behavior modification in the natural environment.* New York: Academic Press.

Thousand, J., & Villa, R. (1988). Enhancing success in heterogeneous classrooms and schools: The power of partnerships. *Teacher Education and Special Education, 11,* 144–154.

Thousand, J.S., & Villa, R.A. (1989). Enhancing success in heterogeneous schools. In S. Stainback, W. Stainback, & M. Forest (Eds.), *Educating all students in the mainstream of regular education* (pp. 89–103). Baltimore: Paul H. Brookes Publishing Co.
Thousand, J.S., & Villa, R.A. (1992). Collaborative teams: A powerful tool in school restructuring. In R.A. Villa, J.S. Thousand, W. Stainback, & S. Stainback (Eds.), *Restructuring for caring and effective education: An administrative guide to creating heterogeneous schools* (pp. 73–108). Baltimore: Paul H. Brookes Publishing Co.
Villa, R., & Thousand, J. (1993). Redefining the role of the special educator and other support personnel. In J. Putnam (Ed.), *Cooperative learning and strategies for inclusion: Celebrating diversity in the classroom* (pp. 57–92). Baltimore: Paul H. Brookes Publishing Co.
Voeltz, L. (1982). Effects of structured interactions with severely handicapped peers on children's attitudes. *American Journal of Mental Deficiency, 86*(4), 380–390.
Voeltz, L., Johnson, R., & McQuarter, R. (1983). *The integration of school-aged children and youth with severe disabilities: A comprehensive bibliography and a selective review of research and program development needs to address discrepancies in the state of the art.* Minneapolis: Minnesota Consortium Institute.
Wang, M.C., Reynolds, M.C., & Walberg, H.J. (1986). Rethinking special education. *Educational Leadership, 44,* 26–31.
Wehman, P., Kregel, J., & Zollers, K. (1984). *A follow-up of mentally retarded graduates of vocational and independent living skills in Virginia.* Manuscript in preparation.
West, F. (1990). Educational collaboration in the restructuring of schools. *Journal of Educational and Psychological Consultation, 1*(1), 23–40.
West, F.J., & Brown, P.A. (1987). State departments of education policies on consultation in special education: The state of the states. *Remedial and Special Education (RASE), 8,* 45–51.
West, F.J., & Cannon, G.S. (1988). Essential collaborative consultation competencies for regular and special educators. *Journal of Learning Disabilities, 21,* 56–63.
West, F.J., Idol, L., & Cannon, G. (1989). *Collaboration in the schools: An in-service and preservice curriculum for teachers, support staff, and administrators (Instructor's manual).* Austin: PRO-ED.
Will, M. (1986). *Educating students with learning problems—A shared responsibility.* Washington, DC: United States Department of Education.
Wojciehowski, T., & Burton, L. (1985). *The special education teacher as consultant. Who? Me!* Monograph.
Zins, J.E., Greden, J.L., Curtis, M.J., & Ponti, C.R. (1988). *Helping students succeed in the regular classroom.* San Francisco: Jossey-Bass.
Zollers, N., Conroy, J., Hess, C., & Newman, E. (1984). *Transition from school to work.* Philadelphia: Department of Health and Human Services.

13

Trying To Play Together

Competing Paradigms in Approaches to Inclusion Through Recreation and Leisure

Bruce C. Blaney and Elissa L. Freud

The study upon which this chapter is based drew upon the experiences of 12 people with disabilities to discover what factors promote successful community inclusion in recreation/leisure activities and settings. What emerged from the case studies was the interaction of and often contest between two distinctive approaches—what the authors eventually came to call the recreational paradigm and the community membership paradigm. To the extent that the recreational approach was dominant, a platform for social inclusion was put in place. The realization of community membership and relationships, however, seldom occurred. In those case studies, in which the community membership paradigm was widely shared and understood, an impressive level of community inclusion was achieved in recreational activities settings.

The following case studies of Barbara Anne, Paul, and Brian illustrate that there is much to celebrate. The issue at hand has less to do with inclusion versus segregation and more to do with what is meant by inclusion and how to achieve it. At the same time, the personal stories here are sobering in that they reveal that the key words of the so-called new way of thinking—choice, membership, and, above all, inclusion—represent more of an ambiguous straining toward a new values base than guiding principles for policy and practice. Indeed, as the embracing the-

This chapter is based on research supported by Grant #90DD0178/01, funded by the Administration on Developmental Disabilities, to the Human Services Research Institute in Cambridge, Massachusetts. All names and places appearing in this chapter have been changed to protect confidentiality.

sis of this book suggests, the field is in the midst of a paradigm shift. Therefore, it continually will be confronted by old practices couched in new language and new practices that struggle for language not yet invented. The research presented in this chapter aspires to shed light on some mighty abstractions by taking a person-centered and analytic look at specific examples of what actors in the field of developmental disabilities currently describe as successful social inclusion through recreation and leisure.

A WORKING DEFINITION OF SOCIAL INCLUSION

We met Barbara Anne, Paul, and Brian through a national search for individuals who had experienced exemplary social inclusion through recreation and leisure. The key guide in this search was an operational definition of social inclusion that the authors conceptualized as occurring across the five dimensions described below:

- The frequency with which an inclusive activity occurs is a consideration. An activity that occurs on a weekly basis, such as attending a neighborhood church, offers far more opportunities for interaction than does an activity that might be very interesting but happens only once a year, such as attending a state fair.
- The duration of an activity affects the level of inclusion. While it is true that there is some level of inclusion that comes from short interactions between people with and people without disabilities, it is also true that longer duration offers greater opportunities for interaction. Thus, other things being equal, a relatively long activity, such as an evening visit, is likely to offer more inclusion than a relatively brief exchange in line at a grocery store.
- Intensity of interaction is more difficult to measure. Social science researchers are used to counting frequencies and timing durations. However, intensity of interaction is a more ethereal dimension. Imagine two situations with identical frequencies and durations, but clearly different levels of intensity. For example, once a week, two pairs of people spend an hour with each other. The two people in one pair ride a bus together, sit side by side, but do not speak and barely acknowledge each other's presence. The two people in the other pair are engaged in a special time that they reserve each week to be with each other as best friends. Clearly, the intensity of the latter experience makes it more inclusive than the former.
- Proportion is a dimension of inclusion because of the importance of promoting experiences for people with disabilities in situations in which there is a natural proportion of people with and without disabilities. One or two people without disabilities at a recreation program that serves 100 people with disabilities cannot offer as much inclusion as a situation in which one or two children with disabilities are an integral part of a neighborhood soccer team composed mainly of children without disabilities.

- Symmetry can be seen as the highest order of the various dimensions because it addresses the relative status of the individuals involved in the inclusive activity. There are three types of symmetry; they are described below:

  The person with a disability is a recipient. This type of relationship is often promoted by big brother/big sister types of programs. In this type of relationship, the person without a disability clearly is there as the helper, and the person with a disability is seen as the recipient of some form of assistance.

  The person with a disability is equal with the person without a disability. This type of relationship is a true peer relationship. An example is including a child with a disability as a regular member of a sports team.

  The person without a disability is a recipient. In this type of relationship the person with a disability is not the recipient in the relationship, and not only equal in the relationship; rather that person is what may be called the benefactor in the relationship. These relationships are far rarer than the previous two.

It is important to note that the authors' definition of social inclusion at the outset was much closer to what they later would conceptualize as the community membership paradigm. What the authors did not anticipate was that the dominant paradigm informing the case studies, which they named the recreational paradigm, while taking account of the frequency, duration, and proportion of inclusive activities, was unclear about and typically ignored the higher order dimensions of intensity and symmetry. The latter represent a focus on enduring and deep relationships and on the achievement of valued roles in one's community as a contributing member. As discussed below, inclusive efforts concerning people with disabilities remain caught in the instrumental and physical aspects of recreation/leisure, while consciously encompassing the social and existential dimensions is left to a small number of exemplary pilot projects and individuals.

BARBARA ANNE BECK

Carole Beck described her daughter, Barbara Anne, in the following way:

> Barbara Anne has cerebral palsy. She is severely handicapped. She is nonverbal. She cannot walk or sit, and she cannot use her hands. She is completely dependent on others. She is also beautiful, intelligent, and has more courage than anyone I know. Barbara Anne is now 13.

Barbara Anne Beck and her family live in Woodsville, Tennessee, a small town outside of Nashville. Her mother is a homemaker and her father, a professional. For the past 2 years Barbara Anne has been a cheerleader for her middle school. And, as her friends hasten to add, she is not just a cheerleader, but an outstanding cheerleader. In addition to cheerleading, Barbara Anne enjoys close friendships and an elaborate social life including slumber parties, girl scouts, and boyfriends. Barbara Anne's life appears rich and full in terms of activities, roles, and relationships rooted in mutuality, respect, and love.

The Key Role of Barbara Anne's Mother, Carole

Carole Beck describes her role in her daughter's life as leading Barbara Anne where Barbara Anne wants to go. And Barbara Anne wants to go where everybody her age is going. Listening to Carole's story, one is impressed with her mindfulness of planning. She explains, "First I decide what Barbara Anne wants from the experience, and then I make a list of all the things I need to do and put in place to make sure she has the kind of experience she wants." In order to ensure that Barbara Anne was where she wanted to be, the family moved from another town, from a school system where Barbara Anne "stayed shut up all day and never saw normal children." They moved to their current community because the special education regional director and school principal were known to be committed to social and educational inclusion.

In Barbara Anne's afterschool life, her mother is equally mindful of planning: In order to create a context of reciprocity in which Barbara Anne might meet her future friends on both an equal and mutually enjoyable plane, Carole would plan settings that would be fun for both Barbara Anne and her friends and include activities such as helping Barbara Anne to rent videotapes, make popcorn, or go swimming. Carole is a gifted designer and organizer of natural supports—a gifted natural. She combines active listening to her daughter's desires and interests with the capacity to create settings that support fulfilling them. She does all this systematically and consciously, though the planning has at this point become second nature.

Barbara Anne's Friend as Emergent Bridge-Builder

For most of Barbara Anne's childhood, she has had close friends without disabilities. Patsy, who is 12 years old, has known Barbara Anne since the 1st grade and is one of her closest friends. What is striking about Patsy is what might be described as her sense of mission in the friendship. Patsy experiences her commitment to Barbara Anne not out of a concern for Barbara Anne's disabilities but from a deep regard for Barbara Anne's abilities, gifts, and talents. Patsy explained:

> Barbara Anne doesn't want people to do things for her. She types her own homework on her computer. I can always figure out what she's saying. She points and has great facial expressions. She loves to dance and cheer. She knows when there's something wrong: When her brother was in Desert Storm, Barbara Anne comforted her mother. She's like me, only she can't walk or talk. I learn from her all the time.

Patsy's role in the conversation in which she made these comments was to introduce us to her friend as a person we would love to come to know, someone just like us, with all sorts of attractive qualities. Patsy has become an impressively effective bridge-builder, which she demonstrated when she was the key person in enabling Barbara Anne to become a leading member of the cheerleading squad. She explained:

> Barbara Anne wanted to try out for cheerleading, and the principal said it was O.K. The judges, cheerleaders from other schools, didn't choose her for the squad, because

> they had never met anyone like her. So I and another friend of Barbara Anne's went to the cheerleading coach and asked her to let Barbara Anne join the squad. The coach made up a new position for Barbara Anne called the "spirit leader." But the other kids who had tried out for the team and had not make it were mad because Barbara Anne was getting a special deal. Barbara Anne heard about their hurt feelings and decided not to join. But we told her that we really wanted her on the squad, so she finally joined. Something you should know is that Barbara Anne is not only a cheerleader but one of the best cheerleaders. At first we noticed that in the practices Barbara Anne was there but on the sidelines. So we went to the coach and asked her to put Barbara Anne at the center of the squad. She let us do that. Now, Barbara Anne dances and cheers better than most of the squad. The girls who had been angry about Barbara Anne aren't angry now because they know that she is a better cheerleader than they could ever be.

Patsy has become a conscious teacher and advocate for her friend and for the core insights and values of the new paradigm: Supports have to do with choices and gifts, not paternalistic controls and deficits. Patsy expresses these key principles more articulately and passionately than the professionals in Barbara Anne's life.

A Partnership for Inclusion at the Woodsville School

Barbara Anne attended the Woodsville School, where everyone, from the regional special education director, to the principal, to the special education teachers, to the regular education teachers, to the classroom aides, to the bus driver is committed to students with disabilities being in the center of all school activities. This value is expressed in an active and well-supported inclusion effort, using, for example, a classroom aide who accompanies Barbara Anne to her classes and a disability awareness curriculum beginning in kindergarten. Cathy Potts, leader of the special education effort in the region, prides herself on an assertive commitment to eliminating all forms of labeling and was the initiator of the disability educational program. She explained:

> Woodsville, as is true with many small towns, has no formal recreation providers, making the school system (and frequently religious organizations) the key nexus for formal and informal information, referral, and, in many cases, actual provision of recreational opportunities for kids. The values and knowledge base, including the quality of the leadership of the school system, is even more important in such communities than in urban areas, which offer more options. In this instance, the school staff was eager to develop a partnership with Barbara Anne and her parents to support and challenge her to join the Woodsville community through its recreational opportunities, especially Girl Scouts and cheerleading.

The View of Family Support as a Private Matter

There is much to affirm in Barbara Anne's story: her mother's gifted planning, her friend Patsy's growth in understanding and contribution to Barbara Anne's quality of life, the partnership among the school staff, Barbara Anne, her family, and her friends, all combine to create the richness, texture, and quality of Barbara Anne's life. But the glass is half full and half empty. The fragile nature of the foundation for all this is captured in the following anecdote told by Barbara Anne's mother:

> During my recent illness the staff of Barbara Anne's school really rallied around her and our family. The bus driver and bus monitor lifted Barbara Anne onto the bus each morning. The special ed. teachers and aides assisted in Barbara Anne's attending after-school events. And on several occasions teachers took her on overnights to spend with their families. As soon as I had recovered, all these responsibilities were suddenly mine again—all the planning, all the lifting and transporting, all the assistance with her recreation. My husband and I have not had a date in the past 10 years. I am tired.

Both the vulnerability and opportunity in Barbara Anne's life, are contained, on the one hand, in the near exhaustion of her mother, who is her key support person, and, on the other hand, in the commitment and capacity of those in Barbara Anne's school community to provide an effective network of support. The problem is that these supports are seen by those who provide them as extraordinary interventions required by a health crisis, rather than as supports that are, quite simply, necessary most of the time if the Becks are to have anything resembling a normal family life. "Family support is whatever it takes to experience the quality of family life enjoyed by families who do not have members with a disability" (Agosta, Bradley, & Knoll, 1992, p. 1). Included are the provision of routine family supports such as respite, transportation, futures planning, and case management. All these supports and many more are the responsibility of the Beck family, specifically Carole Beck. In the main, she feels it has to be this way. The community, including Carole Beck, views raising Barbara Anne and the arrangements for Barbara Anne's social and recreational life to be a private matter. Indeed, Carole Beck was surprised to learn that some parts of the United States do provide family supports that would address much of the emotional and physical depletion she is experiencing.

A Limited Vision of Inclusion

Although both Barbara Anne's mother and the staff of her school were delighted with the extent of Barbara Anne's inclusion in the recreational life of the community, a clear and widely shared vision and understanding of social inclusion were missing. Specifically, the school highly valued and uncritically promoted Barbara Anne's participation in the Special Olympics, a segregated program.

The vision that currently guides Barbara Anne's mother and the school staff is that Barbara Anne should have fulfilling, even exciting recreational experiences. Such experiences are viewed as the primary goal of supportive arrangements. But in this view, whether such experiences are socially inclusive or segregated is less prominent, or, more often, a nonissue. This lack of an in-depth understanding of social inclusion constitutes one of the major vulnerabilities in the supports around Barbara Anne. A widely shared understanding of community membership and personal relationships as the goals of recreational activities rather than the current belief that the recreational experience is a goal in itself would represent a crucial safeguard for the gains that have occurred for Barbara Anne and her community.

PAUL HUNT

Paul Hunt is such an impressively competent 38-year-old man that it is difficult to discern what motivated his mother's physician to discourage her from taking him home, by saying, "If you take him home, he'll die." Paul went from his birth hospital to the hospital at Pinecrest State School, still the largest institution in Louisiana, for people labeled as having mental retardation. When he was 15 he returned to Baton Rouge to live with his family. His father ran a small sign-painting business out of their home, which, over the next 23 years, was Paul's main source of employment and income.

By the time he was in his 30s Paul had outgrown the opportunities offered within his family and was communicating his frustration through various anti-social behaviors. Four years ago his sister heard about a supported living project beginning in Crawford, a small town not far from Baton Rouge, and invited Paul to explore the possibilities of a more independent lifestyle.

The Community Opportunities Project

Paul has lived in Crawford for more than 2 years with the assistance of Community Opportunities, a pilot project funded by the Louisiana Developmental Disabilities Planning Council. Described as supported living, the pilot is intended to lead the Louisiana disability service system (which has the second highest rate of institutionalization in the United States and, in addition, has relied heaving on ICF/MR models for its community-based services) into a new paradigm emphasizing self-determination, personalized supports, and community membership.

Since moving to Crawford, Paul, whose life had been defined entirely in terms of relationships and roles within the orbit of his family and of the institutional system, has entered a variety of new roles and relationships, including the following:

- Church member
- Fiancé
- Health club member
- Good neighbor
- Regular at Fred's Country Western Bar
- Regular at the town coffee shop
- Self-advocate with state-wide recognition

At the intersection of all these roles and relationships, Paul is experiencing himself in a different way. He no longer stutters, nor is he now painfully shy, nor does he feel the need to communicate through upsetting people around him. Perhaps most notably, Paul has developed a believable and powerfully motivating picture of his future as a family man with a life of rich and responsible involvement in his community.

Self-Determination in the Supported Living Paradigm

Paul has respect in his community and has self-respect as an interesting, talented, and responsible citizen. He plans to marry in April and is confident about the future. People who knew Paul a year ago say that he is a remarkably changed person. Much of his personal growth clearly has to do with his changed living situation and specifically the role of his supported living provider, Community Opportunities.

In designing supports for Paul, the director and staff of Community Opportunities were seeking primarily to remove barriers, that is, the patterns of control and overprotection that had been imposed on him both by his long institutionalization and by his family. Staff described as community connectors acted as guides in exploring his new community; other staff helped him to become more competent in managing his household. Underlying all these efforts was the core value of the supported living paradigm—the commitment to turn over more and more control to Paul for the direction of his life.

New Roles in the Community

William Kelly is a retired carpenter who works part time at the local Arc, which hosts the supported living project. He identifies himself as the town greeter, helping new arrivals to Crawford feel welcome. When William met Paul he sensed Paul's passion to belong in the community, as well as his fears and lack of confidence. Because Paul's apartment was across the street from the South Baptist Church, which William attended, William invited Paul to come with him to the Sunday services and to join him at the Wednesday evening Men's Fellowship. Since Paul had so little social experience beyond his immediate family, William found that Paul needed considerable encouragement and assured him that those in the congregation were "God's people who would go all out to welcome him."

Joining the church represented a breakthrough for Paul in several ways. He found both a community of accepting people and an arena where he was able to make contributions and express his talents. He became one of the cooks for the Sunday breakfast and was able to impress the congregation with his excellent voice as a member of the choir. Among the parishioners, he met a man with Alzheimer's disease and his wife, who lived in his apartment complex. Through his relationship with them, he came to feel needed and depended upon, probably for the first time in his life, becoming a neighbor who could be called upon for all kinds of assistance.

William and the church helped Paul find the confidence to participate wholeheartedly in his community, especially what he called its "great good places," such as the town coffee shop, the health club, and the country western bar, where shortly everybody knew his name. Such participation conferred on Paul for the first time a number of roles, which, taken together, represented a new identity and set of expectations both from others as well as from himself. Paul had become a citizen of

Crawford, whereas, only a year before he had been known as the "mentally retarded son," the child-man of the Hunt family.

The View of Freedom as the Removal of Barriers

The major weakness of the supports for Paul grows out of the major strength of the supported living paradigm, that is, the commitment to choice and personal empowerment. As interpreted by the Community Opportunities supported living project, personal freedom and choice were synonymous with the elimination of barriers, especially controlling rules and expectations. Once such barriers were eliminated, the supported living project staff took their cues from Paul's expressed satisfaction with his various experiences, for example, enjoying attending church. Those providing support through the project viewed Paul's recreation/leisure activities and settings as his affair as long as he seemed happy. When Paul entered the social arena, he quite simply disappeared from the view of the project staff, which had pitfalls.

Paul's experience at church is a revealing example. Not long after he joined the congregation, several parishioners organized a segregated Sunday school class for all the parishioners with disabilities. Paul's support staff did not discover this development until long after it had occurred and were not particularly disturbed by it because he seemed to like the segregated class. According to the project's outcome criteria of freedom of choice and personal satisfaction, Paul was doing well. The problem is that Paul had been resegregated without the project's knowledge, and the project had neither strategies nor intentions for responding.

Choice versus Informed Choice

Choice, personal freedom, and personal empowerment are the rubrics that, perhaps more than any other, signal the presence of the new way of thinking or the new paradigm in the design of supports to people with disabilities. Paul's story invites analysis of these core values. Such an analysis must walk a tightrope between two persisting patterns of the past: 1) the arrogance of professional dismissal of the expressed desires and interests of people with disabilities, and 2) the rationalization that choices for social isolation and segregation in the absence of experiences of inclusion are actually free choices. In his essay, *Individual Freedom as a Social Commitment* (1990), the social policy analyst Amartya Sen identified support to personal capacity-building as the core strategy in a social policy committed to freedom. He explained:

> The freedom to lead different types of lives is reflected by the set of alternative combinations of functioning from which a person can choose; this can be called the person's "capability." A person's capability depends on a variety of factors including personal characteristics *as well as social arrangements* [italics added]. A social commitment to individual freedom must involve attaching importance to enhancing the capabilities that different people actually have. (p. 38)

One might argue that Paul has been freed from certain patterns of control, but he has not at the same time been supported in developing the personal capabilities to choose equality over inequality or inclusion over segregation. Without the life experience for capabilities, the past, which in Paul's case was extremely circumscribed, remained the crucial, though invisible, determinant of his current choices. Paul had not experienced regular Sunday school classes for adults; therefore, he had no basis upon which to choose whether or not to participate in a segregated class for people with disabilities. The Community Opportunities project had not helped Paul learn of the value of inclusion for his personal and social growth. Finally, the project had not attempted to engineer inclusive opportunities in any of Paul's recreation/leisure activities.

Given the absence of this experiential base, Paul's subjective reports of satisfaction are only a partial criterion for assessing project effectiveness. His most accessible experiential standard is his comment, "At least it's not Pinecrest or staying home with my parents." In order for personal satisfaction to be utilized as the key criterion for assessing project effectiveness, Paul would also have to experience inclusive settings and relationships. His reports would then provide information relevant to improving the quality of his community inclusion. That Paul is happy with segregation, in the absence of extensive inclusive experience, should be a red flag to the project rather than an indicator of its effectiveness.

The project has, in a sense, done half the job. It has eliminated barriers to inclusion, but *informed* choice and active support for inclusion that is mindful of planning are missing. Instead, the project has been defined by its commitment to personal freedom and choice, acquiescing to significant patterns of constraint, as in Paul's ongoing social and personal segregation. In this regard, one must conclude that Paul's remarkably improved quality of life, in terms of his roles and relationships in his community, derives primarily from his own activity and commitment without the consciousness or effort of the Community Opportunities supported living project. The vulnerability of the project is, indeed, concealed by Paul's competencies. There seems to be little that would safeguard an individual less committed to community participation or, perhaps even more significant, less able to pursue it on his or her own, from being captured by segregated environments and activities.

BRIAN DAVIS

Brian Davis is a young adult who lives with his family in a small town in Connecticut. Having recently completed high school, Brian is now looking around for a job. In the meantime, he and his friend from high school, Jackie, have received funding through a local grant to scout out, photograph, and finally prepare a booklet on walks in the Greater Hartford area where "people in wheelchairs can go and enjoy nature with their nondisabled friends." Besides preparing the book, Brian also enjoys sports, computers, art, and fishing with his father.

Brian has severe cerebral palsy. He needs help with all aspects of his personal care. His speech is impaired to the extent that strangers have difficulty understanding him. He uses an electric wheelchair which he can steer deftly. Brian is also a handsome 6-foot-tall man with an infectious sense of humor. He is capable of understanding and participating in the conversation around him, and his warm and playful attitude brightens a room. Brian seems to surprise others continually by how much he knows, understands, and can do.

Brian spent most of his educational years in a segregated, hospital-affiliated school. However, with the help of Northspring Consulting, a small consultation and training organization in Manchester, Connecticut, Brian was able to chart a new course. Northspring is led by George Ducharme; he and Beth Mount are the leading writers and trainers nationally in the approaches to empowerment, planning, and community-building that are known as personal futures planning. George helped Brian assemble and direct his own circle of supports, that is, people close to him who met regularly to explore his talents, gifts, and interests; to shape his vision of the future; and to develop strategies for realizing his vision. Propelled initially by the vision of Brian's brother Jason, the circle's first project was enrolling Brian in his neighborhood high school. Although achieved with much difficulty, courage, and persistence, Brian enjoyed a rich and fulfilling high school career, including membership in the computer club and several close friendships.

What was graduation for his friends turned out to be aging out for Brian. While his peers went off to college, Brian experienced isolation and loneliness, mollified somewhat by his loving family. During one dreary spell when most of his friends were away at college and when repairs to the family van kept Brian indoors, he became discouraged. One particularly unhappy day he called Jackie, whom he had met in a class when they collaborated on a report. Brian still remembers the name of the first girl paired with him, who blew him off. Brian's aide asked Jackie to team with Brian and helped her to understand Brian's speech. They prepared a report on disability and continued to socialize regularly in school. But it was only after Brian called Jackie that their friendship deepened. Jackie became a frequent visitor to the Davis home where she found the family to be "the nicest people" and "great" to be with.

Not long afterward, through Brian's connection to Northspring Consulting, he and Jackie applied for and were awarded a grant to pursue one of Brian's dreams, to become an author. In the next several months, they composed and published a book. Together, Brian and Jackie used his computer to design a logo and sent out inquiries to local towns for information on accessible walks that would be described in the book. With Brian's mother or father driving, Brian and Jackie would go out on weekends in search of accessible backroads, bridlepaths, and hiking trails.

Jackie calls Brian her best friend, and, indeed, the two seem to share the private jokes, intimacy, and interpersonal knowledge that only close friends experience. She calls Brian whenever she is upset and finds comfort in his good-hearted sense of humor. Thanks to her friendship with Brian and his family, Jackie feels she is now less shy and more able to assert herself on behalf of other people with disabilities in her community. Although her friends and family sometimes wonder why she is spending so much time with Brian, generally they are accepting, and she is encouraging them to explore relationships with people who have disabilities.

MODEL COHERENCE AS A FRAMEWORK FOR ANALYSIS

O'Brien (1987) and Wolfensberger (1982) have urged that the assessment of quality in supports to people with disabilities examine not only individual supports and outcomes but the global issue of project or model coherence. Assessment of coherence should focus on the extent to which support components interact harmoniously and effectively toward outcomes defined by the choices, interests, and life situations of those using the supports. O'Brien refers to this focus as the issue of "fit," that is, whether a project organizes its resources, including its vision and values, in ways that create an optimal fit with the interests and choices of the people served, and whether each component and the interaction of the components fit the interests and choices of the people served.

Through this kind of analysis of the 12 case studies, the key patterns to emerge were the fundamental roles of two very different value systems and support paradigms that determined the configurations of each of the 12 case studies, and affected not only outcomes but also the roles of support people and the support process, that is, the entire "how to" of arranging supports. The authors have named the first pattern the community membership paradigm; it has been described extensively (Bradley & Knoll, 1990; McFadden & Burke, 1991). They have named the second pattern the recreational paradigm.

The Community Membership Paradigm

Like the recreational paradigm, the community membership paradigm seeks to remove barriers to access and support people with disabilities in being physically present in recreation/leisure activities and settings. Another point in common with the recreational paradigm is supporting growth-promoting and fulfilling experiences.

Unlike the recreational paradigm, the community membership paradigm views access and physical presence as means to social relationships and membership roles rather than ends in themselves. Therefore, the measures of effectiveness are framed in terms of the quality of the relationships and roles enjoyed by a person with disabilities.

The arrangements and outcomes for Brian Davis exemplify an effective approach through the community membership paradigm. For Brian the focus was on nurturing a close and reciprocal long-term relationship between him and Jackie. And within that relationship Brian was also able to enter the role, in addition to that of close friend, of collaborating author and highly respected member of his community. The focus was not on Jackie as the support person during Brian's research travels, that is, as a support person in a recreational experience; rather, the travels provided the foundation for Jackie and Brian coming to know each other and developing a close relationship. The relationship was the goal of the supports; Brian's recreational activities and experiences were the means to that goal. His access to community experiences was the precondition for his developing a personal relationship and a respected role.

A view through the community support paradigm would be critical of outcomes of the recreational paradigm as illustrated in aspects of Paul Hunt's situation. (Table 13.1 shows the major aspects of the two paradigms.) To be sure, Paul joined a church and was present in the congregation. However, he was socially segregated in a Sunday school class for people with disabilities. He was kept in the role of person with a disability despite his physical presence in the church. Because they operated through the recreational paradigm, the support staff did not attend to Paul's segregation and continued to view his situation as successful. They based this assessment on the fact that Paul was present in the church and said he was satisfied with the experience. They failed to take into account the fact that the limited extent of Paul's community experience gave him little or nothing to judge his church experience against.

The Recreational Paradigm

The core of any coherent value system or paradigm is a specific definition of the goal that the paradigm was designed to achieve. The overarching goal at the core of the recreational paradigm is accomplishing the physical inclusion of people with disabilities in recreation/leisure activities and settings by eliminating the attitudinal and physical barriers that prevent their physical presence. The outcome is people having enjoyable, growth-promoting recreation/leisure experiences. There are two assessment measures of the outcome. First, an assessment of the quality of the experience itself is needed. Typically, this measure entails soliciting the opinion of the participant by asking how exciting and growth-promoting the experience is and how much impact on self-esteem it has. The second measure concerns the achievement of the person's physical presence in the activity or setting. This measure calls for examination of frequency of attendance, duration of participation, and effectiveness of support for long-term involvement.

From the perspective of the recreational paradigm, Paul Hunt had a successful outcome. He was physically present in community recreation, he was having a good time, and he was becoming more competent. His supported living project aimed to remove barriers to his participation in community recreation by eliminating patterns of control and exclusion; assisted him in exploring his community; and introduced him to various recreational settings, including church and the local health club. Whenever he was interviewed Paul described his involvement in those activities in positive terms, especially in contrast to the recreational life he had experienced previously in his family and during his lengthy institutionalization.

Table 13.1. Aspects of the recreational paradigm versus aspects of the community membership paradigm

Recreational paradigm	Community membership paradigm
Major goal	
To enable a person to be physically present in an inclusive recreation/leisure activity or setting	To support the person in developing relationships with people without disabilities in inclusive recreation/leisure activities or settings and to assume the role of contributing member
How accomplished	
Planning supports, including adaptive environmental design and technology Use of paid staff and volunteers to provide transportation and on-site assistance Training and technical assistance to staff and being with participants without disabilities	The support context unites a clear vision of community membership with *collaborative* and planning support (e.g., circles of support) The setting is defined as only a *means* to meeting or being with potential friends and associates Potential friends are never used *primarily as a means* to support a person in being in a recreational activity; such relationships are not reduced to serving another goal; they are the goal
Support role	
Recreational or rehabilitative assistant with a focus on accomplishing and supporting access to the desired recreational experience	Community connector or bridge-builder, a well-connected person gifted in creating introductions and supporting friendships between people with and without disabilities
Outcomes	
Increased self-esteem New interests and activities New and enhanced competencies	Friendships Role as contributing member Enhanced self-esteem New and enhanced competencies
Key assumptions	
The key benefit of recreational activity is the enhancement of self-esteem and competencies	The primary goal of inclusive recreation is support to personal relationships and membership
That community is defined as a *site* for recreational activity, desirable because community provides a richer learning environment than does a segregated setting	Community is defined as networks of relationships and roles rather than as a site for recreational activities
That the accomplishment of physical presence in settings utilized by people without disabilities will *spontaneously* lead to the formation of personal relationships and membership roles	Physical inclusion will not naturally or spontaneously lead to social inclusion; social relationships and membership must be supported with the same degree of consciousness and mindfulness of planning typically associated with rehabilitative activities

Everyone who knew him attested to the remarkable improvement in his self-esteem and social skills.

VISION AND VULNERABILITY

Barbara Anne's mother and closest friend were both gifted naturals in fostering community membership and personal relationships. One could convincingly argue that Barbara Anne's personal vision of her own future and quality of life, a vision deeply shared and affirmed by her mother and best friend, was deeper and more compelling even than Brian's and far more apparent than Paul's. How quickly such a vision and the relationships and roles generated by it may disappear is illustrated in Brian's situation. He aged out of public school, the arena in which he had enjoyed close friendships and all sorts of respected roles, and within weeks he was alone and discouraged.

What was lacking for Barbara Anne is what was crucial for Brian, that is, a support effort going beyond committed family, friends, and professionals and even beyond a compelling and shared vision. When Brian's life fell apart, he was able to convene his circle of support to improvise some exciting projects and directions, including friendship and the role of author. In addition, Brian's circle had the opportunity to become informed about the pitfalls and vulnerabilities of any effort at community membership—especially the ubiquitousness of segregated organizations and activities. The circle of support was, therefore, both a platform for change and an ongoing safeguard against settling for social isolation or segregation.

Although they shared a vision of Barbara Anne's future, the key people in her life typically acted in isolation, except when faced with the crisis of her mother's illness. Acting alone, even though out of love and vision, was bringing her mother to exhaustion. The potential for collaboration and effective mutual support were vividly apparent in Barbara Anne's life and were, in fact, mobilized in an emergency. However, such collaborative support was called for also by the ordinary circumstances of realizing a good quality of life for Barbara Anne *and* her family.

Brian's situation attests to the power of a collaborative effort focused through a common vision. Barbara Anne's situation is a reminder that a vision without collaborative and mutual support is vulnerable. Also, Paul's situation affirms that collaborative effort is ineffective in supporting social inclusion in the absence of an informing vision of community membership.

Like all the children in our study, Barbara Anne was without a focused and informed support effort beyond her family. Two realities conspired to prevent such an effort: the belief that support is a private, family matter except in emergencies, and the lack of needed information and a critical perspective on segregated recreation. It was mostly the children in the study who lacked focused and informed support, which raises the issue of family support options working toward socially inclusive recreation/leisure and the knowledge and values underlying, as embryonic and lacking resources. In the main, this subgroup of children describes the energetic and solitary activities of mothers struggling to support their children in typical lifestyles. In every case, the parents were tired and at risk for burnout.

A related vulnerability, illustrated in Barbara Anne's situation, concerns the parents' lack of a critique of segregated recreation and their approach mainly through the recreational paradigm. The emphasis upon the recreation/leisure *experience* at the heart of the recreational paradigm makes that paradigm inclined toward utilizing segregated activities and organizations. One cannot deny that segregated recreation/leisure activities are capable of generating experiences that both are satisfying and enhance competency. Within the context of their own imminent exhaustion and lack of a critique of segregation, the parents turned to extensively supported, segregated recreation/leisure opportunities such as the Special Olympics. In the absence of both material and educational support for inclusive options, highly visible segregated organizations, in combination with the influence of the recreational paradigm, constituted a powerful magnet away from the inclusive opportunities these families had pursued with such energy.

CONCLUSION

Generally, there is progress toward community inclusion. More and more people with disabilities are being included in community life and becoming leading members of communities. Even the recreational paradigm, which in effect constitutes a barrier to supporting full inclusion, does not represent a commitment to segregation. The core challenge is to extend and build upon the current commitment to physical inclusion to include an in-depth understanding of social inclusion. Staff who support Paul could be retrained and supervised to plan and act to support relationship and membership for him rather than mere presence. For Barbara Anne, those committed to her with such a compelling vision could be shown how to begin a systematic collaborative effort to support her family as well as safeguard her in the face of both predictable crises and the ubiquitous invitations of segregated recreation/leisure environments.

One note of caution is in order. The recreational paradigm, while not able to promote membership or relationship, is able to generate quite powerful experiences of enjoyment and self-esteem. However, there is a knowledge base that permits transcendence of mainly subjective assessments of what is effective and desirable. Efforts toward recreational/leisure participation that promote or accept social isolation, even if they enhance competence or are exciting, are no longer acceptable goals.

Furthermore, some skepticism is appropriate given that the recreational and community membership paradigms, while committed to very different goals and strategies, use a similar language. Therefore, mission statements and various other verbal commitments to inclusive recreation are not reliable indicators of an understanding of inclusive outcomes. The authors recommend that the two paradigms be studied and then every effort be made to realize the visions and outcomes of the community membership paradigm.

REFERENCES

Agosta, J., Bradley, V., & Knoll, J. (1992). *Toward a positive family policy*. Cambridge, MA: Human Services Research Institute.

Bradley, V.J., & Knoll, J. (1990). *Shifting paradigms in services to people with developmental disabilities*. Unpublished manuscript, Administration on Developmental Disabilities, United States Department of Health and Human Services.

McFadden, D., & Burke, E.P. (1991). Developmental disabilities and the new paradigm: Directions for the 1990's. *Mental Retardation, 29*(1), pp. iii–vi.

O'Brien, J. (1987). *Frameworks for accomplishment*. Lithonia, GA: Responsive Systems Associates.

Sen, A. (1990, May 12). Individual freedom as a social commitment. *New York Review of Books,* p. 38

Wolfensberger, W. (1982, April 16). *Workshop in model coherency,* Syracuse.

14

Organizational Transformations

Moving from Facilities to Community Inclusive Employment

Kristen Magis-Agosta

The idea behind community inclusive employment is simple: to "provide individualized support to help businesses keep people with significant disabilities in regular jobs" (Rhodes, 1990, p. 1). This level of community inclusion cannot be achieved simply through physical inclusion, but must also provide opportunity for cultural and social inclusion and for self-determination (Lakin et al., 1989). Since 1982, organizations across the United States have moved toward a further realization of this vision by changing over their services from those based in facilities, such as sheltered workshops and activity centers, to those that emphasize community inclusion.

These efforts have demonstrated repeatedly that, given proper supports, people with severe disabilities can work in real jobs in the community (Kiernan, McGaughey, & Schalock, 1986; Wehman, Kregel, Revell, & West, 1990). To succeed, professionals must identify suitable opportunities within community businesses and develop the supports that individuals require to keep their jobs. Such supports may involve a range of specialized services (Bellamy, Rhodes, Mank, & Albin, 1988), as well as the creative use of the supports offered directly by the employer or helpful coworkers (Nisbet & Hagner, 1988; Rusch, Johnson, & Hughes, 1990). Despite programmatic and economic arguments in favor of supported employment arrangements, as of 1990 only 9% of the persons with developmental disabilities in day and employment programs across the United States were reported to be in supported employment. Over 90% remain in facility-based arrangements (McGaughey, Lynch, Morgenstern, Kiernan, & Schalock, 1991). Many states have adopted policies in favor of supported employment. However, they have had considerable difficulty seeing to the transformation of their day service systems pursuant to this policy. Much of the difficulty lies in converting agencies from facility-based service providers to providers of supported employment arrangements.

Facility-based organizations attempting such a changeover are challenged to create a favorable context for change while negotiating an array of counter forces. The standing organizational culture and mission must be redirected, and those affected, including staff, persons with disabilities, and family members must come to accept the prospective change. Old administrative structures and behaviors must be abandoned in favor of entirely new policies and actions (Albin & Magis-Agosta, 1990).

Change projects must address the complex, interrelated, and highly dynamic nature of organizations (Mohrman et al., 1989). Service providers must approach change projects holistically (Kilmann, 1987), by simultaneously balancing the multiple organizational dynamics keyed to change, and by permanently replacing old values, systems, and behaviors with those that directly contribute to the new vision.

Based on the author's experience and consistent with the observations of others, a *holistic approach* to managing change must encompass five elements: 1) establishment of a *vision* of the desired future (Egan, 1988; Kouzes & Posner, 1991); 2) strong *leadership* keyed to that vision (Kouzes & Posner, 1991; Nadler & Tushman, 1989); 3) an *action-bias* dedicated to change (Peters & Austin, 1985; Peters & Waterman, 1982); 4) development of a supportive *learning culture* (Deming, 1982; Handy, 1989; Harvey, 1990); and 5) continuing realignment of *administrative and programmatic systems* consistent with the new vision (Kilmann, 1987; Mohrman et al., 1989).

Community agencies across the United States are attempting the changeover from facility-based services to community inclusive employment, some more successfully than others. The purpose of this chapter is to explore the positive change experiences by two community service agencies in Oregon, Polk Enterprises, Inc. and Bonney Enterprises, Inc. What follows is a description of these agencies and the changes they experienced and analysis of the process using the above framework. Discussion and concluding remarks complete the chapter.

THE EXPERIENCE OF CHANGE: TWO CASE STUDIES

In late 1991, three people from the two Oregon community service agencies were interviewed: the present and preceding executive directors of Polk Enterprises,

Inc. and the executive director of Bonney Enterprises, Inc. A series of nine open-ended interviews were conducted with these three people lasting approximately 12 hours. Interview questions were developed to capture the dynamics of change noted above, as well as agency history and demographics. To complement the information gathered through the interviews, relevant documents—mission statements, notes from staff retreats, and organizational policies—were reviewed.

Information about Polk and Bonney is presented below; it describes agency demographics, past and current vision, history briefly, the major barriers each encountered, and current outcomes. Subsequently, an analysis of how the organizations managed in these five elements is presented.

DESCRIPTIVE INFORMATION

Polk Enterprises, Inc.

Polk Enterprises, Inc., a vocational program incorporated in 1972, is located in Independence, Oregon, a town of about 5,000 people. Polk has an annual base budget of $600,000. It supports 79 individuals with developmental disabilities. Ranging in age from 21 to 58 most of these individuals have moderate to intensive support needs; some have complicating physical, emotional, and medical conditions.

Polk Enterprises employs 24 staff people. Polk's mission is to help the individuals it serves to participate in their communities and develop meaningful relationships with others. Staff pursue this mission by helping individuals gain paid employment or play other valued, albeit nonpaid, community roles. Presently, 40 individuals hold jobs in local community businesses and receive varying levels of support from Polk staff, while 39 are supported in the agency's vocational facility. Polk's goal was to have all people supported in the community by July 1992. The plan was to sell the facility at that time and use the revenue exclusively to support individuals in their communities. Polk's growth into community inclusive employment has spanned 10 years, from meek beginnings with a new idea to a 100% commitment to community inclusive employment for all those they serve.

In 1981, Polk employed five staff people to provide day activities and prevocational services to 32 individuals. Management hired that year dismantled the day activity and prevocational model and initiated plans to convert the program into a revenue generating workshop providing individuals full employment within the facility. By 1984, the program had acquired a facility, a van, and enough subcontract work to keep all individuals working. During these years, staff were also being introduced to community-based activities, first in the form of community access and then in terms of actual community jobs. In 1985, the state awarded Polk a grant that enabled establishment within Polk of a division devoted to community inclusive employment.

Polk's attention to the values and tenets of community inclusive employment greatly intensified that year and culminated in a management decision in 1986 to completely changeover from facility-based to community-based employment services. Since 1987, Polk has struggled to effect this change, to reach this vision. Their efforts to change have not, however, occurred in isolation. They have received training and technical assistance through the Oregon Supported Employment Initiative, a federally funded changeover grant.

Daily operations within the facility have continued to demand attention and resources. Meanwhile, the agency initiated Total Quality Management (Deming, 1982), a consumer-centered management philosophy and system that requires at least the same amount of energy and focus as the changeover from facility to community-integrated services. Complicating matters further, as Polk proceeded with their changeover plans, they confronted still other demands. In 1989, Polk initiated services for a group of individuals who were being relocated from the state's institution. This initiative required a great amount of resources.

Polk currently supports approximately 20 different businesses employing individuals with disabilities. Most people are employed in individual jobs, though two groups of four share two jobs. Jobs range from courtesy clerk to food preparation, to mail room attendant, to horticulture. While the agency's efforts to change have not been easy, the staff's commitment to individuals and to the values of community inclusive employment has grown even stronger. Moreover, as a result of their continuing efforts, the staff's skills and abilities have grown significantly.

Bonney Enterprises, Inc.

Bonney Enterprises, incorporated in 1969, closed their facility-based operations in October 1991. Their $750,000 annual budget allows Bonney to provide support to individuals ranging in age from 21 to 81 and who have developmental disabilities and other associated medical, emotional, and physical complications. Nearly two thirds of these individuals require significant support. Bonney's vision is to enable and support the community in including individuals into community businesses and life.

Bonney employs 25 staff people to support 61 individuals in community jobs and to run six small businesses administered by Bonney in Corvallis, Oregon, a town of about 40,000 people. The six businesses are a packaging firm, janitorial services, landscaping services, a nursery, bookbinding services, and a bakery. Approximately 50% of those served are supported in Bonney's small businesses.

The businesses were purchased, and individuals with disabilities were included in the current work force. Other businesses withdrew from the job site, but agency staff assisted coworkers and individuals in establishing supportive working relationships and in continuing relationships outside the work sites. Staff remained available to coworkers as needed. Individuals participate in delivery, sales, labor, customer service, quality control, materials handling, typesetting, and craftwork. Other people are supported by community employers in individual placements. They have jobs ranging from grounds maintenance, to shipping and receiving, to food manufacturing, to office clerical work, to grocery assistant, to assembly.

Bonney, like Polk, did not convert from segregated to inclusive services overnight. The change process officially began in 1986. Prior to that time, Bonney had experimented with crews composed of groups of individuals working together on projects in the community. They had also discussed community employment, both at the staff and board levels. Their initial commitment to changeover was based on a desire to give individuals more choices in services, rather than an intense desire to achieve the values of community inclusive employment. As they experimented with changeover, they discovered that it also greatly improved staff working conditions and staff morale. And as individuals started succeeding in the community, Bonney realized that community employment was much more than just another service option. In 1988, Bonney formally committed to a 100% changeover. By 1989, most staff at Bonney equated inclusion with a civil rights movement, and the value of community employment is now deeply ingrained throughout the organization.

Bonney has worked hard to accomplish their vision. Since 1987 they have added services for 25 individuals, more than doubled their staff, started four new businesses, and abandoned the philosophy and structures of the facility-based model of services. Like Polk, Bonney received support from the Oregon Supported Employment Initiative.

Yet, change did not come easily. Numerous barriers were encountered in the process. While the facility was still in operation the demands it made needed to be met and balanced against those generated by the new vision. In addition, services for persons with significant support needs who were being relocated from the state institution also needed to be established and stabilized. This particular effort was extraordinarily difficult, and along the way a lawsuit was filed against the agency. Moreover, during this time, both staff and service recipients were injured physically, and staff morale suffered.

Bonney staff were forced to seriously reevaluate their values about community inclusion for all people. After doing so, they renewed their belief in the value of community inclusion and restated their commitment to the individuals they served and to each other. They were resolved to translate their vision into practice for all people, regardless of the intensity of supports required. Bonney's current goals include incorporating Total Quality Management into their operations, exploring consumer-owned and consumer-run businesses, and pursuing natural supports for individuals employed in the community.

ANALYSIS OF THE CHANGE EXPERIENCE

Both Polk Enterprises and Bonney Enterprises have experienced successes in their move to provide persons with developmental disabilities opportunities for community inclusive employment. Polk's goal to support all individuals in the community has been achieved. Bonney has now totally converted from facility-based services to community employment. Analysis of these two experiences shows how they have managed to include a vision for change, leadership, action-bias, learning culture, and constant realignment of administrative and programmatic systems as part of their system change process.

A Vision of the Future

Any process dedicated to change starts with a vision of what the future might be. Often such vision is born of a passionate belief in some human value, in this instance, the right of all individuals to participate in interdependent relationships with other community members and to hold valued jobs with community employers. The vision is an image of the ideal, an expectation of the possible. It proclaims what should be, not what currently exists or probably can be.

During their interviews, people associated with Polk and Bonney Enterprises conveyed a deep personal commitment to persons with disabilities—to their indisputable right to participate in their communities and to their ability to contribute positively and share in the splendor and struggles of life. These beliefs fueled an emergent vision that centered on a dedication to community inclusive employment.

Once established and articulated, this vision inspired the will to commence, and the strength to complete, an unknown and arduous journey from present practices to those more consistent with the envisioned ideal. Though the visions held at Polk and Bonney did not provide a detailed map for the imminent journey, they embodied subtle nuances, which, when discovered, served to guide the change process and focus the organizations' energy. Through constant analysis of what the vision meant in daily life, each agency learned about the parameters for action and the criteria against which to measure efforts and outcomes.

In both organizations, the emergent vision of the future provided guidance right from the start. It revealed the proclivity of facility-based services to consume essential program resources, resources that then could not be applied toward the vision. Yet, while the costs associated with facility maintenance were easy to see, the cost to those served was more subtle and, in nonfiscal terms, even greater.

In the facility, individuals were required to choose from an extremely limited variety of jobs. Individuals whose needs or preferences did not match the available options or who did not want to be in the facility at all had no choice but to accept these limitations. If they became frustrated or angry, they might be introduced into a specialized behavior control program designed to make them more compliant.

Both organizations responded by investing only as necessary in their facility's physical plant. They also provided other options, including ventures out of the facility and into the community and individual choice as to whether or not to work on available facility subcontracts.

But as useful as a clear vision might be for pointing the way to a new future, it does so at the expense of exposing the status quo—the prevailing vision—as unacceptable. The conflict between the new vision and the old vision may well create dissonance and trepidation among agency staff and others with a stake in the agency's directions (e.g., parents and other service providers). Before the new vision, the organization has focused its entire energies on fulfilling the old one. The difficulty the agency will have in abandoning it and refocusing on the new vision relates directly to the amount of energy invested in creating and fulfilling that old vision (Kuhn, 1970). Until the new vision is firmly established in the organization, the struggle for survival and dominance over the old vision will act as a drain on the entire organization.

Consider the experience of Polk Enterprises. Only a few years prior to Polk's commitment to convert to community employment, staff had invested an extraordinary amount of energy transforming the organization from a prevocational and work activities service into a viable workshop offering in-house work for all its consumers. Their hard work paid off in lucrative subcontracts and the acquisition of a new facility and vehicle. It was in the afterglow of these accomplishments that inclusive community employment was first considered.

At first, dismantling the workshop and erasing all of these hard won accomplishments was inconceivable to Polk staff. And so, for several years they attempted to follow the dual visions of facility and the community employment programs. However, they found their efforts and resources constantly divided and at odds. Eventually, they came to understand that community inclusive employment was not just an alternative to sheltered work, but in fact, an essential and *primary* requirement for individuals to be included in their communities. This realization led them to conclude that the facility had to be closed and that all the agency's resources should be focused on community-based supports. Polk had successfully managed the complete adoption of its new vision and the total displacement of the old vision.

Leadership

In stable times, management is employed to handle the affairs of the organization, that is, to direct and control resource utilization and systems operations. During periods of organizational change, however, staff attitudes and practices must be reshaped and organizational systems retooled. During these times, an additional quality is required: leadership (Kouzes & Posner, 1991). Both Bonney and Polk have benefited from strong leadership, at first from the executive directors, and now from many throughout the organizations.

Leaders from both Polk and Bonney project an intense and unwavering focus on their vision of community inclusive employment, an undying belief that it will become reality, and a solemn conviction that their organizations will succeed. These leaders are explorers and adventurers. They are personally challenged by the journey and invigorated by change and growth. They have had the courage to challenge prevailing practices and the strength to lead their organizations through change when neither the tools nor the methods were fully understood.

From the very beginning, they established community inclusive employment centrally within their organizations. At Polk, for instance, evidence of leadership's commitment to change was displayed in numerous ways, including posting frequent and varied written messages about the agency's new mission. The commitment to change gained high profile; it dominated conversations and became a key topic at agency meetings. Staff could only conclude that the agency's leadership was dedicated to change and that all barriers could and would be overcome. In fact, at Bonney, the board officially gave the executive director license to take risks and to make mistakes. This freedom, then passed on from management to staff, enabled the organization to experiment with new and unproven ideas and to apply the lessons learned from these experiments.

Leaders at Polk and Bonney worked to provide a favorable environment for others to discover the tools and methods necessary to make their vision reality. For instance, leaders at both Polk and Bonney established various forums for staff to discuss problems and alternative solutions and to test innovative ideas. They also provided resources for staff to implement new strategies by devoting revenues generated by their workshop and by acquiring new resources (e.g., grants) to support the conversion. They constantly reinforced staff efforts, provided support in rough times, and cheered their successes. Leaders at both organizations committed to stand by staff as they struggled with their new roles and relationships.

Action-Bias Dedicated to Change

An action-bias is a prevailing preference among staff for action rather than extended discussion (Peters & Waterman, 1982). Ultimately, a vision, even where supported by dedicated leadership, is only an image of the future. It is soon fatally endangered without real evidence of its transformation from concept to actual practice. It is actions, both large and small, occurring on a daily basis, that transform the vision into a reality. Action has been the cornerstone at both Polk and Bonney.

More than simply articulating agency positions from on high, leaders at Polk and Bonney inspired in other people the same passion that consumed them, beginning with a consistent modeling of preferred new actions. For instance, the leaders at both agencies spent an enormous amount of time listening and learning about the fears, needs, and aspirations of their staff. Subsequently, they demonstrated how the agency's new vision would address the staff's needs and preferences. They used the vision to guide daily decisions, to revamp organizational structures, and to provide direction during crises. Such modeling enabled others to visualize and experiment with their own new roles.

Staff actions to realize the vision have always been instrumental in shaping the organizations' formal administrative and programmatic policies and systems. Moreover, those systems are then frequently modified as the result of lessons learned through taking action. For instance, immediately after Bonney's decision to convert their workshop and before a formal plan was developed, each staff person assumed responsibility for five individuals. The staff's job was to discover the interests and aspirations of these individuals and to advocate for them. The lessons they learned from taking such positive action helped to create the agency's formal plans for changeover.

Also, Polk first believed that community employment would work only for people who did not have significant support needs. So the initial target for conversion was set at just 50% of those supported. However, as new ideas were tested, individuals with disabilities taught staff that anyone could work given the correct supports. The actions Polk took led them to realize that no consumer should be excluded from the community and helped to clarify what must be done to support all individuals in the community. As a result, Polk shifted their goal to 100% conversion and proceeded to acquire grant monies to support their efforts. Bonney and Polk, though strong believers in the value of discussion and debate, place the most value on actions, which led to the realization of their vision.

Supportive Learning Culture

A positive learning culture generates opportunities for staff to build the many skills needed to implement and cope with change. First, staff need to understand the rationale for the change and the fundamental concepts and values central to the new vision. Second, they need to acquire the attitudes and skills needed to transform the vision into reality. Third, they need skills to balance the requirements of the old vision with those of the new. Fourth, they need skills to cope with the emotional stress produced by the change process. If the vision is to be realized, a culture that facilitates this learning must be established and nurtured.

In both organizations, learning occurred through successive approximations of the vision, creative thinking, innovative experimentation, and challenging discussions. Mistakes were seen as almost inevitable steps in the learning process, and successful innovations were embraced as paths to the vision. Staff were provided with systematic instruction and technical assistance keyed to the new vision. They participated in formal peer support groups to share and learn from other organizations attempting to reach the same vision. All of this learning led to the continual improvement of the organizations' efforts and outcomes, as well as improving staffs' understanding of the vision.

Two requirements of a positive learning culture are that staff be treated with respect and that the leadership convey a willingness to learn—that it does not have all the answers (Moss-Kanter, 1983). There must be a feeling of pride and a common zeal for excellence. Organizational cultures that treat staff as commodities, that employ the hands not the minds, that criticize or devalue identifying problems, that punish mistakes, or that elevate the leader to super human status can damage or destroy the learning culture. Both organizations have worked to develop and maintain a positive learning culture.

After they initiated conversion to community employment, Polk Enterprises started another journey. They became deeply involved in Total Quality Management. This management philosophy places great value on organizational growth and improvement, which necessitates a strong and vibrant learning culture. Incorporating quality improvement tools and procedures into their daily operations started paying off almost immediately. The complexity of their systems and paperwork was significantly reduced. They also developed a more knowledgeable and skilled workforce by increasing opportunities for timely and appropriate staff training. Staff turnover decreased from 63% to 25%. These changes enabled the agency to eliminate three mid-level management positions and to delegate the responsibilities to direct line staff. Savings from these and other improvements in their organization saved Polk $79,150 in the first 1½ years alone. Additionally, staff became more vested in the organization as they developed their skills and became more intimately involved in setting policies and establishing procedures.

Bonney's leadership has continually expressed a genuine interest in staff. Working conditions are constantly monitored and adjusted to ensure that staff feel supported and respected. In 1988, this commitment to staff was formalized into the QISS program, Quality is Success and Satisfaction. The program was designed to increase job satisfaction and illustrate how all staff contribute to the organization's mission, including the quality of services. Barriers caused by the organization were systematically reduced and supports to staff were increased. Communication channels were improved, giving staff access to information previously retained within management. And staff were given more responsibilities, such as participating in developing service plans for individuals.

The program established a strong culture that has since matured and yielded great benefits for the organization. Because staff feel respected and valuable, they are highly motivated to contribute to the organization. They regularly assume leadership roles in identifying and implementing improvements in organizational operations and in the quality of their work lives. This commitment has resulted in an organization-wide wellness program, a retirement plan, and a profit sharing option for all staff.

Continuing Realignment of Administrative and Programmatic Systems

Systems, both administrative and programmatic, must be strong enough to provide direction and to support organizational operations, yet flexible enough to adapt to program change. The executive directors of both Bonney and Polk view systems as a means to the end. As a result, staff have developed administrative and programmatic systems only as needed, monitored them to ensure that their intended effects are achieved, and changed or abolished them when they ceased to contribute toward reaching the vision.

One purpose of administrative structures is to delineate and clarify roles and responsibilities throughout the organization. Both organizations have changed their structures several times in an attempt to find one that best accommodated their visions. At Polk, the organizational structure was redesigned in a way that could be represented by a star. At each point on the star, people representing administration, marketing, job coaching, and the workshop joined to provide support to several individuals. This helped staff better understand the multiple and related dimensions of individual lives and how they should collaborate in their efforts to help individuals fulfill personal and employment ambitions. It also helped staff learn how those in various positions functioned, discover their natural interdependence, and recognize how the whole network related to the organization's vision.

Another administrative dimension concerns the salary and status accorded their staff. With dramatic change in service practices, new staff positions are created while others are eliminated. New types of knowledge grow in value while the knowledge associated with the displaced service model loses its value. Some staff advance and gain status in the organization; others lose. Though a supportive and vigorous learning culture may ease the transition, there is no escaping the reality that the new service model demands changes in administrative hierarchies, job descriptions, career ladders, and salary structures.

These changes were made in both organizations, but with regard and respect for staff. Staff were involved in recreating the organizational structure and various job descriptions. People were given choices regarding the functions they would like to fill in the new structure and were supported even when they did not feel comfortable taking the new positions. New positions were added as old positions were vacated. People were not forced into positions.

Regarding programmatic operations, both agencies started their conversion efforts using the various community employment models designed in the early 1980s, including individual placements, work crews, and sheltered enclaves within businesses (Bellamy et al., 1988). Over time staff grew dissatisfied with these group models. Contracts for work were negotiated between the employers and the agency, not with individual employees. Individuals were paid and supervised by agency staff, physically isolated from their coworkers, and excluded from social events such as staff meetings and company picnics. These factors led individuals to be labeled as different, as apart from the real work force, and as expendable. Employers did not seem to develop an investment in them, supervisors and coworkers did not develop relationships with them, and when layoffs occurred individuals with disabilities were always first to go. The group models apparently had inhibited individuals' opportunity for social inclusion.

In response to these observations, Polk started to approach employment exclusively one person at a time. Aside from focusing on their small businesses, Bonney also focused on individual placements. Now, businesses hire, supervise, and provide training and support to individuals. Individuals work beside coworkers and participate in business events, both formal and informal. Polk and Bonney have discovered a new role for themselves. No longer are they the lead partner in the employment process. They are now supporters of the two main employment partners, the employer and the employee. They are being challenged to redesign systems that promote opportunities for social inclusion and to design and experiment with totally new systems to facilitate their new role in the community. For example, the traditional job coach position is being replaced with a community support person, direct training of individuals is being replaced with training co-workers and supervisors, and direct intervention in problems and crises is being replaced with support to enable people to solve their own problems.

DISCUSSION

Organizational change does not follow directly and immediately from the decision to adopt a new vision. Change is complex and dynamic. It takes time. It cannot be isolated from the myriad of other forces, both external and internal, affecting the organization. At Polk and Bonney the change process has spanned more than a decade, and has been intertwined with many other events all competing for attention and resources and affecting the nature and process of the change. Forces external to the agencies, such as federal and state laws and policies, new technologies, local economies, state and local politics, the demands of advocates, and changes in business management philosophy have all had their impact. Internal forces affecting the change process include the agency's own historical values and approaches to service delivery, their policies and systems and their dominant culture, and the crises that inevitably arise.

While advances in the approaches taken by agencies to provide community inclusive employment have exploded over a decade, little attention has been directed to the actual dynamics and processes of effecting successful and enduring organizational change. In this chapter, the process of organizational change has been considered in terms of the experiences of two community agencies. The author believes that these organizations were successful largely because they had vision, leadership, an action-bias, a learning culture, and continually realigned administrative and programmatic systems to fit their changing situations. But more than that, their experience suggests that these elements must be part of a holistic change process.

This changeover seems an overwhelming and impossible task. However, close examination of Polk and Bonney leads to the conclusion that *effective change is holistic,* and that it can be approached successfully without overwhelming the organization. Holistic change occurs through a continuing cycle of successive approximations of the vision, and the subsequent balancing and realignment of both the change processes and the organization. Through *approximation and alignment,* the entire organization grows and changes one holistic step at a time.

During approximation, a small but holistic step is taken to produce small-scale change in values, systems, and behaviors throughout the organization. Complex change is managed in steps that are small enough to foster success. As each step is implemented, it influences and, in turn, is influenced by both organizational and environmental events. Subsequently, during alignment, the changes are allowed to settle into the organization. Values, systems, and behaviors that do not contribute to the vision are modified or eliminated and replaced with those that do.

Next, the organization is challenged to ensure the changes are permanently integrated into the organization (Harvey, 1990).

This cycle of approximation and alignment results in organizational lessons that act to stimulate and direct the next cycle. These lessons include identifying strategies that did and did not work, analyzing interactions generated by the implemented strategies, and determining opportunities and challenges stimulated by the change. Analysis of these interactions leads the organization to conclusions as to how to design and implement the next step of the change process. The cycle is repeated until the change is successfully completed.

Throughout, there will be great danger of resistance and regression, so daily decisions and actions need to be closely monitored to ensure that the majority of tradeoffs made are in favor of the new vision. Consider the competition for resources that emerges between facility operations and new community employment initiatives. Until the facility is closed, the organization's resources are divided and depleted by running two disparate businesses. If the organization is to succeed in its transformation, decisions in favor of community employment must continually outweigh those in favor of the facility. For example, both Polk and Bonney turned down opportunities to bring work into the facility, preferring instead to have individuals leave the facility for work in community businesses. More people acquired community jobs; however, others still in the facility lost opportunities to work. This process of decision and tradeoffs is further exemplified in the conversion strategy chosen.

Each agency chose different strategies that resulted in different tradeoffs, with new challenges and barriers to negotiate. Polk, placing great value on inclusion, continued to pursue individual placements exclusively, but the stress from continually dividing their limited resources finally took its toll. As they consistently made tradeoffs in favor of the community, resources available for individuals in the facility grew so limited that individuals there had opportunities neither for inclusion nor for community employment. Polk recently determined that the tradeoff to these individuals was too great, so they decided to close down the facility, rather than wait to find placements for everyone. Polk's challenge will be to ensure that all individuals are included in the community, whether in jobs or unpaid, valued community roles.

Bonney chose a different conversion strategy. They placed high value on immediate employment for individuals requiring the most significant supports but were concerned about the time involved in generating community acceptance and opportunities. Rather than pursuing individual placements exclusively, they chose to purchase small businesses and employ these individuals therein. This strategy permitted individuals quicker access to community experiences and employment. However, there were tradeoffs, one being the departure from the standard employer–employee relationship in which wages and benefits are earned for work completed, resulting in mutual participation and gain. In service agencies, staff provide services to recipients. The relationship is that of rehabilitation professionals and clients. Bonney's challenge is to provide supports to individuals and business personnel without negatively affecting the employment relationship.

CONCLUSION

The analysis above described how Polk Enterprises and Bonney Enterprises are successfully effecting change in their organizations. Through successive approximations of their vision, they have come to understand community inclusive employment not as just a good idea for some, rather as a right of all people. They have been willing to take risks, and constantly to change their organizational structures and program approaches to approximate their vision more clearly. They have much more to do. Polk still must ensure that individuals have opportunities for career enhancement and social inclusion. Bonney still must make it possible for individuals employed in their small businesses to experience a normal employer–employee relationship. And both need to continue to adapt their organizations to service their evolving understanding of their visions, while continually improving the quality of their services.

Nonetheless, they have demonstrated that, approached holistically with a strong vision, effective leadership, an action-bias, a supportive learning culture, and continuing realignment of administrative and programmatic systems, facility-based providers can transform themselves into effective agents for community inclusive employment.

REFERENCES

Albin, J., & Magis-Agosta, K. (1990). *Self assessment for changeover to supported employment: A troubleshooting approach.* Eugene: Oregon Supported Employment Initiative, Specialized Training Center, University of Oregon.

Bellamy, G.T., Rhodes, L., Mank, D., & Albin, J. (1988). *Supported employment: A community implementation guide.* Baltimore: Paul H. Brookes Publishing Co.

Capra, F. (1982). *The turning point: Science, society and the rising culture.* New York: Bantam/Simon & Schuster.

Deming, W.D. (1982). *Out of the crisis.* Cambridge: Massachusetts Institute of Technology.

Egan, G. (1988). *Change agent skills B: Managing innovation.* San Diego: Pfeiffer.

Handy, C. (1989). *The age of unreason.* Boston: Harvard Business School Press.

Harvey, T.R. (1990). *Checklist for change: A pragmatic approach to creating and controlling change.* Boston, MA: Allyn & Bacon.

Kiernan, W.E., McGaughey, M.J., & Schalock, R.L. (1986). *Employment survey for adults with developmental disabilities.* Boston: Developmental Evaluation Clinic, Children's Hospital.

Kilmann, R.H. (1987). *Beyond the quick fix.* San Francisco: Jossey-Bass.

Kilmann, R.H. (1989). A completely integrated program for organizational change. In A.M. Mohrman, S.A. Mohrman, G.E. Ledford, T.G. Cummings, E.E. Lawler, & Associates (Eds.), *Large-scale organizational change* (pp. 200–228). San Francisco: Jossey-Bass.

Kouzes, J.M., & Posner, B.Z. (1991). *The leadership challenge: How to get extraordinary things done in organizations*. San Francisco: Jossey-Bass.

Kuhn, T.S. (1970). *Structure of scientific revolutions*. Chicago: University of Chicago Press.

Lakin, K.C., Jaskulski, T.M., Bruininks, R.H., Menke, J.M., White, C.C., & Wright, E.A. (1989). *Medicaid services for persons with mental retardation and related conditions*. Minneapolis: University of Minnesota, Institute on Community Integration.

McGaughey, M.J., Kiernan, W.E., Schalock, R.L., Lynch, S.A., & Morgenstern, D.R. (1991). *Natural survey of day and employment programs for persons with developmental disabilities: Results from state mental retardation and developmental disabilities agencies*. Boston: Training and Research Institute for People with Disabilities, The Children's Hospital.

Mohrman, A.M., Mohrman, S.A., Ledford, G.E., Cummings,T.G., Lawler, E.E., & Associates. (1989). *Large-scale organizational change*. San Francisco: Jossey-Bass.

Moss-Kanter, R. (1983). *The change masters*. New York: Simon & Schuster.

Nadler, D.A., & Tushman, M.L. (1989). Leadership for organizational change. In A.M. Mohrman et al. (Eds.), *Large-scale organizational change* (pp. 100–119). San Francisco: Jossey-Bass.

Nisbet, J., & Hagner, D. (1988). Natural supports in the workplace: A reexamination of supported employment. *Journal of The Association for Persons with Severe Handicaps, 13*(4), 260–267.

Peters, T. (1987). *Thriving on chaos: Handbook of a management revolution*. New York: Alfred A. Knopf.

Peters, T., & Austin, N. (1985). *A passion for excellence*. New York: Warner Books.

Peters, T., & Waterman, R.H. (1982). *In search of excellence: Lessons from America's best-run companies*. New York: Warner Communications Company.

Rhodes, L. (1990). *Oregon supported employment: A growing labor resource for business and industry*. Eugene: Specialized Training Center, University of Oregon.

Rusch, F., Johnson, J., & Hughes, C. (1990). Analysis of co-worker involvement in relation to level of disability versus placement approach among supported employees. *Journal of The Association for Persons with Severe Handicaps, 15*(3), 32–39.

Wehman, P., Kregel, J., Revell, G., & West, M. (1990). The national supported employment initiative. *OSERS News in Print, 3*(3), 7–13.

15

From Facilities to Supports

The Changing Organization

Derrick Dufresne and Bob Laux

Failure is not fatal, but failure to change might be.

—Coach John Wooden

What made a company great 40 years ago will kill it today.

—IBM

The field of developmental disabilities has changed. It is undergoing a vast and rapid change in the way it approaches its business. Never has there been a time of such anxiety, hope, possibility, and frustration. While there may be a need for rehabilitation in the 1990s, this is likely to have much more to do with professionals than with people who have disabilities.

In working with almost 100 agencies from 1982 to 1992, the authors have seen many different approaches to (and some avoidance of) these changing trends. They have seen some agencies embrace change and prosper and others fight change and go out of business. Many agencies still are unaware of the challenges and may be experiencing the calm before the storm. The only thing the authors feel able to say with certainty is that the current changes experienced are not the culmination of historical evolution, rather, they are more likely to be harbingers of the impending revolution.

In their work, the authors have seen some common elements that are embodied in organizational values of agencies that are transforming themselves from facility-based programs to systems of support. In this chapter, the authors will share some of the fundamental principles of organizational change as well as sto-

Derrick Dufresne and Bob Laux are consultants who have worked closely with a number of organizations nationally that are rethinking their missions, service approachs, and service configurations.

ries about some of the agencies with whom they have worked that have embraced this journey. Their stories are not without pain but are capable of giving hope and guidance to others who may be poised on the edge of the decision to embark on organizational change.

PRINCIPLES OF ORGANIZATIONAL CHANGE

For some time, we believed that perhaps some of the responses we were seeing in agencies involved in change were unique to nonprofit organizations or the field of developmental disabilities. The longer we look, the more we realize that many agencies are dealing with the results of a more generic form of organizational change and the personal issues and values that emerge as a result of such change. Some basic principles may assist in understanding that these are not disability issues or nonprofit issues; rather, they are personal issues and values in response to changes in the human organization.

Several writers have identified some of these organizational issues in a context that may help in understanding why organizations change or do not change. David Gleicher (Bekhard & Harris, 1977) has a formula that helps in understanding the impacts of change on organizations: $C = (abd) > X$.

In this particular model, "*C*" equals change; "*a*" equals level of dissatisfaction with the status quo; "*b*" is the clearly desired goal; "*d*" represents the first practical steps toward the desired goal; and "*X*" equals the costs of change.

Thus, in order for true change to take place, there must first be some level of dissatisfaction with the status quo. Examples almost everyone can relate to involve losing weight, stopping smoking, or leaving a bad relationship. Second, there must be a clearly desired goal (e.g., losing 20 pounds, stopping smoking completely, or being free of a relationship). Third, one must take the first practical steps toward that goal, (e.g., starting a diet, cutting down on smoking by two cigarettes per day, planning for life without a previous relationship). *The most critical point is that all of these factors must be greater than the cost of change.*

LACK OF COMMITMENT TO CHANGE

For too many agencies, this last factor is the one that hinders fundamental change. An experience we had working with an agency in a midwestern state is an example. This agency operated a large dorm-like campus that served people with various disabilities. We were called in to meet with the management team who had decided to close one dorm and place all individuals into the community.

Throughout the day, we talked about financing options, individual futures planning options, and strategies that could be employed to accomplish this goal. Toward the end of the day, we asked the question, "What are you planning to do with the building after it is closed?" We anticipated hearing a response such as, "We are going to turn it into office space," or "We are going to tear it down."

Instead, we heard, "Oh, we have a grant to serve 'the deaf-blind' and will be opening up a new program within the next 2 months." At that point, we realized that they had embraced the "Titanic" version of management: the ship is still going down, but we get a better view.

What had become clear was that the agency was not truly committed to change; it was committed to expanding its services. Somehow the administrators could not see the contradictions inherent in moving one group of people out of a small institution into the community while moving another group of people into their place because they had greater disabilities.

All too often in our work with organizations, we have found that at the upper levels, particularly the executive director and board levels, there is not enough dissatisfaction with the status quo. In our experience, many executive directors either founded the agencies that they now head or were brought in at a time when the field was still in the thick of the developmental model. As a result, these administrators embrace what we call the incremental approach to change. That is, we will change, but at our own pace and in a way that is safe and will keep us viable. This caution is based on some real fears including:

- A direct loss of income related to reducing staff
- Less stability, more uncertainty, and more headaches dealing with property turnover
- Disposal of a single-use asset that may not be marketable to the general public
- Learning to manage a decentralized system

As a result, an agency might commit to trying the new paradigm by developing a small number of supported employment jobs or allowing several individuals the opportunity to move into a supported living setting. These attempts to change its services are largely viewed as experiments or exceptions to the norm. Through these attempts, the agency does not have to commit strategically to a new direction, but simply a small reallocation of resources that allows it to expand its scope of services.

In a related approach, the agency that currently runs a number of residential facilities might make grandiose announcements about the cessation of such efforts, such as: "We will build no more ICFs/MR," "we will own no more buildings," or "All of our new development will be in the area of supported living." Among vocational providers, we hear, "We will not build any more additions to our workshop," or "All of our new vocational development will be in the area of supported employment."

On the surface, this seems not only like a plausible path, but also an advisable one. What many of these executives do not realize is that in setting up this new paradigm, they have failed to erase the old one. As a result, two systems are created: one that is based on current technology and values and one that rests on historical trends and old thinking. These executives work under the mistaken notion that they will be able to develop new approaches, and at the same time all of what they are currently doing is held harmless. Nothing could be further from the truth.

These agencies experience significant amounts of stress and internal hemorrhaging as they try to maintain two systems that run off two different sets of values. This causes an increasing and unrelenting tension and confusion among staff, funders, people with disabilities, and management. The reason for this conflict is that these two models are incompatible and force an agency to speak one thing and do another.

ATTITUDES AND VALUES

The way to explain this situation is to discuss the difference between attitudes and values. People tend to speak their attitudes and live their values. Thus, an agency's mission statement, public relations material, and proclamations, which reflect its attitudes, might speak of individualized programs, consumer choice, quality services, and a wide scope of services. At the same time, its actions, approach, and results, which reflect its values, may foster something quite different. *In our opinion, one of the greatest indicators of an agency's values is its budget.* Where does the money go? How much of the resources are tied up in building, capital, and management? How much of the resources go to people, particularly those who have the most contact with individuals with disabilities?

What does its strategic plan look like? If it is running residential, vocational, or educational facilities, are there plans in place to close them? Does the agency see the conflict between owning the housing and also providing the services? And, finally, what role does the agency see for itself in the future in a system that will largely be controlled by people with disabilities acting as *customers* purchasing services as opposed to agency- and facility-driven approaches that provide for *clients*?

How does this agency explain to the individuals it serves why some are in supported employment and some are not? How does this agency explain to the individuals it serves that certain people have a choice of housemates and where to live and others have to remain in the residential facility? Ultimately, they have no explanation, and, for many of these agencies, the costs of transforming the entire system, including closing residential facilities and workshops, is simply too great. Colleen Wieck, Executive Director of the Minnesota Governor's Council on Developmental Disabilities, has characterized the resulting resistance to change as "the edifice complex."

Examining boards of directors shows that most executive directors control the information that goes to their boards. Most board members are volunteers who have an interest in a general sense or have family members with disabilities, which gives them a personal interest as well. If the executive is the major conduit of information to the board, then the executive's values will largely govern and reflect those of the board.

Unfortunately, too many executive directors, in the name of channels of command, limit the interaction with other staff and people receiving services and/or educational opportunities with the result that many boards are not aware that there is much they do not know. Therefore, decisions made tend to be more reactionary than strategic in nature.

Ideally, the attitudes and values of those governing an organizational structure would dictate the direction, spending, and management of the organization. The executive director, although a key player in the organization, should be employed to initiate the mission (implementation of values) of the organization. All other staff, from managers to those offering services, should know and represent those values as they carry out the mission in their capacities.

CLEAR MISSION

One way to test the entrenchment of values is to ask any assembled group of staff and/or board members in the organization this simple question: "Who can recite the mission of the organization?" See how many people in the group can recite, word for word, at least the major tenets of the organization's mission. *In our experience, less than 20% of all people at any level in an organization are able to recite even a portion of the organization's mission.* As a result, these organizations tend to be objectives-driven rather than values-driven.

Another pitfall awaits organizations that use the approach of going slowly and changing just a little at a time. Many of these organizational managers have the mistaken notion that if they have a clear goal in mind, they can manipulate change in incremental steps that can be organized, catalogued, predicted, and controlled. While their plans initially may have the enthusiastic support of staff and consumers, such support may erode over time as unpleasant suprises begin to occur.

Though the managers may be prepared for some rough spots along the way, many agencies we have worked with are shocked to find out that, in many cases, things not only do not improve quickly, in some cases, they become much worse.

In the path of change, the point at which the path dips below the status quo is the point that we call "critical mass." Here the agency reaches its low point. The goal seems the furthest away. Staff members who used to be friends are fighting. The agency is in significant turmoil and conflict.

In our experience, this occurs because the agency has left its plateau of security and has taken off on a path where it can see the summit but is faced with many unanticipated roadblocks and deadends. These are clashes of cultures, values, and approaches. Differing viewpoints emerge and different methods are started and stopped as the agency faces the most frustrating part of organizational change. At the point where people feel that the goal is unattainable they must continue to keep their eyes on the prize. There is no easy way to do this. In these uncharted waters for an agency, adaptations that are not based on old habits and old successes must be made.

Fortunately, in our experience, critical mass does not last a long time. If an agency can stay committed to its principles and continues to focus on the future and remembers its missions and values, its struggle will be rewarded.

THE NEW MODEL

The disability field is currently using models that are 30–40 years old. Group homes, sheltered workshops, and segregated schools are all ideas whose time has come and gone. They are extensions of the current model called the developmental model that still has independence as the highest and greatest good. Many people with severe disabilities will never live independently. But almost no one is truly independent. Almost everyone to varying degrees depends on the support, concern, and resources of those around us as part of our daily lives.

Unfortunately for people with disabilities, the term, independent, has largely come to mean without staff. In addition, where a person lives has largely determined the level of support afforded. In this old model only high functioning, ambulatory people who do not need 24-hour care are considered to be capable of living in an apartment independently. In this model, only the few who can make it through a continuum from most restrictive to least restrictive are considered successes. It is a facility-driven model that first acquires a piece of land to build a group home without regard to where the potential residents would like to live or with whom.

It is precisely the agencies that are not only challenging this old model, but are also offering specific suggestions and solutions that not only will survive, but will thrive in the 1990s. The reason is that they have changed the model.

A year before the Wright brothers took off at Kitty Hawk, they almost gave up on their quest for flight. They retreated to their garage in Dayton, Ohio, disillusioned because they still had not put a person in flight. It was back in their garage rather than on the hills at Kitty Hawk that they really learned how to fly. They were successful because, unlike their predecessors, they were willing to try something new. After their first flight, Orville Wright said that the thought of flying was actually more exciting than flight itself.

In order for organizations truly to become change agents, they must first transform themselves. Unfortunately, in too many organizations we have seen what we call, "reverse, get ready, play it safe planning." This involves making incremental plans based on a series of ifs such as: "If the state finds a new director, things will be better," "If we receive more money next year, we will reduce operations of the workshop," "If this state ever changes its funding formula, we will get out of our ICFs/MR." *What we see lacking in this approach is not a lack of money but lack of a clear statement of mission: vision, values, and direction.*

COMMON ELEMENTS OF MOVING TOWARD CHANGE

We continue to see pockets of excellence across the United States. We have seen small, loosely knit agencies, large established agencies, parents and people with disabilities themselves who have taken charge of their destinies. Other parts of this book deal with change at the level of the individual, the family, and state and national organizations. We focus our comments on private, for-profit or non-profit agencies that have made a commitment to move from a system of facilities to services and supports. There are definitely some common characteristics that have propelled these organizations to action. Some of these are discussed in the following sections.

A Sense of Urgency

For years, Gerry Provencal, Executive Director of the Macomb-Oakland Regional Center in Mount Clemens, Michigan, has said that real change takes place only when there is a sense of urgency. For instance, some of the agencies with whom we work have changed as a result of budget difficulties. Others have changed as a result of increased pressure from their constituencies. Still others have changed because they took a hard look at their values.

There was some sense of urgency in all these agencies that caused them to take immediate action. Long-range plans are fine, but if people do not know what they are going to do right away to reach the ultimate goal, then the level of discomfort that will cause action toward change simply does not exist.

A Commitment to Vision, Values, and Mission

The agencies that have been the most successful have a sense of common purpose that is embodied in their missions, missions based on the values of choice and community inclusion. Whether the mission is written or unwritten, we find in successful agencies that there is a universality of understanding that the work is being done for a specific purpose that is strategically planned for and long-term in nature. These agencies are not preoccupied with quick fixes for how to pass the next inspection or keep funding. They are struggling to develop an approach that is coherent and consistent with their espoused mission.

Truly transformed agencies tend to use the words "all people" when speaking about community participation and full inclusion. There is no caste system, no readiness, no incrementalism in their approach. They feel as passionately about the participation of the individual with the most severe disabilities as they do about the individual who is easiest to support.

Action, Not Study

Far too often, we have seen agencies that have strategic plans that stretch from months to years to decades. Whenever we hear that an agency wants to do something by the year 2000, we feel it will be best to revisit them in the latter half of 1999.

Agencies that are truly committed to change are action-oriented. While they certainly have plans, these plans have target people responsible and dates that are determined by months, not years. The short-term actions are strategic in nature and lead toward clearly defined long-term goals. Their evaluation of success is not in the eloquence of their words but the adequacy of their actions.

Holistic, Not Piecemeal Change

While agencies might start with transforming a piece of their organization (e.g., closing one dormitory, moving 10 people out of the workshop), they also recognize the importance of not recreating the very problems that they are attempting to solve. Thus, they do not add to the facility at the same time they are trying to reduce its operation and close it.

While these agency administrators realize that there will be a period of change, frustration, and transition shock, they realize that they cannot turn back. They see it as incompatible to have individuals in supported living and have a 200-person workshop still in operation. They see it is a conflict to have adults in supported employment and still be operating a segregated school. While their strategic plan may call for phasing in the changes over a period of years, they clearly understand that eventually all services to all people need to be transformed to be consistent with their mission.

Willingness To Take Risks

No change occurs without taking risks. It is our experience that agencies that are sitting on the sidelines, waiting until others take the lead, calling what is currently held out as exemplary practice a fad, are sealing their own fate.

In much of what we have learned about organizational change, it is precisely the people who are out in front who are likely to have the greatest impact on change. Agencies that jump in at the beginning are more likely to be at the table writing rules and regulations rather than being targeted by them. Agencies that are in at the beginning are likely to detect mistakes earlier and, therefore, correct them sooner.

These agencies realize that the lessons of the past may not be helpful in predicting the future. Finally, they do not see their primary role to be to keep people safe (although this is important); rather, they see their role as being to encourage people to be free and to shape their own lives.

Flexibility

The agencies with whom we have worked that have accomplished the most significant transformation have also been the most flexible. While they have a clear mission, they realize that not every plan will go exactly as predicted. Not every step will be clearly defined. As a result, they realize the need for flexibility. Because of their ongoing communication internally and externally, they are able to adjust and adapt to changing situations in the midst of organizational change and, as a result, accomplish more than if they had stuck with an original plan simply because it was the expectation at the time that they started.

Person-Driven, Not Facility-Driven Planning

Several years ago, we heard a provider say, "We are really into supported living, we plan on building a number of supported living facilities!" *Supported living facilities*—this is probably the ultimate oxymoron. There are many providers who speak the right words, but whose actions do not match.

Change-oriented agencies start with one individual and continue to plan one individual person at a time. They do not go to seek housing in the community until they find out where an individual would like to live and with whom. Their planning process is built not only upon needs but upon expressed preferences. They realize that some of the best planning takes place not around a table but in the community.

One of the difficulties in planning with people with disabilities, even if we ask what individuals want, is that their responses may be only repeats of their current and past experiences. Therefore, rather than asking whether or not an individual wants to live in a single family home or apartment, it may be important to take the individual physically to show him or her the difference between the two.

Ultimately, these plans have flexible. Choices of housemates, jobs, and level of support needed are fluid, not stagnant decisions. If 53% of the American public have the choice of changing their minds about marriage, then certainly people with disabilities should have the right to change their minds about housemates, level of support, and what services they desire.

Finally, we see these agencies going beyond just the participation of people with disabilities in their plans. In some of the most change-oriented agencies, we are seeing individuals direct the preparation of their plans. In some cases, this includes actually leading the team meetings, selecting who will attend the meetings, and interviewing and making final decisions on who their staff will be.

These agencies no longer see their role as being the hub of services but as being one of the spokes. The individual with disabilities needs to be the conductor of a symphony of support that changes in intensity, frequency, and tempo with his or her ever-changing world, instead of being an object of service provision.

CONCLUSION

Any real organization transformation and new approach must ultimately come down to a shared mission that is grounded in the future, not in the past. Our work with organizations has changed more in the last 2 years than in the previous 20. To keep resting on our past accomplishments, our history in the community, and our current stability is to miss the point. The fundamental issue is no longer whether people with disabilities are ready for this new way of thinking. In our experience, most of the resistance to change these days is coming from professionals, not people with disabilities.

REFERENCE

Beckhard, R., & Harris, R.T. (1977). *Organizational transitions: Managing complex change*. Reading, MA: Addison-Wesley.

16

Strategies To Help Agencies Shift from Services to Supports

Jerry Kiracofe

This chapter draws upon the experiences of "change agents" at the Human Services Institute (HSI) in Maryland in their work to help private agencies serving persons with developmental disabilities to move from traditional modes of service to an individualized support approach. Doing so entails a change from deference to professional judgments to more personalized relationships with people who have developmental disabilities and a deference to them as customers. The strategies outlined grow out of the institute's consultations with a service agency in Maryland and two service agencies in Delaware.

Before elaborating on these case studies, however, it is important to provide a context for the change that these agencies undertook. Therefore this chapter begins with an examination of the factors that indicate a willingness to change, moves to an exploration of the level or degree of change that may be necessary, and concludes with an outline of essential actions needed to make the transformation to the new paradigm.

WHY CHANGE?

The shift to a supports orientation is motivated by a desire to move from doing things in the right way as dictated by professional and bureaucratic mandates to doing the *right thing* for people with disabilities. The definition of the right thing depends on whose perspective or against what assumptions or criteria current

Jerry Kiracofe suffered an accident leading to his death prior to completing the chapter. The description of the Delaware Community Living Project was added by Pamela Butler-Stone, an associate.

models are assessed. Service providers and professionals may not see the system's failures, while people with disabilities and their families may be acutely aware of them.

If there is no acknowledgment by at least a few key administrators in a provider organization of the need for substantive, not merely cosmetic, change, then real change is unlikely to occur. Several internal factors or experiences may contribute to the realization by agency administrators that change is necessary. These include listening more intently to the customer (clients), staff dissatisfaction, learning about best practices, in-depth program evaluation, effective strategic planning, and reflecting on basic values and beliefs. The agency that seeks change solely in response to external forces without an understanding of some of these internal factors may prove to be a less than fertile field.

To begin the process, it is not necessary to understand fully all of the changes needed or even to have a clear picture of the desired alternative, but there must be sufficient recognition that the current way of doing things needs to be improved. Basically, there are three stages of awareness that an organization goes through in order to be ready for real change to take place. They are listed below:

- An *acknowledgment* that the current way of doing things does not work very well or needs improvement
- Some *awareness* of a better way or best practices in the field
- A substantial level of *commitment* to discover or explore new and different ways of doing things

Once there is a readiness to change, it is important to have some level of understanding about the degree of change that may be necessary. This is important to explore and clarify because there is a common tendency for organization executives to look for superficial change or quick fixes, such as reorganization, when major or framebreaking change is needed. The latter goes to the heart of the organization's mission and involves a reconceptualization at operational levels throughout an agency.

LEVELS OF CHANGE

For such a reconceptualization to take place, there needs to be not only some level of acknowledgment, awareness, and commitment, but some shared understanding of the depth of change that is desired or necessary. This is important since some within an agency may be amenable to change in one aspect of the operation but adamantly opposed to it on another level. Following are the four types of change that Thomas Bennett (1962) described as helpful in thinking about change in human services agencies:

- Change in structure
- Change in technology

- Change in behavior
- Change in values and assumptions

Change in Structure

A change in the structure of the organization is simply reorganizing the existing people or program elements. Such change may consist of moving a program from one location to another or reassigning or redefining the jobs of people who are responsible for various programs. For example, the change issue might be whether to keep the supported employment program under the director of the workshop or create a new supported employment department, or whether to maintain a separate residential program and individual support program or combine them into one community services department. Such considerations, while perhaps improving organizational efficiency, may amount to only a rearrangement, not a change in mission and substance.

Change in Technology

A change in technology is described by Bennett (1962) as an "adaptation" or "modernization" of the way to do things. These changes could be capital or physical in nature, for instance, acquiring the latest model heat-sealing equipment for a workshop production line to increase productivity, or training staff in the latest behavior management techniques to reduce disruptive behavior. Technology changes can be characterized as efforts to change or improve effectiveness.

Both change in structure and change in technology can be described as first-order change. While they may improve the efficiency and effectiveness of the organization, they do not address fundamental paradigm issues such as purpose, mission, or the basic beliefs that guide the organization. John O'Brien (1987) has characterized first-order change as simply exploring the question, Can we find "a faster, easier way to dig the hole you are standing in?" (p. 6).

Change in Behavior

Bennett (1962) also described change in behavior, which is a change in *how* things are done in the organization. For instance, an organization may change from a hierarchical, top-down decision-making process to the use of participatory management or quality circles, or may move from plugging people with developmental disabilities into predefined slots to designing individualized supports.

Sometimes changes in structure and/or technology can lead to changes in behavior; this may be deliberate or unintentional. However, changes in behavior almost always entail changes in structure and technology. For instance, an organization that moves from services to supports will find that its traditional, compartmentalized staff structure will constrain the new thrust.

Changes in Values and Assumptions

Changes in values and assumptions are the most profound level of change because they involve a shift in values or a renewed understanding of the operational ramifications of values already held. This level of change brings about a new way of thinking about the organization's customers and its role in responding to their expressed needs. This may mean a change from seeing people with disabilities as commodities in the program to seeing people as citizens of the community. This is a second-order change. It is important to emphasize that this is not just a change in language or terminology; rather, it is a fundamental change in how staff see people with developmental disabilities and how staff relate to their customers.

Bennett (1962) points out that a change in values and assumptions is essential for true change in behavior. For an organization, change in behavior means an unmistakable change in the culture of the organization. The culture of the organization is like the personality of an individual. When a paradigm change occurs, it is clear and obvious to all those involved. It may be manifest in a dismantling of conventional programs, a new individual planning approach, a commitment to retraining, or a refocus on mission and vision. There is no going back to the old way. It may take time to sort out all the pieces and implications of the new way, but that discovery process is an essential part of the paradigm change itself. John O'Brien (1987) refers to this level of change as second-order change, or, rather than how much wider or deeper we dig this hole we're standing in, the question becomes, Why are we standing in this hole?

STRATEGIES: TOP DOWN VERSUS BOTTOM UP

Human services agencies typically are organized in a traditional top-down hierarchical structure. In this structure a few people at the top (i.e., policy-makers, board members, executive directors, and program directors) have the power to control the organization. With this power comes the authority to mandate or bring about change. When change is ordered from the top down it usually results in first-order or structural/technical change. Behavioral change, which is needed to create a more collaborative partnership between staff and customers, is harder to bring about by fiat. Changes in behavior, as well as changes in values, usually grow out of experience shared across the organization. It is this bottom-up transformation of values and assumptions that triggers real change and eventually alters the behavior and culture of the organization.

However, bottom-up change without top-down support amounts to insubordination at best or revolution at worst. A few well-intentioned direct service workers struggling alone will find it very difficult, if not impossible, to force change on the administration or on established practices of the organization. Organizational inertia or overt control can frustrate change from the bottom, discouraging, redirecting, or even squelching the seeds of change before they develop. Such frustration of reform may be very damaging to the morale of the organization.

In addition, an executive director cannot make direct care or supervisory employees change their personal values and assumptions any more than a judge can make a bigot stop being prejudiced. Change that is dictated from the top down or forced from the bottom up results in frustration, low morale, and high staff turnover. An organization with this much dysfunction can have a devastating impact on the lives of the people who rely on the organization for support.

A strategy that HSI has found to work best is a holistic approach that combines both top-down and bottom-up principles. A process aimed at second-order change must have the blessings and active leadership of the board of directors, executive director, and other key people at the top of the organization and must also allow for real participation and discovery from the bottom up.

The most important roles for top and middle management are to provide leadership, to create and support a shelter for innovation to take place within the organization, and to provide an opportunity for the changes in values and assumptions to be discovered and understood at all levels of the organization. These conditions do not occur for everyone all at once, rather, they begin with a few key people and then spread rapidly and contagiously throughout the organization, shaping and influencing the values and assumptions of others as the shared experiences grow. Over time, this momentum results in a holistic change in the culture of the organization, that is, a paradigm change.

ELEMENTS FOR SUCCESSFUL CHANGE

Changing paradigms is difficult, tricky, and full of surprises. Managing this change takes strong leadership, good planning, an experienced guide, ample time, and a willingness to bend rules and take risks. Each of these qualities is greatly enhanced by the presence of strong individual commitment. Commitment is strengthened by personal experiences that reinforce the validity of the new ideas.

The key element of real paradigm change in an organization is the opportunity for key people to experience the change personally. These people then can become pioneers for change within the organization. The greater the number of influential people who become pioneers, the greater the likelihood that the change will be lasting. In designing a plan for organizational change, the challenge, then, is to create the opportunities that are likely to lead to these personal changes and channel these shared experiences of personal changes into a force or movement that can overcome the inertia and the investment people have in the current program.

HSI found that the best way to spawn a change in thinking is to go back to basics and start all over again with the people for whom the service exists, or, as Peters (Peters & Waterman, 1982) points out in *In Search of Excellence*, "the excellent companies really are close to their customers" (p. 156). This approach allows people to see or perceive through the eyes of the customer. This requires coming to know the person with a disability as a unique individual rather than as a collection of predetermined limitations associated with his or her label.

HSI's basic strategy is to guide a few key people through paradigm change, focusing initially on a limited number of customers. Focusing on just a few people as pioneers makes the change more manageable. The number of people selected in an organization can be as few as 5 or upward of 25, depending on the size of the organization, leadership, and the levels of commitment to change. These focus people become the pioneers who guide the rest of the organization through the change process. This pioneer group of staff and customers need to break out of old paradigms and to discover the efficacy of the organization's changing role for themselves.

HSI has now worked with over 10 private agencies and 10 local and state governments in exploring and guiding organizational transformations or paradigm change. Each situation was unique in politics, history, awareness, leadership, commitment, and the personalities of key leaders. Each situation required a somewhat different approach. However, there are eight important steps to promoting paradigm change and to creating a context for change to occur; they are listed below:

- Step 1. Establishing commitment
- Step 2. Building ownership of key stakeholders
- Step 3. Setting the tone
- Step 4. Trying a new way
- Step 5. Reflecting and sharing
- Step 6. Follow-up training and consultation
- Step 7. Analyzing findings and implications
- Step 8. Developing an action plan for constructive change

In the following sections, each of these steps is explained briefly and some experiences in applying each one are recounted.

Because real organizational transformation has its roots in the values, beliefs, assumptions, and behavior of its key people, no one process can guarantee a successful paradigm shift. An effective process can, however, create the opportunity for people to see things differently and experience paradigm change. If enough people come to see things differently, the stage is set for more systemic change.

Step 1. Establishing Commitment

It is critical to obtain a significant level of commitment to change from the executive director and other key stakeholders. The importance of this step cannot be overemphasized. The organization is really being asked to commit to the process of learning about a new way of doing things and to studying the implications of these new concepts for the organization. In other words, the organization needs to commit to a journey of discovery. Leadership must create an environment that will allow something creative, exciting, and different to happen and then learn from it. Businesses would call this research and development or planning for innovation.

Step 2. Building Ownership of Key Stakeholders

An organization is its people. Significant change is likely to occur only when key stakeholders in the organization are invested in the process and are willing to share in the learning, the analysis, and the implications. Therefore, HSI has found that the formation of a leadership team or change team is essential. Participants on the leadership team should represent all levels of the organization. Typically, the leadership team includes board members; key staff, such as the executive director, program directors, and coordinators; direct care staff; people receiving services; and some family members. Several interested community citizens should also be recruited to serve on this team. Since the emerging paradigm in the field is grounded in community, it is important to build active partnerships with community leaders. The leadership team should meet regularly throughout the discovery process, which may take from 6 to 18 months or longer. The length of time depends on many variables including size, history, leadership and management capability, time commitment, and overall scope of project.

Step 3. Setting the Tone

The change process should focus on a group of direct care supervisors, staff, and people served by the agency. These are the pioneers whose discovery process, hopefully, will filter through the entire organization. To set the tone, a series of events, including a kick off session, should be held to introduce the change process. These initial sessions serve to challenge the organization as well as build expectations and excitement about the endeavor.

Step 4. Trying a New Way

Paradigm change is most likely to occur when staff have positive experiences that challenges their vision of the people they serve and their relationship to them. The crux of the change process is these experiences.

Typically, service agency staff come to know their clients through the individual program planning process. Through this process they conduct their assessment, establish the person's needs, set goals, and plan a strategy for implementation. The planning process is the tool that links the person to the organization. Individual planning is a very valuable and practical thing to do. It is through the planning process that the organization's values and beliefs are operationalized on behalf of an individual. The individual planning process, therefore, is the place to begin the organizational change process.

To discover a new way of coming to know their clients as people, the participating staff must be introduced to a tool that is grounded in the values, beliefs, and assumptions of typical citizenship and community. HSI has found that personal futures planning, developed by Beth Mount (1992) (see Chapter 6) is the process most likely to raise the core issues that lead to paradigm change. Individual planning has three main stages: 1) preparation, 2) developing the plan, and 3) follow-along. Instead of a deficiency orientation to this process, personal futures planning stresses a person's gifts, capacities, and dreams. It is a plan for everyday community life—for citizenship. While personal futures planning is widely recognized as an individualized planning tool, HSI has found that it is also an effective discovery tool when linked to the larger strategic planning or discovery process integral to organization/systems change.

As part of the change process, the pioneering staff are given intensive training in the values and assumptions that underpin personal futures planning, as well as instruction in the planning process itself. The actual personal futures planning meetings are usually led by a change facilitator. It is HSI's intention that during the change process, some of the participating staff become competent facilitators for the future. Having these initial personal futures planning meetings run by an experienced facilitator enhances the quality of the planning meeting and serves as a model for staff in effective team leading and facilitation skills.

Step 5. Reflecting and Sharing

After all or most of the initial personal futures planning meetings have been held, HSI schedules an opportunity for people to come together and share what they have experienced and learned. This sharing is a forum for participants to celebrate their successes, share their frustrations, identify the obstacles and challenges they face, and renew their commitment to carry on. This forum also provides an opportunity for the guides and consultants to take a good reading on progress to date in order to make determinations about additional training, consultation, and other strategies that may be necessary to keep the change process on track.

Step 6. Follow-Up Training and Consultation

There are many variables that can influence the organizational change process. They may be manifest at the personal level, program level, organization level, or systems level. Each project presents a unique set of issues and challenges that must be addressed to keep the project on track and to maximize the opportunities for learning and change. The key to real success (first-order, rather than second-order change) is the role of the independent change agent or consultant who is guiding the change process. Every organization responds differently to the change process. An experienced guide will be able to identify critical opportunities and obstacles, as they surface, that provide key opportunities or "learning windows" for the pioneers. Based on experience, one can anticipate some of these opportunities and plan for them, though every change project brings unexpected windows that do not stay open long. This follow-up training and consultation stage provides a flexible, creative space in the process to respond to the issues that have surfaced along the way. This response may include a combination of additional training, retreats, and meetings or take the form of special assistance to one person or groups of people as necessary.

Step 7. Analyzing Findings and Implications

The previous steps are designed to create the opportunity for creative learning to take place. The organization has allowed the pioneers to try things differently and included the training and consultation necessary to maximize the learning opportunities. Now, the key participants, especially the leadership team, begin to analyze what has been learned and to study its implications for the organization now and in the future. Questions explored have to do with what worked, what did not, and why, and what should have been done more, less, or in a new and different way.

As a result of this analysis stage, the organization begins to understand the types of change that may be necessary to achieve paradigm change over time. While many of these changes are changes in structure or technology, particular attention must be given to identifying and exploring desired changes in values, assumptions, and behavior.

Step 8. Developing an Action Plan for Constructive Change

As noted, success ultimately depends on an organization's commitment to change. The agency places that commitment on the line as it prepares an action plan for constructive change. The process will undoubtedly produce a number of opportunities and challenges for the organization. Each organization will respond differently to what it has discovered through the process. Some will proceed cautiously with small, easily manageable steps as they move toward a new way of doing things. Other organizations will embrace bold initiatives designed to transform the organization fundamentally as soon as possible. Listed below are some of the factors that influence an organization's response:

- The initial commitment to the change process
- The effect of the individual experiences during the process
- The number of champions for change who emerge and their roles in the organization
- The degree of comfort with risk-taking that exists among key managers
- The degree of support generated from the board of directors and other key stakeholders
- The presence of leadership and the ability to manage

The action plan need not be a lengthy, complex document. A simple, straightforward plan that sets a clear direction for the future and the steps to be taken toward it is important. The plan should be brief, simple, and easy to read. The final plan should be put in the hands of all staff as well as other key people. The greater the number of people who are aware of the changes and have an opportunity to participate, the greater the likelihood that change will occur. The action plan can be used in staff training, orientation of new staff and board members, staff meetings, planning sessions, performance review sessions, and in many other creative ways. The plan becomes a symbol, as well as a tool, for change. It represents the organization's commitment to move toward lasting paradigm change.

STORIES OF PARADIGM PIONEERS

In thinking of pioneers, those early European settlers in North America who risked life and limb to chart new territory come to mind. They represented a small percentage of the larger population. They were willing to place themselves at risk in pursuit of a better life for themselves or others. They were willing to leave the security of what they had to reach for the unknown. They were carving a path for others to follow. They surely had fear, but they learned to live with it. They were bold, adventuresome, determined, and courageous.

That pioneering spirit lives on in many ways today, even though the context is very different, in those individuals and organizations willing to risk the security of the status quo and pursue a better way. They are willing to take risks, bend rules, and do whatever else is necessary for improvement. They wear their values on their sleeve; their vision of a better future is bright and clear. They are charting a path through a forest of regulation bureaucracy and social stereotypes. They often risk position and reputation in order to bring about changes in assumptions, structure, and behavior. These pioneers represent a small percentage of the professionals and organizations in the field; they are leaders who are willing to overcome their fear and take the bold steps necessary to discover a new way that eventually others will follow. The following sections describe some of what HSI learned from a few pioneering individuals and organizations with whom it has had the privilege of working.

The Citizenship Project

The story of Alternative Living, Inc. (ALI) and the Citizenship Project has been written about and shared at many conferences and workshops. The focus of the stories has been on the impact of the project, what ALI learned, and what they are doing about it. While this information is valuable to share and can be inspiring to others, one of the most important aspects, the discovery process, has not been described. The eight steps in that process are described below.

Background ALI is a private, nonprofit agency with a 10-year history of carrying out their mission to "provide quality residential services to people with developmental disabilities in Anne Arundel County, Maryland" (Alternative Living, Inc., 1978, p. 1). Before the Citizenship Project, with the exception of a group home serving six people, individuals lived in two- to three-person apartments or houses called alternative living units scattered throughout the United States. They served people, mostly adults, with a wide range of disability labels, primarily mental retardation. By all standards ALI was a well-run agency that provided quality residential services.

Carol Beatty, Executive Director of ALI, while proud of their programs and services, continually searched for new ideas and best practices in the field. This searching led her to question the true quality of their services, based on the emergence of a new way of thinking about the quality of life for people with disabilities. Though ALI met or exceeded the system's minimal standards for quality, ALI was not affording the people it served the opportunity to make basic lifestyle decisions that most people take for granted, such as where to live, with whom to live, what to do during the day, with whom to spend free time, and where to spend free time. Struggling with these and related issues brought the agency to a readiness for change. Carol sought out the assistance of HSI to design a strategy that would guide ALI on a path to renewal and redirection. Funding under a grant from the Maryland Developmental Disabilities Council made it possible for HSI to work with ALI, which gave birth to the Citizenship Project to discover a new way of providing services and to restructure the agency for pursuing this new direction.

Establishing Commitment While the desire for change was Carol's and the design for change was HSI's, the commitment to change needed to come from the key stakeholders in the agency, especially the board of directors. As is typical with most boards, there was mixed response to the ideas of the Citizenship Project. But Carol knew her board well. She had a strong relationship with the president, who shared her enthusiasm for the value of this change process. She had earned the trust of the board over the years and was able to secure the support and commitment needed to begin.

Building Ownership of Key Stakeholders As mentioned earlier, the best environment for change to take place is one in which there is leadership and support from the top, learning from the bottom up, and participation in the discovery process throughout the agency. To create this environment, ALI established a project team consisting of key people representing all levels of the agency: people receiving service and family members, direct care staff, mid-level supervisors, managers, and board members, as well as key people from outside the agency such as service coordinators, state government representatives, and community leaders. Much consideration was given to the recruitment of people who would be open to change and who were excited about the possibilities presented. The team members were asked to make a commitment to meet regularly throughout the project. They provided guidance, ideas, information, and support.

HSI has found that such a team is critical to the change process. It is important that the team be made up of people who are supportive, creative, and willing to take some risks. This team is not the place to put people who are opposed to change but whom the pioneers hope to bring around. There are effective ways to involve these people in the process, but bringing them on this team is not one of them. Because the road ahead is rocky, it is important to have creative thinkers, allies, and supporters on this team.

Setting the Tone The change process can be scary. Even the thought of change causes many to withdraw or resist. This response is unavoidable to some extent, but much can be done to set a tone that helps to alleviate some of the fear and even put some people at ease. People's fear is exacerbated when they are asked to accept some unknown future. Therefore, people should first be focused on the process, not the outcome. In fact, the outcome is an unknown for all involved in this process of discovery. The people invited to be a part of that discovery process will have a unique opportunity to chart the path the organization will take in the future.

Setting the tone at ALI was accomplished through a series of trainings and social gatherings. The social gatherings were open to all people involved with ALI: people served, family members, the board of directors, staff, and the community. These gatherings were designed to kick off the project by informing people of the commitment of ALI to the people they serve, to the learning process, and to pursuing a new standard of quality for the future.

The Citizenship Project was designed around 12 clients or focus people initially. Later three more people were added. A series of trainings and retreats were held for the key staff people (approximately 40 people) who worked with the focus people. The training, conducted by HSI, addressed broad issues including values, inclusion and community building, self-determination, and quality. The training focused on the individual planning process. The training provided a critical analysis of the existing individual program planning process and contrasted it with the personal futures planning process that was to be used in this project. This training set the tone for a new way of thinking, provided the framework for the discovery process, and introduced the nuts and bolts of the new way of planning.

Trying a New Way People can learn a great deal through training, but discovery takes place by putting what is learned into action. Staff were given an assignment during the training to spend time with the focus person with whom they would be working to come to know the individual again as a person, not as a client. Coming to know the person and see his or her capacities and strengths is a key part of the personal futures planning process. Personal futures planning is whole-life planning around a person's dreams and vision of a desirable future. It does not focus on the person's disability. Therefore, before planning can take place, a relationship and understanding must be developed. ALI selected a mix of focus people who represented all people served by the agency. Some of those chosen were clear about what they wanted and were seeking change. Some people provided great challenges, and it was difficult to figure out how to serve them well. Both children and adults were chosen. Some people had family involvement; some were totally dependent on staff.

Upon completion of this "capacity hunt," personal futures planning meetings were scheduled for the focus people and led by HSI. The personal futures planning meetings demonstrated a dramatically different way of listening and empowering the person with a disability, honoring what the person said, creating a vision for the future, and redirecting staff energy toward the desired vision.

Some meetings revealed dramatic information about a person that had been lost or undiscovered, for example, learning that Mary had a son with whom she was later reconnected. Some people's dreams appeared, on the surface, to be unrealistic. For example, Herbert wanted to run an ice cream store. Eventually, he operated his own ice cream cart. Others' dreams were very concrete and realistic, like Joe's desire to live in his own apartment, with his name on the lease, with no staff. Eventually, he realized that dream. The effectiveness of the personal futures planning process as a person-centered planning tool and a new way of coming to know people became evident. Each person's plan served to focus the agency's attention on him or her as an individual.

Reflection and Sharing Personal futures planning is generally recognized as an effective means of bringing people together to celebrate one person, to learn about his or her life, dreams, and desires for the future. Additionally, the personal futures planning process was used as a strategic planning tool, to generate learning from the bottom up.

Several retreats were arranged to provide opportunities for staff to share their experiences. These retreats not only provided learning opportunities, they allowed people to celebrate their accomplishments, share their frustrations, and build momentum and enthusiasm for what they were undertaking. It became clear early on in the process that something exciting was happening and that these staff were proud to be part of it. While HSI had anticipated that there would be some meaningful changes in the lives of the focus people, they had not anticipated the significant positive impact these changes would have on the morale of the staff. Some staff were so moved that they felt a need to make a public confession to their coworkers of their initial doubts and their new found belief.

These were moving expressions of personal paradigm shifts. For some it was dramatic and all at once; for others it was subtle and happened over time. For some, their experiences reaffirmed what they always believed and reminded them why they had entered the human services field to begin with. For a few the changes were so threatening that they eventually left the agency.

Follow-Up Training and Consultation Another reason for holding the retreats was that they provided an opportunity for the consultants (guides) to learn how things were going, where people were stuck, and what additional information and/or assistance would be helpful. As a result of what was learned during those retreats, several follow-up trainings and discussion groups around specific issues were conducted. There were also numerous formal and informal meetings, one on one and in small groups.

Quick access to information, consultation, and support is critical during difficult times in the change process. In addition to providing training, HSI also established a presence at ALI. HSI had a space with little more than a desk, a chair, a few plants, and a large poster with the symbol for the Citizenship Project. The importance of this presence cannot be overstated. During the process of organizational paradigm change, the forces of inertia, resistance, and reverting to the old way of doing things are tremendous. HSI's presence symbolizes ALI's commitment to change, to finding a new way.

Analyzing Findings and Implications Not until after 15 months of listening and discovering from the focus people did the agency turn to analysis and planning. IT is critical that adequate time be spent to allow staff to internalize and share their experiences, to really come to know the people they serve, to renew their commitment to them, and to discover that they are not responsible *for* people with developmental disabilities but responsible *to* them. The paradigm shift occurs with this realization. ALI experienced this shift during the 15-month period. Even many staff who were not directly involved were touched by what was happening. The shift did not occur for everyone in the agency during this period, but it happened for most of the key stakeholders. A large retreat was held with all the people who were involved in the project to not only share once again what they were learning, but also analyze it. Issues examined were the implications of what they were learning, and what changes would be needed to be more responsive to people's desires and dreams. A great deal of time and thought went into this analysis. It was learning from the bottom up, with an eye to redefining ALI's purpose and mission.

For many of the people involved, the way of thinking changed early on. This was captured in the executive director's update to the board of directors not long into the project. Carol reported that she was not sure where they were going to end up as a result of this, but she knew there was no going back. ALI would never be the same.

Developing an Action Plan for Constructive Change As exciting and as significant as the learning was to this point, it could all have been dismissed as simply an interesting project, diffused through competing interests and demands, or been allowed to die from lack of constructive action. Often, the best of intentions are lost because there is no plan of action.

All steps, up to this point, served to make the agency ready to plan for the future based on a new set of assumptions and beliefs. ALI was not ready for fundamental change. Leadership and key staff were determined, and felt obligated, to climb out of the hole they were in and set upon a new path.

Strategic planning is a process in which an organization reexamines its core assumptions and beliefs, creates a shared vision of a desired future based on these beliefs, establishes a clear mission to guide the agency toward that vision, conducts an analysis of the gap between where they are now and the desired vision, and commits itself to the constructive actions necessary to move toward the vision. In many ways, a strategic plan for an organization is like a personal futures plan for an individual. Now that ALI had rediscovered itself, it was ready to plan for a desired future. HSI guided ALI through the planning process. The project team, the board of directors, and other key stakeholders were involved. A key part of the process is to create a shared vision and establish a new mission. All planning then is setting goals to accomplish that mission. Part of the change in ALI's new mission statement was from "a provider of quality residential services" to a dedicated agency set up to: "empower, enable and support the people who rely on ALI to establish and maintain a lifestyle of their choice in the community" (Alternative Living, Inc., 1988, p. 7). ALI in turn identified the need for organizational changes to fulfill this mission.

The agency still faces many obstacles and challenges internally as well as externally. They are still in the throes of change, still on a journey of discovery. However, the process of discovery now has a charted course and definitive destination.

The Delaware Community Living Project

As in Maryland, there were several leaders in Delaware who felt an increasing sense of discontent with the existing ways of delivering services to people with disabilities. The Delaware Community Living Project (DCLP) emerged from a shared commitment by these leaders to discover more innovative and effective ways of providing services in Delaware.

This commitment found a vehicle for action through a 3-year grant from the Delaware Department of Public Instruction. Funding was awarded to two residential provider agencies, the Salvation Army and Ken-Crest Services, both of which work in partnership with the Delaware Division of Mental Retardation (DMR). These agencies then turned to HSI for assistance in designing a long-term change strategy that would be implemented on a small scale. HSI, Ken-Crest, the Salvation Army, and DMR designed a 3-year demonstration project with the personal futures planning process as the cornerstone.

The project was designed to focus initially on only six individuals with disabilities. However, the resulting changes in the lives of these six individuals were so positive that people throughout the state began questioning why the current system did not facilitate this kind of change. What they realized was that the current individual program planning process did not support an active and meaningful dialogue with the person receiving services about his or her hopes and dreams for the future. In contrast, the personal futures planning process was seen as a forum where not only did that dialogue occur, but follow-up action on the part of the person and members of his or her support system resulted in real change that had previously been considered impossible.

Consequently, the DCLP expanded its scope to become a full-scale systems change strategy, built upon the personal futures planning approach, to have a positive impact on the quality of life for all people with disabilities in Delaware. As in the Citizenship Project, the design incorporated the eight core steps to create a fertile environment within which paradigm change could occur. However, an added feature of the DCLP was the active and ongoing involvement of state-level representatives from DMR on the DCLP leadership team. Their participation provided an important conduit for bottom-up change to have direct impact upon state policies and regulations.

One watershed event in the 2nd year of the project was a statewide retreat designed to broaden the base of support. Project participants as well as top administrators from all agencies and advocacy groups were invited. The retreat began with the creation of a shared vision of a desirable future for Delaware. This vision was of people with disabilities empowered to be full citizens with their lives centered in community.

While there was a high level of energy and excitement about the vision, many retreat participants, especially direct service workers, were concerned that there be clear strategy for translating the vision into concrete and effective action. Therefore, as a next step the leadership team drafted a set of clear guiding principles to provide a new frame of reference for decision-making at all levels in the system, from direct service to the top levels of policy-setting. The resulting Proclamation of Beliefs and Guiding Principles reflects a high level of input from all levels within the system.

The retreat provided two essential underpinnings to the project. Equipped with the new vision and guiding principles, the leadership team realized that there was still a need for a more intensive plan of action to bridge the gap between the vision and the way services were currently being delivered. The team therefore recommended the formation of a Coalition for Change, directed to the steps listed below:

- Identifying key areas in which current practices violate, impede, or interfere with the adopted guiding principles
- Analyzing the gaps between existing practices and the desired guiding principles
- Recommending constructive strategies that will help close the gap between the current reality and the desirable future of the Coalition

The members of the Coalition represented people who receive services, family members, human services professionals, and legal advocates.

The work of the Coalition resulted in 13 bold and far-reaching recommendations with key action steps and proposed time frames. These recommendations ranged from modifying policies, to revamping the individual program planning process, to reviewing procedures for ensuring consistency between contractual services and guiding principles, to ensuring that people with disabilities have control over their finances.

Implementation of these recommendations has already begun. For example, all intermediate care facilities for persons with mental retardation (ICFs/MR) in one county have been converted to smaller homes. This was done by shifting existing resources and required no increase in funding. DMR has underscored its commitment to follow through on the recommendations by creating a vision paper for the state. Some key elements of the vision paper are listed below:

- DMR services in the future will enable people with disabilities to exercise maximum choice and independence, with the Proclamation of Beliefs and Guiding Principles as the frame of reference.
- DMR's administrative services will become streamlined, with fewer layers between the individual and top administrator, thus ensuring more direct communication and more responsive services.
- Policies and procedures will be rewritten to be fully congruent with the Proclamation of Beliefs and Guiding Principles.
- All ICFs/MR in the state will be converted to smaller homes that provide an environment that reflects the individual's own personal lifestyle and choices.
- Contracts with provider agencies will include performance standards based upon the Proclamation of Beliefs and Guiding Principles.

Delaware has embarked upon a major paradigm shift for the way services are delivered. This shift will be reflected in lifestyles encompassing choice and empowerment for people with disabilities in Delaware.

SUMMARY

As evident from the ALI Citizenship Project, shifting from facility-based residential service operations to person-centered operations is a major undertaking. It takes leadership, time, and an approach mindful of planning. Outside assistance can be of considerable benefit in guiding the organization through this challenging process. Building the ownership and commitment of agency leaders and key stakeholders is critical. The personal futures planning process is invaluable as a means of gaining a true understanding of the supports paradigm and experiencing and witnessing its rewards firsthand. Training opportunities and planned opportunities for reflection and for sharing the experiences throughout the organization are also important in order to maintain momentum.

As indicated by the Community Living Project in Delaware, organizational change projects have the power to affect the course and pace of change systemwide. As demonstration projects and with the active involvement of the state leadership, the projects can lead to important changes in state policies and programs and to replication by similarly situated organizations throughout the state.

REFERENCES

Alternative Living, Inc. (1978). *Articles of incorporation.* Anne Arundel County, MD: Author.

Alternative Living, Inc. (1988). *Strategic plan.* Anne Arundel County, MD: Author.

Bennett, T.R. (1962). *The leader and the process of change*. New York: Association Press.

Mount, B. (1992). *Person-centered planning: Finding directions for change using personal futures planning. A sourcebook of values, ideals, and methods to encourage person-centered development*. New York: Graphic Futures, Inc.

O'Brien, J. (1987). *Discovering community: Learning from innovations in services to people with mental retardation*. Lithonia: Responsive Systems Associates.

Peters, T., & Waterman, R. (1982). *In search of excellence*. New York: Harper & Row.

17

Field in Search of a Home

The Need for Support Personnel To Develop a Distinct Identity

James A. Knoll and Julie Ann Racino

The following dialogue is an example of conversations that are occurring with increasing frequency in colleges and universities as individuals who have been defining best practices in community support for people with disabilities attempt to pursue higher education.

Student: Hello, Professor. I'm interested in enrolling in your graduate program in community support for people with disabilities.

Professor: Thanks for calling. A number of the faculty are doing research related to services and supports for people with disabilities, but our degree programs are associated with the various professional disciplines at the University: special education, social work, rehabilitation counseling, psychology, family studies, occupational therapy, public administration, nursing, and so forth. At the institute we have a course on community inclusion which students from all of these departments take as an interdisciplinary elective. Why don't you tell me a little about your work and your interests. Let's see if we can figure out what program is appropriate for you.

Student: Well, OK. I've been working in services for people with disabilities for about a dozen years. I have a bachelor's degree in psychology and was planning

This chapter was prepared with partial support from the Administration on Developmental Disabilities, United States Department of Health and Human Services under Grant No. 07DD0368, and from the Research and Training Center on Community Integration, Center on Human Policy, Division of Special Education and Rehabilitation, School of Education, Syracuse University, through Cooperative Agreement H133B00003-90 from the National Institute on Disability and Rehabilitation Research, United States Department of Education. No official endorsement of the opinions expressed here by either the United States Department of Health and Human Services or the United States Department of Education should be inferred.

to go on to graduate school after working for a year or 2. In my senior year I started working as weekend relief staff in a group home for people with severe multiple disabilities. After I graduated I worked there full time, and after about a year I was made house manager and later became assistant director for residential services. During the next 3 years I helped to set up our respite program, took a few graduate courses, and wrote our agency's proposal for a supported employment program. When that was funded I moved into the role of coordinator for that program until I became assistant director of Connect, a new supported living agency. At that point, my director suggested that I really needed to get that graduate degree. So here I am.

Professor: That's great experience. I'd love you to be here as a full time student working on our community inclusion project. But as to an appropriate graduate program, I am not sure what has the best fit with your career. When I faced a similar dilemma, I was working as a teaching aide so I didn't have any problem using special education as a jumping off point for my broader interests in community support. Somehow, I don't get the feeling you view an education degree as an option.

Student: No, not really. I did think about it, but my interest has little to do with schools, and none of the other disciplines seem quite right either. When I heard about your course and got the mistaken impression it was part of a new program, it seemed ideal. The whole idea of a program that focused on understanding the lives of people with disabilities within the community context that taught students how to develop strategies for building support systems and creating change seemed right on target. I've worked with a lot of psychologists, occupational therapists, social workers, rehabilitation counselors, and educators and little pieces of what they do seem to fit my needs. But going into a program in one of those fields seems off target for me; after all, I am pretty clear on my career. Well, thanks for your time. I've got to think about this and see if there are any other options. I hope you'll start that program in community inclusion.

Professor: Thanks for calling. I will let you know if I come up with another solution that fits your needs. And I will give that program in community inclusion some thought. Good-bye.

Those personnel who are employing best practices are discovering that in their daily work they are defining a new role—perhaps a new profession. In pursuing higher education they are discovering that the traditional programs either have not responded to this new reality or have responded with minor modifications of existing programs.

The emerging supports paradigm offers people with disabilities, policymakers, administrators, family members, friends, advocates, and service providers a new perspective to use in re-examining the relationship of agencies and the system of services to people with disabilities. At its most basic, this fundamental re-examination reflects the realization that, until the 1980s, community services were defined by institutional models. In the 1980s, as states such as New Hampshire (see chap. 7, this volume) began to realize a goal of institutional closure and increasing numbers of people with disabilities and their allies began to challenge group homes and sheltered workshops as the archetype of community living and work, the fallacies inherent in the predominant institutional model became evident.

Only by finally abandoning institutional models and striving to actualize the concept of community inclusion has the field begun to appreciate the power of the old paradigm. It has taken a generation of struggle with the meaning of concepts like choice, control, quality of life, personal satisfaction, and community membership to begin to understand the power of the program/facility-centered model and the extent to which it reflects a way of thinking that is fundamentally alien to the way human beings wish to live.

One aspect of the emerging paradigm has been the rejection of terms like "community-based alternatives" and "home-like environments." Once the segregation of the past is finally rejected, the field can assert that: 1) there are no community-based alternatives, the only alternative is the *community*; and 2) service systems should not develop homelike environments for groups of people; rather, they should figure out how to support individuals in *their own homes* (O'Connor & Racino, 1993; Racino & O'Connor, 1994). In other words, the supports paradigm is once and for all in and of the community.

Nowhere is the reality of the supports paradigm more evident than at the level of direct interaction between the person with a disability and his or her service provider. In fact, it is at this micro level that the new way of thinking was defined (Bradley & Knoll, 1990; O'Brien & O'Brien, 1992; Racino, O'Connor, & Walker, 1993; Taylor, Bogdan, & Racino, 1991; Traustadottir, 1991). For it has been in personal one-to-one interactions that the inherent and unresolvable tension between a program-centered model and the hopes and dreams of an individual must be confronted. At the macro level, state and federal regulators, funding agencies, and university training programs largely continue to do business as they always have.

This chapter contends that a new, distinct role that focuses on community support is indeed evolving. The authors hope to stimulate further conversation about how the field, and particularly the traditional human services disciplines in higher education, can and should respond to these new challenges. While the authors feel that no single response to this developing challenge is the right one, they do feel that the development of a systematic approach to educating support personnel is crucial to continued progress.

CRISIS IN THE COMMUNITY WORK FORCE

In a paper entitled, "Crisis in the Community," Smull (1989) cogently summarized the significant challenges confronting efforts to develop a true community system of services for people with developmental disabilities. He concluded that the multiple fiscal, work force, regulatory, programmatic, and community problems inherent in the proliferation of group homes and other facility-centered models argued for adoption of a new approach to community services based on the concept of support. This new way of thinking with its rejection of the historical continuum and its mobilization of the unique array of supports each individual needs to live in his or her own home and participate in the life of the community is a new insight

(Ferguson & Olsen, 1989; Johnson, 1985; Klein, 1992; Minnesota Governor's Planning Council on Developmental Disabilities, 1987; Taylor, 1988; Taylor, Racino, Knoll, & Lutfiyya, 1987). In its simplicity and novelty it continues fundamentally to challenge practices in a service system that is still driven by program-centered models.

In a relatively short time supported living has moved from small local efforts to being touted as the new Jerusalem, the cost effective salvation for federal agencies, state departments, and local providers overwhelmed by demand for services. There has been widespread support for this movement by organizations and individuals confronting the demand for quality services (National Association of Private Residential Resources, 1991, 1992; Smith, 1990). Additional validation of supported living is seen in Medicaid's exploration of the concept through the eight Community Supported Living Arrangement (CSLA) projects.

Although many organizations and individuals have changed their vocabulary, the actual operation of agencies and the style of individual professionals remain substantially the same. The authors feel that the basic values of personal choice and control, individual quality of life, valued roles, and full community participation for people with developmental disabilities do indeed require the fundamental transformation of words and practice inherent in the supports paradigm. However, this promise will be lost if the field does not re-educate itself and develop new workers who both are imbued with this new way of thinking and have the skills needed to undertake the far-reaching changes that lie ahead.

Sense of Mission

Smull (1989) highlighted work force issues as one symptom of the crisis in the community. He pointed to the size of the needed work force, the cost of salaries, and issues of the quality of the work force pool as major barriers to developing a nationwide system of group homes that could begin to meet people's needs. Later, Braddock and Mitchell (1992) provided a data base that validates the significant work force problems confronting the system of community services. The authors feel that these work force issues become even more acute in striving to establish support as the basic organizing paradigm for services to people with disabilities and their families. The supports paradigm, by increasing reliance on informal supports and the generic resources of the community, may alleviate some of the pressures related to the number of employees needed in a system of traditional residential services. However, the quality and skill of the smaller number of individuals who will play full time roles in this new system of support become all the more crucial. The authors feel that the way in which this work force crisis is addressed will make or break this wave of change.

As in the early days of deinstitutionalization, many of the people currently involved in defining what it means to provide support are guided by an evangelical zeal (e.g., O'Brien & O'Brien, 1992). They have a sense of mission. But, as the process of deinstitutionalization has demonstrated, *a permanent system cannot be established and maintained solely on the fervor of the first generation of reformers*. The history of services to people with disabilities contains too many examples of reform efforts that lost direction either after the departure of the charismatic leader or when the supposedly reformed system encountered fiscal or programmatic barriers. Then the protective asylums became custodial institutions; the local Arc home became a highly regulated restrictive intermediate care facility for persons with mental retardation (ICF/MR); community inclusion and participation were translated into a special bowling league; and, finally, personal choice and self-determination were somehow transformed into a rationale for abandonment in substandard housing in a marginal neighborhood. The sense of mission is crucial, but structures, such as a broader base of training in higher education, must be set in place to communicate this mission and ensure that direction and quality are maintained as new workers and administrators come into the field who lack personal knowledge of, and experience with, the models and problems of the past.

Capacity Building

While there is growing pressure to replicate the success of organizations that have adopted a supports mission, major gaps in the system needed for this expansion seriously threaten the field's ability to respond. Because of the origin and nature of many of the organizations that have begun to define the supports paradigm, relatively little effort has been put into developing mechanisms to communicate their lessons to the rest of the field.

It must be remembered that the very concept of supported living did not evolve from university-based demonstration projects or mandates from within the formal system of services. Rather, this reform had its origin in grassroots efforts of people with disabilities, their allies, and service providers who were disenchanted with the restrictions and limitations put on them by the status quo. In their efforts they passively, and sometimes very actively, sought to work around the barriers to true choice, control, and community membership erected by the system within which they were forced to operate (cf. Taylor et al., 1991).

The net result is that much of what is central to the lives of these organizations is very alien to the standard programs of professional preparation and the inservice training agendas of the typical human services agency. What they are doing is rarely discussed in special education, social work, psychology, rehabilitation counseling, occupational therapy, public administration, or other classes in universities. The required program of inservice training continues to place a major emphasis on developing skills for direct care workers, which are slightly different from the training programs required for institutional attendants. Most of these programs yield trainees with little or no basic orientation to their central role as working *for* people with disabilities to support community participation (Knoll & Ford, 1987). For these reasons organizations that have embraced support as their mission have rejected the traditional training vehicles and set up their own programs of personnel development often based on mentoring of new employees by more experienced workers (Racino, 1990).

This lack of sufficient training capacity does not augur well for the development of a national cadre of people well prepared to transform the traditional system of services for people with developmental disabilities into a system of person-centered supports. Universities are not preparing enough people with this orientation; inservice training is not geared in that direction; and, while the ground breaking organizations provide a base of experience to build on, they are not geared to the massive education effort that is needed. Only by realizing that support is taking its rightful place in the mainstream can the field begin to address the need to develop support personnel.

As first steps in discussion of this realization, the rest of this chapter explores the identity of the type of personnel the field needs and the body of knowledge that defines this field and finally returns to the issue of an appropriate home identity for support personnel.

FORMING AN IDENTITY

The truth is that the field of services for people with developmental disabilities has not yet come to terms with the fact that, within the community context, it is developing a unique identity and a body of knowledge that is not currently owned by any of the traditional disciplines that have in the past defined the field. Central to this has been a corporate process of consciousness raising which an increasing number of authors have seen as meeting Kuhn's (1962) criteria for a paradigm shift, a basic re-orientation of a particular field (Bradley & Knoll, 1990; Racino, 1992; Racino, Walker, O'Connor, & Taylor, 1993). This transformation has occurred as organizations and individual professionals have begun to see the community and not the program—whether the clinic, the special class, the group home, or the workshop—as the proper arena of their activity. This process of consciousness raising involves the ultimate in community inclusion, that is, breaking down the visible and invisible barriers of the disability ghetto.

A Change of Consciousness

As the field has moved out of the disability ghetto, where everything was defined in reference to individual deficits, specialized services or interventions, or the negative stereotypes often imposed on people with disabilities and the individuals working with them, it has been forced to grapple with real estate, public relations, self-help groups, employer incentives, public transportation, concerned neighbors, union representatives, and a myriad of other topics seldom discussed in many special education, rehabilitation, psychology, or social work classes. Field professionals have found themselves, with all their professional credentials, needing to turn to people with disabilities, neighbors, and family members with no advanced degrees to learn the lessons essential to succeed within the new community context.

Working for People Most workers in the field have found their relationship with people with disabilities turned on its ear. They were trained to be professional helpers by assessing and teaching people with disabilities, designing individualized plans and programs for them, and modifying their behavior. But once workers in the field went outside the ghetto, once they started really listening to people and their families, they started hearing that people wanted education, homes, jobs, friends, and family. These goals, which were written off as unrealistic expectations, were only unrealistic within the context of the ghetto. Field workers quickly began to learn two very important lessons: 1) their carefully managed, normalized environments were one of the major limitations imposed on the people they said they were committed to helping; and 2) individuals with disabilities had a different view of what was truly supportive to them (e.g., Kennedy, 1993; Moore, 1993).

Once workers in the field moved beyond the limits of the ghetto and started letting themselves learn from people with disabilities, they found their roles being redefined as assisting people who might have very significant physical and mental disabilities in achieving the most natural, and varied, human goals. Workers now find themselves trying to figure out what it means to work *for* people with disabilities. The term "client" is no longer a meaningless euphemism that thinly disguises the fact that the people so identified are commodities traded on the human services market (Biklen & Knoll, 1987; McKnight, 1987). Those who assume helping roles in community services now are called on to act as agents both for specific individuals to assist them in resolving the problems of housing, food, health care, income, education, employment, transportation, recreation, and human relationships, and for groups as they act to make the agencies and systems that effect their lives more responsive.

New Priorities The profound nature of this change in consciousness leads to a complete redefinition of the priorities for people in these new roles. No longer do workers in the field concentrate on identifying deficits; they now concentrate on identifying individual and collective strengths. Unrealistic expectations based on diagnostic categories are abandoned in favor of exploring personal hopes, dreams, and goals. Minimal expectations in terms of the achievement of programmatic goals are superseded by high expectations related to personal goal attainment. A crisis intervention mentality is replaced by an aggressive crisis prevention perspective, which identifies formal and informal resources, develops multiple back-up strategies, and is based on the premise that support is not a program that ends, but a long-term commitment. Finally, and perhaps most important, the priority traditionally given to documenting effective intervention is supplanted by the need to foster and develop positive relationships.

Being of the Community Reframing the relationship workers in the field have with the community is at least as profound as the new relationship with people with disabilities. The community is no longer seen as an adversary, like the irate neighborhood association opposing the group home; rather, it is seen as a group of potential allies who have the same desires and dreams and confront the same problems of neighborhood safety, affordable housing, quality education, effective governmental services, access to health care, and job security. Workers in the field are forced to balance the role of being assertive advocates seeking to break down barriers, with becoming effective allies in helping to design cooperative solutions to common problems.

Increased immersion in the community leads to the awareness that a simplistic understanding of the term "independence" as rugged individualism, and "productivity" as solely full-time paid employment, plays into a competitive frame of mind, which is particularly dangerous for individuals with severe disabilities. The necessary antidote is a deeper, cooperative perspective that defines community in terms of *interdependence; contribution; valuing difference;* and *respect for diversity of views, values, and approaches.* Not only does this cooperative perspective better serve the needs of people with severe disabilities, it highlights the fact that people with disabilities do contribute to the community and provides a basis for the kind of reciprocity that nurtures the development of the informal supports currently lying dormant in many neighborhoods.

An Evolving Role

As Bradley and Knoll (1990) have outlined, the change in consciousness has been an evolutionary process as people with disabilities, advocates, and professionals have learned from three distinct stages in the 30 years of reform from the 1960s to the 1990s. The initial effort was largely motivated by reaction to the abuse endemic in institutions and forced a definition of a minimal standard for *quality care.* The success of new community programs fostered the era of deinstitutionalization; this saw the articulation of standards for *program quality,* which was defined by consistent client growth through achievement of developmentally appropriate goals. Today brings the challenge of supporting *full* community membership and *quality of life* for people with disabilities. Each of these three stages has seen a concomitant evolution in the competencies required of professionals in the field and changes in the definitions of the direct care worker and the case manager. The evolutions of these three roles contribute directly to defining the new role of support personnel.

Professional Role Efforts to identify the appropriate competencies for professionals working in the field of developmental disabilities have paralleled the three stages in the modern history of the field. This process finds concrete form in the changing mission of university affiliated programs (UAPs) and their mandate to conduct interdisciplinary education of professionals. Within the UAP network the construct of interdisciplinary education has become the vehicle for identifying the specific body of knowledge relevant to providing effective services to people with developmental disabilities who are "frequently un-served or underserved" by standard programs of professional preparation.

The establishment of UAPs by the Developmental Disabilities Act of 1970 (PL 91-517) clearly was guided by efforts to provide quality care for people with developmental disabilities. The concept of being "interdisciplinary" was used to capture the nature of services needed by people with developmental disabilities. These individual's disabilities were described as requiring a complex, lifelong, coordinated array of health, psychological, educational, and social services. Therefore, any professional who was to have a primary focus on serving this group of people had to be able to work cooperatively with a variety of professionals in other disciplines. In practice, the concept of being interdisciplinary was actualized in UAP assessment and evaluation clinics, which had a largely medical focus and demonstrated the effectiveness of the team approach to develop a comprehensive picture of each person's needs.

During the era of deinstitutionalization and community-based program development, the experience of UAPs in developing and refining interdisciplinary team process provided a firm basis for defining one of the crucial characteristics of a quality program. As community programs developed, the construct of interdisciplinary process was broadened from the traditional clinical setting to any residential, educational, or vocational program that served individuals with complex, lifelong disabilities. Simultaneously, the educational efforts of UAPs were able to refocus interdisciplinary education to this somewhat broader agenda. What remained constant in this evolution was the firmly established disciplinary identity of the team members (e.g., as physicians, psychologists, nurses, educators, and therapists) and the primacy of the team in establishing developmentally appropriate goals for the people in the program.

The current reform effort seriously challenges the interdisciplinary team as the dominant model for decision-making in all programs supporting people with developmental disabilities. The source of greatest concern is the way the current structure maintains a hierarchical relationship between the professionals, the person with a disability, and the family and does not provide for participation by members of the community. As noted, workers engaged in support work find such professionalized models dysfunctional as they work within the community.

While the concept of interdisciplinary education as a vehicle for developing professionals seems increasingly important, it is evident that the meaning of the term and needed competencies for professionals must continue to evolve to meet the challenge of the supports paradigm. Structures such as the national research and training centers (RTCs) play an important role in the development of a cadre of trained personnel through their coordinated programs of research, training, and information dissemination that are designed to promote state-of-the-art practices. However, research continues to take precedence over systematic efforts at personnel preparation, and the relationship and influence of the RTCs on training programs remains a difficult challenge. It is evident that not only must the needed competencies of professionals evolve to meet such challenges, but that major changes will be necessary in formal, well-established organizations, with strong ties to traditional disciplines and models of training and organizational values and structures that conflict with a supports paradigm.

Direct Care Role The direct care worker in the field of developmental disabilities has been regarded with a remarkable degree of ambiguity. At times the literature and the rhetoric of professionals highlights the interaction of direct care personnel and people with disabilities as the crucial relationship in any program. Yet, professional behavior in team meetings as well as in the literature on effective programs tends either to totally disregard the individuals providing direct care or to regard them with disdain as mere ciphers. This latter attitude and the dubious title of "paraprofessional" reflects the marginal status that this culture typically confers on people who fulfill these caring roles.

It is this frequently marginalized group of direct care workers who have made a major contribution in challenging the status quo in services and helping to define support. This contribution comes from the fact that it is direct care workers who personally experience the barriers to full community membership inherent in the typical approach to services. They are the ones who really know and experience the communities in which they live and work with people with disabilities. And, most important, they are often the only ones sitting in a team meeting who really know the person for whom the team is planning. Once organizations begin to treat direct care workers as more than mere functionaries, who implement the programs designed by professionals, and give them a clear mandate to support people, they will be able to rise to the occasion and help set direction for the whole field.

In briefest summary, this group has moved from being attendants to program aides to the realization that this type of work entails at least two very distinct roles. The first role is captured by the position of personal care attendant, an individual trained and hired by a person with a disability and accountable to that person. The second role, which has evolved from the traditional group home worker, is the community worker; the person who helps make connections, mobilizes resources, and plans back-up systems. The field must realize that the two roles are distinct and are essential. The first has been well-defined by the independent living movement. The second is evolving and still needs clarification. Part of the process of clarification involves understanding the relationship between these two roles, that is, whether they are mutually exclusive, and if not, how they can both be fulfilled by the same person.

Case Management When the role of support personnel is described, the initial reaction is often, "Oh! You mean a case manager." While it is true that in some organizations an individual with a title like case manager may fulfill a central role in providing support, most case managers perform primarily bureaucratic functions that are inappropriate for support personnel.

The role of case manager has undergone an evolutionary process that parallels the other two roles discussed. Typically, the social worker on an interdisciplinary team in an institution or clinic explored a person's social history and relationship with family, identified appropriate service agencies, and developed and monitored discharge or community placement plans. Within the facility, coordination of care was usually provided by a nurse, psychologist, or special educator.

As community placement became the norm, the mandates for quality programming caused a radical shift in the social work role and the term "case manager" appeared with increasing frequency. Now these individuals were indeed charged with managing "cases," providing follow-up to ensure that planned services were being received, and reviewing records to confirm that individualized plans were being implemented. In this role, the case manager was often the person legally mandated to convene and chair the interdisciplinary team meeting and finalize the plan. He or she was also required to ensure that there was effective communication among the various professionals and agencies involved in the person's life. In essence, case manager was a role created by deinstitutionalization. This role was established to ensure that the promise of program quality was kept in the community. Increasingly, the crucial nature of this role led progressive voices to highlight the potential of the case manager as a key actor in the process of building bridges to the community (Lippert, 1987).

Unfortunately, the promise of case management to support community membership by pulling all the pieces together has largely been lost because Medicaid and other funding sources reimburse for case management that is closer to "managed care" as seen in the health insurance industry. This can be seen in the proliferation of case managers in every agency associated with people with developmental disabilities. A study in progress documents up to 15 case managers in the lives of some families of children with developmental disabilities (Herman, Thompson, Linklater, & Hazel, 1992).

In summary, much of the literature on independent case management and best practice in individual agencies provides a model for consumer-centered service coordination and brokerage. However, the responsibilities entrusted to this position brought with them increased caseloads and paperwork requirements that made it impossible to attend to crucial outcomes such as personal choice, friendship, and personal goals, which were not being achieved in people's lives. Responsibility for truly consumer-centered attention to these outcomes is devolving to the people being called support personnel.

Support as a Unifying Theme

In reviewing the roots of the developing role of support personnel, it should be evident that the roles of interdisciplinary professional, direct care worker, and case manager have all contributed to the evolutionary process. What should further be apparent is that no one set of competencies fully encompasses the skills needed by support personnel. The numerous individuals supporting people with disabilities and their families, friends, and communities have learned from each of these roles. They have achieved a new synthesis that merits full recognition in its own right.

As Ferguson and Olsen (1989) pointed out, support has found currency as a unifying theme in all the most progressive efforts related to people with disabilities. Although the discussion here has been focused on developing the work force needed to provide supported living, in reality the work force issue is just a single aspect of the larger phenomenon of providing support. In reviewing the literature related to the best practices in family support, supported employment, and inclusive education, it becomes evident that, although the focus in each of these areas may be different, the strategies and frame of reference are the same. Indeed, a case could be made that the common focus on support may transcend relatively minor differences specific to the field of endeavor.

Supported Living Central to the emerging role of the professional in supported living is a basic shift away from creating dependence on human services. The field must not seek to be all things to the people served. The field is becoming more precise in defining its appropriate role, that is, it is not landlord or real estate agent, but community workers knowledgeable about disability issues. Its role is to provide support, to work with people to identify and obtain whatever it takes for them to obtain a high quality of life, and to work with the community in becoming more inclusive. Organizations assuming this role use a wide range of titles for this position, including community support worker (Options in Community Living, Madison, WI); primary staff/connectors (Residential Support Program, Weld County, CO); community facilitator (Community Mental Health, Midland, MI); or social pedagogue (Scandinavia). Regardless of the title, the clarity of mission and the work is the same.

Family Support The development of family support as a new way of thinking about the relationship between the service system and people with disabilities and their families completely parallels developments related to supported living. Indeed it can be effectively argued that these two movements are not distinct but expressions of the same global change (Bradley & Knoll, 1990). As the emerging issues in family support are explored, key concepts such as family empowerment, flexibility, family-centeredness, family–professional partnerships, and natural community supports stand out as exactly paralleling the concepts found in the mission of supported living organizations. The principal limit on this connection is that family support is typically directed toward maintaining the family, and the person with a disability is often a minor (Bradley, Knoll, & Agosta, 1992). The developing role of what might be called the family support specialist or family agent consistently uses the same tools as the individuals working in supported living (cf. Agosta & Ellison, 1988).

Supported Employment Initially, supported employment was marketed as a demonstration of the way people with severe disabilities could break the grip of sheltered employment and be fully integrated in competitive jobs. Increasingly, individuals involved in this endeavor have self-critically evaluated why the full potential of supported employment is not being realized (Nisbet & Hagner, 1988). This reassessment has led to a redefinition of the role of the job coach with a movement toward a natural support approach to employment (Hagner, Rogan, & Murphy, 1992; Nisbet & Hagner, 1988). The individuals in this role are called on to allow the employer to provide the job coaching and concentrate their energies on facilitating inclusion at the job site. As in other areas listed here, the mission of the human services professional shifts from doing the task to developing the support system needed for the person to achieve his or her goals.

Inclusive Education Education is a situation somewhat different from employment but only because the educational system requires people working in it to be credentialed as teachers. A reaction to the failures of mainstreaming and the continued segregation of children with severe disabilities, more than 15 years after the passage of PL 94-142 (the Education for All Handicapped Children Act of 1975), has provided impetus for the so-called regular education initiative or inclusive education. This movement takes as its fundamental premise that schools are places for the education of all children (Gaylord-Ross, 1989). People sharing this perspective see the goal of education as preparing all students to function effectively in a heterogenous society and assume that this goal can be reached only if students learn together in heterogenous classrooms (Biklen, 1992; Stainback & Stainback, 1990). Within this framework, special education is a resource that is applied to all classrooms for the benefit of all students. The refocused special education role calls on support facilitators (they may be called teacher consultants or resource teachers, among other titles) to assist in redesigning the regular classroom to include students with a full range of disabilities. Although the arena of activity is the somewhat more circumscribed environment of the local school, the mission and most of the strategies used by educators in this role are the same as those of any other type of support personnel.

Family Resource In moving out of the disability ghetto, it is important to note that the disability field is not the only one struggling with the definition of the support role. The national family resource movement, with its focus on support for *all* families, is attempting to redefine the relationship of helping professionals and families, all of whom they feel are at risk in the United States. Their issue is not community inclusion, since often families are absolutely submerged in the community. Rather, the issue is basic community organization and grassroots empowerment which it defines as:

> an intentional ongoing process centered in the local community, involving mutual respect, critical reflection, caring, and group participation through which people lacking an equal share of valued resources gain greater access to and control over those resources. (Cornell Empowerment Group, 1989, p. 3)

The words are somewhat different from those expressing the goals of the disability field, but the intent is the same. The group of professionals who support this process are transforming their roles, and their transformation mirrors the change in consciousness in the disability field (cf. Barr & Cochran, 1992).

In all of the areas discussed above there are human service workers who have undergone the same change of consciousness as their responsibilities have increasingly immersed them in the life of the community. There are people with very different instrumental focuses (e.g., work, housing, education, family support) using the same skills and strategies to assist children and families, adults, and the community in identifying resources and mobilizing themselves to gain control over their own destinies. Throughout the United States, individuals with a wide range of educational and personal experiences are on a daily basis supporting individual choice and control, facilitating planning, mobilizing resources, building connections, fostering relationships, and organizing. Aside from the difference that, in some systems, most notably education, these workers are required to have specific credentials, it seems apparent that these people are doing many of the same things in different sites and contexts. While they might be called case managers, facilitators, family support specialists, community workers, job coaches, teacher-consultants, or family resource specialists, they are all, in fact, providing support.

DEVELOPING A KNOWLEDGE BASE

Their evangelical zeal notwithstanding, people working to build community supports are not saints doing good work for disadvantaged people with disabilities. They are committed individuals systematically working in alliance with people with disabilities, families, and community members to achieve very specific accomplishments. Over and above their sense of mission they have developed a concrete body of knowledge, skills, and problem-solving strategies that can be taught to others to guide implementation of the support process. The need to synthesize this body of knowledge and effectively communicate it to current and future professionals is a central challenge in making a focus on support one of the centerpieces of services to people with developmental disabilities.

As a first step in that direction, the authors have attempted to provide an initial catalog of theoretical perspectives, program practices, strategies, and tools of the trade that begin to form the body of knowledge that support personnel consistently use. This outline is drawn from the literature in the fields of supported living (Racino et al., 1992; Smith, 1990; Taylor, Biklen, & Knoll, 1987; Taylor et al., 1991); family support (Bradley et al., 1992; Dunst, Trivette, Starnes, Hamby, & Gordon, 1991; Turnbull, Garlow, & Barber, 1991); supported employment (Hagner et al., 1992; Nisbet & Hagner, 1988); and inclusive education (Biklen, 1992; Stainback & Stainback, 1990); and the authors' experience interacting with people working as support personnel. The intention is not to pontificate on the essential knowledge needed to be identified as a support facilitator, but only to begin the discussion.

Holistic Perspective

The holistic or ecological perspective provides an overall theoretical framework for much of what support personnel do (Bronfenbrenner, 1979). Rather than seeing behavior as either caused by some internal drive or a mechanistic response to external stimuli, the holistic perspective views the way people and communities act as resulting from the complex interplay of multiple factors that impinge on their daily lives. Based on this premise, most of the limitations on people with disabilities are imposed by society rather than being intrinsic to an individual's functional deficit. From this perspective disability can best be defined as resulting "from a discrepancy between . . . skills and abilities and the demands or expectations of . . . [the] environment" (Apter, 1982, p. 2). As a result of this broadened definition of disability, there are three possible avenues for intervention: 1) changing the person, 2) changing the environment, or 3) changing societal attitudes and expectations. Traditional services focus most of their efforts on changing the person. Support personnel look for ways to change environments and attitudes.

Empowerment and Self-Determination

Organizations providing support have made a commitment to self-determination for individuals and grassroots empowerment the foundation of their mission. Many of the other strategies outlined in the following sections are mechanisms to ensure that an individual with a disability has the opportunity to exercise choice. Developing and enhancing these strategies and developing the skills to support grass roots empowerment are at the heart of the support mission and in many ways present the greatest challenges to this emerging field since they run counter to the way professionals have traditionally operated.

As a response to the enormity of this role change, an international think tank of change-focused philanthropic foundations, community organizations, and academics convened in the Netherlands in 1990 to begin a process of describing the professional role in supporting empowerment through family support and community development. They identified the following nine competencies for professionals to master in transforming their role to support empowerment:

- Ability and commitment to identifying strengths in people and groups
- Genuine respect for diverse perspectives and lifestyles
- A capacity to listen and reflect
- An ability to subordinate one's own ego (to put one's self aside in the interest of the group)
- Skill and creativity in helping people become more aware and confident of their own abilities
- Appreciation of when to step back and the ability to help the individual or group assume decision-making and action
- Ability to analyze power relationships and help others to do so
- Knowledge about how to gain access to information
- Ability to reflect on and criticize ongoing processes, including one's own role in those processes (Cochran, 1990, p. 25)

While these competencies are not specifically focused on working with people with disabilities, they offer direction to any professional who seeks to support the empowerment of any group of individuals who have traditionally been denied access to power.

Transdisciplinary Skills

By its very nature the support role needs to incorporate the perspective of a variety of disciplines. The interdisciplinary team may be one vehicle for blending a variety of skills, but the need to function as an individual agent immersed in the community and to integrate knowledge beyond the realm of the traditional human services makes that model unworkable. Therefore, support personnel need to develop as individual professionals who can integrate a broad spectrum of knowledge in their interaction with people with disabilities and communities.

Facilitator Role

Support personnel are very clear that their mission is to help connect people with communities. In an earlier period, a professional in the disability field might have seen integration as a means to develop social skills. Today there is much agreement that community membership is an end in itself. From this perspective the support profession looks at all activities as potential vehicles for building personal connections and strives to set the stage so that relationships have a chance to grow.

Consultant Role

A critical review of the literature on support might take the position that all this talk of inclusion is fine, but people with disabilities have specific limitations, problems learning, and difficulty communicating. Their special needs are being lost sight of in the rush toward the utopia called community membership. One of the authors' rationales for asserting the importance of support personnel is to respond to this very criticism. Support personnel are the advisors/consultants who ensure that a person's specialized needs are met by connecting them to any needed specialized services. But, perhaps more important, they are the consultants with both generalized and specialized knowledge who can act as a resource to people with disabilities, community agencies, roommates, employers, and neighbors to assist them in problem-solving.

Community Organizing

The support role can trace some of its roots to the work of people like Saul Alinsky (1971) and Si Kahn (1982) and their efforts at community organizing, and Paulo Freire (1982) and his "pedagogy of the oppressed." From this point of view, disability is not primarily a physical characteristic but one of those distinctions like wealth, gender, and race that society uses to rank people and exclude certain groups and individuals from access to power. There is a deep-seated awareness of oppression and the varied forms it can take. A major component of this awareness is the knowledge that two of the principal strategies for control are to create a competition between various disenfranchised groups for limited public resources and to constantly reinforce a view that an issue is an individual problem and not the concern of the community. Within this framework, bridge-building is necessarily much more than helping to connect individuals with disabilities to communities. It entails supporting all disadvantaged groups and all local communities as they mobilize to gain control over their own destinies.

Person-Centered Perspective

While community organizing is a major role for support personnel, their activity remains firmly grounded in bringing all that they do back to the experience of specific individuals. This is not individualism, but true person-centeredness, which sees that people are at the intersection of all the myriad forces that affect community and family life. The concrete experience of individuals, rather than abstract goals or concepts, remains the constant measure of success or failure. At its most basic, a person-centered perspective is an antidote to the abstraction that is so often referred to as the community. Support personnel need to see the community in very concrete terms as a series of concentric circles with one person at the center.

Anti-professionalism

This consideration is as universal as any other, but might be seen as a bias rather than an identifying characteristic. Because of negative association with the dominant paradigm of service and strong identification with communities, there is great resistance among support workers to professionalization and human services. McKnight (1987) and others who have been powerful voices in the development of the support role have continually argued that human services by their nature, and human services professionals because of their training and orientation, erect barriers between people with disabilities and communities. For this reason many people in the support role assert their lack of background in or total rejection of professionalized services. This bias notwithstanding, the authors feel that this chapter and the others in this book demonstrate that support personnel have developed an identity that begins to describe a new profession. Perhaps in itself the roots of this anti-human services professional bias is enough to argue that support personnel should maintain this distinction and not seek a home within traditional human services disciplines. Rather, they should take on the struggle of carving out new ground in academia in order to develop the support personnel of the future.

Tools of the Trade

Part of the identity of any field is the specific tools with which someone in that field is expected to be conversant. The following sections discuss five skills that are generally used by support personnel. Some support personnel may not be familiar with these specific terms because they have mastered these skills in the field and have never placed them into categories. Nonetheless, the authors feel this list captures the basic methods that all of these people use to do their jobs.

Qualitative Research The idiosyncratic nature of most support organizations, the unique nature of each person's life situation, and the complex, dynamic life of communities have led to the primacy of qualitative methods for applied research and evaluation related to support programs. There is real concern that the richness and essence of what support has to do with would be lost in the need for the generalizability inherent in quantitative methods. In addition, the storytelling style of qualitative methods retains the degree of accessibility that is crucial to communicating effectively with people in the field and with community members and is particularly useful in times of change for identifying new concepts and directions.

Planning for Personal Supports There are a variety of technical and human relations skills or evolving processes that support personnel need to know about their role and those of others in planning for personal supports. These skills aim to provide assistance to the individual with disabilities or family member either directly or indirectly through the mobilization of other resources. Specific examples include personal futures planning (Forest & Lusthaus, 1989; Mount & Zwernik, 1988; O'Brien, 1987); strategies to plan, develop, and monitor support services; facilitating community connections and personal relationships; and providing nonintrusive support services and specialized supports. As the planning process is understood today, support personnel need knowledge about personal futures planning or processes that go beyond the traditional team meeting. They need knowledge about social mapping or network analysis to begin to understand the relationships in a person's life; discrepancy analysis to systematically analyze the fit between the person and the environment; bridge-building strategies to support people's connections with each other; and nonintrusive interventions congruent with the social and community environments in which people participate.

Facilitating Dialogue and Problem-Solving Moving toward a supports approach will require bringing together people with diverse viewpoints in a variety of forums, including groups. Support personnel will need to work with others to plan meetings, facilitate interaction, assist in resolving conflict and seeking common ground, and work together with community organizations and associations. This must be done so that the thoughts and perspectives of the participants, not the professional, are reflected in the outcomes, and so the orientation is toward the community rather than toward human services.

Resourcefulness This skill is based on knowledge of the resources in the community and the ability to stimulate creative problem-solving. It involves seeing beyond the limitation of the current situation, that is, not being confined by the way things have always been done, and assisting others in developing this vision. Furthermore, it requires awareness of the dilemmas inherent in supporting people with disabilities in full community participation, such as the tension between independence and interdependence or between personal autonomy and safeguards (cf. Racino, 1990), and the ability to work with others to resolve these tensions.

Leadership and Change Strategies Support personnel will be working in traditional systems and attempting to play a role in change toward new relationships between professionals and individuals with disabilities and families. This will require knowledge about how systems and communities work, including their potential social and economic context and specific strategies on adapting, modifying, and changing the ways in which individuals with disabilities and families are included in all aspects of community life. The skills must include a basic knowledge of community organizing strategies, which encompass the development of support networks through personal contacts; support for group development; and analysis of critical relationships and tools for personal, agency, systems, community and societal change. Like any leadership role in a grassroots effort, the support role demands the ability to ease out of the picture and nurture the growth of new leaders from the community.

Although they lack a home in academia, the individuals and organizations who are defining support as a new relationship between service providers, people with disabilities, and communities have produced a theoretical framework and a body of knowledge as well developed as those in many established disciplines. So the question remaining concerns identifying the best approach to nurturing, developing, expanding, and spreading the word about this field of endeavor.

FINDING A HOME AND AN IDENTITY

There appear to be the following three primary options for finding a professional and academic home for support personnel: 1) doing nothing and maintaining the current identity as an underground discipline, 2) developing a concentration within the most appropriate academic discipline, or 3) forming an identity as a totally new discipline and developing training programs within universities and colleges. The following sections briefly review these options and highlight some of the pros and cons of each.

Maintaining the Status Quo

The current interest in support as an organizing construct guarantees that the status quo will not long be maintained. If people who have taken leadership in identifying support as a new way of operating do not take a lead in developing a training capacity and defining support for the next generation, this opportunity will be seized by others. If this happens support will be redefined to fit the agenda of the definer. There have been numerous normalized institutions; normalizing physical restraint programs; normalizing electric shock behavior modification programs; and organizations touting normalization in their missions statements, but in which all the residents pursued the same meaningless program goals for 10 years. If there is no action to reinforce the meaning of support, there will soon be, for example, "Support, Inc.," a sheltered workshop; "Supported Living ICFs/MR"; and the "Family Support Program," which offers the single "option" of out-of-home respite twice a year when scheduled 6 weeks in advance.

It may well be that the current montage of publications, consultants, inservice training, and courses will be sufficient, along with effective advocacy, to complete the transformation already underway. However, the vested interest of the large system of community facilities leaves serious doubts about the ability of a relatively small group to transform this system without also preparing professionals who find it unacceptable. Currently, the vast majority of programs of professional preparation are not meeting this challenge. Maintaining the anti-professional purity of support personnel does not seem to be sufficient reason to jeopardize the future. Somehow the concept of support must be infused into college and university programs.

Programs Within Existing Disciplines

As noted, many academic departments have bits and pieces of the skills and perspectives that inform the support role. If those fields that have a limited clinical focus are eliminated from consideration, there seem to be five possible departments or programs currently found in universities that have the background and commitment to people with disabilities that would be needed to house a program for preparing support personnel. These are discussed briefly below.

Special Education Numerous individuals working in support have come to the field with a background in special education. Furthermore, a number of university special education programs have provided a base for reform efforts related to supported living and supported employment and have small training programs in place. Even though a program to prepare support personnel would need to maintain a very distinct identity from a program of teacher preparation, a strong case could be made that some special education programs would be very appropriate homes for support personnel preparation.

Social Work The rich tradition of macro level community work, traced back to Jane Addams and the origins of the profession, demonstrates that some schools of social work would be appropriate for the preparation of support workers. Indeed, some of the leaders of agencies who have helped to define support were initially trained as social workers. However, the issue of credentialing, that is, licensing of social workers, and the increased emphasis in social work on training individual therapists raises concerns about the right fit with the support agenda.

Rehabilitation Counseling The role of traditional rehabilitation counselor, with a focus on meeting the mandates of the state vocational rehabilitation agency, is not congruent with a support role. However, reform pressure within the rehabilitation community, redirection of the Rehabilitation Act of 1973 (PL 93-112), and the increasingly diverse positions held by people with this credential make it clear that these programs would be just as appropriate an academic home for support personnel preparation as either special education or social work. Again, the issue of credentialing, that is, certification as a rehabilitation counselor, and the strong emphasis on the individual counseling relationship raise serious questions about the ability of these programs to nurture professionals with a social change/community organizing perspective.

Rehabilitation/Independent Living Perhaps more appropriate than programs in rehabilitation counseling are those programs that use the broader construct of rehabilitation as their organizing framework. These programs typically include counseling as one option in a range of clinical emphases. Where they have attempted to develop an option that specifically deals with the independent living movement (DeJong, 1978), they probably have already taken a major step toward creating an appropriate home for training support personnel. The major concern in these programs would be balancing their traditional clinical focus with the social focus inherent in support.

Interdisciplinary Programs The other option for an academic home for support personnel preparation is the increasing opportunity for interdisciplinary certification being offered by UAPs and other specialized programs. As in the option last described, these efforts have traditionally had a strong focus on clinical practice, but a few have already begun to expand their efforts with a focus on support as an organizing framework. These programs have the disadvantage of having a low profile and being distinct from degree programs, therefore they must be taken as electives. However, their interdisciplinary nature enables them to draw on resources from across the university. One variant of this option would be for UAPs to offer an interdisciplinary degree program for the preparation of support personnel.

While there are a number of opportunities in the universities, there are some limitations inherent in trying to build a new program within the territory of an existing discipline. First, the expertise needed to develop a program for support personnel typically is not found in any one of the existing programs. Second, most disciplines have a well-developed identity that is reinforced by licensure or other program certification, thereby making it difficult to create something that would deviate from these standards. In other words, disciplines are conservative by nature and have developed structures that are resistant to new roles. Third, the field of community support for people with disabilities is not the primary focus of most traditional disciplines, therefore there is likely to be a lack of commitment to developing a new program that might be challenged within the university structure. Fourth, in the authors' experience some of the basic issues raised by individuals providing support tend to be reframed by many professionals in terms of the dominant paradigm of their disciplines. These professionals then are unable to see the problems of support personnel preparation that need attention. Fifth, regardless of the academic home, an effective program of support personnel preparation would challenge the standard practice of some senior colleagues. This tension might not be supported or even tolerated.

Developing an Identity as a New Discipline

Seymour Sarason and John Doris (1979) wrote about the status system in academia that uses ambiguous and socially situated criteria to determine what "windows on the world" merit standing as academic disciplines. Specifically, they pointed out that the window of disability, while a perfectly valid organizing framework, has been ignored or relegated to secondary standing in universities. Perhaps the post-Americans with Disabilities Act era is an appropriate time to challenge this discrimination at the heart of the university.

Based on the material outlined above, a strong case can be made that the work of support personnel merits standing alongside any of the long-established professional disciplines. Certainly, the theoretical framework and professional practices associated with support are as well developed at this early stage as those of many established disciplines. The curriculum of a department of community support could be structured around this framework as well as the significant body of work that has been generated by programs in disability and community studies.

Admittedly, this route may be the most difficult to pursue given: 1) the current dispersal of people with relevant expertise both geographically and within the universities; 2) the conservative nature of the universities, which makes it difficult to establish new programs; 3) the current budget problems facing many universities resulting in a reticence to expand programs; and 4) the resistance of people in the field to professionalization and their fear that institutionalizing a curriculum would stultify their dynamic efforts. However, an equally strong case could be made that a higher degree of visibility and far greater long-term benefits will be realized in choosing to pursue this route.

CONCLUSION

Periods of transition and growth in personal development are fraught with tension and fears in facing the challenges of new stages in life. The security of childhood must be left behind and identity formed in adolescence. The relative freedom of adolescence is relinquished so that the responsibilities and rewards of adulthood can be confronted. As it is with individuals, so it is with fields of human endeavor. It is one thing for individuals and organizations to challenge the status quo, to cherish their identity as the radicals who are showing the rest of the field how to do things the right way. It requires other efforts when those points of view are validated and the rest of the field asks how to take action. The battles fought by the pioneers in providing support are by no means over, but a point of transition has been reached.

Although institutions continue to hang on, their days are numbered. The authors believe it is becoming very evident that the system of community-based facilities, built by the process of deinstitutionalization, is a white elephant that will survive for quite some time but will fade. There will be continued battles, but it is already known that people with disabilities who have never been in an institution and have had access to free, appropriate, public education (increasingly in their local schools) are not interested in going into a facility. They want a system that is of the community and will support them in homes, jobs, and relationships of their choosing.

If the endeavor of providing individualized support is to succeed, providing support cannot be just an esoteric activity that can be conducted only under the guidance of a charismatic leader. It must become the core of a new system marked by a clear sense of mission that challenges the current boundaries of what is called human services. This chapter has demonstrated that support work has a specific body of knowledge that can be effectively communicated to people currently working in the field and to the next generation of workers. The increasing acceptance and respectability of support as an organizing framework requires that support workers begin talking with each other and ascertain how best to set the stage for a new generation of people with disabilities, professionals, and their allies to mature and reform the issues of the supports model.

REFERENCES

Agosta, J., & Ellison, M.L. (1988). *Making the pilot project work: The role of the family agent.* Cambridge, MA: Human Services Research Institute.

Alinsky, S. (1971). *Rules for radicals.* New York: Random House.

Apter, S.J. (1982). *Troubled children, troubled systems.* New York: Pergamon Press.

Barr, D., & Cochran, M. (1992). Understanding and supporting empowerment: Redefining the professional role. *Networking Bulletin: Empowerment & Family Support, 2*(3), 1–8.

Biklen, D. (1992). *Schooling without labels: Parents, educators, and inclusive education.* Philadelphia: Temple University Press.

Biklen, D., & Knoll, J. (1987). The disabled minority. In S.J. Taylor, D. Biklen, & J. Knoll (Eds.). *Community integration for people with severe disabilities* (pp. 3–24). New York: Teachers College Press.

Braddock, D., & Mitchell, D. (1992). *Residential services and developmental disabilities in the United States.* Washington, DC: American Association on Mental Retardation.

Bradley, V.J., & Knoll, J.A. (1990). *Shifting paradigms in services for people with developmental disabilities.* Cambridge, MA: Human Services Research Institute.

Bradley, V.J., Knoll, J.A., & Agosta, J.M. (1992). *Emerging issues in family support.* (American Association on Mental Retardation Monograph No. 18). Washington, DC: American Association on Mental Retardation.

Bronfenbrenner, U. (1979). *The ecology of human development.* Cambridge, MA: Harvard University Press.

Cochran, M. (1990). The transforming role. *Networking Bulletin: Empowerment & Family Support, 1*(3), 25.

Cornell Empowerment Group. (1989). Empowerment through family support. *Networking Bulletin: Empowerment & Family Support, 1*(1), 2–12.

DeJong, G. (1978). *The movement for independent living: Origins, ideology, and implications for disability research.* Boston: Tufts New England Medical Center, Medical Rehabilitation Institute.

Dunst, C., Trivette, C.M., Starnes, A.L., Hamby, D.W., & Gordon, N.J. (1991). Family support programs for persons with developmental disabilities: Key elements, differential characteristics and program outcomes. *Family Studies Intervention Monograph 3.* Morganton, NC: Center for Family Studies, Western Carolina Center.

Ferguson, P.M., & Olson, D. (Eds.). (1989). *Supported community life: Connecting policy to practice in disability research.* Eugene: Specialized Training Program.

Forest, M., & Lusthaus, E. (1989). Promoting educational equality for all students: Circles and MAPS. In S. Stainback, W. Stainback, & M. Forest (Eds.), *Educating all students in the mainstream of regular education* (pp. 43–57). Baltimore: Paul H. Brookes Publishing Co.

Freire, P. (1982). *Pedagogy of the oppressed.* New York: Continuum.

Gaylord-Ross, R. (1989). *Integration strategies for students with handicaps.* Baltimore: Paul H. Brookes Publishing Co.

Hagner, D., Rogan, P., & Murphy, S. (1992). Facilitating natural supports in the workplace: Strategies for support consultants. *Journal of Rehabilitation, 58*(1), 29–34.

Herman, S.E., Thompson, T.L., Linklater, A., & Hazel, K.H. (1992). *Family support services in Michigan: Community mental health family support services.* Lansing: Michigan Developmental Disabilities Council.

Johnson, T.Z. (1985). *Belonging to the community.* Madison: Options in Community Living.

Kahn, S. (1982). *A guide for grassroots leaders: Organizing.* New York: McGraw-Hill.

Kennedy, M.J. (1993). Turning the pages of life. In J.A. Racino, P. Walker, S. O'Connor, & S.J. Taylor (Eds.), *Housing, support, and community: Choices and strategies for adults with disabilities* (pp. 205–216). Baltimore: Paul H. Brookes Publishing Co.

Klein, J. (1992). Get me the hell out of here: Supporting people with disabilities to live in their own homes. In J. Nisbet (Ed.), *Natural supports in school, at work, and in the community for people with severe disabilities* (pp. 277–339). Baltimore: Paul H. Brookes Publishing Co.

Knoll, J., & Ford, A. (1987). Beyond caregiving: A reconceptualization of the role of the residential service provider. In S.J. Taylor, D. Biklen, & J.A. Knoll (Eds.), *Community integration for people with severe disabilities* (pp. 129–146). New York: Teachers College Press.

Kuhn, T. (1962). *The structure of scientific revolution.* Chicago: University of Chicago Press.

Lippert, T. (1987). *The case management team: Building community connections.* St. Paul: Metropolitan Council.

McKnight, J. (1987). Regenerating community. *Social Policy, Winter,* 54–58.

Minnesota Governor's Planning Council on Developmental Disabilities. (1987). *A new way of thinking.* St. Paul: Author.

Moore, C. (1993). Letting go, moving on: A parent's thoughts. In J.A. Racino, P. Walker, S. O'Connor, & S.J. Taylor (Eds.), *Housing, support, and community: Choices and strategies for adults with disabilities* (pp. 189–204). Baltimore: Paul H. Brookes Publishing Co.

Mount, B., & Zwernik, K. (1988). *It's never too early, it's never too late: A booklet about personal futures planning.* St. Paul: Metropolitan Council.

National Association of Private Residential Resources. (1991). *Supported living.* Annandale, VA: Author.

National Association of Private Residential Resources. (1992). *Supported living, Volume II.* Annandale, VA: Author.

Nisbet, J., & Hagner, D. (1988). Natural supports in the workplace: A reexamination of supported employment. *Journal of The Association for Persons with Severe Handicaps, 13*(4), 260–267.

O'Brien, J. (1987). A guide to life-style planning using *The Activities Catalog* to integrate services and natural support systems. In B. Wilcox & G.T. Bellamy (Eds.), *A comprehensive guide to The Activities Catalog: An alternative curriculum for youth and adults with severe disabilities* (pp. 175–189). Baltimore: Paul H. Brookes Publishing Co.

O'Brien, J., & O'Brien, C. (1992). *Remembering the soul of our work: Stories by staff of Options in Community Living, Madison, Wisconsin.* Madison: Options in Community Living.

O'Connor, S., & Racino, J.A. (1993). "A home of my own": Community housing options and strategies. In J.A. Racino, P. Walker, S. O'Connor, & S.J. Taylor (Eds.), *Housing, support, and community: Choices and strategies for adults with disabilities* (pp. 137–160). Baltimore: Paul H. Brookes Publishing Co.

Racino, J.A. (1990). Preparing personnel to work in community support services. In A.P. Kaiser & C.M. McWhorter (Eds.), *Preparing personnel to work with persons with severe disabilities* (pp. 203–226). Baltimore: Paul H. Brookes Publishing Co.

Racino, J.A. (1992). Living in the community: Independence support, and transition. In F.R. Rusch, L. DeStefano, J. Chadsey-Rusch, L.A. Phelps, & E. Szymanski (Eds.), *Transition from school to adult life: Models, linkages, and policy* (pp. 131–148). Sycamore, IL: Sycamore Press.

Racino, J.A., & O'Connor, S. (1994). "A home of our own": Homes, neighborhoods, and personal connections. In M. Hayden & B. Abery (Eds.), *Community living for persons with mental retardation and related conditions* (pp. 381–403). Baltimore: Paul H. Brookes Publishing Co.

Racino, J.A., O'Connor, S., & Walker, P. (1993). Conclusion. In J.A. Racino, P. Walker, S. O'Connor, & S.J. Taylor (Eds.), *Housing, support, and community: Choices and strategies for adults with disabilities* (pp. 355–366). Baltimore: Paul H. Brookes Publishing Co.

Racino, J.A., Walker, P., O'Connor, S., & Taylor, S.J. (Eds.). (1993). *Housing, support, and community: Choices and strategies for adults with disabilities*. Baltimore: Paul H. Brookes Publishing Co.

Sarason, S., & Doris, J. (1979). *Educational handicap, public policy, and social history: A broadened perspective on mental retardation*. New York: Free Press.

Smith, G. (1990). *Supported living: New directions in services for people with developmental disabilities*. Alexandria, VA: National Association of State Mental Retardation Program Directors.

Smull, M. (1989). *Crisis in the community*. Alexandria, VA: National Association of State Mental Retardation Program Directors.

Stainback, W., & Stainback, S. (Eds.). (1990). *Support networks for inclusive schooling: Interdependent integrated education*. Baltimore: Paul H. Brookes Publishing Co.

Taylor, S.J. (1988). Caught in the continuum: A critical analysis of the principle of the least restrictive environment. *Journal of The Association for Persons with Severe Handicaps, 13*(1), 41–53.

Taylor, S.J., Biklen, D., & Knoll, J.A. (Eds.). (1987). *Community integration for people with severe disabilities*. New York: Teachers College Press.

Taylor, S.J., Bogdan, R., & Racino, J.A. (Eds.). (1991). *Life in the community: Case studies of organizations supporting people with disabilities*. Baltimore: Paul H. Brookes Publishing Co.

Taylor, S.J., Racino, J., Knoll, J., & Lutfiyya, Z. (1987). *The nonrestrictive environment: A resource manual on community integration for people with the most severe disabilities*. Syracuse: Human Policy Press.

Traustadottir, R. (1991). *Supports for community living: A case study*. Syracuse: Center on Human Policy, Syracuse University.

Turnbull, H.R., Garlow, J., & Barber, P.A. (1991). A policy analysis of family support for families with members with disabilities. *The University of Kansas Law Review, 39*(3), 739–782.

IV

LEADERSHIP AND EMPOWERMENT

What is perhaps most remarkable about this section's reflections on leadership in the 1990s is the shift in voice they signify. The authors, as well as the leaders they describe, are predominantly people with disabilities or their parents. The same material, written even a brief 10 years ago, might well have concerned aspiring to such leadership roles for people with disabilities and their families; however, the authors, would likely have been all professionals, and the events they recounted would have described the efforts of professionals on behalf of people with disabilities. The current period is responding to a "different voice." The so-called paradigm shift may, after all, reflect this actual shift in perspective, what Kendrick, in Chapter 21, describes as the imperative to think and plan by "placing the user of such services at the center of leadership concerns."

One hallmark of the current period is the struggle to develop images and language to describe an alternative vision to the segregative community system. Written in the different voice of those so long excluded, the reflections in this section in themselves embody such visions. Rooted in the everyday realities of coping with disability and working for change, these authors describe images of and pathways to the future that are compelling in their vivid detail and sense of veracity. The advice offered here is, therefore, notably useful. "Empowerment," for example, appears less as a platitudinous bullet in a mission statement and more as a description of exactly how people, like Gagne in Chapter 18, who had no influence over their personal or public lives have gained such influence. The authors move easily from the conceptual level of circles of support, as in Chapter 20 by Ducharme, Beeman, DeMarasse, and Ludlum, and strategies for supporting shared visions, as in Chapter 22 by Farber and Marcel, to the level of organizational action, such as methods for arranging telephone trees or conducting meetings, as in Chapter 19 by Bowen.

Farber and Marcel, and Ducharme, Beeman, DeMarasse, and Ludlum, in their co-authorship, as in their insights, exemplify an emerging pattern of collaboration and partnership between professionals, people with disabilities, and communities. Within this partnership, the fundamental role of the professional is to create contexts that support the self-determination of people in their personal lives and the leadership of parents, people with disabilities, and community members in social change. Indeed, the unifying role (and voice) is less a variant of either user of services or professional; rather, it is that of the *citizen* engaged in making his or her community more hospitable and inclusive for us all.

18

A Self-Made Man

Raymond J. Gagne

My name is Raymond J. Gagne. This is a true story. I was born on January 10, 1945, in Attleboro, Massachusetts. I am a person with cerebral palsy. I lived with my mother, grandmother, uncle, two brothers, and sister in a large house. I don't remember my father ever living at home, although he sometimes came to see me and took me out for rides.

EIGHT YEARS OF POWER

My mother always worked, sometimes during the day, other times at night. When she worked at night, she slept all day. I would see her when she woke up. Often, my mother took me in the baby carriage to see people, or to go shopping, or on other errands. One day we went to the post office. I climbed out of the carriage and crawled all around. My mother found me and put me back in the carriage.

My godfather owned a food store. Sometimes I visited him with my mother. If I did not go, I would hit and bite my mother.

My mother felt that there was something wrong with me. She took me to many doctors and hospitals to see if they knew how to help me. They told my mother I would never walk.

When I was home, I used to sit in a rocking chair next to a yellow window. I would sit there for hours watching people and cars go by. When the family went out, they put me in my baby carriage and usually included me in the activities. My brothers and sister went to school. At the time, there was no school for me. I stayed home with my grandmother, who took care of me. She had her hands full. I could not walk, talk, feed myself, or dress myself. She had to carry me upstairs each time I had to go to the bathroom. I crawled on the floor to get around.

When I was 8, my mother told me I was going away. She put my name on my clothes and packed my new suitcase. I remember the night before I left, I was bathed and my fingernails and toenails were cut. On February 19, 1953, two ladies picked my mother and me up for the drive to a state school. I didn't know where we were going. My mother had just told me I was going away and that I would be better off.

A LIFE OF NO POWER: EIGHTEEN YEARS IN AN INSTITUTION

After arriving at the state school, I was put in Building 7. An orderly brought me to a ward. He put me on a bed and took all my clothes off. He put a johnny on me. My mother left, and I didn't see her anymore that day. I was scared because I didn't know where I was or why I was there. I had arrived early in the afternoon. The rest of the day and night, I was in bed. The bed was different from mine at home. At home, I had slept in a crib with the side up. This was so I would not fall out of bed. My bed in the ward was high off the floor and didn't have side railings. After the orderly put me in bed, I froze and did not move all afternoon or night. I was afraid of falling off the bed. Maybe that is why I am still afraid to lie down on doctors' examining tables.

The ward itself was drab. The windows were high with white shades. There were no curtains or decorations on the wall, not even a clock or calendars. There was a radio. The first song I heard was, "Pretend You're Happy When You're Blue." It made me sad to hear it. I cried for 3 days.

After having a physical examination, personnel asked me if I wanted to move to a different building. I said yes, and they moved me to Building 15. They put me on the floor. The other patients stepped all over me. I cried all day because I wanted to go back home. At lunch time, I didn't eat because I was too upset. For dinner, they brought me the lunch tray warmed over. I didn't like the food.

That evening they gave me a group bath with five other boys. The bathtub looked like a bird bath. There were water sprayers all around the inside of the bath. I was put to bed after the bath. At midnight, the attendants woke everybody up to go to the bathroom. I hated that, but I went.

Every morning we would wake up at 6:00. An attendant would help me put on the clothes he had laid out the night before. I didn't have any say about what I wore. What they put on, I wore. Sometimes they wouldn't put underwear on me. My mother used to buy my clothes. At the state school, I'd wear them once, and the next day I would see them on someone else.

The first time I had a visitor was a month after being left at the state school. My mother came to visit me. I cried all the time she was there. I told her I wanted to go home; I was angry and told her I didn't want to stay. She didn't say anything. During this visit, she asked about taking me home for a 1-day visit. I promised not to act up when the day was over. At the time I didn't realize I was lying. When the visit was over and they got ready to take me back, I acted up. I hit and bit my mother. I also hid underneath the bed so she couldn't get me. She finally returned me to the state school.

As I look back on my childhood, I realize that I have been on my own since I was 8 years old. Some people would disagree and say that I was taken care of for many years. However, I felt as though I had no love or understanding from anyone.

While I was at the state school, I was often sick. I had the measles, chicken pox, yellow jaundice, plus many other diseases. When I was sick, I was alone all day. It was very lonely for me to be by myself. The other people were in the hall until 5:00 P.M. each day.

That spring, I went to the dentist for the first time ever. The dentist pulled out eight teeth. He did not use any Novocain or any pain killers. I tried to be brave and not cry.

In the summers, they would put me and the others out on the playground from 9:00 in the morning until 4:00 in the afternoon. Some people were left to go to the bathroom in their pants; others would vomit all over each other, even me. We would stay like that until we went back inside. Also, the times employees hit me were mostly on the playground. They hit me with a wet towel. When 4:00 came, we went inside and were put to bed by 5:00, even in the summertime.

On Sunday afternoons in the summer, I used to spend the day lying on the floor of the ward waiting for company. No one ever came. Even my mother didn't visit much in the summer because she spent Sundays at the beach with her boyfriend. Even now, summer is not my favorite time of the year.

At age 8, I went to nursery school for 1 hour a day. It was then I started to walk. It took me a long time to walk because I had to teach myself. Nobody helped me. I wanted to be with the rest of the class, but the teacher refused because I couldn't get around.

Once I waited a full day for my mother to come and pick me up. I had to wait on a bench all day because the attendants didn't know when my mother was coming. During my visit, my grandmother fell down the steps and had to be hospitalized. A few days after I returned to the state school, my grandmother died. I wasn't told until Christmas Day, 5 months later.

Holidays were not fun for me. I remember spending my whole first Thanksgiving at the state school in my bed. We had a big dinner but that was all. My first Christmas I went home. That was the day I learned my grandmother died. I stayed home for 4 days. When I learned I had to return to the state school, I acted up. Looking back, I feel my strength and stubbornness helped me to survive these years of my life when I had so little control. When I returned to the state school, I brought my presents. I had them for 1 day. The next day, the attendants put them in the cellar. They told me I had too much stuff. I never saw my toys again. Not only did they take my toys away, they also took my privacy. In general, I never had any private room. I shared my bathroom with 32 other people. There was nowhere to go when I wanted to be alone.

I went to Building 5 and saw that people had more freedom there. I asked the staff if I could move to this building. They said I could. While I was at the new building, I felt better. In the new building, I could go to bed at 9:30. When I was in the other building (Building 7), I was often moved between the large and small ward. This happened as often as each week and was done to give a bed to an older person who might come in sick from another building. I never actually had my own personal bed. It made me think that, even in prison, you at least have your own cell. At the state school, I didn't have any living space of my own.

One of the nice things I remember is that we had parties once a month. An outside public group brought food each month and helped put on the parties. The parties were fun, and the food was better than I was used to. Each month, they would ask us what we would like the next month. It was one of the only times we were ever given a choice about anything.

I didn't have to take group baths in this building. We were allowed to take a shower once a week. After I'd take a shower, they would inspect me. Also, once a month they weighed you. If you lost weight, the attendants said it was because you were playing with yourself too much. The attendants would yell at the residents and call people dirty. Now I know that masturbating is normal. But back then they punished you for it. They made me feel dirty and embarrassed; I think that is true for a lot of people at state schools.

I stayed in Building 5 for about 7 months until the Nursery Building opened. Everybody went to one of the nurseries to live except for me. I couldn't walk so they didn't transfer me. The nurseries were where small children lived. I moved back to Building 7.

They set up a school and let me go one day. The next day they didn't let me go back because they didn't think I could complete the school work. Most of the people were older than me, and there was only one teacher for many students.

The staff who worked at the state institution were insensitive and cruel. There was one attendant who would take me to a back room and beat me up. Other times, he would hit me right in front of everybody. Another attendant hit the residents on the head with his keys. However, the most abusive employee was a man who had 14 lockers filled with candy bars. He didn't buy the candy with his own money. He bought it with our canteen cards. If you did some work for him, he would pay you with candy bars he had bought with our money. One night a group of us broke into the lockers and took the candy bars. The next day we got punished by the man, though we felt a great deal of satisfaction.

Three times a week I had to go to exercise class. I hated the woman who taught the class. We had to take off our clothes and exercise in our underwear. One day, I told the attendant on my ward that my back hurt. After looking at it, he told me nothing was wrong and sent me to the class anyway. When I got to the class, I told the exercise teacher about my back, and she sent me back to my building where I was punished for going over the head of the attendants. This is one of many examples of punishment for my trying to advocate for myself.

Another injustice occurred when I was 18 or 19 and I worked in the mailing room. I worked a half day, 5 days a week, plus all day Saturday. My job was to deliver mail throughout the institution. I didn't actually get paid for my work. Instead, you got credit on your canteen card. That was the only form of money available to us. One day I was fired. I was hurt because I had just worked a holiday and because I had worked there 5 years. The reason for my being fired was that I stole a resident's jacket for a staff member who promised to pay me for doing it. Staff often stole. They would steal televisions, clothes, shoes, and food. During the jacket incident, the staff member never did pay me, and when my boss found out I had stolen something he fired me. He never asked or found out about the staff member. I felt rotten about this incident. Everybody talked about it, and I went out to the woods and cried.

The staff never seemed to prepare me for living outside the institution. They didn't seem to think I would make it on my own. Up until the age of 14, I wasn't allowed to go to school. I spent most of my day going to physical therapy or sitting on the floor in the back room. One of the things that saved me from boredom and loneliness was that I had a radio and listened to it often.

I never had support, role models, or mentors to guide me in growing up. Very few of the staff ever assisted me in developing my identity, creativity, or self-esteem. Their roles were more of full-time caretakers, and if I obeyed their rules they were good to me. From the very beginning, I felt isolated and had trouble in social situations. I had a few friends but received no encouragement in learning good social skills. The staff did arrange game activities, and I participated in some recreational activities, but it still doesn't seem like much.

For as long as I can remember I was considered to have mental retardation. I didn't do too well on some tests, didn't learn how to walk until I was 10, and had trouble adjusting to the institution. Therefore, no one ever expected much of me.

At age 14 I started to go to school 1 hour a day. At this time, I could not read or write. During this hour I put together puzzles. I still don't know why I had to do this. I didn't learn anything to help me prepare for the future. The next year I started going to school 3 hours a day. I began to learn my ABCs but there was no individual help for students, and many of the teachers read newspapers during class. I continued to go to school 3 hours a day for 4 years. When I was 19, I went into an all-day pilot school program. During this year, I learned more about reading, writing, and arithmetic. I felt good about this year. The next year I was returned to a 3-hour school day. That spring I quit school to work in the workshop. I worked in the workshop for 1 year. We put nails in boxes and then sealed the boxes. The workshop was not unlike the workshops that are around today for people with mental retardation. I got paid $30 a week. This was the first real money I had to call my own. Within the year I was promoted to the position of supervisor. I learned good work habits such as being on time, doing good work, responsibility, and getting along with others.

Although I learned some good things at the workshop, many basic skills were never taught. These included budgeting skills, personal grooming skills, and almost any other skills that a person needs to live outside an institution. The director of volunteers, whom I liked and spent many hours with, was the first person to help me deposit my money in a bank account.

TWENTY YEARS IN THE REAL WORLD: A STRUGGLE FOR POWER

The year I worked in the workshop, I went to a brand new halfway house on the weekends. The halfway house was owned by the institution, but at least one man who worked there had confidence in my abilities. When I visited the halfway house I hung out and relaxed. That man was transferred to my building after about 6 months. He and I talked about moving out of the state institution. I said yes. He told me I didn't need the halfway house, although I felt unprepared to leave.

The day I moved out, some staff told me I would be back in a month. They may be still waiting for me to come back. I lived in an apartment for 3 years on my SSI income and the income from my job in the institution's workshop. I lived with two apartment mates. They were from the same institution. My two roommates had lived in the halfway house and helped me learn many of the basic daily living skills I needed. I helped them with their banking and shopping. The institution did not have professionals coming to help make the move easier. To be honest, I only saw my social worker a week before I moved. If one of us had a question we could call the halfway house.

After I shared an apartment for 3 years, the staff of the halfway house asked me to move into the house to help five men move out on their own. While I was working at the halfway house I met an employee named John. After he was hired we broke all the rules in the book. One night he allowed beer into the house. Another night he took my friend and me to a bar. The bartender refused to serve me because he thought I was drunk. John paid the bill and walked out. This was one of the first times that I felt I was important.

That same year I went on a vacation to Washington, D.C., by myself. This was the first time I had ever done this.

During the fall, the five men I was helping and I moved into our own apartment. I quit the workshop job and began working full time to help these five men learn banking, cooking, and shopping skills. I was in the apartment 24 hours a day, 7 days a week. I helped them in whatever they needed. If I had a day off, I did not know where to go or what to do.

At this time John and I started a friendship. However, we did not get close overnight. One day I asked John where I could get a different job. John referred me to a state vocational rehabilitation agency. They wanted me to go to a workshop that I did not want to attend. Even John and I had a fight over this. Within that year I finally agreed to go to the workshop. It was boring. After 4 months I quit. They told me either I stayed at the workshop or I could stay home and do nothing. I stayed home.

During that fall I moved into my own apartment after a counselor at a camp for people with cerebral palsy told me she thought I could. I did well in living alone for 3 years. During that time I didn't work. I spent most of my time watching television. I didn't interact much with the community.

While I was in the institution I had contact with my family. I usually had visits with my sister or my mother twice a month. Visits with my brothers were less frequent. My mother died 1 year before I left the institution. She never got a chance to see me on my own. When she died my sister and I became closer. Even though my sister felt some responsibility for me, I don't think she really thought I could make it on my own. When I left the institution, it took a while for my family to understand that I could live successfully on my own. For a number of years changing their beliefs was hard, but they slowly began to see me as a person.

After living alone for 3 years, I decided to move near the city where my sister lived. While there I became involved with the local chapter of United Cerebral Palsy (UCP). I became involved with UCP 3 weeks after I moved. When my typewriter was stolen I went to UCP for another one. They didn't have one, but I met the new executive director, who asked me to volunteer at UCP. I helped complete mailings and coordinate the UCP local telethon. I learned about Section 504 of the Rehabilitation Act and helped found an advocacy group named the Massachusetts Coalition of Citizens with Disabilities. I learned the skills of leadership, advocacy, consumer organizing, and assertiveness by watching people, participating in group meetings, and asking questions. My ability to communicate my ideas and to facilitate work toward changing the status quo developed over time.

My social and recreational skills also increased. I joined a bowling team of people with disabilities. Also, I joined a church. I attended most of the services and activities that were offered. While at the church I worked with a youth group. During this period of my life I had the greatest amount of personal growth ever. It was during this time that I began to develop friendships.

In terms of work, I worked at a camp for people with cerebral palsy in maintenance or the dining room. The summer months were the only months I was employed; the rest of the year I volunteered my time and survived on my SSI and SSDI checks.

After 4 years, I moved twice more. I continued to learn new skills and became more involved in self-advocacy and consumer advocacy. I moved to New Bedford, Massachusetts. I was interviewed by the Arc directors and was hired as a public information coordinator. This is an impressive title, but the job paid me only $30 a week. I was responsible for developing a positive public image of people with mental retardation through public speaking, training, and creation of written material. Unlike the staff at the institution, the human services professionals I met at this job treated me with respect. They gave me a chance to contribute my input and feedback and believed in many of my ideas. My colleagues also adapted the working environment to help me communicate with them. After several years I became the staff liaison to a self-advocacy group of adults with mental retardation. I worked at this job for 6 years.

Through my job I met many people who have become friends. I began to get involved in national issues. In 1988 I was selected to be the National Chairperson of the Self-Advocacy Advisory Committee for the National Association of Retarded Citizens (NARC). I helped coordinate a successful voting rights campaign and assisted in promoting self-advocacy initiatives within NARC. I also lectured on these issues at Harvard University.

After 6 years of not having enough money or moving ahead I decided to look for another job. I discussed this with some people from Harrisburg, Pennsylvania. I visited their programs and talked with employees and consumers. I was hired as a training specialist. My duties included providing self-advocacy and social skills training to over 200 residents and employees at residences for people with mental illness/mental retardation. I assisted in the development of a training program focusing on community involvement and social role valorization. My colleagues at this present job treat me well and have made adaptations so I can do a better job.

Moving so far away from my home state and meeting and getting to know totally new people has been difficult. Getting around, learning the new city, and finding and moving into a new apartment have been major challenges.

I wrote this story to let people know what it was like growing up in an institution from the 1950s through the 1970s. The total lack of power in making decisions about my life made me angry, and I was treated as an outcast. The staff's abuse, neglect, and insensitivity kept me from being educated and learning the other basic skills that many children learn from caring adults. When I got into the real world, I wasn't sure what my role was. Nobody ever talked to me or taught me how to be successful. I learned to survive mostly on my own and with the help of a few good people.

I feel that what happened to me should never happen again. I have been working in human services teaching self-advocacy techniques for 10 years and still see people in state institutions who should not be there. Most people, with community support, can live successfully in the community.

Furthermore, staff are still abusing residents emotionally, physically, and sexually. This needs to stop! Self-advocacy and better monitoring of staff activities is essential. People's attitudes must improve. There has been a slow change in attitudes, but people with disabilities are still made fun of and kept out of many places in the real world. People with disabilities are gaining choice and control, but there is still a long way to go. I hope this story helps people understand conditions in the past (and sometimes present) and how people with disabilities and those who care about them can help eliminate the kinds of experiences I had.

19

The Power of Self-Advocacy

Making Thunder

Jean N. Bowen

One more time we lost Barbara, this time for good. She is a warm, pretty woman, adamant about making her own choices and decisions. But her sister was embarrassed by her disability and by her public declarations of independence. Barbara's sister promised family trips, a vacation to Florida, shopping excursions with other sisters and family. After many years of separation from them, living apart in an institution, Barbara left People First of Connecticut. After all they were family, she told us; they would love her. Barbara's sister is her legal guardian, appointed many years earlier by a probate court judge in Connecticut. Even though Barbara lives in her own apartment, holds down a responsible job, uses public transportation, and had the opportunity to become a leader in the self-advocacy movement, her sister makes the decisions for her. Barbara hates this but loves her sister. She left People First.

Members of People First in the chapters across Connecticut were shocked, hurt, then angry. How could this happen? The vulnerability of self-advocates once again haunted members and advisors. Personal preference, opportunity, choosing where to live and with whom, spending time at home or with friends, in other words, the most basic choices and decisions may be made by others when a person is labeled as having mental retardation. Guardianship became a hot issue. The threat to freedom to have control and be legally recognized to authorize consent to outsiders hit home. T.J. Monroe, President of People First of Connecticut, spoke at meetings and shared Barbara's story. If this could happen to Barbara it could happen to anyone.

Being scared and angry sometimes has its benefits. In community organizing it is a necessity. In Connecticut as well as other states, spirited and concerned men and women met in public libraries, senior centers, apartments, and at the institutions to share their fears, frustrations, and anger. Word spread rapidly through the group homes and sheltered workshops about coming to a meeting. There people would have a voice, be heard, and be treated fairly. This new movement of people with disabilities was borne of denial and discrimination. The proliferation of services that developed from new laws and litigation was not enough; the option to direct and determine a choice of independent supports was left out of every plan.

Many learned from Barbara's experience. Nancy remembered growing up with Barbara at the institution. Nancy also had a guardian appointed over 20 years ago; no one ever questioned this, and no court ever reviewed this decision—until Nancy spoke up.

Nancy lived at the institution in Southbury, Connecticut. It is still one of the largest in the United States, with a population of 913 men and women with disabilities. Nancy moved there when she was 9 years old, and at age 52 she finally got her freedom.

Nancy was described by staff as pushy and bossy. She organized the life of everyone in her building, including that of her long-time boyfriend, Richard. She worked in the community in a sheltered workshop and kept track of production for herself and those working around her. Being pushy and bossy has its advantages. She is a natural leader and ran the new self-advocacy group at the institution with precision and fairness. As leader she got to participate in the ever-increasing opportunities in the community, and she spoke at conferences, to the legislature, and to the press. She spoke her mind, shared the joys in her relationship with Richard, and shared her dream to live in the community. Interested group home administrators called and asked to meet her and invited her to come to a home for a visit. Her guardian said no. Nancy's friends and advocates remembered Barbara.

THE PEOPLE FIRST CONFERENCE: MAKING THUNDER

On September 15, 1990, in Middlebury, People First of Connecticut held its first statewide conference for people with disabilities. This 1½-day meeting took place after months of planning by a committee of self-advocates and advisors, its accomplishment complicated by the enormous logistics of planning, such as how to distribute information and printed materials to people who, for the most part, could not read and depended on others for transportation. As it turned out, 350 people came from all over the state. They came from a wide range of living arrangements; some lived on their own, or with their families, others lived in group homes or in shared living arrangements, and still others resided in state institutions. The conference hotel was beautiful, the menu carefully selected to offer choice and real variety. The surroundings were important and assisted in creating an atmosphere of dignity. Conferees rose to the occasion.

T.J. Monroe led the organization through a long day of passionate pleas, training and workshops, awards, speeches, and its first annual meeting:

> You have to do two things today. You have to make this room thunder. You have to speak for your rights. You're not gonna get in no trouble speaking for yourself, because there aren't going to be laws in this room. I want to hear thunder!

Nancy heard thunder and she remembered Barbara. Nancy's guardian is also her aunt. Only two other people are left in her family. She is extremely emotional about her family. They are dear to her. Her aunt is growing older and cannot manage as much as she would like. She remembers Nancy's mother's wish for her daughter to be safe and protected from the harsh world. Her pledge is to a family long gone. The institution has changed. The world in which it functions is vastly different and so are the children who moved there in the 1940s.

Nancy struggled with her feelings and affection for her aunt. Her choice to challenge a probate court guardianship with her own attorney and advocates was an extraordinary act of courage. It was an emotional roller-coaster for 2 years. After numerous hearings, misunderstood conversations, team meetings, hours of telephone calls with her aunt, angry letters to the institution administrators from her aunt and from a cousin she had not seen since she was 10 years old, the Southbury Probate Judge reduced and limited the plenary guardianship, giving Nancy the right to make important decisions and the right to tell an apartment program that she wanted to live there and to sign the proper consents. Several months later Nancy moved to a town near her aunt and to live with a family who would help her to re-enter community life. She continues to be active in self-advocacy and attends weekly meetings with people who live in apartments on their own and with roommates. Now she is confident and very happy. When she is ready she will find an apartment and choose a roommate. She will decide when.

One of the conference resolutions called on People First to "take a look at obstacles of the current guardianship process." Nancy's leadership will make it easier for others to carry out that resolution. They should not have the burden of proving their capabilities and competency.

Revolution and the Enthusiasm of Self-Advocacy

T.J.'s challenge to make thunder provided an opportunity for many to question the world of providers and caregivers, to learn from their experience, and to take the message of change to the "Bosses of Administration." The new degree of B.A. was initiated that day. This B.A. was the first degree conferred on caregivers by this new collegiality. Larry, a change agent and articulate teacher, described the personal control that those with a B.A. would have to acknowledge and support:

> I feel group home life is better than institutional life. I want to move out on my own to either an apartment that can be supervised, but where there are few rules. To do things after a long day or on the weekend but on my own. However, if I want to or don't want to go out, instead want to be home, that is my decision to make.

In the workshop session "Where Do the Rules Come From?" participants described the many obstacles to normal, everyday living:

> There are many people who argue when they live together and I think they should talk. You can't have sex with a woman. I work hard and earn money but if I get a raise the state will take the money. In my supervised apartment there is a rule I can't watch TV and work at the same time. Some of our clients are pretty good, but if we want a snack or even get silverware, we have to keep everything under lock and key because of one person. If the food is open, he will get into the cabinet and steal all the food because he has this thing in his head to go get! At work we aren't allowed to sing or be happy. There's a rule against happiness or humming.

T.J. called on the self-advocates to set goals and vote on resolutions, but somehow this always came out "revolutions." These "revolutions" were at the heart of organizing a new generation of advocates in the disability movement. Resolution One read like a mission statement: **The right to live on our own, and have relationships and the right to have jobs in a way that our rights are not being taken away from us.**

In the session organized by Vice-President Peter Kirsche to offer advice and suggestions to improve personal relationships and to learn "How to Flirt," Peter offered advice to alleviate the agonies that all people share in making friends. He explained that making eye contact is also a way to make friends. Men can do this to men. It is on the same wavelength as flirting. You can find out that you have the same wants and needs. He said, "I never had eye contact with women because I was scared. I couldn't face up to it or myself. I thought I was doing wrong by flirting. If you want to compare it to getting a new job, it makes me sweat or get cold feet."

T.J. encouraged people to speak at every opportunity, saying, "Self-advocacy means you have the words to speak; this is a free country in the United States. You might need help, but you can speak for yourself."

Larry reminded everyone that in this new group of activists there are similarities to other civil rights movements.

> I used to think people with disabilities couldn't make it in the outside world, and to listen to Martin Luther King, Jr. speak about how people should have the same rights has really helped me to learn it, and I feel greatly influenced.
>
> My home is on a real street; it's not set apart; it's like being in public. It relates the same thing that JFK tried to stress in the 1960s where he said blacks have the same rights to work in the same place with white people.

To accomplish a political agenda and make changes in an immense service delivery system is a huge task for any organization. For people with disabilities this challenge is met with enthusiasm and by using all the principles of organizing a community of people who come together with similar issues and a need to implement change. T.J. explained the impact of a large membership and coalition-building.

> Everybody came here today, self-advocates, bosses, executive directors and staff. We need everyone to help us. We have people who want to come but can't get here. Go to

> your local meetings; tell your staff; tell them you want to go. You have to get up and march for a lot of issues. We need to get serious now. You have to make it work; we are the people and you are the persons with disabilities with the right to make choices.

In the foyer during the day, participants had an opportunity to network with other organizations invited to exhibit and engage conferees in linkages they would not usually have had the opportunity for. Legal Services offered information on guardianship and made referrals to local offices. The League of Women Voters helped people register to vote and offered instruction on sample ballots. The Jaycees, the Institute for Human Resource Development, and the Connecticut Coalition for Action Groups provided information on job opportunities, community fundraising events, health care reform, and legislative action. This was the first time these organizations had the opportunity to recruit members of People First, and their enthusiasm for the task during the day was infectious.

The Plenary Session

With over 350 people in an elegant banquet hall, more than half of whom had never attended a local or state meeting of People First, the advisors wondered how the plenary session was going to work. But with T.J. at the microphone and advisors running around the room with portable microphones, the comment period and open testimony were a joy and tremendously productive. They were also eye-opening for visitors.

A man rises and asks, "What about the name change? How many would like the Arc to change their name?" There are cheers. Another asks, "Why can't we change DMR" [Department of Mental Retardation]? "How many people would love to see DMR change?" The cheering is louder. "I can't hear you. Do you want that to be another revolution?" Craig from New Haven asked, "How come DMR has cut housing?" T.J. called on the Commissioner of the Department of Mental Retardation to answer this. She responded:

> I hope that all of you [come] who want to see a name change and want to see enough money in our budget so that we don't have to cut opportunities to your colleagues; see you at the legislature to pass laws on this.

Seeing an opportunity here, T.J. asked the crowd, "Do you want to see that as a revolution?" A chorus of cheers and arms waving resounded through the room. "We are going to be there!" The result of this emotional response was the passage of another resolution calling on People First of Connecticut: **To be present at legislative meetings and to lobby for increased funds to enable people to live more independently.**

The issues that generated the most discussion in the plenary session and in the workshop sessions were, not surprisingly, issues about better paying jobs and the benefits to go with them. Larry was one of the few with a better job. He explained:

> As a file clerk, I have a good supervisor. I am proud to fit in with people who are not handicapped. I do not feel out-numbered at all. I belong in a place with normal people which is where I stand now in the world of business.

But many self-advocates complained that the regulations of the Social Security Administration and Connecticut's regulations for Medicaid make it difficult to work in full time positions and live more independently. A Hartford man expressed the pride he had in his work, saying, "I work at a car dealership and I make 90 bucks a week but I can't save too much because they will take it away." Often group home providers encourage dependency, evidenced by Ellen's description of her situation: "They don't want me to take outside jobs because they get paid by the state." Encouragement came from Treasurer, Cathy Juni: "You can still make it if you don't earn more than $500 a month."

A show of hands revealed that almost no one had a paid vacation, paid sick time, or health insurance paid by an employer. Many self-advocates work along side other workers who receive these benefits. It is a real sore spot. Uneven wages from sheltered workshop employers bothered others. Nunzio demanded, "Every job should get paid the same every week." Marilyn practically spat out a similar message, "Nobody wants to work there because the pay is so low."

But no other issue received as much attention and discussion as living in places where there was more independence. At every step to greater independent living, people were proud to describe their accomplishments and to share their goals for the next opportunity.

The leaders of People First of Connecticut and its 14 chapters grew up at Southbury Training School. Many participants still live there or at Seaside Regional Center. At the meeting they wisely congratulated valued staff for their care, asked for more money for them, and asked for their own place in the community. Nunzio reported on his move to a group home: "And a couple of weeks later I'm cooking lasagna." The biggest cheers of the day rose for the next resolution: **People should leave the institutions and live in the community.**

The community network of group homes and supervised apartment programs offers greater access to the world but with many limitations, rules, and the feeling that the home is definitely not your own. Larry spoke of some problems:

> Another thing I am looking into for myself is to live in an apartment by myself or a group home with a lesser number of people and choose my own housemates as opposed to the housemates I currently live with.

People described their success in making it to an apartment or place to live with greater independence and the choice of whom to live with. A young woman from East Hartford said, "Living in a group home there are a lot of problems, and in my own apartment there are hardly any." Diane and Judy stood to announce the purchase of their new condominium in Danbury and reminded listeners that this accomplishment was based on two things: "We have our own rights and we are on our own." Peter is confident about his move, saying,"It is the best thing that has ever happened to get out on my own." Rose shared, "We can go anytime we want, we don't have to check in or out. We can go to a nightclub."

Conference Accomplishments

During the conference, there were many people in the wings offering assistance as helpers to participants who needed directions to the next workshop or to move from room to room. Most were invited to attend because they have a B.A. They were there to listen. This was a benefit and offered an edge in lobbying and networking for self-advocates. Those who lived in institutions had the opportunity to meet people who could introduce them to group home administrators in their region. A self-advocate looking for a better job and higher wages found the opportunity to have lunch with potential employers. The networking went on all day. People exchanged telephone numbers on cocktail napkins, and self-advocates regularly collared the Commissioner and the Regional Directors from the Department of Mental Retardation. People First members offered them evaluations of the services they received; these evaluations were better than any established quality assurance system. People First members turned out to be the best lobbyists. For instance, DMR puts in a great deal of time training staff people to encourage a more open and meaningful team process for people served by the state. But People First members told the bosses this was not working for them. Jim described the shortcomings of the team process: "I'm on my own but I don't seem to be getting anywhere. We have an OPS [Overall Plan of Service] but nothing is being done. I want to get out on the weekend and after work, to be away from the group home."

The annual meeting came to a close. The issues covered were work, benefits, relationships, living more independently, and making real day-to-day choices. T.J. could not pronounce "resolution." He continually said, "Let's make a revolution" as soon as it became apparent that the self-advocates had reached consensus or had raised a vital issue. T.J. had it right all the time. To this day he smiles when asked to pronounce the word resolution. Here are the "revolutions" as they were developed by over 350 persons from across the state:

1. The right to live on our own, and have relationships and the right to have jobs in a way that our rights are not being taken away from us
2. To change the name of ARC/US and ARC/CT
3. To change the name of DMR
4. To be present at legislative meetings to lobby for increased funds to enable people to live more independently
5. Paid sick time, vacation time and holidays
6. People should leave the institutions and live in the community.
7. Take a look at obstacles of the current guardianship process.
8. Transportation must be provided for people in suburban areas to go out locally and to other towns.

FOSTERING SELF-ADVOCACY

Important issues abound for advisors of self-advocates. The latter's message is so powerful that it does not have to be interpreted. The fostering and support of this vital movement, the role of advisors, and the necessity to take seriously what is being expressed so eloquently are essential issues. Being an advisor is hard work. It requires the ability to organize and balance a million details of transportation and materials distribution. Multiple and frequent telephone calls are almost always necessary to provide follow-up and to ensure participation and success. This kind of meaningful support is essential for a group of self-advocates to come together in the local library or church hall and to go to a statewide meeting. Ensuring this level of attention to detail is necessary if self-advocacy is to be a success, and this is an obligation of the advisor. It does nobody any good to send an announcement to area group homes, work programs, and families without a plan of outreach to the persons advisors are helping to become organized. Much of this can and should be done in conjunction with self-advocates themselves if the group is young. Later, members will assume more responsibility for the logistics. Follow-along support may continually be necessary. The self-advocacy movement is still in its infancy in most regions. Only a few organizations are totally on their own, without advisors or helpers.

The telephone tree is an old organizing tool that self-advocates can arrange and plan as a means to contact each other about upcoming meetings and organizational alerts. This tool has the benefit of increasing social contacts and networking opportunities for people. It can enhance an individual's skill in communication and increase skills in the ordinary use of the telephone. It can also increase the understanding of the rights of people among residential staff. In large and segregated facilities, use of the telephone is often limited to staff, and restrictions of residents' use of the telephone may be an obstacle. Self-advocates can exercise their new advocacy skills here. This obstacle may seem simple to hurdle, yet in many group homes residents are forbidden to use the telephone after a certain hour, or they have access to it for a limited time. Staff have been dismayed by a caller's request to speak to a "client" member of the household. Family members may think it is cute or amusing to receive telephone calls for their self-advocate relatives. When such rules or attitudes exist, an advisor can run interference when necessary and model new behaviors for staff and families as well as offer explanations and insight into what self-advocates are accomplishing.

Whenever possible it is important to hold meetings in a community setting apart from service providers such as Arc and state facilities. Assisting the coordinator/leader of the group in making arrangements by identifying the correct contact in city hall or the public library offers an enabling experience and directly increases the sensitivity to self-advocacy in city hall.

The next contact should be made with the press. The local newspaper can run the meeting announcement and agenda. This also may spark interest by reporters to a new and interesting event. People organizing themselves who traditionally have been labeled "retarded" is news. Inviting a local legislator, or city council representative, or other issue-oriented leader and program speaker can offer public education and a systems advocacy opportunity for people with disabilities.

Cultivating a relationship with the press is an important advantage for People First; this is the obligation of the advisor and leader. Bringing the press to meet and interview participants individually or at People First meetings can give the reporter the individual focus needed for a story. It also provides a gold mine of opportunities to educate readers on disability rights issues, increases public awareness and sensitivity, and recruits members and allies.

If there is any question about the reporter's attitude toward people with disabilities, running interference again may be required of the advisor. An advisor can assist in asking the questions and redirect the reporter to the members. Sometimes a political translation and summary can be provided by the advisor, but the responsibility for answering questions and discussion of issues is with the People First member. Media guides on disability are available in many states and offer guidance to well-meaning but uninformed reporters and writers on appropriate disability language.

Minutes can offer another tool for advocacy. An advisor or helper can assist a recorder/secretary in capturing the comments of the members. If the group thinks it is appropriate, the minutes can be sent to B.A.s for an opportunity to understand the thinking and clarify self-advocacy issues for them. The group may need to be selective about which minutes are sent, however. Some administrators are not interested in or amused by criticisms of their work and programs.

Everyone enjoys refreshments at a meeting and self-advocates are no exception. Some groups organize their meetings successfully around a meal, and others restrict food from their meetings because it can be a distraction for people who are regularly denied sweets and caffeine. Whether food should be served at a meeting should be discussed and decided by participants. They should also share or assume the responsibility of arranging for refreshments. Making them available at the beginning of the meeting or at the end of the meeting should be their choice. Social time at People First meetings enhances friendship and increases skills in socialization.

There is at least one natural leader in every group. Assisting those leaders in running the meeting requires a delicate balance for advisors. Good advisors know instinctively where to cross the line and enter a discussion, assist in defining a problem, or redirect an ongoing conversation. All advisors struggle with this support issue. Guidance may also come from the leader of the group, who will provide direction to the advisor and ask for help and assistance when needed. Tuning in to the sensitivity of the leader–advisor relationship requires work and balance as for any cooperative relationship.

Transportation presents a logistical nightmare for advisors and leaders. Advance planning and plenty of lead time is required. Providers, friends, and community transportation sources should be on the mailing list and telephone tree for People First and self-advocacy meetings. Follow up will always be required to ensure that arrangements are completed. There should be plans for last minute pull-outs and problems. Often self-advocates find their voice on access to improved transportation by dealing with the many obstacles they face in assembling.

Also, providers create obstacles to participation. Meetings held in the evening may overlap shift changes. Participants are at the mercy of staff who drive them to meetings and may experience the embarrassment and frustration of having to leave early. Advisors can assist self-advocates in speaking out on this problem and help find alternate transportation as well as encourage the provider to respect the scheduling of the meeting.

SUPPORT FOR THE PEOPLE FIRST MOVEMENT

Supporting People First and other self-advocacy organizations requires more from advisors than just helping to organize a conference. Conferences are truly wonderful events for self-advocates, but they become another sweet memory if follow-along support to implement their goals is denied. However exhausting a conference may be for advisors and the planning committee, the real impact comes not just from the conference itself but through organizing self-advocates to follow through on the advocacy strategies that they decide will best make their messages a reality to B.A.s and policy-makers.

When People First of Connecticut developed and adopted their agenda of eight resolutions, this really did cause a revolution for service providers, administrators, and families. When labor and local townspeople in Mansfield, Connecticut joined in a last ditch effort to keep Mansfield Training School open for the remaining 140 people, People First of Connecticut moved quickly. These last 140 individuals, on their way to the community after years of waiting, were threatened by this coalition. People First went to the capitol to visit legislators to ensure their goal was realized and people could leave the institution. In Governor Lowell Weicker's office they asked for his support and won him over. They took the time to discuss with him their jobs, educate him on sheltered workshop low wages, and ask for help in obtaining benefits.

Since People First held its first conference in 1990, a greater number of self-advocates have obtained supported or competitive employment where they receive benefits. In addition, service providers are responding to the request for holiday and sick leave with pay. Nancy's highly visible struggle to reduce her guardianship has resulted in greater awareness by the probate courts and the interdisciplinary teams to present an individualized approach to competency questions and wider use of limited guardianship. After several years of organizing, self-advocates convinced parents and members in the Association for Retarded Citizens/US to drop the offensive "R" word and change the name. Connecticut People First brought the same resolution to Arc/CT. T.J. was right, self-advocacy is about revolution.

In order for self-advocates to achieve the changes they are looking for in services and obtain natural and self-directed supports, first, the obligation to truly listen to their message must be met. Bringing people together or appointing one person to a committee or board is not enough, and scheduling self-advocacy as a program in the service-delivery system is not correct. Listening to self-advocates' message requires stripping away the usual trappings of the "we versus them" attitude. The strengths and capabilities of the people purportedly served must be acknowledged. Real self-determination is a goal that can be shared with self-advocates. Supporting and developing self-advocacy and this emerging disability rights movement are powerful tools for change.

20

Building Community One Person at a Time

One Candle Power

George Ducharme, Pat Beeman, Regina DeMarasse, and Cathy Ludlum

In the fall of 1986, John McKnight, David Wetherow, and Beth Mount came to Connecticut as the keynote speakers at a conference titled, *Beyond Community Services: Toward Full Community Participation*. The 3 days of the conference were spread over the months of September, October, and November at the Knights of Columbus Hall in Newington, Connecticut, and changed the way we (the authors) interact with children and adults with disabilities.

Through a grant from the Connecticut Developmental Disabilities Council, we began to walk with people toward their vision of the future. Beth contributed her positive futures work and shared a concept developed by Judith Snow and Marsha Forest called circles of friends or circles of support. We contributed our knowledge of Connecticut community life and the networks of professional and community groups we have built up through a lifetime as Connecticut residents. We chose five people and began a journey that has led us to a greater appreciation of the power of the ordinary, natural, spontaneous caring that is possible when one person commits a little time and energy to the life of another. The stories we are living (two of which will be recounted later in this chapter) are filled with the joy, pain, risk, sadness, and thrill of a journey toward a vision of the future, which is unique to each person. What we have learned in the 5 years since we began our journey is documented in six monographs published from 1988 to 1991 (Mount, Beeman, & Ducharme, 1988a, 1988b, 1988c, 1991; Mount et al., 1990; Mount, Beeman et al., 1991; Mount, Ludlum et al., 1991).

The elements that we believe to be essential for supporting children and adults with disabilities in full community inclusion are expressed in the six-step process we call "One Candle Power." When one candle (the gift of a person) lights (empowers, stimulates) another, it intensifies the glow. This process enables community members to empower each other, to light the way toward building bridges to participation in community life for a person with a disability by creating a circle of support.

Step 1 focuses on *giftedness* or *capacity*. Without denying the disability and all the difficulties surrounding it, we spend our energy finding and building upon the gifts of *everyone* in the circle of support.

Step 2 involves asking the person or family who wants to begin a circle of support to develop a vision or dream *of the future* as they wish it to be. The following questions are helpful in developing an image of the future:

- *Relationships* What are the relationships in your life? Who are the people who care for you? Consider not only service providers, but also neighbors, people in a house of worship, people at school, and so forth.
- *Places and activities* During a week how do you spend your time? Where do you work? What community activities are you involved in?
- *Preferences* What do you find engaging, enjoyable, or motivating? What do you find frustrating, upsetting, or boring?
- *What is the vision for the future* Do you want to become more involved in community? Do you want a job? Do you want more friends? Where might you like to live?
- *Things that will help* What opportunities do you want?
- *Things that are challenges/fears* What do you worry about?

In step 3 the *circle of support* is developed. The members of a circle of support are usually friends, family members, coworkers, neighbors, people at a house of worship, and sometimes service providers. The majority of people in a circle of support are not paid to be there. They are involved because they care about the person or family and they have made a commitment to work together on behalf of the person or family. The circle members come together to pursue the vision by identifying and understanding the challenges and opportunities and working on strategies to overcome certain obstacles and take advantage of opportunities.

The first meetings are very revealing because circle members become aware of the barriers faced by the person with a disability. Following each meeting and brainstorming session, a list of specific strategies is divided up among members. Individual members make commitments to work on what they feel comfortable with, according to the amount of time they have available, even if some people have only enough time to be present at the circle meeting. Just being present is very important.

Step 4 is *getting connected* or building bridges. This is the ongoing process of walking with a person into the heart of community life to reach places, groups, and organizations that the person or family would like to be involved with. Circle members and others who are interested act as guides into community.

Step 5 is a reminder that *starting small* is fine. Too many of us think we cannot do anything significant if we do not have the professional degrees or we are not the experts, so we do nothing. It has been our experience that *every* person's gift (candle) is important. We encourage everyone to share their gifts, however small they might think they are.

Step 6 is changing the system. In some instances, we might have to participate (in our small way) in efforts *to change government or another system* in order to continue the journey toward reaching the vision. The stories of Regina DeMarasse and Cathy Ludlum, presented in the sections following, describe the use of these steps in daring to dream.

REGINA DEMARASSE'S JOURNEY: BIG DREAMS AND COMMUNITY CONNECTIONS

I (Regina DeMarasse) have always had a gift for not making sense. In my youth, I had big dreams, like attending New York City's High School of Music and Art, despite the fact that an early childhood spinal tumor had rendered my fingers clumsy on the piano. My own mother suggested I try art, but I insisted that I wanted music, which whispered, and stirred, and roared through my veins. I auditioned . . . and was accepted!

Money was tight in our family. Still, I wanted to attend college, "a small, private one in a rural setting," I would say. "You and everyone else," my friends responded. But I was insistent. Why not pursue a scholarship? After all, I had worked hard (sometimes) in school. Along with Mom, I researched the possibilities and applied to several sources. I was rejected by some but won a full financial aid package to attend my first choice, Antioch College in the little town of Yellow Springs, Ohio.

And why not start off by taking a course in human physiology, despite my lack of background in biology and the possibility of failure? I came close to failing some of it, but I still learned enough to consider it invaluable a couple of years later when I was grappling with understanding my doctor's explanation of the vicissitudes of my own serious illness.

And why not become involved in some civil rights activism years later, believing the part I played really could change things? Through persistence in a telephone campaign and letter-writing to the proper authorities, the door was opened to a group of students with disabilities who had previously been denied opportunity.

Policy-makers often rely upon all kinds of formulae to help them make decisions. Over the years, I too have developed a formula to make my dreams come true; it seems to have excellent results. It is shown below:

A dream + naiveté + ignoring what others think + work + sharing the dream/soliciting the help of others + more work + still more work + time + patience + still even *more* work = A dream come true.

When I found myself living in a rehabilitation center/nursing home later because I had become blind and quadriplegic, I saw no reason why I should be stuck there. They called it a home, but it was not. I shared a room with three other people, all with different channels on their televisions, all with their own aides, nurses, therapists, friends, families, and other assorted members of the human race traipsing in and out of *my* room, all hours of the day and night. It was not exactly the quiet, contemplative life. I had little privacy and little control over when I got up in the morning, when I went to bed at night, what I ate, who fed me, who washed me, who dressed me, or how much and what I could do in a day, or even where and when I could do it! Perhaps others thought it was the only place for me, some might even say "the best place for me," but I had my doubts.

Since it was a rehabilitation center (of sorts), the institution had an independent living facilitator (ILF), Lori. She was fairly eager to assist me by coordinating appointments and transportation to independent living centers (ILCs). By the time I traveled down to one of them, she had left for a position elsewhere. Mary Beth, the social worker, accompanied me instead.

The counselor at the first of the centers asked, "If any Section 8 housing becomes available in the next several years, what kind of arrangement do you want? One with a social worker on the premises, one with recreational activities, one that provides transportation?"

"Yes," I replied.

"Yes what?"

"All of them."

"Look, if you want to get on a waiting list you might be able to get into an apartment building with one of these features. You've got to decide which kind of stuff you want, and then make application."

"Umm, I don't know. What are the neighborhoods like?"

"I have no idea," she answered, tapping the desk. "What'll it be? What kind of features do you want?"

"I don't know; I've never done this kind of thing before."

"Well, why don't you give us a call when you decide."

"But I don't know how to judge."

Our point–counterpoint went on a few moments more and I could hear her voice shifting as she moved her head about, apparently looking one way, then another. I politely thanked her and left, hoping the other ILC would offer me better counsel.

At the second ILC, the counselor was far more amicable, but in answer to my questions, she had little more to say than, "Gee I wish I could help you on that, but I'm kind of new at this, myself. I can give you some literature, though, if you like."

"Does any of it come on tape? I'm blind."

"No, I'm sorry. I wish it did; I have a visual problem myself."

Back to the institution we went. I carried with me not only reams of paperwork to sort through with Mary Beth, when she had the time, considering all her other duties, but also the good wishes of all the friends I had been with that day. (I had arranged for my appointment to occur the day of a luncheon given by the college program I had been a part of before I left New York. I believe in having it all.) The feeling was bittersweet—so many supporters, so little knowledge as to how to reach independence. Mary Beth and I never did get to sort through that material. Within a month she left for bigger and better things, as did most of the staff eventually.

Two ILFs and a case manager later (and I'm not sure how many social workers), I was still exploring possibilities. I inquired about my sister's area in upstate New York but never got an answer on that from the new ILF, much as I hounded, nagged, and reminded her that it was important to me. I inquired about a congregate living situation in Connecticut, as well, but no one left on staff even took that inquiry seriously—no one except for the psychologist, who knew I was going nuts.

"Have you considered a circle of friends?" he suggested.

"Well, I've heard about them, but I don't really see how a bunch of my cronies sitting around discussing my plight is really going to help."

"But it's worth a try, isn't it?"

"Anything's worth a try," I responded, deciding to talk with two of the other residents, who had a circle going around them.

Later that month I attended the circle of friends meeting of Connie and Stan, a married couple who were determined to leave the institution. By the end of my first experience attending their meeting, I was convinced they would. Here they were, surrounded by folks who believed not only that it could happen, but that it *should* happen. The 10 or so members of Connie and Stan's circle sat brainstorming, strategizing, building, and creating options.

Beth Mount, one of the circle facilitators, explained to me that she had three large sheets of newsprint tacked up on the wall. One was labeled Things That Work, and she had listed items there in green. Another was labeled Things That Don't Work, and the items listed there were red. A third column was labeled Strategies; she had written there in purple.

I was impressed. Still, I had strong reservations about this approach working for me. After all, Connie had Stanley. Stanley had the use of his hands and eyes; Connie had the use of her eyes too. I had neither. I had nothing but dreams and, I later realized, some raw indignation. It was that raw indignation that drove me to call Beth 2 weeks later.

"On my drive over here today," she said as we sat in the quietest spot we could find, "I was getting thoughts about there being a lot of people out there in the spiritual community who want to be of use but don't know in what way. I think your situation will provide that way."

For the next 2 hours we talked about my goals, my dreams (e.g., to live someplace quiet and countryfied, yet near enough to the convenience of a city, and with vegetarians), my gifts, my interests, and my penchant for "not making sense." Beth took it all down and took it seriously. She also took down all kinds of information about the people I knew and the possible networks. We set a date for my first circle meeting with Beth, Pat Beeman, and George Ducharme, to which I invited six or so friends.

We decided the conference room at the ILC would be the most convenient place to meet, since I would not need transportation there. We met in the same room where I had met on numerous occasions with "the rehab team" to discuss my therapies and other activities. The team and I did not always agree!

The circle was different from the rehab team. My friends saw me as capable, needing not therapies, but *real life* aspects, like purposeful work, purposeful leisure, dependable help, personal choice, autonomy, control of my life, and the means and atmosphere in which to have it all. They saw me as having a right to self-determination and a right to a home of my own, living with people with whom I choose to live, taking medicines and nourishment of my choice, and being in an atmosphere of my choice with the peace and quiet I need. They believed in my leading a full, productive life. Never before had I met with such an exhilarating group!

By the next circle meeting, however, once again, I had my doubts. I wondered how all this really was going to work, how I could achieve independence when so much was needed. I needed not only a place to live, but paid personal care assistants and someone to train and supervise them in the areas that I could not verbally explain or see. I needed someone to handle my finances, to be there when paid help was unavailable, to turn and reposition me in the middle of the night, and to care for me when I was sick. Essentially, I needed to live with a devoted friend (or two). But where does one find such friends?

George began, "We discussed a lot of things last time. Is there anything specific you would most like to cover tonight?"

"Well, none of all the wonderful things we talked about last time can really happen if I don't have a place to do them, like my own room and my own home and the personal care assistance (PCA) I need to live there. I mean, I can't even get to a phone, or depend on getting any messages around here. Even if I got some kind of phone I could operate, sharing a room with three other people, their aides, their visitors, housekeepers, and all the rest of the world coming and going as they please just doesn't cut it for confidentiality if I want to work as a counselor. Before I can even think about where to live, I need to figure out how I'm going to do it, especially if the number of personal care hours is so limited by the state. I'm going to need a roommate or someone who's willing to be my eyes and to fill in at times when I don't have an aide."

We tossed around that idea, pursuing the classified ads in all kinds of New Age journals that George's guest, Marty, brought. I observed Richard, my friend with whom I had shared a study group for the last 5 months, shifting in his chair beside me. Several times he leaned forward and took a breath as if about to speak, but someone else always spoke first; we were so full of ideas. At last, he got his chance:

"Regina, Sherri and I have been talking this over, and were wondering how you would feel about coming to live with us?"

Well, if that wasn't a show-stopper.

It was late September of 1988; we set a discharge goal of June 1, 1989. That would give us plenty of time to put all needed services and supports in place, including remote control equipment with which I could operate a telephone, a computer, my talking book machine, a radio (music is vital to my health), a fan, and so forth. The advocacy group to which I belonged was working on convincing legislators to agree to a direct pay PCA program, which would enable me to select attendants with whom I could feel comfortable and whom I could depend on and trust. Also, because it would not require any middleman agency, it would mean more hours for the same money.

I wanted to tell the rehab team at the center my plans. It just so happened they were having my monthly case conference the very next day. Unfortunately, they were having it without me, since it was being held when my psychology class met. After all, I couldn't expect them to change their schedule to suit me, even if it was my life they were discussing.

I did tell my case manager and she conveyed my plans to the team. I think no one other than the psychologist wanted to believe them. The team members were all a little afraid for me, with many what ifs: What if it does not work out? What if they decide it is too much for them? What if you get sick? What if there is an emergency? What if there is a fire?" It was kind of like a game of "Name that Fear."

The months that followed were more active than any since I had acquired my disabilities. We had circles, mini-circles, legislative meetings, friendly meetings, forums, parties, concerts, and sleepovers—I and my friends. Sherri and Richard came to the rehabilitation center and learned just about every aspect of my routine. They practiced on every leave of absence the institution would grant me. We then decided to move the discharge date up to May, not trusting the center to keep things moving quickly enough to meet the June date. I could not have left a day too soon.

It has been nearly 3 years since I left the institution and close to 4 since I became involved in this circle "nonsense." Since then we have succeeded in having a direct pay PCA program instituted. I have written a book, dozens of poems, and a dozen articles and stories, all on a computer I operate by puffing the Morse code into a special device (frequently late at night when no institution would allow it). As a member of the Connecticut Poetry Society, I have participated in readings of original work at the public library. I am facilitating a listening sensitivity support group and counseling a young man as part of my internship at the University of Connecticut, as well. Next year I hope to attend graduate school.

The fact that I have many things to do now that I am back in the community does not mean that starting a circle will cause thing to fall into place automatically and miraculously. Like most things in life that work, circles require commitment and effort. They also require dreamers with determination who are not afraid of "not making sense."

My circle has not met in months; there is little need to meet these days since I can now attend to most things on my own or with the help of others here and there. I *have* community connections! Sometimes, I cannot even remember, anymore, where the circle left off and community began.

CATHY LUDLUM'S JOURNEY: COMMUNITY BUILDING AND COMMUNITY THINKING

People with disabilities, their families, and their service providers have routinely been taught to think of the community as an unfriendly place. When I (Cathy Ludlum) started college and later graduated and went to work, I was told to expect people in the community to be apathetic at best toward my presence. It was usually suggested that my needs could be met more easily and efficiently in specialized service systems, and for years I believed that. Yet, ultimately, I was deemed "too disabled" by these very systems and ended up turning to the community as my one remaining option.

When I dreamed of moving out on my own, I always thought of it as a question of money. At 16 I already knew that I would need an incredible amount of support to live independently, and in my mind this meant 24-hour paid staff. I had never known anyone who hired his or her own assistants, so all I had to go on was the vague notion that I could hire people. But I also felt that no one person could support me adequately over a period of time and feared that people would not show up when they were supposed to. I thought the answer was to find enough cash, hire enough people, and pay them well enough to make them act responsibly toward me.

I developed preliminary comparisons between my earning power and the money I felt I needed to move out. This proved depressing, however, since I always came up many thousands of dollars short. I needed so much support, partly because of the severity of my physical disability itself, but especially because of the presence of significant breathing problems. The idea of having difficulty breathing without a trained person present was more than I could handle. It never occurred to me that anyone who was willing to listen could help or that many of my needs could be met informally.

Six years of pursuing my dream on my own resulted in nothing but disappointment and a bleak vision of my future. I wrote or called every innovative living program I could find, both inside and outside of Connecticut. I went for occupational therapy evaluations and independent living counseling sessions. I was referred everywhere, but everyone said the same thing. My needs were too extensive, my concerns about survival well based. The experts all agreed that I could not function in the community apart from the specialized support of my mother.

I spent the next 2 years trying not to think about what was going to happen. My mother was growing older, and I could easily foresee the day when she could no longer care for me at home. A nursing home seemed inevitable, and at 24, I dreaded it.

Then I went to a conference on community inclusion of people with disabilities. I went reluctantly, as part of my job, not expecting to hear anything new. But John McKnight, the first speaker, jarred my attention by saying that paid services were not the answer. Funded services are crucial to helping people remain in their communities and have control over their lives, but without ordinary relationships, no amount of services will make a person safe. John talked about community, and how neighborhoods and associations are more complete when all people are welcome to participate. He spoke, not so much of what people with disabilities needed from the community, but of what the community needed from all its members. And he told stories, wonderful stories about people being together just because they wanted to be.

The second speaker, David Wetherow, described how housing cooperatives were being used to generate informal support around people with disabilities. In coops, everyone is expected to contribute to the maintenance and management of the property in whatever way he or she is able. By working together, all the members become neighbors in the true sense and routinely make arrangements that are beneficial to one another. I grabbed this concept and wrote on the conference evaluation form, "Please call me if anything like this is coming to Connecticut!"

Beth Mount, the third speaker, pulled all the previous ideas together by making drawings of people's lives. Paid services were depicted with red triangles, while community activities and resources were in green, often accented with brilliant rainbows, hearts, and clouds. I realized, after a time, that my focus in moving away from home had always been on the red, having enough paid staff time to make me feel secure. But I slowly realized that a life concentrated in red will always lack the mystery of friendship, the joy of celebration, and the challenge of striving toward a dream.

A few months later, conference organizers Pat Beeman and George Ducharme contacted me. Along with Beth Mount, they came to my house and asked me questions about where I wanted to live, whom I wanted to live with, what I wanted to do, and what would make me happy. This was quite a switch from all my previous talks with experts who thought that hardly anything was possible.

Beth, Pat, and George challenged me to dream, so I did. I said I wanted to live in a housing cooperative, with enough personal assistance services to do more than merely survive. I wanted a job where I could make full use of my writing and speaking skills, education, and interests. I wanted to travel, go to concerts and movies, be outdoors, and do more things with my friends.

Beth, Pat, and George not only accepted my vision, but treated it as my roadmap to a better life. They suggested I invite some friends over and share the vision with them. At first, this seemed to be an innocent request. I expected that people would come, and they did. I assumed that they would be supportive of my goals, and they were. But I could not have anticipated the depth of their commitment to me, to my vision, including helping me stay out of a nursing home. Since then, some people have dropped out, and new people have come in, but our journey has lasted for 5 years.

My primary goal was to move into a housing cooperative, and we all mobilized to contact everyone we knew who had any experience with housing. Suddenly, there were more meetings and excursions than anyone could have imagined. It became obvious very quickly that all these trips were putting a strain on "Ludlum's Taxi Service" (i.e., my mother driving my lift-equipped van). The issue came up in a circle meeting as to whether someone else could learn to drive the van. There was no reason why not; we simply never had thought of it. Over the next few months, nearly everyone in my circle started driving my van and helping me follow up on housing leads. Gradually, invitations to concerts and parties came to include the key phrase, "I'll pick you up in your van." I was now free to come and go with my friends, without having to worry about the time, or the distance, or whether my mother felt like going. It was as if a whole new world had opened up for me!

As time went on, people became interested in hearing about our journeys, and those of us who had circles were invited to speak at conferences in a widening geographical area. When a 45-minute trip to New Haven came up, I dreaded it. I had not done much traveling without my mother and could think only of all the things that could go wrong. My van could break down or I could have trouble breathing. But someone in my circle had an expression, "We'll deal," and after a while I just automatically thought, "We'll deal," whenever I weighed an opportunity against a risk.

In 1988, a group of us drove to a conference in Baltimore, Maryland, to talk about circles, and someone who heard us at that conference invited us to Ohio the following year. As my friends and I traveled farther and longer and had consistently positive experiences, it dawned on me that my mother was not the only one who could provide me the necessary assistance. All I needed was to be with people who were willing to listen to me.

With my circle in the background for support, I began to hire some personal assistants. My fears about the reliability and competence of strangers were still there, but at this point I was ready to try. I knew that even if my first few experiences were disastrous, I was not alone. Any problems could be brought before my circle, and together we would come up with new options.

To my surprise, almost all my employees turned out to be wonderful, caring people who went out of their way to ensure the success of whatever I was doing. People were willing to negotiate new arrangements, willing to help out in a crisis, and much more dependable than I could have predicted. As a result, I had a new level of independence. I could now wash my hair, change my clothes, and go somewhere of my own choosing without having to consult with my mother, or even coordinate with another member of my circle. With my assistants, I took off for meetings all over the state, went to the park, went roller-skating, and ran long and complex errands. When I had an opportunity to speak in Montreal, Canada, I invited an assistant and we went.

The combination of my circle, my assistants, and my own increased confidence made me feel much more secure than I had at any time in the past. But the test came in April of 1989, at 10 o'clock on a Saturday night, when my mother had difficulty breathing. At first, she told the ambulance drivers that she did not want to go to the hospital because she could not leave me home alone. I just kept saying not to worry because my circle would help me.

As soon as my mother had left for the hospital, I was on the telephone starting to coordinate the support I would need over the next few days. I called one of my assistants and woke her up. She came immediately and stayed overnight, and during the following week she put in many hours she refused to let me pay for. By the time I went to bed that first night, people in my circle were already scheduled to stay over through Tuesday, providing personal assistance, cooking, driving me to work and the hospital, or doing anything else that had to be done. No one thought twice; everyone just jumped in and helped. By Tuesday, the crisis had passed. Mom came home and was able to resume many of her previous activities. But my circle had come through when it mattered most, and we still talk about what a significant period that was for all of us.

Before my involvement with circles, I thought I could find safety in the service system, in its regulation and funding. Yet none of what happened during those days in April could have been mandated by any legal contract or service agreement. I was able to remain in my own home for one reason, that is, because I had some people in my life who cared about me.

The changes brought about by my circle continued to spread out into different areas of my life. One part of my vision was to find productive and challenging work. I wanted to stop using Social Security Disability Insurance (SSDI), mostly because of the earning limits and other restrictions the program imposed on me, but I kept running into the problem of health insurance. I could not afford to lose my Medicare coverage as long as private insurers continued to reject people with pre-existing conditions. So I joined a statewide advocacy group to lobby for accessible, affordable health insurance for everyone.

Meanwhile, I was constantly receiving offers to write on, speak on, edit, and advise on a number of issues related to inclusion. All these projects were exciting in their own right, and I dove in eagerly. I was already earning the SSDI maximum of $190 a month at my regular job and refused additional compensation because I felt it would threaten my income. This made all of us unhappy, but I wasn't willing to risk losing my benefits.

The members of my circle had always stressed my talents instead of my limitations, and gradually, against my better judgment, I began to think my time was worth something. The SSDI rules became more unbearable than ever as I realized I had some marketable skills. About this time, however, new regulations took effect that allowed earnings of $500 a month, some limited spend down provisions, and a buy-in formula for Medicare. This seemed to be the perfect opportunity to spin all the loose ends into a small consulting business. So these days I am running around speaking or working at my computer and being paid for it!

As all of this was going on, I was still trying to find a way to move into a housing cooperative. There were so many obstacles that it looked impossible for months at a time. Although there were already a number of coops in Connecticut, none had ever deliberately included someone with a disability. This was partly because coops were not wheelchair accessible, and partly because a few hundred hours of "sweat equity" (e.g., working on insulation, painting, and landscaping) were needed as a down payment, and people with physical disabilities supposedly were not able to fulfill this requirement. But in reality, the reason people with disabilities were not living in co-ops was that because no one ever suggested it. Once developers were made aware that people with disabilities were being left out, they started planning accessible units into most of their projects and recruiting people to apply for these units.

Hopes rose and fell over several years as my circle and I sought a co-op for me to apply to. Then, finally, word came about a co-op in Manchester, Connecticut, that was perfect in every way. I filled out a long and intimidating application; then there were 6 anxious months of interviews and credit checks. Finally, I was accepted, along with 15 other families, as a co-op candidate. We have spent the last 7 months contributing sweat equity and attending weekly membership trainings. During this time, we have begun to create a sense of community, which will continue to grow stronger after we move in. Four of the 16 units are fully wheelchair accessible, and the remaining townhouses are accessible on the first floor to encourage people to visit one another.

My sweat equity was contributed by members of my circle and other friends. Although I was reluctant to impose further on busy people, they went out of their way to ask me if they could work on my behalf. Everyone was excited to help make my vision a reality.

The co-op is now nearing completion, and we hope to move in within the next few weeks. I already feel at home in my new community. I have joined a church in the area, and I am learning where things are and what there is to do. I have a great live-in assistant, and other details are slowly working themselves out.

Now it is time to dream new dreams, only this time I will not start by thinking of anything as impossible. I have already seen impossible things happen!

Over the last 5 years, I have learned a great deal about myself, about the nature of the community, and about the service system. I have learned that, when people think of me in terms of my capacities instead of my deficiencies, doors seem to open everywhere I turn. My new home, my job, and many other opportunities all were reachable because people were able to see me for what I could offer instead of what I lacked. This is not to ignore the realities of my situation, but simply to recognize what I have going for me. And one of the best things I have going for me is the support of my circle. Over time, it has transformed the way I think of myself.

Five years ago I could not have imagined staying alone in my apartment for any length of time because of my breathing problems. But my confidence now has increased to the point where I can be on my own for hours at a time. I have several back-up plans in case of emergency, and these days that is enough. In my travels and at home, I have dealt successfully with big and little crises, and I know I can handle whatever comes up. As a result, I feel free to take some risks in the process of living.

I now think of community as a place where people's capacities blend in an infinite number of wonderful ways. When people meet, whether for roller-skating, bagpipe practice, or planning a festival, they have a natural tendency to complement and compensate for one another, and most of the time no one realizes this is happening. The concepts of giving and receiving become blurred, and everyone goes home feeling that they have gained something.

Contrary to what I once believed, the community has almost unlimited reservoirs of acceptance, kindness, and creativity. I have found people to be keenly interested in what I was doing but also eager to become involved. For example, I met a woman who knew how to do computer graphic layout. When she learned that I was starting a communications consulting business, she gave me informal lessons just because I was new and she wanted me to succeed. I have also been surprised by the flexibility of my assistants, many of whom are college students, servers, or school teachers, and whose contact with people with disabilities has been minimal. Time and again, they have shown up on short notice, stayed late, donated time, and asked how they could help.

I have learned that the only programs worth creating are those that empower people and set them free to pursue their own dreams in their own ways. The best services are not tied to places or agencies and do not have completely predefined specifications; services should provide the vehicle but let people do their own driving. I am on a program that pays me a monthly amount to hire personal assistants. The only requirements of the program are that I work at least 20 hours a week and fall within the earning guidelines of $4,000–$30,000 a year. Other than that, I have complete control over whom I hire, how much I pay, and how I manage the whole process.

CONCLUSION

Circles do not provide all the answers. Perhaps one of their greatest strengths is that they do not claim to. What they do provide is an opportunity for one person to dream and for his or her friends to share in the journey toward making that dream a reality. As with many long journeys, there are no timelines. Dreams often take shape gradually, and the process is destroyed when it is rushed. What counts, ultimately, is the commitment to walk together, flexibility to accommodate changes in direction, and patience to wait for the dream to come to fruition. As Judith Snow, who has her own experience with circles, says, "The dream will be changed by reality, but the dream will also change reality."

REFERENCES

Mount, B., Beeman, P., & Ducharme, G. (1988a). *What are we learning about circles of support: A collection of tools, ideas and reflections on building and facilitating circles of support*. Manchester, CT: Communitas.

Mount, B., Beeman, P., & Ducharme, G. (1988b). *What are we learning about bridge-building? A summary of a dialogue between people seeking to build community for people with disabilities*. Manchester, CT: Communitas.

Mount, B., Beeman, P., & Ducharme, G. (1988c). *One candle power: Building bridges into community life for people with disabilities*. Manchester, CT: Communitas.

Mount, B., Beeman, P., & Ducharme, G. (1991). *Person-centered development: A journey into learning to listen to people with disabilities*. Manchester, CT: Communitas.

Mount, B., Ludlum, C., Beeman, P., Ducharme, G., DeMarasse, R., Meadows, L., & Kilroy, R. (1990). *Dare to dream: An analysis of the conditions leading to personal change for people with disabilities*. Manchester, CT: Communitas.

Mount, B., Ludlum, C., Beeman, P., Ducharme, G., DeMarsse, R., Meadows, L., & Riley, E. (1991). *Imperfect change: Embracing the tensions of the person-centered work*. Manchester, CT: Communitas.

21

Public and Personal Leadership Challenges

Michael Kendrick

This chapter discusses the leadership challenges that arise from reliance on the agency-based service system developed in the late twentieth century. It is written from the perspective of persons who use services standing at the center of leadership concerns. From this perspective emerge a number of fundamentals to guide the commitment of those in leadership roles on behalf of persons in the client role. While this chapter does outline several great challenges, it places them in the broader context of societal and personal change. Thus, systems change is itself dependent on more profound changes in who we are and how we live.

LEADERSHIP CHALLENGES IN SYSTEMS CHANGE

Leadership is central to any process of change, whether the leadership arises out of individual charisma; preexisting agreement on leadership because of common values, goals, and interests; or the urgency of necessity. Often the existing resources that potential leaders could utilize will go unutilized because the focus that leadership can bring to a situation is lacking. Leaders must always be concerned with the question of how to make use of resources available in the situations they face. Otherwise, the potential of a situation may not be mobilized.

Leadership must be judged not as a factor outside of the flow of history, but as a factor of deliberate human agency within history that causes events to take a particular direction. The challenges facing leadership are rarely those preferred by leaders; rather, they are usually obstacles, opportunities, and hardships determined by prior events. These inherited circumstances contain intrinsic challenges that the potential leaders choose whether or not to address. The worthiness of leadership is judged against the emerging issues of the situation. Naturally, all judgments of this kind arise out of pre-existing beliefs and assumptions about what leaders should address.

THE RISE OF COMMUNITY SERVICE SYSTEMS

In the field of disability and in other fields in the United States a noticeably massive configuration has arisen since the 1970s called community services. A comparable process has occurred almost simultaneously in many countries in often strikingly similar ways. These community services are quite varied and in many localities are arranged as systems of services that aspire to be comprehensive; that is, they seek to address all of the life needs of particular subgroups of persons with disabilities. To call these arrangements systems, however, may assign a greater rationality and relevance to them than they can live up to. The reality is often that systems grow helter-skelter in an incremental manner, the net accretion being described as the system.

What is remarkable about such systems is that largely they are novel and unprecedented. Never have people had to rely on anything quite like community service systems to address the life needs of persons with disabilities. Because this system of services has become the norm, society forgets that it is peculiar to the late twentieth century. There has not been much long-range experience in managing such complex systems. Still many in the disability field now see community service systems as a massive part of public life, so that it seems impossible that any leadership would not encounter the problems posed by such systems at some point, even if these systems are variously abandoned, demolished, replaced, or reconstituted.

In large part, the growth of such services has been intertwined with the transfer of social responsibility for services to the state. The growth of such services and systems has been fueled (and limited) predominantly not by charitable sources, as was formally the case, but by governments increasing their taxes to support various versions of the welfare system. This has created entitlements to assistance that heretofore either had not existed or had been left as the ambiguous prerogative of families and other concerned persons. In the name of abstract public personal assistance, the government was expected to undertake responsibilities greater than what most strangers might normally do for other strangers. In many cases this level of responsibility might well exceed what is expected of a devoted but imperfect family in caring for its members.

The sheer scale of such activity and responsibility has meant not only a vast increase in public expenditures, but also a compelling increase in the scale and dominance of the mechanisms of administration of the resources. The service bureaucracies have expanded both directly by adding personnel and responsibilities to public agencies, and indirectly by contracting with pseudo private agencies. These private agencies typically are dependent on the state and, thus, are seen more realistically as extensions of the state rather than expressions of a pre-existing independent private interest. In all likelihood their growth and standing has arisen from capturing public expenditures and legitimacy rather than from private interests that would have prevailed irrespective of what the state did. Their growth, character, and identity have been shaped massively by the character of governments.

THE CHARACTER OF AGENCY-BASED SERVICES

Out of the wide range of ways which societies have chosen to assist their members throughout history, the method used at present is distinctive. Broadly speaking, the pattern of service is agency-based, that is, it relies on creating agencies to act on people's behalf when they are unable to or unlikely to act on their own. The mediator of this process of services is largely the state, which causes the service system to be characterized as a public, collective, politicized, and abstract undertaking.

Since the essential context for services typically is a public agency (notwithstanding its superficial trappings as a private effort), it is noteworthy that, almost by definition, it is impossible for a service not to involve formality in its exercise. Whether such formality arises out of, for example, contract obligations, eligibility, or formal legal requirements, it is structurally impossible for services to be informal or to arise out of the unmediated interactions of individuals. In a symbolic sense, the government is present as a silent participant in each interaction, even if the participants are informal in their conduct. In this way a formal, independent relationship exists that neither participant can be free of by assuming a relaxed manner.

Furthermore, regarding informality of assistance, currently, much talk is heard of natural supports. This approach to assistance is often problematic because "natural" in this sense usually means something unmediated by or not dependent on service bureaucracies. Service bureaucracies are not unnatural nor are informal services rendered by one person to another on a private basis natural. Both are creations of culture and can be seen logically as intertwined with a larger social system. Whether that which is characterized as natural is more efficacious, moral, or otherwise superior cannot be determined simply by its tie to, or its distance from, a service bureaucracy, unless one simplistically equates agencies with malevolent purposes.

Additionally, virtually all agencies, in one manner or another, are bureaucratized. While advantages may accrue from bureaucratic organization, few would deny that bureaucracies contain powerful obstacles to functioning. Common bureaucratic dysfunctions include goal displacement, poor coordination of effort, learned irrationality, rules fixation, turf wars, and inefficiency.

Added to these dysfunctions is the fact that employees of bureaucracies are normally strangers who are not encouraged to deliver personalized service. While such arrangements of paid service are not unheard of throughout history, the scale of service being undertaken in this impersonal and commercial manner is unprecedented now. Put another way, the client of services is now utterly dependent on a whole complex of strangers for their assistance. Many people appear to favor this impersonality because of the perceived drawbacks of obtaining assistance from family members or other familiar people with whom they already have an intimate and perhaps problematic relationship. Similarly, many believe that social distance ensures objectivity. Objectivity in this sense usually means accurate, fair, and not in conflict with other interests and needs.

Intertwined with service bureaucracy is the related phenomenon of professionalization. Service bureaucracies are inhabited by classes of workers whose work identity exists only in roles in such systems. Were it not for these agencies many professions would not have an ecological niche. For example, an employment specialist could not exist without supported employment services, and a service coordinator could not exist without disparate services to coordinate. While the differentiation and rationalization of tasks is classically associated with bureaucracies, this does not mean that professionalization per se is a synonym for usefulness, efficiency, or relevance. Equally, professionalization is always mediated by interests that are at variance with the general public good as well as the good of those cast in the role of consumer.

Service agencies frequently are hierarchical not only in the administrative sense, but also in the sense that organization of power and of control is such that the consumer typically is at a disadvantage. This may be expressed further in the absence of mechanisms with which the consumer, his or her friends and allies, and the broader public can direct what assistance they receive. Agencies may create participatory mechanisms to compensate, but this does not change the common reality that the agency is dominated by its own internal hierarchies and seeks advice at its own discretion. Under such conditions, strong community control and direction and commensurate empowerment become very unlikely unless they are deliberately pursued.

As the state has expanded into the role of service provider, it has generated a simultaneous increase in the number of agencies and their size. Increased size alone has led agencies to become more complex, exert more control, consume more public resources, become more distant from the consumer and local communities, and become increasingly bureaucratized. While the absolute growth of public expenditures to feed such aggrandizement will eventually reach some limit, the vast majority of agencies have not deliberately restrained their own growth, and many run as if this expansion poses no dangers. While this may be due in part to naiveté, it is striking that predictable tendencies toward, for example, empire building are so rarely discussed as factors in agency aggrandizement.

Community services sometimes are so large-scale that they are incomprehensible to average citizens. This may be so not only because professionals encourage mystification of service activities, functions, and interests, but also because large-scale alone renders service agencies difficult to comprehend, monitor, shape, and rehabilitate in the community interest. Curiously, some community agencies serve so many people that the consumers are literally anonymous and even innumerable. This is compounded by the presence of large "community" agencies operating in many communities including, more and more, communities literally on the other side of the continent. It is reasonable to question whether the word *community* should be used to describe services on a scale too large for them to be ultimately molded by local communities to fit local needs. Localization of service, decentralization, and superficial participatory structures do not change the reality that the local community has increasingly become merely the site for an outlet of a mega-agency. The character of such agencies is now effectively expanded beyond local direction as opposed to arising out of it. Thus, characterizing large-scale services as community services is an incorrect portrayal of who actually owns the services.

TRUST IN THE COMMUNITY AS A CORNERSTONE OF COMMUNITY SERVICES

While there has generally been a wholesale expansion of public services since the 1950s, the rationalization for this metaprocess in the field of disability has drawn heavily on ideology that emphasizes community contexts. Expansion has taken the form of deinstitutionalization, as well as greater inclusion of people with disabilities in the clientele of community resources. Such broad ideological goals make for diverse interpretations for specific community hopes and expectations, ranging from near utopian expectations of rapid social inclusion to continued existence in punitive segregation.

Just as in the reality of services, there are many realities of community life for all citizens that are problematic. While it is true that institutions are rife with disadvantages, the presumption that community life does not have its own problems is invalid. Furthermore, institutional problems are reincarnated in somewhat modified forms in everyday community life. Therefore, the community may not be the fulfilling context that is hoped for. For instance, community living may routinely subject people with disabilities to continued social devaluation, rejection, exploitation, disregard and neglect, abuse, segregation, abandonment, poverty, powerlessness, and so forth. It is noteworthy that so many advocates of community living seem incapable of being truthful about these predictable constancies in the human condition.

Many reformers seem to believe in a community free of this neglect and oppression. This view of community can have an unromantic basis because there are massively important and positive ways in which people can be perceived and included in community life. However, this enriched view of community does not take into account the situation in which people with disabilities are present in the community but have social roles that devalue and degrade them. This situation, in turn, brings up the question of what elements of life in the community to emphasize in order to ensure persons with disabilities a quality of life at least commensurate with that available to other citizens.

LEADERSHIP CHALLENGES POSED BY AGENCY-CENTERED SERVICES AND COMMUNITY LIVING

The term *system* commonly is used in referring to an organization but can refer to any pattern or order. For example, the term system is used in ecology to depict the logical interdependence among elements of the environment and the life forms that it sustains. Regarding services, the broad context of the cultural order of which services are a part could be referred to as a system. Leadership is addressed here in the context of the character of the broader social system rather than simply as a problem of managing services.

The Problem of Social Devaluation

The cultural order that has produced agency-centered service systems has dealt only in part with the fact that, historically, it filled its residential institutions with largely unwanted people whom it collectively devalued. Those not in institutions were scarcely more socially valued, though, typically, they were far less dispossessed and debased. Inclusive ideologies and community services have been only partially effective against this social devaluation. The system of services as well as a disembodied ideology of empowering inclusion may well obscure and accommodate to a deeper and continuing ambivalence toward persons with disabilities. Broad compliance with legal and other imperatives for inclusion has not brought about deep social acceptance.

A closer look at communities reveals that most people with disabilities are not viewed as equal members of the human race. This is manifest every time these individuals' wants, needs, and entitlements are assumed to be less than those recognized for others. The test of true social valuation has to do with whether the social valuation of a group is comparable to that of people in the general culture.

This test partly concerns whether sufficient leadership and leadership interest exists in creating the true heart of community as opposed to more superficial and unconvicing expressions of tolerance. Leadership toward a community with true heart is necessary to bring about community life in which people with disabilities are not automatically thought of as tragic, pitiful, burdensome, or unattractive. In communities with this kind of leadership perhaps prospective parents would choose not to abort their children with disabilities. Similarly, public gatherings without people who have disabilities would seem odd.

These examples are among the values that society must affirm to ensure relative security for people with disabilities in community life. Affirming positive values involves exposing false values. Effective leadership is needed in both cases. This leadership will emphasize repeatedly the identity and needs of people with disabilities. A moral relationship between ideological leaders and people with disabilities is presumed here. Leaders involved in this relationship include people with disabilities themselves, families, advocates, dissident professionals, visionary politicians, journalists, artists, and others acting either individually or collectively in challenging society at the level of its values.

Creating and Sustaining Valued Social Roles

Successful values leadership involves more than adopting pleasing slogans. Real change establishes and enhances valued social roles for people with disabilities in community life. This goal is not a service goal; rather, it is a broader attribute of culture and social relations. Furthermore, it is utterly entwined with the internalization of authentic values change and its expression in the conduct of ordinary people.

Valued social roles will be established and enhanced through generations of effort. This long-term effort calls for a sustained effort at leadership by many ordinary people acting out of their specific circumstances. Consequently, prospective leaders should focus attention on circumstances of everyday life in which people with disabilities are forced into devalued social roles or are taking positive, valued roles. These circumstances are flashpoints for moments of decision on personal action and, more broadly, resulting collective behavior. In this way everyday life is a litmus test of values authenticity.

Ordinary Citizens and Everyday Responsibility for Social Inclusion and Support

As discussed above, the presence of impersonal services indicates that citizens have failed to be responsible for each other. However, social acceptance, inclusion, and the accordance of personal worth do not primarily come through agencies. Rather, these qualities of life require the will and commitment of ordinary people. When these qualities become the norm, then a commensurate change in social pattern will occur. The leadership challenge is to mobilize people to comprehend and consider this prospect and eventually decide where they can make a contribution.

As people's responsibility to each other has been supplanted by agencies, people without disabilities have been encouraged, thereby, not to concern themselves with the lives of individuals with disabilities. Changing this situation means no longer embracing agency-centered services as a social remedy. Rather, people should be encouraged toward personal responsibility to one another within the range of appropriate personal obligation. People with disabilities have needs relevant to work, income, family, security, accomplishment, growth, and so forth, which are the same needs other people have. Addressing these needs can be accomplished in normative ways. Leaders have the task of initiating and encouraging the change in consciousness needed to bring about this type of commitment of people and resources.

Encouraging individuals without disabilities to reconsider their relationship with people who have disabilities speaks to people's characters. The process of relationship involves people's positive and negative traits. Thus, there will always be situations of partial, incomplete, or ill-advised inclusion. Consequently, critique, challenge, and guidance are needed to keep values and actions in check.

Ordinary people taking responsibility for one another could be construed as an alternative to agency-centered services. This alternative is workable for some people, but the practical means for taking the full extent of responsibility for all people with disabilities will not be available to other individuals. The huge investment of social resources in agency-centered services prohibits this availability. These same resources would have to be reinvested in supporting the ability of ordinary people to assist each other. As it stands, small, citizen-based and citizen-directed measures have little funding because agency-centered services receive so much.

However, this proposed reinvestment of resources would only curtail agency-centered services. Though professional and agency activities could be undertaken as community efforts, communities may prefer not to become involved, thereby creating a role for an agency. Furthermore, the practical competence of many professionals and agencies exceeds that of unsupported, disorganized, and inexperienced citizens. Finally, even if some people do not devalue people with disabilities, the fact that others do impedes the ethos needed for people to be responsible for each other.

Listening to the Concerns of People with Disabilities

People who have disabilities and all people who experience social devaluation usually are not taken seriously when they complain or suggest improvement. While paternalistic approaches in the field may bring about improvement, change is limited if it does not consider the will, insights, and aspirations of people with disabilities. Understanding that people with disabilities are entitled to self-determination does not mean viewing this or any other socially devalued group as infallible, superior, and unchallengeable because they have lived under oppression.

The sounder attitude is that people with disabilities must be accorded the common dignity of self-determination to the extent that most other people are. The leadership challenge is more than to promote self-advocacy groups; it is to promote an attitude of basic regard that includes the needs and preferences of people with disabilities with the priorities that shape the culture. Thus, as people do speak for themselves, leaders are needed to encourage others to listen. In a curious way, good listening is proactive self-advocacy. If people are heard and understood as a matter of course, they do not need to speak up in a deliberate sense. Being heard protects, for example, equal educational opportunity, universal access, freedom from stereotyping, and the lives of people unwanted because they have disabilities. Leadership is essential to building these qualities of life into the fabric of community.

The Contributions of People with Disabilities

Perhaps one of the most perverse roles society puts people in is that of "client," in which they are perceived entirely as receiving the charity of society rather than contributing to the virtue and richness of society. People with disabilities, like many other groups of people cast as "needy," are given the function of providing those who assist them with what could be construed as a reason to congratulate themselves. Whether some of the assistance given is at all useful may be arguable. Still, those who provide it reward themselves with self-congratulation and other psychic rewards.

This condecension negates the intrinsic value of people with disabilities and precludes their opportunity to contribute to society. Thus, any constructive leadership strategy must grapple with the problem of society's perception of people with disabilities because it presumes that they cannot, and are unwilling to, contribute. In reality, people with disabilities can make contributions as varied as anyone else's. While the actual contribution is important, society's underlying perception of ability and willingness to contribute is even more important.

SERVICES THAT TRULY ADDRESS THE NEEDS OF THE PEOPLE USING THEM

It is not entirely clear that services can be free of certain struggles in addressing people's needs appropriately; people are imperfect and so are the systems they create. Still, creating favorable conditions for providing appropriate services can be accomplished. However, being able to create these conditions is by no means assured by agency-centered or professionalized services or by resorting to informal, natural supports only.

The process of service emerges out of interests, limitations, intents, capacities, and values that routinely may be incompatible. Agency-centered services are invariably suffused with competing interests, which often causes the practicalities of serving consumer interests to be subverted by the practicalities of serving other interests. When this happens, the service provider comes to view the interests of the consumer as a low priority. Informal supports also may sacrifice the interests of the individual supported when varying interests exist. In families this may mean that the interests of other family members are given priority over those of the family member whose interests are least convenient to attend to.

While the concept of interests or needs is understandably complicated, it is clear that services often fail to provide what the individual truly needs. The service provided may be irrelevant to the individual's actual needs or relevant but not addressing needs that are basic to the individual. For example, discounted telephone service would be of no use to someone who is homeless. The more fundamental need to be addressed for this person would be the need for a residence.

Society invests extensive resources in services, so its failure to address needs appropriately should cause great public concern. This failure to address needs appropriately can waste resources by forcing useless services on people and even harm people by forcing them to use services that are damaging. Wasted resources are unavailable for valid uses. Effective leadership can help keep service delivery on track. Leaders are faced with the challenges of both keeping services as relevant as possible and detecting, critiquing, and eliminating irrelevant or inadequate services.

SAFEGUARDS AGAINST SERVICE DYSFUNCTION AND FAILURE

There will always be ideologies, mythologies, and interests that portray services as incapable of breaking down or otherwise failing those in the role of client. Some ideologies are rooted in the belief in a level of human conduct (on the part of individuals or collectives) that precludes decadence, error, perversity, dysfunctionality, and ineptness. For example, many organizational specialists seem to perceive all human conduct as able to be socially engineered. An engineering analogue applied to human behavior can be deceptive.

While some services may not be dysfunctional or harmful either in principle or in day-to-day reality, it is quite another matter to suggest that services are incapable of harming those they are intended to serve. With the lives of vast numbers of human services clients now massively bound up in the system of agency-centered services, it would be irresponsible for leaders not to ponder the disturbing issue of service dysfunction and failure and how to prevent or correct it. This is essential, especially when few clients can now do without formal services.

There is a history of people with disabilities being abused and neglected in institutions and by the community. It is crucial that safeguards be built into services to ensure protection for individuals being served. Making the effort to learn from history maintains a conscious link to the continuing reality of human nature. Far from precluding abuses and failures, this link points out the possibility of their existence and highlights their actual existence.

CONTROL OF SERVICES LYING WITH THE INDIVIDUALS SERVED

As indicated earlier, truly respecting the dignity and autonomy of those using services entails listening when they voice their needs. There is something unalterably profound and equalizing in giving due respect to the voice and humanity of people whose identity is unrelentingly devalued in everyday life. Those battling stigma, neglect, impoverishment, powerlessness, and dehumanization are further harmed by services intended to help that ultimately disempower them—obviously or subtly. Furthermore, the rhetoric of person-centered services may substantially obscure the actual disempowering effect of services.

In order for those who use services to have more control over them, a great deal of change in the values, structure, and alignment of interests of service systems will be required. Many attempts to give more control over services to the individuals who use them fail because they do not make these changes. The solution, therefore, is not found in restructured service measures alone but necessitates fundamental societal realignment of ideology, power, and interests. This includes the realignment of control of services in such a way that those served can shape the character of services. This logic is not predicated on the assumption that consumers always know best; rather, the assumption is that services must be coherent, understandable, and relevant to them. Furthermore, services are more likely to have these qualities if they are designed based on the experience and priorities of those who use them, rather than these individuals being relegated to the position of being put upon by professional judgments. The process of breaking up the exclusive control over services that is held by human services managers will entail changing vested interests, practice, and structures through fundamental changes in belief and attitude about the capabilities of people on either side of formal services. Human beings have great difficulty changing on a fundamental level, so leaders will have great difficulty stimulating service personnel in these more progressive directions.

REDUCING BUREAUCRACY IN SERVICES

The notion that people can help each other only through the mediating influences of service bureaucracies is dominant currently. Therefore, more informal ways of helping each other sometimes are not even comprehended by those accustomed to bureaucracy. It falls to leaders to discover effective forms of assistance that are nonbureaucratic.

Not all alternatives to bureaucracies replace them effectively. For example, individual funding schemes may provide for those who use assistance to have greater influence on it, but these schemes are still embedded in a bureaucratic service system. Also, group homes typically are more embedded in a bureaucratic service system than adoptive homes, which function for the most part outside of service bureaucracies and in a manner that is more culturally normative. Similarly, a situation in which an individual uses a special needs allowance attached to his or her fixed income to hire neighbors for personal assistance is far less bureaucratic than assistance from neighbors being enlisted by community agencies. Neither is entirely separate from service bureaucracies, but the former provides assistance much more naturally.

Effective alternatives to service bureaucracies will not always be clear. Leaders face the challenge of pressing for those alternatives that free society from the disadvantages of making service delivery through bureaucracy a necessity. Even where there are elements of service bureaucracies that have some effectiveness, it is still useful to probe whether this same effectiveness could be obtained without the drawbacks of bureaucracy.

THE SPIRIT OF SERVICES

Services are usually embedded in agencies, but they are delivered by human beings. The human character of providing services encompasses some quality of spirit in terms of regard for the worth and dignity of those using services. Inevitably, this spirit will dominate the relations between those using services and those delivering them. It is essential that this spirit be genuine and positive for services to address people's actual needs.

Leaders can have their effect at fundamental levels. They can inspire service providers to deliver services in a manner that is encouraging, but they can also have a negative influence. Negative service situations do not necessarily result from absence of leadership. The leadership may be competent but lacking a positive spirit. One of the ways in which this positive spirit may take form is through legitimation of the issue of recognizing the intrinsic value of the lives of people using services and actually listening when they express their needs and concerns.

SUMMARY

In these times of reverence for science and its assorted technologies, there is often an attempt to reduce problem-solving to a formula. Leadership through a strategy of mechanical oversimplification poses great risk. The leadership challenges presented here are intimately tied to questions on deeper levels. Quick fixes and minimizing leadership issues into superficiality are unlikely to produce enduring, relevant leadership. Leadership challenges call for attention on all levels.

Ultimately, organizational and conceptual tinkering will not alter much without changes in the way people think. With this type of change comes leadership that is not so much altruism as a reflection of a connection to the deeper currents of the psyche of prominent people and ordinary people alike. The issues identified in this chapter are both greatly public and intensely private. Therefore, addressing these issues is a challenge to public life as well as personal life. Fortunately, this broad continuum of consequences permits many people to rise to the challenges as their positions allow.

22

Parent Power

Change Through Grassroots Networking

Anne Farber and Kay Marcel

In 1988, parents of children with disabilities in Louisiana began an odyssey to change a system that offered little support to the majority of families whose children lived at home. Louisiana's system was and still is dominated by institutional services. The state has the highest proportion of individuals living in large facilities for persons with mental retardation, a rate that is twice the national average (Lakin, White, Prouty, Bruininks, & Kimm, 1991). Although limited respite services and a very small family subsidy program were available in 1988, state officials believed that the education system had the primary responsibility for providing services for children ages 3–21. The state had not identified family support as a component of the system to be developed.

Families felt alone, frustrated, and powerless. They experienced extreme emotional and financial stress. Children often went without needed services because families wanted to keep them at home. Additionally, siblings and other family members lived with unmet needs. Over a period of time the stress took its toll on families, and many were forced into making placement decisions about their children with disabilities. One parent testifying before a legislative committee expressed the painful choice eloquently:

> Eight years ago, the hardest thing we had to do was place our daughter in an institution. Our choices were dismal. Do I continue with my job and career, or do we keep

Preparation of this chapter was supported by a grant from the Administration on Developmental Disabilities, United States Department of Health and Human Services. The contents of this chapter do not necessarily reflect an official position of this agency.

our daughter at home; do we have financial security in our family or do we keep our daughter at home; do we raise our other child in a normal, healthy, adjusted environment, or do we keep our daughter at home; do we take family vacations together and have fun like other families, or do we keep our daughter at home; do my husband and I have a happy marriage, or do we keep our daughter at home; do we have a family with emotionally, physically, psychologically, healthy lives or do we keep our daughter at home? (Joint Committee on Health and Welfare, 1991)

People with disabilities and their families, of course, knew their own situations concerning their strengths and needs. However, they did not know about community and family support and what it could mean for them and their families. They felt individual frustration and anger about the critical needs they faced. They lacked organization and had no way to communicate their needs and ideas with each other or with policy-makers.

DEVELOPING A VISION

A statewide conference on community integration held in 1988 provided the needed information and impetus for change. The conference was sponsored by the Center on Human Policy at Syracuse University through a federal grant, and co-sponsored by several Louisiana organizations and agencies. Speakers shared information about the principles and components of community and family supports and described programs that implemented those philosophies. These programs espoused the belief that children, regardless of their disability, need families, and whatever families need to care for their children at home should be provided. These programs also recognized that families know their needs and should make the decisions concerning their children. The conference participants heard about programs that recognized that adults with developmental disabilities can reach higher levels of independence, productivity, and integration into the community when provided with individualized supports that give them opportunities to make decisions for themselves and exercise their full rights and responsibilities as citizens.

These programs sounded like an unrealizable dream to people in Louisiana. However, an awakening began. Conference participants wondered about having similar programs set up in their state. But people in other states had heard about wonderful programs in other states at conferences and then seen no change in their own state service systems. This conference, however, gave participants the opportunity to develop their own vision of a service system that would meet their needs. In a session on systems change, participants shared their own visions of what they wanted for themselves or their families 15 years in the future, a time far enough away that something new seemed achievable, but not too far away to be totally unrealistic. In small groups, participants shared their needs and what was required to address those needs. Each group focused on a different area, either family support, supported living for adults, personal assistance services, or service coordination. As the groups came back together and shared their visions of what the service system should look like in 15 years, the energy and enthusiasm in the room multiplied. A common vision had been developed, which each individual recognized as his or her own. One participant, a father of an infant daughter attending his first such conference, spoke out and asked what was going to happen to all the things they had written down and talked about; he wondered if they were just going to remain written on pieces of paper.

The session facilitators challenged the leaders from the Louisiana advocacy groups present to channel this energy and enthusiasm into actions to make the vision a reality. The advocacy groups, with some trepidation about what lay ahead, accepted the challenge and formed a steering committee whose membership included parents, advocacy groups, and representatives of state agencies. The steering committee chose the name, Louisiana Citizens for Action Now, or LaCAN, which represents the energy and positive direction of the group.

REALIZING THE VISION

LaCAN began by developing a work scope and timeline for activities. The members identified major stakeholders to be educated, such as state agency officials, legislative leaders, potential opposition groups, and supporters. Strategies to identify and contact these stakeholders were brainstormed and a plan of action developed. The steering committee divided into work groups to refine the vision statements on family support, community supports for adults, personal assistance services, and service coordination. Family members took leadership roles in these work groups and spent a great deal of time clarifying what they wanted to see developed in Louisiana.

To solicit feedback, the steering committee circulated the vision statements to various organizations and sought public involvement through regional forums. Over 150 persons attended the eight regional forums, which parents organized and led. The parents scheduled the date and location, invited participants, and presided at the forums.

At the forums, participants separated into small groups and developed their own visions of community and family support. Next, the small groups shared their vision statements, and then the vision statements developed by the LaCAN steering committee were presented for feedback. Forum participants were energized when they discovered that the visions they developed were very similar to those drafted by LaCAN. The concepts in the vision statements represented the basic needs and beliefs of families. These forums enabled the steering committee to strengthen their vision statements and to identify supporters.

Translating the Vision into Legislation

The steering committee compared current state laws and the visions to determine what changes in the law were needed to fill in the gaps. Members of LaCAN also held meetings with state agency officials as well as legislators to gain support for the visions. Committee members were encouraged when two legislators expressed a strong interest in helping to change the law. One state representative had a solid track record of working with family, children, and disability issues. He was, in fact, chairman of Louisiana's Interagency Coordinating Council. Both legislators brought a strong commitment to seeing that the concepts in the vision statements became reality in Louisiana and agreed to sponsor legislation.

LaCAN set its goal to have legislation introduced into the 1989 Louisiana legislative session. The LaCAN steering committee drafted the legislation, providing parents the opportunity to craft a bill that reflected their beliefs. The draft legislation established the principles of family support and supported living and outlined a planning process to implement these systems.

Representatives of the Parents Association for the State Facilities, a powerful group in Louisiana, expressed concern over some provisions in the bill, thus threatening the chance that the bill would pass. Several negotiating sessions were held to develop language that was acceptable to both sides involved. While some compromises were made, the integrity of the bill remained, and the Parents Association withdrew their objections to the bill.

Another community integration conference was held in the spring of 1989 to continue to share the vision and gain more supporters. Again, information on community and family support was presented along with an emphasis on self-advocacy. This conference also served to re-energize current supporters of the vision.

The bill had its first hearing in the House Health and Welfare Committee. LaCAN members attended the committee hearing to testify and show their enthusiastic support. The presence of supporters was important, but, as it turned out, little testimony was needed. Committee members had been lobbied effectively prior to the hearing by families and advocates who were their constituents. For the most part, they came into the hearing with their minds already made up about how they would vote. Seeing supporters in attendance with their children reinforced the committee's decision. The committee voted unanimously to report the legislation favorably, and committee members signed on as co-sponsors of the legislation. LaCAN members celebrated their first victory!

After celebrating this initial success, it was time to get back to work. The support of the entire Louisiana legislature had to be won. Families continued their advocacy efforts and making contacts with legislators. The primary concern of legislators was the potential cost of the bill, so information had to be presented on several occasions to address this issue. The Community and Family Support legislation passed unanimously, and, on June 29, 1989, Governor Charles "Buddy" Roemer signed the bill into law at a press conference that was attended by families of children with disabilities and other advocates.

The signing of this legislation was another cause for celebration. A formal celebration was held at a luncheon hosted by Governor Roemer for members of the Developmental Disabilities Council, LaCAN, and their families.

In a little over 1 year's time, Louisiana's parents moved from anger and frustration over the lack of supports for their families to defining and enacting a solution to their problems! Families now felt empowered to make a difference in the lives of their children with disabilities and the service system that would serve them.

The Community and Family Support System Act

The Community and Family Support System Act, Act 378 of 1989, provides for the development of a plan for a system of community and family supports for persons with developmental disabilities and their families and calls for implementation of the plan by the Department of Health and Hospitals in cooperation with the Department of Social Services.

Act 378 specifies that services for persons with developmental disabilities should be responsive to the needs of individuals and their families, rather than fitting people into existing programs. The act outlines two basic principles:

> Children, regardless of the severity of their disability, need families and enduring relationships with adults in a nurturing home environment. As with all children, children with developmental disabilities need families and family relationships to develop to their fullest potential.
>
> Adults with developmental disabilities should be afforded the opportunity to make decisions for themselves and to live in typical homes and communities where they can exercise their full rights and responsibilities as citizens. (Louisiana Revised Statutes 28: 821[B], 1989)

The act specifies ideals and guiding principles for the development of the Community and Family Support System Plan and lists an array of community and family supports to be made available to families and adults. The act also has time frames for the development and implementation of this plan.

DEVELOPING THE PLAN

The Louisiana State Planning Council on Developmental Disabilities had responsibility for the development of the plan to implement a Community and Family Support System. As authorized under the act, the council appointed an advisory committee to assist in the planning process. The advisory committee included the major stakeholders: parents of children and adults with developmental disabilities, adults with disabilities, advocacy organizations, representatives of the various agencies responsible for implementation of the plan, and legislators. The advisory committee formed four work groups to address specific components of the act. The full advisory committee met bimonthly to develop recommendations for the plan. At meetings, experts spoke of model family support and supported living programs in Michigan, Illinois, and other states.

At the March 1990 Community Integration Conference, conference participants reviewed the draft plan and provided input into its provisions. That same spring, LaCAN parents held a second round of regional forums around the state to obtain further input and commitment to the plan.

The Community and Family Support System Plan reflected the values and beliefs of the many families and individuals with disabilities who participated in its year-long development. One advisory committee member, a mother who had been working for several years to develop supports for her adult son to live in the community, expressed surprise that the plan, when published, actually reflected what the advisory committee had recommended. That remark was an unsettling commentary on how unresponsive the system had been to the needs of those who used its services.

In the area of family support, the plan made the recommendations listed below:

- Families with children who have severe disabilities should receive a cash subsidy to offset the extraordinary costs of their child's care.
- A system of service coordination to facilitate family support activities should be developed throughout the state.
- A range of services to support families should be provided that would be flexible to allow for the unique needs of each child and his or her family.
- The agencies responsible for implementing the family support system are: the Division of Mental Retardation/Developmental Disabilities, the Division of Mental Health, and the Handicapped Children Services Program.
- Uniform application procedures across agencies should be created to spare parents the time and emotional costs of filling out multiple requests for services.
- In each region of the state there should be an agency that can direct families to the supports and services they need.
- To successfully implement the plan, training should be provided to staff on the philosophy of family support.
- Implementation of the system should begin in July, 1991, with full implementation in July 1993.

For adults, the plan made the five recommendations listed below:

- The eligibility criteria for individualized supports should be based on the definition of developmental disabilities and should extend to individuals who had disabilities before the age of 55.
- Adults with severe disabilities should receive a range of supports to assist them in living in their own homes and their own communities.
- The agencies responsible for implementing the system of adults supports are: the Division of Mental Retardation/Developmental Disabilities, the Division of Mental Health, and Louisiana Rehabilitation Services.
- Support for adults should be phased in on a pilot basis.
- Training should be provided to potential providers of supported living.

Several recommendations were made to ensure that the system would be responsive to the needs of families and individuals with developmental disabilities. These were that regional and state advisory councils be established, that an annual external evaluation be conducted based on consumer satisfaction and performance indicators, and that an appeals process be developed.

In August 1990, the Developmental Disabilities Council submitted the Community and Family Support System Plan to the Secretaries of the Department of Health and Hospitals and the Department of Social Services, who reviewed and approved the plan. The secretaries then sent the plan to the Senate Committee on Health and Welfare, the House Committee on Health and Welfare, and the Joint Legislative Committee on the Budget, as called for in Act 378.

The timeline for completion of the plan was scheduled to coincide with the annual state budget development process. The state agencies submitted requests for new programs based on the recommendations for the first year of implementation of the plan. The budget requests were in the hopper, but the probability that they would be funded appeared low because of projected budget deficits.

TRAINING PARENTS TO INFLUENCE PUBLIC POLICY

While the plan was being developed, Louisiana was awarded a technical assistance grant from the Human Services Research Institute to assist parents in educating policy-makers. Specifically, the aim of the project was to help parents communicate with policy-makers about what is needed for families with children with disabilities to keep their children at home. The council saw this project as an opportunity to increase and enhance the parent advocacy efforts for community and family support that would be necessary to gain legislative support for funding. During the first meeting, held in October 1989, the parents identified barriers to communicating with policy-makers. They felt that legislators would not listen to them or even schedule appointments with them. They talked about the training components needed to overcome some of these barriers.

At the second meeting, a training session held in January 1990, on the first day parents were briefed on current federal and state programs, legislation and national trends in family support, and the Community and Family Support System Plan. The second day centered on citizen participation in the legislative process. The morning program took the group through the legislative process and coached them on how to go about preparing to give testimony at committee hearings. In the afternoon, parents worked directly with three legislators. First, parents formed work groups to develop issues and position papers for presentation to lawmakers. Each lawmaker met with two groups to hear their presentations and discuss the issues. The legislators provided feedback to the parents on their presentations and gave them pointers on how to communicate their ideas more effectively.

The legislative training was the second turning point in the odyssey after the initial conference on community integration in 1988. The experience of talking to legislators who volunteered a Saturday afternoon to listen to parents and help them learn allayed the parents' fears and helped them find the confidence to approach their own legislators. The legislators were touched by what they heard and the sincerity of the parents. The entire Louisiana Legislature of 144 members had been invited. The three legislators who attended were members of the House and Senate Health and Welfare Committees.

Developing a Structure for Effective Parent Power

During the first year of legislative activity when the authorizing legislation, Act 378, was enacted, parent members of LaCAN had acted as an informal network, contacting legislators and enlisting others to do so. However, no structure existed to mobilize a grassroots effort. It was clear that there had to be an organized effort for the monumental task ahead, which was to obtain funding to implement the Community and Family Support System Plan.

In September 1990, LaCAN established regional teams with parents of children with developmental disabilities as the chair and vice chair. They were provided with job descriptions for their roles, responsibilities for the regional teams, and information on the legislative process and on legislators. Fact sheets on the Community and Family Support System Plan and a slide presentation on the plan were also developed for their use in the regions. Each team sent five representatives to a legislative training session in November 1990, which utilized the techniques learned through the Technical Assistance Project on Family Support. Five legislators attended this event and coached parents on communicating their ideas. This larger group of parents were educated and motivated to make a difference in the lives of their children and others.

Mobilizing the Grassroots Structure

In the fall of 1990, LaCAN regional teams began their grassroots efforts. They met with their legislators, first targeting the members of the committees that appropriated funds. They described the Community and Family Support System Plan and urged support of the plan. They shared their personal situations and how implementation of the plan would help their families. They also spread the word, enlisting other parents, relatives, neighbors, and friends in their efforts. Additionally, they established telephone networks that could be activated when legislative contacts were needed.

When the Joint Legislative Committee on Health and Welfare scheduled a hearing on the Community and Family Support System Plan in March 1991, the grassroots network was in place and ready to mobilize people to attend and give testimony. The hearing was a great success. Over 100 families and advocates attended the hearing, demonstrating the widespread support for the plan. Six parents and two adults with disabilities gave compelling testimony as they spoke from their hearts about their experiences. The testimony delivered the message that people with disabilities and their families had waited too long for the state to provide supports and services and that they should not have to continue to wait. The legislators were visibly moved and unanimously supported the plan. Each legislator individually and publicly pledged support to gain funding for the plan.

Efforts continued throughout the spring of 1991, with the regional teams continuing to make contacts with legislators. LaCAN joined forces with advocates for ChildNet, Louisiana's Early Intervention Program for Infants and Toddlers with Special Needs and Their Families, as they sought funds. The theme of the conference on community integration held in May 1991 was, "Communicating the Vision." Participants learned about the components of Louisiana's Community and Family Support System Plan and heard from professional lobbyists about how to communicate effectively with legislators. They were inspired by the words of a state legislator, who was one of the three legislators who had participated in the first legislative training session and had become a strong supporter of the plan. He became an even more ardent supporter when his first child was born with severe disabilities. Participants then went to the capitol to tell their legislators about the Community and Family Support System Plan and why it should be funded.

Throughout the 1991 legislative session, parents and advocates monitored the budget appropriation of the Community and Family Support System Plan. They attended budget hearings and were given the unprecedented opportunity to testify before the House Appropriations Committee on the need for community and family support. They continued to advocate with legislators, urging their support of the funding.

The Fruit of the Effort

As a result of the grassroots network, in 1991 the Louisiana Legislature appropriated $1.3 million in state funds to initiate individual and family supports. The appropriation was obtained during a year when few new programs received funding because of budget deficits. Implementation of the plan during the first year includes a monthly cash subsidy available to families of children with severe disabilities. Six hundred families were to receive the subsidy in the first year. In addition, service coordination would be available for families.

Implementation also includes a range of supports to assist adults with severe disabilities to live in their own homes and communities. A total of 100 adults were to be served through eight pilot projects and the two supported living projects already begun by the Developmental Disabilities Council. Included in this group are individuals who choose to remain at home with their families or who already have a home and need additional support to remain there.

Additional legislation passed during the 1991 legislative session; Act 1011 authorizes the Department of Health and Hospitals and the Department of Social Services to provide the supports and services outlined in the Community and Family Support System Plan. The legislation also provides for quality assurance methods to include regional and state advisory councils, annual external evaluations, and an appeals process.

LESSONS LEARNED

Successfully developing a grassroots consumer advocacy campaign to realize a vision has taught families and advocates in Louisiana many lessons. They are discussed in the following sections.

Power of Parents

Parents are a powerful force. Legislators listen to parents because their involvement is first and foremost for their child. Legislators understand what parents express from their hearts and their experiences. They accept the honesty and validity of their requests, in contrast to those of bureaucrats whom they view with a jaundiced eye.

Parents have the ability to make contacts that professionals and providers often do not have. Their contacts are usually numerous enough to bring attention. Policy-makers respond to numbers. The message must be valid, the messengers must be somewhat articulate in presenting the message, but of greatest significance is the number of messages. Parents have connections with other parents, extended family members, friends, and neighbors.

Parents are persistent and passionate in their quest. Effective advocates must be involved for the long haul. They must not let delays, setbacks, or disappointments stop their efforts. Parents in Louisiana have an unwavering belief in their issues. This belief is conveyed to legislators in such a way that they cannot be ignored. There may be the offer of a partial answer or a compromise that should be considered and possibly accepted for a time. But the effective advocates will continue their efforts until they reach their ultimate goal. Parents have the level of commitment needed to be persistent. They work with the conviction and passion necessary to ensure success. Families will do whatever it takes. They have the biggest stake in the outcome, that is, their families' survival, their children having the opportunities to develop to their fullest potential.

What Families Need To Be Empowered

Parents are empowered through knowledge, are energized by their common vision, and need skills to use their knowledge effectively and to communicate their vision. The conferences, regional forums, and training sessions described earlier provided these elements for families in Louisiana. These events also provided a mechanism for families to communicate with and support one another as they learned new roles and tackled new challenges.

Validity of the Vision

When parents develop the vision themselves it has more validity. As demonstrated in Louisiana, other parents responded enthusiastically to the concept of family support, quickly becoming actively involved in working for its realization. The movement came to life. This kind of effort does not have to be orchestrated from above; rather, it moves forward, benefiting from the creativity and commitment of the families. One member of a regional team put together a town meeting on individual and family support in her community, and six legislators and over 100 parents attended.

Need for Structure

At the same time, LaCAN learned that an effective grassroots movement needs a structure so that information can be transmitted quickly and people can act using accurate information. The development of regional teams that met periodically and communicated through telephone trees and written communication provided a systematic approach to reaching every Louisiana legislator with a consistent and timely message.

It was also important to recognize that parents could be involved in various ways, and because of personal circumstances and preferences, needed to have this flexibility. Parents were encouraged and supported in whatever ways they chose to be involved. Therefore, more parents were informed and involved. Also, people did not feel left out or guilty about their level of participation. Some parents attended many meetings, like planning and strategy meetings, meetings with individual legislators, and legislative hearings. Others who could not attend meetings helped tremendously by writing letters, making telephone calls, and offering encouragement and advice.

Advantages of a System Designed by Parents

Changing and designing a system to be more responsive to families needs requires family involvement. Families know firsthand their needs and strengths and those of their children. Trying to design a family-responsive system without parental input is futile and will result in frustration for both parents and service providers.

Involving parents in designing the system offers them involvement on a fundamental level and ownership of the system. This approach creates an opportunity for parents to work enthusiastically with agencies toward implementation of the new system.

Parents in Leadership Roles

It is critical that parents truly be the leaders in bringing about systems change. They bring credibility, passion, and conviction. They are willing to take strong positions. When LaCAN initiated the first round of regional forums, parents had to learn new roles and skills. They needed staff support to take on some of these roles; however, they soon became skilled organizers and facilitators. When staff and professionals are involved, it is sometimes difficult for staff to learn to take a background role of support, allowing parents to be the leaders. The combination of staff providing support (i.e., giving information, facts, figures, and help with understanding the system) and the leadership of parents is extremely powerful and is essential for the grassroots movement to be valid.

Look for and Learn from Allies

The impetus for change in Louisiana came from the models of family support that individuals from other states presented. Leaders in the disability movement provided the organizing and communication skills necessary to create systems change.

In Louisiana, many people contributed their advice and skill. State agency leaders helped craft the strategy to ensure that budgetary requests were timed to fit into the state budget cycle. Legislators offered suggestions about the critical players to be contacted. Professional lobbyists provided direction in designing a comprehensive legislative plan. Advocacy organizations lent their assistance by mobilizing their membership to contact legislators.

While the members of LaCAN initially were not a politically connected group of people, they were able to identify two legislators whom they knew from their home towns who were willing to champion this cause. These legislators also had the background and political stature to be effective lead authors of the legislation.

However, the legislators needed the knowledge and support of LaCAN. They frequently requested additional background information, especially relating to the cost of the program and its benefits. They needed effective advocacy with other legislators by constituents.

The parents who initially feared that legislators would not give them an opportunity to meet with them, found themselves becoming trusted advisors of legislators. One parent filmed a television commercial with her son during the re-election campaign of a state representative, stating the commitment of the legislator to persons with disabilities and their families.

Systems Change Is a Long Process

Efforts to change Louisiana's system for individuals with developmental disabilities and their families began in the spring of 1988. Families started to receive supports in the winter of 1992. That progress took 4 years. The first year was spent learning about family support and communicating the vision to other families in Louisiana. The second year was spent developing and passing legislation that established the principles of family support in state legislation. During the third year, these principles were fleshed out in the Community and Family Support System Plan. In the fourth year, funding was obtained and implementation of the plan begun.

To accomplish this feat, a grassroots network had to be developed. There was no existing advocacy constituency in Louisiana that could champion this issue as their top priority. While support was obtained from many other groups, the network of families had to be established to communicate their vision to state policymakers. If a grassroots network exists committed to realizing family support, the process should be significantly shorter.

While 4 years have already been invested to realize family support in Louisiana, the effort has only just begun. There are two major tasks that lie ahead for this odyssey to be successful. First, on the administrative level, the principles of family support must be infused into the polices that are developed to implement the plan. The two strategies being used to address this issue are the involvement of parents in policy development through the Community and Family Support System Plan Task Force and the establishment of advisory councils to provide input on the family support system. These councils will advise the state agencies on policy issues that arise, set priorities, review program effectiveness, and make recommendations on implementation.

Even with these two strategies, infusing a new philosophy into a state system is extremely difficult. Attitudes and beliefs are slow to change and many of the structures needed to implement the new philosophy do not exist. The development and implementation of policies on family support that are truly responsive to families will be a long-term effort.

Second, adequate funding must be obtained to meet the needs of families. Although the plan recommended that 1,500 families receive supports in the first year, the level of funding appropriated will only serve 600 families. Full implementation calls for supports for a total of 4,500 families.

When the availability of cash subsidies was announced in the fall of 1991, over 6,300 families applied. Many families have been disappointed that they did not benefit from the tremendous efforts they put forth to obtain the initial funding. Many more families continue to struggle without adequate supports to keep their children with them at home.

CONCLUSION

When this odyssey began, there was no road map that provided directions to the ultimate goal of creating a system that meets the needs of families. Much of what has happened is based on the courage and belief in this cause. Strategies were constantly devised and changed to tackle the next challenge along the road. Many times people scoffed at the proposals, considering them to be unachievable. While much remains to be done, Louisiana parents and their supporters can be proud that they dared to dream and to work to make family support a reality.

REFERENCES

Joint Committee on Health and Welfare, Louisiana Legislature. (1991, March). Testimony by T. Messenger.

Lakin, K.C., White, C.C., Prouty, R.W., Bruininks, R.H., & Kimm, C. (1991). *Medicaid institutional (ICF-MR) and home and community based services for persons with mental retardation and related conditions (Report No. 35).* Minneapolis: University of Minnesota, Center on Residential Services and Community Living.

Louisiana Revised Statutes 28: 821(B), 1989.

V

MECHANISMS FOR CHANGE

As Gardner explains in Chapter 26, current organizational structures, cultures, and political environments are designed to further the institutional and deinstitutional paradigms; they are not designed to further the supports paradigm. Changing paradigms means changing service systems up and down the line. The chapters in this section describe experiences and related strategies for the changeover of systems from the existing paradigms to the supports paradigm.

To start, in Chapter 23, Ashbaugh reminds us how much the developmental disabilities power structure, driven largely by existing service providers, administrators, and recipients, is locked into the existing system. To wrench it free, the balance of power must shift to unserved and underserved consumers and families. He explains how collaboration is the logical mechanism to exercise this shift and identifies some sine qua nons of such collaborative efforts. In Chapter 24, Kimmich elaborates and adds still other guidance on organizing and maintaining collaboratives to engineer fundamental systems change.

Gardner, as do Kimmich and Bradley in Chapter 25, focuses specifically on quality assurance mechanisms as ready-made tools for leading and guiding the paradigm shift. Gardner capsules the abundant literature on total quality management (TQM). He considers TQM principles and practices as nothing less than "a guide for the successful implementation of the new paradigm." While Kimmich and Bradley do not reference TQM directly, they identify the same principles, that is, a vision and focus on outcomes, and the empowerment of consumers and families to demand service and of front-line workers to respond.

In Chapter 27, Wesely describes how the legislative process was used in Nebraska to bring about fundamental systems change. Carmody, in Chapter 28, describes how traditional administrative mechanisms had to be redesigned in moving individuals from nursing homes to supported living arrangements as part of the Supported Placements in Integrated Community Environments (SPICE) Project. In Chapter 29, Smith describes how states are restructuring their payment systems away from standard facility-based, service-bound schemes to consumer-based support schemes that can be custom designed to suit the individuals served.

23

Removing the Barriers to Supported Service Arrangements Through Collaborative Planning

John W. Ashbaugh

Barker (1992) defined a paradigm as a set of rules and regulations (written and unwritten) that establish or define boundaries and that tell how to behave within these boundaries to be successful. He identifies three stages in the life span of a paradigm in terms of problem-solving and time.

HOW PARADIGMS WORK

First, in stage A, people are thinking that they may have a new model for solving some long-standing problems. There are demonstration and pilot projects. There is not much problem-solving, and there are few established rules at this stage. People are feeling their way. They are figuring out the rules and how to make them work.

Second, in stage B, there is much problem-solving. The demonstration programs become mainstream; discretionary funding becomes base allocations. As this stage concludes, people have figured out the rules and done a good deal of fine tuning.

Third, in stage C, the problem-solving grinds down. Difficult and intractable problems remain. There is the realization that no amount of fine tuning is going to solve these problems. If it has not been apparent before, the need for a new approach is now quite clear.

Consider the driving principles and values espoused for people with developmental disabilities. In looking at developmental disabilities systems in the future, the National Association of Developmental Disabilities Councils declared the following:

> Individual and family supports will be an integral part of a new approach. Supports to individuals will enable choice and selection, help people to stay in their homes and communities, and empower people to obtain what they need to achieve the goals of independence, productivity and integration.
>
> People with developmental disabilities will be in homes that they have selected, will live with people they have chosen to live with and in the neighborhoods and communities of their choice. Children with developmental disabilities will grow up in family homes. Community support and family services will be available to enable people to live in homes and participate in their communities. (1990, p. 5)

A consideration of the developmental model or paradigm shows that individuals are trained, habilitated, socialized, screened, assessed, and assisted through a continuum of educational, vocational, and residential settings. Specialized, professionally staffed treatment arrangements (i.e., small homelike residences and day programs) are established to teach individuals the skills needed to live more independently, and the services of therapeutic and behavioral specialists are employed to help individuals with even the most severe disabilities and emotional instability to develop.

This paradigm is in stage C, so it has gone about as far as it can. Choice is confined to the limited offerings of service providers, most of which are facility-based, segregated, and expensive. There is little movement along the continuum to independence and corresponding savings. There has been very little progress in ameliorating problem behaviors, and many of these behaviors are concomitants of segregated, group arrangements where staff are burned out and the behavior modeling among peers is poor.

Finding and retaining competent and committed staff are increasingly difficult, particularly because of economics. Ensuring the quality of the scattered residential and day programs using the traditional on-site standards compliance review teams is more and more costly, intrusive, and of little apparent value day to day.

The costs of these facility-based developmental programs have escalated considerably over the years and so have the rules established to govern their operation. The average cost per client of private ICF/MR services has risen from $20,040 in 1980 to $44,946 in 1989, an increase of more than 10% annually (Lakin, White, Prouty, Bruininks, & Kimm, 1991). It was expected to reach $63,000 in 1992 (Smith & Gettings, 1992).

And all the while waiting lists are growing. There is increasing doubt that the vast majority of people with developmental disabilities who are not served will ever be served given the heavy commitment of expenditures for these specialized facilities and the widely forecast plateauing of revenues. The economy is in recession. Thirty-six states are in deficit situations, and the recovery is expected to fall short of prior levels. The prospect of a Medicaid cap is real. Resources have plateaued. There is widespread recognition of the fact that the heavy investment in facility-based programs for relatively small numbers of persons is effectively denying services to the much larger numbers of persons living at home.

The capitalization requirements associated with facility-based programs, burdensome administrative demands imposed by Medicaid and developmental disabilities authorities, and the natural tendency of purchase-of-service systems to evolve into oligopolies (Schlesinger, Dorwart, & Pulice, 1986) have led to service systems being dominated by large providers, public and private. They resemble decentralized institutions, characteristically bureaucratic in their dealings with employees and consumers alike and removed from many of the communities they serve.

A consideration of the supports paradigm shows that, instead of surrounding people with services in specially designed and constructed facilities, supports are moved to where people live. Instead of individuals being adapted to special environments, the general environment and supports are being adapted to them as now required under the Americans with Disabilities Act of 1990 (PL 101-336). Rather than focusing on putting people into community programs, the service system is beginning to create networks of formal and informal supports to help meet individuals' day-to-day needs. Parks and recreation departments, YWCAs, and YMCAs are being used increasingly by all citizens. The Red Cross is being used to train and certify respite workers and personal care attendants. Intake and eligibility determination workers are being stationed away from the stigmatizing welfare offices. Home-based options are sought before individuals are placed in homes other than their own. Inclusive day and work alternatives are being sought before individuals are assigned to segregated day or work programs.

Under the supports paradigm many of the problems associated with the developmental model evaporate. Staff requirements, recruitment, and retention problems are typically fewer. The need for facility licensing and other intrusive, burdensome, and bureaucratic quality assurance requirements are obviated. Problem behaviors associated with group arrangements are avoided. Small agencies can better compete with the large given the limited capitalization required by the former. Costs are less for many individuals. Smith (chap. 29, this volume) notes that the same amount of money being spent to support an individual in an institution could support 25 or more families in a typical family support program. Service arrangements can be truly individualized; choice and inclusion are really possible.

Yet, despite the apparent programmatic and economic advantages of natural supports, supported family, supported living, and inclusive employment approaches, these arrangements remain at the margins of service systems. A national survey of mental retardation/developmental disabilities agencies in 1990 found that only 9% of the persons in day and employment programs were in supported employment arrangements (McGaughey, Lynch, Morganstern, Kiernan, & Schalock, 1991). Similarly, expenditures for family support programs in 1988 amounted to little more than 3% of total mental retardation/developmental disabilities agency expenditures (Braddock, Hemp, Fujiura, Bachelder, & Mitchell, 1990).

Barker (1992) explained why is it only now, in stage C, that the supports paradigm is coming to be considered and why so many states are having difficulty shifting to this paradigm. With two exceptions, in private industry, if organizations had not already begun to change to a new paradigm in stage B, they would likely be out of business by stage C. The exceptions are oligopolistic systems and highly regulated systems. State developmental disabilities systems are both. Indeed, it is these two factors that largely explain the slow movement to the supports paradigm and that, together with lesser barriers, conspire to stall the supports paradigm in stage A, keeping it at the margins.

Oligopolistic service systems are systems dominated by a relatively small number of large providers. Developmental disabilities purchase-of-service systems have a natural tendency to evolve into oligopolies. They are easier for developmental disabilities administrations to manage, and large providers have the wherewithal to cope with the bureaucratic burdens imposed by regulatory and contract agencies. Almost without exception, it is these providers, largely invested in segregated, facility-based programs, together with the consumers and families they serve, that are the most powerful developmental disabilities interest groups. Needless to say, the political environment in most states is not warm to the notion of reconfiguring developmental disabilities service systems from less facility-based to more supported arrangements.

In fact, for developmental disabilities system administrators in most states to introduce a plan to move deliberately to non–facility-based arrangements would be nothing less than political suicide. The airing of just such a plan in one state with which the Human Services Research Institute (HSRI), in Cambridge, Massachusetts, was involved was a major factor leading to the resignations of the developmental disabilities commissioner and developmental disabilities council director. The provider associations viewed the plan as a threat to current arrangements with which they were quite comfortable.

They were correct. In the past, the service system would have looked to funding increases to underwrite the expansion of support arrangements. Today it is all the service system can do to keep existing systems in step with inflation. The growth of supported arrangements in most states will have to be at the expense of facility-based arrangements.

The regulatory environment with its rigid and centralized control is anathema to the supports paradigm. If the supports paradigm is to work, consumers, families, service providers, and local administrators must be given increased control over how funds are expended. The notion of giving over this control is unsettling to most state officials. After all, much of the progress made in the development of community-based systems can be traced to state-led, not community- and consumer-led initiatives. Moreover, for many developmental disabilities agency directors, the ability to survive depends on their ability to retain some semblance of control over the system.

It is not possible to predict the extent to which the oligopolistic and regulatory character of today's developmental disabilities systems and lesser barriers to the supports paradigm can be overcome in a particular state through collaborative planning. But it is possible to assert, based on experience, that cultivating the supports paradigm through a sound process of collaboration will increase the chances of success and lessen the risk considerably.

MAKING COLLABORATION WORK

Collaboration involves stakeholders jointly developing a set of goals for making consumer-controlled, supported service arrangements available to consumers; sharing responsibility for obtaining these goals; and using the expertise and wherewithal of each collaborator to achieve these goals (Brunner, 1991). Collaboration demands more than cooperation. Supported arrangements will work only when service providers, consumers, and local system administrators are ready to make them work and when state officials support their efforts.

The following sections discuss six observations having to do with how to make use of collaborative planning in shifting developmental disabilities service systems from the developmental to the supports paradigm. They are borne of the unsuccessful and successful, first-hand experiences of the author and others at HSRI.

Leaders Are Essential

Leaders have the ability to communicate the vision of the supports paradigm effectively and to engage key actors in constructive collaboration toward that vision. Changing paradigms has to do with leadership, not management. Management has to do with having others do what managers want them to do (Kouzes & Posner, 1991). Leadership has to do with having others want to do what managers want them to do. The latter, while not possible in the purest sense, is generally a prerequisite for positive and lasting change. Certainly, leadership is a critical element in converting to the supports paradigm where so much depends on the interest of providers, consumers, families, and local administrators. State developmental disabilities agency administrators have neither the power to command, nor the reach to manage, the shift to supported arrangements.

It is fair to say that few developmental disabilities agency administrators are well positioned for, or capable of leading, a concerted movement to the supports paradigm themselves. As noted earlier, there would be considerable political risk in developmental disabilities agency administrators fronting such an effort. Moreover, there are far more managers among the ranks of developmental disabilities agency administrators than there are leaders. It is for these reasons that champions and opinion leaders must be identified and brought in. It is not enough just to have management behind the change, parents wanting it, and so forth. Leaders need to be willing to commit their reputations and time to it, and be identified with it. Leaders can come from almost anywhere in the system so long as they enjoy some name recognition and a measure of respect and trust.

A Commitment from Leadership Is Critical

Leadership can help convince key stakeholders to become involved. However, obtaining their commitment to stay and contribute is another matter. Most have been involved before and come away dissatisfied. They must be persuaded that the collaborative enterprise has a reasonable chance to succeed with or without them. This might be done any number of ways.

One way not to be used is creating hoopla and fanfare. Often, in an attempt to demonstrate their commitment to an effort and to engender support, officials will issue overblown announcements of planning initiatives promising earth-shattering, revolutionary, and historic change. Certainly, those who have encountered this before have grown skeptical and weary of it. They have come to wonder about the pretentiousness and naiveté of the claimants. Their attitude is to waste as little time as possible on just another planning exercise. Those prone to believing the claims and opposed to the changes envisioned can become unduly anxious and move quickly to derail the process. The most prudent approach is an earnest and deliberate one; claims of success must wait until there is something to show.

More convincing aspects of the situation to present to hesitant collaborators to convince them that they should commit to the change process are the following: 1) evidence that the supports paradigm has something to offer them or the inevitability of the changes contemplated, 2) realistic goals and timetables, 3) adequate commitments of the staff/consultant time needed to support the collaborative effort, 4) evidence that time is being well spent, and 5) the political weight of the organizations involved. Following are discussions of these aspects.

The benefits to potential collaborators of moving to the supports paradigm are very clear. Benefits obviously will be reaped by unserved consumers living at home and families who want to be supported in their efforts to have fulfilling lives at home and in the community. Also, current providers of support services will benefit, as will developmental disabilities agency administrators, elected officials, and their tax paying constituents, all of whom naturally favor approaches that stretch limited public funds. Also, some service providers and consumers of facility-based services will see that moving to supported arrangements will further empowerment and community involvement.

Convincing hesitant collaborators that the advent of the supports paradigm is inevitable means employing an argument that is easily made. The likelihood that developmental disabilities services will escape the widely forecast long-term declines in public revenues is minimal, the cry for increased consumer choice and community involvement is growing louder, and the waiting lists for services are growing longer. The ability of the supports paradigm to stretch resources in response to consumer choice is compelling to state and local policy-makers and budget-makers.

Having a realistic work plan is another important factor in the eyes of hesitant collaborators. Goals and timetables should be specific and achievable, yet reasonably flexible. In the author's experience there are always opportunities for short-term accomplishments consistent with the longer-term objectives (e.g., regulatory changes, statutory changes, obtaining discretionary funding to resolve particularly difficult issues through study or demonstration). In this connection, it is important to plan for short-term as well as long-term successes. Given that most states have a history of failed and minimum-impact participatory planning efforts, potential collaborators need the reassurance that comes with short-term successes in order to remain committed.

Also, the work plan must be realistic in terms of what is expected of the collaborators. At the very least, a collaboration of this magnitude must have staff assigned or detailed to it. The need for staff could be reduced but not eliminated through the use of consultants. A mistake that commonly is made in organizing collaboratives is to include too many people too often in the process and at times when they do not have a contribution to make. Executive committees, steering committees, core committees, work groups—groups on groups—are organized to demonstrate a participative process with little thought given to how the time of the individuals involved might be employed most judiciously. Too often meetings are called according to a set timetable, with little preparation and limited expectations as to what the collaborators are expected to contribute. The result is squandered time; the collaborators' time is valuable so they become disenchanted.

The desire of invited collaborators to be part of the process becomes stronger to the extent that the thousands of unserved and marginally served consumers and families, the natural and strongest proponents of supported arrangements, are organized in support of, and engaged in, the process. A number of developmental disabilities agency authorities have remarked on the power of this constituency to enlist legislative support for family support and supported living programs as part of the nationwide family support demonstration programs, to enlist partners in policy-making programs, and to alter the political balance in their states. In New Hampshire, a former state commissioner identified this constituency, built-up in support of the state's family support program, as instrumental in the state's efforts to move the system away from institutional and facility-based service models. Unfortunately, this constituency is poorly organized in most states. Even state Arcs and United Cerebral Palsy Associations are now heavily composed of members providing and receiving services. Pushed to choose between shoring up or reconfiguring the existing service network in favor of supported service options, many probably would choose the former.

It would be hard for most developmental disabilities agency administrators to justify organizing unserved consumers in order to give them voice in the planning process and build the commitment needed to lever the shift. This would be seen as out of line by many legislators or self-serving by some service providers and consumers; ultimately, this would be seen as a threat. In a very real sense, developmental disabilities agency administrators are captives to the existing system. Ostensibly, they represent the interests of all people in the state who meet the state's developmental disabilities services eligibility requirements; in practice, the interests of those currently served come first.

Yet, developmental disabilities councils and other prospective collaborators have the license, and, even more, the responsibility, to organize unserved families and consumers and have done so effectively in a number of states. Building this collaborative process would be a contribution that councils are well-positioned to make. Some Arcs, United Cerebral Palsy Associations, and other consumer advocacy groups could do the same.

Everyone's Issues Are of Concern

The decision to remain committed to the collaborative process will also depend on collaborator assessments of the extent to which their issues will be heard. Early on, every collaborator must have the opportunity to register his or her issues and concerns. This is a time-consuming and frustrating stage to those who want to get on with the issues of special concern to them. Not long ago the author was working with a state official conducting forums around a state in a study with local administrators and service providers. He was exasperated with what he described as the time wasted hearing about provincial concerns countless times. He was reminded that in this study and on many other occasions the locals were obliged to hear the state's concerns.

The natural tendency of state officials and other system change advocates becoming involved in a collaboration is to assume that their concerns are of paramount importance and that the concerns of others are of concern to those others only. It is critical early on to hear the concerns of all collaborators. Until collaborators understand and accept the concerns of all involved as important to all collaborators, there can be little progress.

The beauty of collaborative approaches is that the broad array of interests represented allows all pertinent issues to be aired. There are five principal parties involved in developmental disabilities systems: 1) state policy-makers and administrators, 2) local administrators, 3) service providers, 4) current consumers, and 5) potential consumers. Each has important issues of concern in moving to the supported and inclusive service arrangements provided for through the new paradigm. The following sections present the more prominent issues of each party. These issues are all connected and can all be resolved.

State Policy-Makers and Administrators Most developmental disabilities service systems today are highly regulated and centrally controlled. The types of services provided and the manner in which they are to be provided are defined centrally. Certification and licensing standards define uniform performance criteria that must be met by agencies providing services. Uniform contract provisions link payments to predefined units of service, service minimums, and costs. Payments for services are authorized at uniform rates or up to established payment caps in order to control expenditures. A battery of standardized reports and management information systems have been developed to monitor the utilization of these services, to account for costs, and to obtain a picture of the delivery system for purposes of strategic planning and policy-making. From the viewpoint of many central state administrators and policy-makers, this makes for a reasonably manageable and coherent system.

Tying appropriations, allocations, and payments to service types and amounts or costs makes it easy for policy-makers to grasp, and administrators to govern and account for, what is funded. The idea of relaxing these controls in order to give local administrators and service providers the latitude needed to provide flexible supports to consumers leaves many state legislators and administrators uneasy.

Local Administrators It is the proclivity of state policy-makers and administrators to seek uniformity and service-based funding and controls that concern local administrators. Appropriations, allocations, and payments tied to standard service patterns work against the provision of services responsive to the needs of some individuals and force consumers to fit approved service patterns whether or not they make individual and economic sense. For example, many states condition payments to day service providers on a minimum number of hours of service. This is designed, in part, to ensure a fixed amount of active service and, in part, to ensure that an individual's whereabouts are known for a fixed period of time each day. While many individuals can benefit from these hours, for others this amount of service is an imposition with very negative effects. When aggressive local administrators take liberties with service definitions and funding rules to fashion supported arrangements, they are at risk of audit exceptions and being found out of compliance with established regulations.

Another concern to local administrators is that state legislators, as a rule, are more comfortable funding well-delineated, facility-based services. Arguments for the appropriation of funds for an unspecified service array are not as compelling as arguments for a fixed services menu. Facility-based services may also appear more urgent and substantial than supports and their rates easier to justify, the perception being that if an individual can manage with just supports, maybe the person's need is not that great!

Finally, funding categories and limits frozen in regulation are too rigid and remote to allow local administrators and service providers to respond in a timely and individualized fashion to the variety of demands and situations that arise in supported and inclusive arrangements. Also, there are many less visible but very real costs associated with developing and maintaining supported arrangements, necessitating that services adapt to consumer situations rather than the consumer being forced to adapt to a set service pattern. Case managers have to be afforded the time and training needed to serve as effective consumer advocates. Residential or day programs will be called upon to accommodate consumers in supported employment arrangements during periods of unemployment whenever they lose their jobs or choose to quit. Short-term supervision and housing will have to be arranged when live-in companions and family caregivers become temporarily indisposed. Special personal care arrangements will have to be made in times of short-term illness. Behavior management services and back-up supports will be required in times of crisis. Revenue may be foregone while families and consumers decide whether a proposed roommate is acceptable. Local administrators worry that these costs will go unrecognized and uncompensated by the state, leaving consumers at risk and the local administration to blame.

Service Providers Service providers share the concerns of local administrators when it comes to the predictability and adequacy of funding and payments for supported and inclusive service arrangements. The greater the scope of responsibility assumed by service providers in supporting consumers, the greater their risk and concern.

Aside from the blow to professional pride that may be felt at the prospect of bowing to consumer choice and at the prospect of working for rather than caring for consumers, service providers have a number of practical issues of concern. The ability of service providers to survive in the resource-limited world of developmental disabilities services depends on the ability to predict and control demand and related expenditures and keep expenditures in line with projected revenues. This predictability is possible under current rate payment systems and facility-based service arrangements in which service demand and payment levels are governed by the state. However, under supported arrangements, consumers are free to demand other services, more services, fewer services, or no services at all. Service providers can find themselves in unpredictable and untenable situations where they are no longer able to count on revenues, plan expenditures, and budget accordingly. Providers of traditional residential and day programs could lose consumers. Those heavily invested in residential and day facilities could lose their ability to retain their assets, their net worth.

Current Consumers Just as many residential and day program providers fear the loss of consumers and fiscal stability, many consumers and families fear the loss of their service providers. The vast majority of consumers and families are satisfied with current arrangements. Day program schedules fit well with family work and vacation schedules. Job turnover and freedoms associated with inclusive employment could play havoc with family schedules. Families value the stability and supervision available in group homes and worry that they themselves or the consumer would not be able to assume responsibility for managing a household. For these reasons, many families and consumers prefer the status quo than experimenting with new service arrangements.

Potential Consumers There are many families and consumers who receive little more than follow-along services through which assistance may be requested and provided only in times of crisis. Many more receive no services at all. Some are desperate for services, any services; others would like more services. Most have resigned themselves to little likelihood of receiving services for some time, if at all, given current resource limitations.

These potential consumers are sleeping giants. In many states once they found that their need for supports might be heard, they became very active and effective state-level advocates for the supports paradigm. Their involvement is of paramount importance at the local level. While the state can provide regulatory relief, funding flexibility, and support, some local administrators and service providers are likely to change only when they sense that the demand is real and unrelenting.

Joint Problem-Solving Versus Expediency

The most quickly identified and workable solutions are those that are resolved collaboratively. It used to be, and still is for the most part, that HSRI, like many developmental disabilities system administrators, believed that the time spent on the many different concerns in the developmental disabilities arena in the course of problem resolution, planning, and implementing system change was only a necessary evil. Now, HSRI makes a concerted effort to engage the specific interests of different parties in the problem-solving process.

Traditionally, considerable time was spent at HSRI examining solutions proposed by one party, with other parties affected, in an attempt to determine whether the solutions proposed were practical and politically feasible. This process continued until enough information was believed to exist for selecting or devising a workable approach. Rarely was input obtained from more than one stakeholder at a time, particularly not from stakeholders known to hold opposing views. Planning groups and study groups would be established to oversee the work or to review and endorse a study or plan, but rarely to problem-solve. As a rule, these groups would endorse the less polemic solutions and register minority opinions on the others.

The resulting study recommendations and plans were certainly acceptable but not nearly as insightful and practicable as they might have been. Consequently, many were not implemented. It is only now that the parties that were overlooked are being actively engaged in the problem-solving process and that the deficiencies of the old process are apparent. In the old process different parties are met with in order for statements of their perceptions or positions to be taken. The aim was to assure them that they had been heard. Rarely was the atmosphere right for exploring the interests that underlay their positions. And yet, doing so is the way to make progress. Positions tend to be hard and fast, with little room for negotiation. Focusing on interests can open the door to a variety of solutions.

For example, many residential program providers take a position opposing supported programs, explaining how few of their clients could manage under such arrangements. Related interests and concerns go unmentioned. Concerns are that they will lose clients, lose revenue, and lose stability as the supports paradigm takes hold. Further concerns have to do with residential staff recruitment headaches, licensing requirements, and facilities management responsibilities. Allow them to retain their consumers and revenues by themselves becoming providers of supported living services, and many would become willing participants. In Colorado there was a fivefold increase in supported living arrangements from 1987 through 1990 (from 167 to 937) (Ashbaugh & Rice, 1992). Many of these were voluntary conversions from group homes. Other states have made similar gains.

Conflict Should Be Managed, Not Avoided

The essential point is that workable solutions do not come through the exchange of positions, but through a process of purposeful deliberation and negotiation designed to identify acceptable solutions. It is true that consensus is critical for facilitators. However, often, plans and recommendations are kept at a level general enough to avoid the conflict that comes with specificity. Consequently, many of the solutions proposed or planned are never brought to the operational level, so they are never implemented; others prove impractical. Facilitators must accept Harvey's maxim, that resistance to change is inevitable; if there is none, then certainly the prospect of change is but an illusion (Harvey, 1990). Collaborators must flesh out proposals in detail in order to bring conflicts to the surface and work them through. In this way workable solutions are more readily identified and are defined at a level where they can be more readily operationalized.

Level of Involvement

Until 1990, HSRI established typical consultant/client relationships with state and local officials wherein they would identify issues and problems and contract with HSRI as the outside expert to recommend solutions. Generally speaking, the commitment to implement the study recommendations and plans prepared by HSRI hung on those officials who commissioned the study. In those areas in which these officials had the influence needed to see the implementation process through, change occurred. In most cases, they did not have the reach necessary to implement far-reaching changes, so these changes never occurred. In still other cases, these officials left or fell out of favor, and nothing was implemented.

Much of HSRI's work in problem-solving is now undertaken in collaboration with state and local officials. Issues and problems are jointly defined and resolved with the client. In contrast to those authored solely by HSRI, the proposals and plans derived by the collaboratives enjoy a much broader base of involvement and support. The reach of key collaborators generally has been sufficient to implement even the far-reaching changes. Moreover, the follow through on plans and recommendations has not been dependent on a few key people.

The efforts in building supported living, supported employment, family support, and natural support require a strong sense of local commitment. Local administrators must be willing to devote the extra measure of time and effort required to administer these highly individualized and ever-changing arrangements. Case managers and service providers must be willing to listen and respond to the wishes of families and consumers. Local businesses, community groups, families, consumers, and significant others must be willing to play a more active role in the service process. Licensing, regulations, funding incentives and sanctions, and other traditional approaches to change do not foster this commitment. Local commitment to move to the supports paradigm will depend on the extent to which there has been local involvement, on the extent of opportunity to become locally invested in it, and on where there is recognition of that investment.

CONCLUSION

Despite the clear programmatic and economic sense of the supports paradigm, most developmental disabilities systems are trapped in the current developmental paradigm; all but a small percent of their resources expended for people with developmental disabilities are committed to the current network of facility-based service providers as part of what is commonly termed the *base allocation*.

State and local officials, service providers, and consumers alike face potential risks or losses in adopting the new paradigm. For them to open the door to the supports paradigm, their concerns must be addressed. Collaborative planning and negotiating are well suited to addressing their concerns. Joint problem-solving can reduce the perceived risk and uncertainty to the point where state and local policy-makers, administrators, service providers, and consumers can find acceptable avenues for change. Moreover, introducing the large constituency of unserved consumers and families into the process can provide the political muscle needed to carry the shift through.

The lessons culled from experience with the paradigm shift are listed below:

1. Leaders/champions are essential and can come from almost anywhere.
2. Building collaborator commitment to stay with the change process through the early and difficult stages is critical.
3. In a collaborative enterprise everyone's issues must be of concern.
4. Joint problem-solving, not merely noting different positions, is needed to move beyond irreconcilable positions to solutions.
5. Conflict should be managed, not avoided.
6. The level of stakeholder commitment to the systems change solutions, proposed or planned, corresponds closely to the level of their involvement.

The potential of collaboration as a vehicle for shifting developmental disabilities systems to the new supports paradigm is enormous. However, the prospect for failure is just as real. There have been an overwhelming number of anemic attempts at collaboration. To work, it must be well organized, planned, and managed.

REFERENCES

Ashbaugh, J., & Rice, P. (1992). *Study of Colorado's system of services and supports for people with developmental disabilities*. Cambridge, MA: Human Services Research Institute.

Barker, J.A. (1992). *Future edge. Discovering the new paradigms of success*. New York: Morrow.

Braddock, D., Hemp, R., Fujiura, G., Bachelder, L., & Mitchell, D. (1990). *The state of the states in developmental disabilities*. Baltimore: Paul H. Brookes Publishing Co.

Brunner, C. (1991). *Thinking collaboratively: Ten questions and answers to help policy makers improve children's services*. Washington, DC: Education and Human Services Consortium.

Harvey, T.R. (1990). *Checklist for change: A pragmatic approach to creating and controlling change*. Needham Heights, MA: Allyn & Bacon.

Kouzes, J.M., & Posner, B.Z. (1991). *The leadership challenge: How to get extraordinary things done in organizations*. San Francisco: Jossey-Bass.

Lakin, K.C., White, C.C., Prouty, R.W., Bruininks, R.H., & Kimm, C. (1991). *Medicaid institutional (ICF-MR) and home and community based services for persons with mental retardation and related conditions: Report #35*. Minneapolis: Center for Residential Services and Community Living, Institute on Community Integration, University of Minnesota.

McGaughey, M., Lynch, S., Morganstern, D., Kiernan, W., & Schalock, R. (1991). *National survey of day and employment programs for persons with developmental disabilities: Results from state MR/DD agencies*. Boston: Training and Research Institute for People with Disabilities.

National Association of Developmental Disabilities Councils. (1990). *The 1990 reports: Forging a new era*. Washington, DC: National Association of Developmental Disabilities Councils.

Schlesinger, M., Dorwart, R.A., & Pulice, R.T. (1986). Competitive bidding and states' purchase of services: The case of mental health care in Massachusetts. *Journal of Policy Analysis and Management*, *5*(2), 245–263.

Smith, G.A., & Gettings, R.M. (1992). *Medicaid in the community: The HCB waiver and CSLA programs*. Alexandria, VA: National Association of State Mental Retardation Program Directors, Inc.

24

Collaboration in Action

Madeleine Kimmich

As conventional, single-thread intervention strategies in human services become less and less effective in addressing the multi-faceted problems facing vulnerable families and individuals, policy-makers and researchers alike need to breach the gaps among categorical programs, combine funding streams, and develop teams across administratively separate agencies. Across the United States, service organizations are seeking ways to serve families more effectively through coordination, collaboration, and integration.

THE EMERGENCE OF COLLABORATION AS AN IMPORTANT STRATEGY FOR SYSTEMS CHANGE

A 1990 survey (Robison, 1990) of state agencies serving children and families found that in 74% of the states, "coordination among agencies or departmental divisions is viewed as a *major* problem area, that . . . policy makers throughout the country are calling for more collaborative responses to troubled children and families . . . and that the potential of collaboration is just beginning to be explored" (pp. 20–21). Indeed, the interest in collaboration as a vehicle for systems change is exploding, as evidenced by the range of national organizations with a major interest in this area and the number of state and local entities that are tackling reform through collaborative decision-making. A list of relevant national organizations follows:

- Academy for Educational Development, Center for Youth Development and Policy Research
- American Enterprise Institute (begun under the Bush Administration White House Working Seminar on Integrated Services)
- Carolina Institute for Child and Family Policy
- Center for the Study of Social Policy

- Child and Adolescence Service System Program Technical Assistance Center
- Child and Family Policy Center
- Council of Chief State School Officers (CCSSO)
- Council of Governor's Policy Advisors (CGPA)
- Council of Governor's Policy Advisors
- Danforth Foundation
- Education and Human Services Consortium
- Family Impact Seminar
- Foundation Consortium of School-Linked Services
- Home, School, Community Connections Project, Southwest Education Development Laboratory
- Institute for Educational Leadership
- Joining Forces
- National Academy of Public Administration (NAPA)
- National Center for Networking Community-Based Services
- National Center for Service Integration
- National Civic League
- National Commission for Employment Policy (NCEP)
- National Early Childhood Technical Assistance System
- National Health/Education Consortium
- National Maternal and Child Health Resource Center/National Resource Center on Community-Based Service Systems
- National Resource Center for Community-Based Service Integration
- Policy Studies Associates, Inc.
- Program for Community Problem-Solving
- The Bush Center on Child Development and Social Policy
- The White House National Performance Review, Task Force on Services Integration

The flurry of collaborative activity for systems change since the mid-1980s is actually part of a fairly long history in human services. The beginning can be traced to the service integration initiatives at the federal level that began in the 1970s and carried into the 1980s (e.g., the Allied Services Act, the Services Integration Pilot Projects[1]). The movement today comes with somewhat different guiding principles and functions in a different environment. Specifically, there is a broader population focus; efforts are coming from the top down and from the bottom up; new computer technology is being used to further the technical aspects of integration; fiscal constraints are a strong motivating force; and, perhaps most dra-

[1] The Allied Services Act, an unsuccessful 1971 legislative proposal by Department of Health, Education, and Welfare (HEW) Secretary Elliott Richardson, would have allowed HEW to make planning and implementation grants to state and local governments, to waive certain federal requirements, and to transfer funds among categorical programs. The Services Integration Pilot Projects, authorized by Congress under the Deficit Reduction Act of 1984, were designed to help individuals and families achieve or maintain self-sufficiency; grants were awarded to Arizona, Maine, Oklahoma, South Carolina, and Florida (Ooms & Owen, 1991).

matic, there is a clear focus on the importance of the family as both target and partner in the intervention, rather than only the individual as customer (Ooms & Owen, 1991). From the Children and Adolescent Service System Program (CASSP); to the Individuals with Disabilities Education Act (IDEA) (PL 101-476, 1990), Part H; to the Head Start Collaboration Grants; to the Child Welfare Reform Initiative,[2] every segment of the human services community is engaging in some form of collaboration, usually across agencies, to better assist individuals and families.

These reform initiatives are characterized by four predominant themes: 1) family and community empowerment, 2) clarifying and assessing outcomes, 3) systems thinking, and 4) collaborative action. Woven throughout the systems change efforts is "the assumption of shared responsibility for individual and family well-being which cuts across traditional professional, organizational and bureaucratic boundaries. These reforms involve both vertical and horizontal integration and new processes of collaboration and partnership—across program sectors, between different levels of government, between private and public sectors and between providers and clients" (Ooms, 1991, p. 3). This chapter brings collaboration into the forefront as a change strategy, perhaps the primary change strategy in these times of increasing interdependence and fiscal austerity.

The following section reviews the literature on collaboration and services integration, drawing insights from a number of different service arenas. The section following describes some experiences of the Human Services Research Institute (HSRI), in Cambridge, Massachusetts, in applying collaborative planning strategies to specific systems change efforts in particular states and localities. Following are descriptions of four projects of greatest relevance:

1. In Arizona HSRI has been working for 3 years with the Governor's Council on Developmental Disabilities to design and implement a quality assurance system for services to people with developmental disabilities. Through the efforts of a collaborative planning group composed of all the major stakeholders in the service system, HSRI has targeted licensing and monitor-

[2] CASSP: The Child and Adolescent Services System Program, a small federal program begun in 1984, promotes comprehensive community-based systems of services for seriously troubled children, with emphasis on developing strong linkages among the various systems serving children and on having families participate fully in planning and service delivery. IDEA Part H: Originally enacted in 1986 as the Handicapped Infants and Toddlers Program under the Education of the Handicapped Act Amendments (PL 99-457), now amended to be called the Individuals with Disabilities Education Act (IDEA), Part H provides for a state-wide, comprehensive, coordinated, multidisciplinary, interagency service system for infants and toddlers with disabilities and their families. It also "proposes a long series of reforms in the delivery system of services itself, changing the relationship of client and professional and modifying the practice of many professionals" (Harbin et al., 1992, p. 1). Head Start Collaboration Grants: Federal funding began in the late 1980s to encourage Head Start agencies to develop collaborative relationships with other state and local agencies to improve services and to reach more families. Child Welfare Reform Initiative: A 5-year effort of the Annie E. Casey Foundation to assist states in improving their services for children and families, the initiative emphasizes the importance of interagency collaboration and decategorization of funding to develop community-based, comprehensive, flexible services to meet the needs of children and families at risk.

ing activities and case management, both primary responsibilities of the state Division of Developmental Disabilities.

2. In 1992, HSRI assisted the Montgomery County, Maryland, Department of Family Resources to evaluate its current service system for adults with developmental disabilities in terms of responsiveness to consumers and families. HSRI worked through a core advisory committee representing all key sectors and reached out to the broader community through regional forums.
3. As consultant to the Maryland Children and Family Services Reform Initiative, funded by the Annie E. Casey Foundation, HSRI is assisting with development of integrated service efforts among the major agencies serving children and families at risk (i.e., social services, juvenile justice, education, health, and mental health), with the goal of improved outcomes for children at risk for removal from their families. HSRI has been working at both the state and local levels through collaborative working groups made up of representatives of the four traditional agencies as well as the Services Reform Initiative office itself, which has no direct service responsibility but considerable persuasive power over policy and fiscal matters.
4. In South Carolina, HSRI assisted the Department of Mental Health and the Department of Social Services to develop and evaluate a demonstration collaborative project providing mental health services to adopted children with special needs. The project involved both direct intervention with children and families and training for mental health and adoption workers.

The last section of the chapter discusses some of the common pitfalls in the use of collaborative techniques and offers guidelines for deciding when to proceed with collaboration.

WHAT IS COLLABORATION?

Although the term *collaboration* is often used interchangeably with the terms *coordination* and *cooperation*, it signifies more. A collaborative strategy is used when the "need and intent is to change fundamentally the way services are designed and delivered throughout the system" (Melaville & Blank, 1991, p.14), that is, when the goal is systems change. In *cooperative* arrangements, partners help each other meet their respective organizational goals, without making substantial changes in services or in regulations; no effort is made to establish common goals. *Collaborative* partnerships, in contrast, "establish common goals; . . . agencies agree to pool resources, jointly plan, implement and evaluate new services and procedures, and delegate individual responsibility for the outcomes of their joint efforts" (p. 16). Collaboration may mean that agencies "reformulate professional expectations, job descriptions, and program design" in ways more sensitive to the differing needs of families. Where cooperatives advocate for change, collaboratives are *empowered* to negotiate those changes. They have the authority to commit resources and the power to alter policies and procedures toward common goals. "The advantage of collaboration over cooperation is the possibility it affords to restructure the expertise and resources of partner agencies and to balance their emphasis on specialized problems" (p. 18).

The term collaboration is used to refer to a broad range of activities, the common thread of which is merging the efforts and interests of diverse groups to create a better package of supports for a particular group of people. Perhaps the clearest model for interagency collaboration is found in Part H of IDEA, which mandates multi-agency involvement to create comprehensive services to infants and toddlers with disabilities. Discretionary monies are the glue for planning multi-disciplinary interagency programs. Part H has a particularly "strong emphasis on coordination and collaboration at all levels of government" (Ooms & Owen, 1991, p. 19), with multiple federal programs and interagency coordinating councils at the federal and state levels. The Annie E. Casey Foundation's Child Welfare Reform Initiative and New Futures Initiative, and the federal Head Start Collaboration Grants likewise seek to bring together multiple agencies that share responsibility for a particular group of people. Collaboration can also bridge gaps within a single agency, bringing together parties from all levels to better serve a particular group. In these cases, collaboration often highlights the need for merging distinct funding streams or modifying organizational structures that foster isolated approaches to serving agency customers.

Bruner (1991) summed up collaboration in *Thinking Collaboratively*, by saying:

> Collaboration is not a quick fix. It is a means to an end rather than an end in itself. It is extremely time-consuming and process-intensive. It occurs among people, not among institutions. It requires creative problem-solving skills. It leads not to a trivial reorganization but to a fundamental reconceptualization of the service system. (p. 26)

WHAT MAKES COLLABORATION WORK?

Since the 1980s much has been written about successful factors in facilitating systems reform efforts. Perhaps the most useful framework is that provided by Flynn and Harbin (1987), who identified five factors that influence collaborative performance, both separately and in combination. These are climate, process, people, policies, and resources.

Climate

The first factor is climate, which refers to the atmosphere in which collaborative efforts are attempted. It encompasses attitudes, priorities, and support of key people. For collaboration to be successful, the agencies and groups involved must recognize the need for the change, be open to change, be willing to engage in joint ventures, and place a high priority on achieving goals common to the entire collaborative group.

An attitude of openness to change requires that each agency have an understanding of what other parties can contribute to their own efforts, that is, what the immediate benefits to collaboration will be. Thus, an early step must be sharing the organizational culture, values base, and identity of each collaborating group. Hagebak (1979) underscored the importance of this step, noting that collaborative efforts are seriously impeded by "barriers of vision," which cause group members to be unable to conceptualize and implement comprehensive programs. His proposed remedy is to make the collaborative activity a voluntary process so that all those at the table are willing partners to collaborative action; explicitly recognize each organization's autonomy at the outset; and have each organization identify its own barriers to collaborative action and design ways to cope with them.

A number of HSRI efforts have highlighted the importance of such cross-agency understanding. In a 1989–1991 South Carolina pilot project providing collaborative mental health and adoption services for children with special needs, an important prerequisite to successful interagency service delivery was found to be that frontline workers understood and respected the roles and professional strengths of other agency staff (Kimmich & Godfrey, 1991). Likewise, in collaborative "vision development" sessions, which HSRI conducted as a consultant to the Casey-funded Child Welfare Reform Initiative in Maryland, representatives of the five state agencies serving children and families at risk all came away with a much broader understanding of, and greater appreciation for, the responsibilities borne by their colleagues in the other agencies.

Melaville and Blank (1991) urged interagency collaborative groups to take the time to really understand the perspectives of all partners and to incorporate them all as much as possible. At the same time, they warned the groups to be careful to make promises they could keep, recognizing that setting attainable objectives creates momentum and a sense of accomplishment vital to sustaining group member commitment. Guthrie and Guthrie (1991) echoed the same theme, pointing out that the collaborative effort, based on common vision, common goals, and shared expectations, must start small, with clearly manageable tasks.

In a similar vein, Bruner (1991) argued that the "two major prerequisites for successful collaboration [are that] collaborators understand each other's roles and agree on shared goals" (p. 19). He elucidated the process for creating a suitable climate for collaboration, that is, collaborators need to create joint goals, which are specific and measurable, to guide their actions, and take steps to meet those goals. Such a strategy resembles that advocated in the interagency collaboratives under Part H of IDEA, which says that each state is to create state-level as well as local interagency councils to coordinate planning and service delivery. Early evaluations of Part H implementation underscore how difficult it is for interagency groups to create specific, viable, and meaningful joint goals (Harbin, Gallagher, & Batista, 1992; Place & Gallagher, 1992).

Establishing joint goals has been a critical early step in many of HSRI's collaborative projects. In Montgomery County, Maryland, the stakeholders in the developmental disabilities system were already primed for making fundamental change. The request for proposals to which HSRI responded depicted the general direction in which county decision-makers wanted to go; they explicitly sought a consultant who had "a very clear philosophy regarding the provision of integrated services" (Montgomery County Government, 1991, p. 3) and who was "abreast of innovative, creative, and consumer-centered programs serving persons with developmental disabilities" (p. 3). It became a matter of bringing the many parties together to turn that general philosophy into a distinct set of principles to guide the changes in the service system and to develop specific action steps for the short term and the long term.

In Idaho, HSRI worked with a collaborative to redesign the state's developmental disabilities services; this offers a more complex example. Initially, this group was a collection of individual interests with conflicting views, but their collaborative process evolved to create real communication. By the end of HSRI's involvement, the collaborative had come to consensus and was poised to make significant changes. While fundamental disagreement remained, the process yielded enough of a common purpose to fuel an array of change-oriented actions. Progress since then confirms the turnaround in participants' views of the problem and of each other, as evidenced by their continued collaboration and commitment to change.

Climate is strongly affected by the political context. The time required to understand each agency's strengths and to develop a joint vision for change may not be politically affordable. If the political leadership is unstable, it is likely to focus on highly visible and expedient activities and to allow insufficient time to create the stable, sustained commitment and support necessary for collaborative efforts to be effective (Ooms & Owen, 1991). This has been a factor in HSRI's work with Arizona's developmental disabilities service system, where the state agency leadership has changed twice in a 2-year period. Soon after HSRI began its work in Arizona, the situation there in developmental disability services reached the crisis point. The state agency was reeling from explosive growth in its Medicaid waiver program, and consumers and families were vociferously demanding a more responsive service system. In working with the Governor's Council on Developmental Disabilities to improve service quality, HSRI brought together a broad-based collaborative planning group, including consumers, family members, advocates, service providers, and local and state staff. Most participants were ready for change at the outset, but repeated administrative and fiscal crises consumed the state agency leadership. As a result, state officials were unable to await the payoff from the long-term collaborative change efforts.

In summary, climate is the factor of collaboration that brings to the fore the importance of mutual understanding and respect among stakeholders, individuals' willingness to commit to a common vision and joint goals, and leadership's ability to make a long-term commitment.

Process

The second critical factor in the success of collaborative efforts is process, which concerns the actions and operations of the collaborative group. Key components are communication, proper planning, and mechanisms for building trust and handling conflict. Because collaborative efforts to achieve fundamental change bring together parties having different interests and perspectives, conflict is inevitable. Indeed, if there is no conflict, the prospect of change is minimal. As one advocate bluntly put it, "Collaboration is cooperating with your enemies" (Buttons, 1992).

Ooms and Owens (1991) addressed similar process issues, identifying turf and ownership problems as a major barrier to collaborative systems change. All parties have vested interests in the status quo of categorical programs: Policymakers are loath to give up their line authority, advocates want to hold on to a discrete program because it has political support and funding, professionals fear a loss of identity to generic roles, and bureaucrats do not want to give up funding control.

Choosing effective communication methods and conflict resolution strategies can make all the difference. It can mean that enemies are not really enemies, that all parties recognize the greater good. Positive methods can allow a group to come to consensus, so that those in the minority feel they have genuinely been heard, and, though they do not fully agree with the majority, they understand the majority view and will support the decision (Schein, 1988). Thus, the ability to reach consensus depends a great deal on how much ownership the individual has in the group process. Those who do not feel the process was valid will not support the group's decision. Lack of consensus can highlight weaknesses in the earlier step of defining common goals.

Consensus-building has been important in every collaborative situation HSRI has faced. On the negative side, in Maryland's interagency collaboration for services to children and families, the traditional state agency representatives were not given sufficient ownership of the content of the Service Reform Initiative and, thus, went about the task of implementing the initiative without enthusiasm. On the positive side, in the Idaho developmental disabilities system, the collaborative process was strong, with conflicts arising and aired and, as much as possible, resolved to consensus. Unanimity was not always reached, yet, by freely discussing conflicting views, the participants clarified the points of division and the areas of common interest, paving the way for eventual consensus.

In Arizona and Maryland, the path to consensus was made rocky by explicit delegation of responsibility to subgroups. The Arizona Core Collaborative established a common set of principles to guide the redesign of licensing and case management activities, but the link between the two groups involved was not strong enough. The detailed recommendations that came from the subgroups became points of division rather than consensus. The solution that is emerging relies heavily on the power of the collaborative process, that is, from among the detailed recommendations, identifying common ground on which to bring all parties back together and to reestablish trust, then allowing the difficult issues to surface naturally. Such a process is occurring of its own accord in the Maryland children and families initiative, as state-level decision-makers begin to revisit the problematic issues of the past (i.e., interagency assessment and service planning) as they arise in the broader context of services integration.

A 1992 study by the United States General Accounting Office (GAO) argued the importance of process to successful collaborative strategies. The GAO concluded, "systems change has been plagued by an inability to obtain political support for change among key officials and to sustain resource commitments from participating agencies" (p. 3). In particular, GAO felt that systems change efforts had been only marginally effective because they were unable to reach consensus on the nature and extent of problems and how to address them, and they were unable to overcome agencies' concerns about protecting their own identities, ideologies, roles, and resources.

In short, interagency collaboration demands a new way of looking at problems and resolving them. There are multiple agencies at the table. "Collaboration requires the abandonment of mechanical decision-making. [S]olutions must be tailored to specific clients and circumstances" (Bruner, 1991, p. 18). Essential to collaboration is flexibility, that is, the ability and willingness to change agendas and strategies as the political situation or the economic climate demands, without losing sight of, and commitment to, the core vision and values. The key strategy in terms of process is to build ownership so that the group can move through conflict to consensus.

People

The third factor in successful collaboration is the people involved in the collaborative effort, an aspect that clearly interacts with the processes being used. Important categories of people include the key decision-makers, the members of the collaborative, and a group facilitator.

The key decision-makers must not only be involved in planning and developing, they must also play a major role in influencing others outside the collaborative to accept and support the proposals. Without influential people on the team, no amount of good process will achieve the systems change goals. The situation in Montgomery County, Maryland, illustrates this point well. From the beginning, the governmental leaders supported the shift toward the supports paradigm, and they put their word on the line, promising to implement the actions stipulated by the county-wide vision development group.

Membership in the collaborative is often a sensitive decision point. Bruner (1991) argued for "more than nominal membership" (p. 17), involving local service delivery representatives "to help assure that planning at the administrative level is connected to implementation at the service-delivery level" (p. 17). Direct care staff should play a major role in the collaborative change deliberations as well as in implementation of the changes. This was a crucial shortcoming of the Maryland Child Welfare Reform effort. State-level discussions of vision and guiding principles did not include representatives from the field, exacerbating already tense relations between state and local agencies. When the state group delegated to the local representatives the responsibility for fleshing out the process and structure for interagency assessment, the local people were skeptical of the state's real commitment to integrated services. Their fears were well-founded. The state group soon balked at affirming its commitment by waiving regulations or providing exemptions from reporting requirements.

Consistency in membership can lead to increased power. In Arizona, representatives of service recipients and service providers have much longer tenure and have been more consistently active in the collaborative than the state office representatives. This has given advocates and service providers increased opportunities to influence collaborative decisions as well as greater visibility to those interested people outside the process.

Melaville and Blank (1991) added an important point, that is, the membership should include not only those with power but also those who will be directly affected by the decisions of the collaborative. This feature has been adopted in HSRI's more recent collaboration efforts. In both Montgomery County, Maryland, and Arizona, consumers of developmental disabilities services have played a central role in the analysis of system strengths and weaknesses and continue to be involved in the design and implementation issues to ensure that the collaborative process remains true to the original joint vision. In Arizona, the local level involvement has been carried even further with the establishment of local case management working groups composed of frontline staff, consumers, and families. Case management changes are being built from the bottom up, with each district defining its own unique needs for changes and designing the best changes they can to share with the others after they see what works. The key has been the overlap between the participants in the local working groups and the state-level core collaborative.

Taking the membership factor to a deeper level, Ooms and Owen (1991) focused on the interactions among collaborators. They singled out three lessons to be learned from the service integration efforts of the 1970s and 1980s. In addition to sustained funding, the crucial factors were strong leadership and nurturing personal relationships among collaborators. Similarly, Johnson, McLaughlin, and Christensen (1982) pointed to the critical nature of personal interactions in the success of collaborative ventures. Stating, "[the] single most important factor [in successful interagency collaboration] is interpersonal relations" (p. 3) they urged use of an outside facilitator to enhance the group's collaborative philosophy, to open communication channels, and to increase trust and risk-taking among participants. Such an external expert can also be instrumental in keeping the group's agenda on track (Melaville & Blank, 1991).

HSRI has placed itself in just such a facilitation role in many states, leading the groups to approach potentially conflicting areas only to realize that their views were not as divergent as they feared. In an Iowa collaborative effort to develop a model for personal assistance services, it became clear that the resistance to increasing consumer choice in personal assistance services was largely due to the belief that such a move would seriously jeopardize the funding. When the discussion focused on the reasons behind the opposition rather than on the apparent intractability of the opposing positions, the group was able to construct a valid change strategy acceptable to all collaborators (Kimmich & Hutchins, 1992). Such a peaceful resolution is not always possible, but airing the conflicts is, nonetheless, essential to progress. Often, the outside facilitator becomes the lightning rod for discontent among the collaborating parties. By keeping the focus on the issues rather than the personalities, the facilitator can keep the change process going in the original direction. Maryland's Child Welfare Reform initiative is now tackling the fundamental questions of how to decategorize funding and merge service interventions, where just a short time earlier the parties were deadlocked over how to share assessment information.

Policies

The fourth factor in fruitful collaborative efforts is the joint policies of the participating agencies, the "governing principles which are established within and among agencies" (Flynn & Harbin, 1987, p. 38). The key question is whether the policies of the various participating agencies are compatible and encourage collaborative planning and use of resources. Of course, just having the policies does not guarantee that such collaborative activity takes place, but without supportive policies it is impossible. In the mental health/adoption demonstration effort in South Carolina, participants found that, in order to foster collaborative services among adoption and mental health service providers, regulatory and procedural changes had to be made to lower barriers between agencies and allow the direct service workers the discretion needed for real front-line collaboration (Kimmich & Godfrey, 1991). In the Montgomery County, Maryland, developmental disabilities system, county officials found they had considerable latitude to change policies and procedures, despite state oversight, once it was clear that the leadership and the other stakeholders wanted to pursue fundamental changes.

The lesson from Maryland and Arizona is that there has to be a conscious and energetic commitment to the collaborative vision. Too often groups struggle to formulate the perfect statement of purpose, the impeccable set of values, only to withdraw to admire their handiwork. The conceptual consensus is the easy part; the real challenge comes in applying that vision and those values systematically to every policy decision. Thus, in Maryland, when the principles of integrated services for children and families were consciously applied to the task of interagency assessment, it became obvious that in a family-centered service system, families must take the lead in assessing their own needs and strengths. Similarly, Arizona's fervent embrace of consumer choice implies that case managers need to have the authority to assist service recipients who want to move out of their group homes and into supported living. Such practical applications of high-flown principles are essential tests of the true mettle of a collaborative.

Resources

The fifth and final factor in successful collaboration is resources, in particular the money, people, and facilities made available for collaborative systems change efforts. The people with control over financial resources are often inadvertently left out of the collaborative, making it impossible to ensure that the needed fiscal changes occur. Similarly, the needed changes to staff and facilities are often beyond the control of the agency representatives, so that obtaining more highly skilled staff or improving the physical plant cannot be ensured by the collaborative.

No matter how strong the commitment is to collaborative service delivery, constraints on resources cannot be fully overcome. A GAO (1992) study of collaborative child welfare reform efforts pointed to the failure to "sustain resource commitments from participating agencies" (p. 3) as a primary reason that fundamental systems change had not occurred. Despite the trappings of collaborative efforts, agencies remained unwilling to address problems jointly by combining personnel and resources. Ooms and Owen raised a similar concern, noting that the variability in state fiscal conditions can certainly be a serious barrier to the initiation and maintenance of new program directives (Ooms & Owen, 1991).

The financial resource barrier was particularly evident in HSRI's work in Maryland, where repeated cuts to agency service efforts kept the agencies in a crisis mode and unable to look beyond their immediate needs. In contrast, however, it has been these very constraints on resources that have stimulated collaborative planning. In South Carolina, for instance, child welfare and mental health agencies realized they would never be able to serve all the families alone, so they tried to pool resources so that they could reach more families with less duplicative effort and with sufficient assistance to make a difference in family functioning. In Montgomery County, Maryland, the prospect of diminished revenues increased the leaders' energy for collaborative systems change. They began to take a serious look at how to continue innovative ventures without new revenues, which led them to rethink all their service priorities and to move away from those least consistent with the collaborative vision for the service system.

The overall message that surfaces from this review of collaborative efforts since the 1980s is that the prerequisites of successful interagency collaboration are a supportive climate, flexible organizational policies, careful selection of collaborators, conscientious use of trust-building and conflict resolution processes, and a workable resource base on which to build reforms. Pelletier (1992) summed this up well from the local perspective by saying that agencies working together to change systems require "perseverance, a clear vision, a willingness to communicate, cross training of systems, pooling of resources, flexible funding and a willingness to look beyond the shortcomings of individual agencies" (p. 5).

Steps in Successful Collaboration

Much has been written concerning the factors that have an impact on collaborative ventures; less attention has been given to understanding the chronological process that a successful collaborative effort follows. Flynn and Harbin (1987) offered the following helpful schema of four developmental stages of the interagency collaboration process: 1) formation, which includes selecting members, creating a cooperative atmosphere, developing a decision-making structure to enhance group functioning, delineating and accepting roles and responsibilities, and agreeing to a general mission; 2) conceptualization, which is articulating and coming to consensus on mission, philosophy, goals, objectives, strategies, and developing a skeleton plan; 3) development, which is fleshing out the plans, including use of pilot projects; and 4) implementation. Melaville and Blank (1991) described two critical activities in this last stage: 1) institutionalizing the changes by incorporating the group's partnership objectives into each agency's own mandates and budgets, and 2) having the group publicize its success, so it attracts support for replication and expansion.

Thus, not only are there multiple and complex factors affecting the success of collaborative ventures, there are also discernible steps in the collaborative experience that need to be considered carefully if the group is to be able to sustain its commitment throughout the evolution of systems change.

PITFALLS OF COLLABORATION AS A VEHICLE FOR SYSTEMS CHANGE

Reflecting on the many collaborative efforts in which HSRI has been engaged brings to light several major pitfalls of collaboration. These include altering the balance of power, impatience, insistence on forward progress, and equating representation with authority.

Altering the Balance of Power

Collaboration can fundamentally challenge the existing balance of power. In locally administered human services programs, the funds may be controlled by the state while practice is largely controlled by the local government or even by private vendors. If state collaborators have not fully committed to the joint vision and goals, when the time comes to discuss waiving regulations or altering allocation patterns, the conflicts among the agencies and among the levels of government can resurface. Such a situation arose in Maryland because agencies were still unclear about the extent of the threat that collaboration posed to their integrity as service providers to people who were only partially served by the collaborative. In other states the increasing recalcitrance of powerful parties was actually a sign of the effectiveness of the collaborative as the threat to the status quo became more real and opponents rolled out the big guns. The way to avoid such situations is to be sure all the key players are at the table from the beginning, even if it means slowing down the process to ensure that everyone is involved.

Impatience

Because building commitment to a joint vision of change is crucial, progress can be slow. Meanwhile, the world marches on, and state agencies continue to promulgate new rules and regulations, conduct training events, and make decisions about the fate of individuals and families. It is sorely tempting to jump over the process necessities of collaborative planning, only reacting to the day-to-day affairs and, thereby, not only losing sight of the larger systems change goal, but also jeopardizing the long-term stability of the collaborative itself. If the collaborative is successful, it will change the dynamic of decision-making in a state or an organization, and then it can have an impact on even the most recently instituted policies and procedures.

Insistence on Forward Progress

Bruner offers a useful typology of first- and second-level collaborative initiatives, referring first to beginning efforts (first-level) at the state level to establish the conceptual basis and parameters for the collaborative venture, and then moving to local demonstration efforts (second-level) where the details are worked out. The danger is ever present that first-level collaborative efforts are merely pro forma and, thus, do not establish the essential foundation for second-level local demonstrations of the collaborative project. This situation often arises because the key players at the second level are not part of the first-level activity. Schein (1988) emphasized this point saying, "The major problem [in group problem solving and decision making] when different people or groups perform [the two levels of tasks] is that the second group may neither understand clearly nor be particularly committed to the proposal or solution that the first group has offered" (p. 67). The lack of connection between the first-level effort and the second-level effort most often comes to light when the demonstration activities generate specific recommendations that are forcefully resisted by the state policy-makers. The important point to realize is that sometimes progress can be made *only* by going backward. Collaborators should not hesitate to go back to an earlier stage when the situation changes. The collaborative may need to rebuild some group identity because players changed or rethink the problem because the politics or the resources changed. "One should be mentally prepared to go back . . . to reformulate the problem, not merely to rush in with more effort or a new solution" (Schein, 1988, p. 68). Change is a dynamic and cyclical process, not a linear one.

Equating Representation with Authority

There is an inherent danger with any representative that the individual does not really represent the views of others and, equally problematic, that the individual does not adequately communicate the conceptual and visionary aspects of the collaborative process to those he or she is representing, so that, when changes are proposed, constituents see them out of context. Collaborators should not assume that the one staff member speaks for all others in the organization, anymore than one representative speaks for all in a community. If that person does not fully or appropriately communicate the activities of the collaborative (he or she needs support from other members in doing this), there is a risk that the support of the key people will not be forthcoming and the effort will, in turn, be undermined. Collaborators can never be sure that a representative is truly empowered to speak for the organization or that he or she takes the role of being the mediating link seriously. One safeguard would be to observe the representative's activities in reporting to his or her constituency. Another might be to take the word directly to the people, through community forums and agency-wide meetings, where the full context of the collaborative initiative is presented and there is ample opportunity for questions and comments. If the representative has done a good job of communicating in both directions, the meeting can offer additional clarification; if he or she has not done well, the meeting could be the essential link between the collaborative and the greater community that will be directly affected by the proposed change.

RECOMMENDED GUIDELINES FOR USE OF COLLABORATIVE PLANNING TO ACHIEVE SYSTEMS CHANGE

Given the pitfalls to collaboration, and the multi-faceted requirements of successful collaborative efforts, it is important to focus on a few critical types of activities to increase the viability of the collaborative venture. The first three concern leadership, membership, and vision and occur early in the collaborative process. These correspond to Flynn and Harbin's (1987) stages of formation and conceptualization, the essential groundwork for successful collaboration. The last two types of activities relate to sustaining the collaborative; they are the grease that keeps the development and implementation machinery going in the latter stages of the collaborative process. Following are discussions of these five types of activities.

Identify the Leaders

"Leaders have the ability to effectively communicate the vision and to keep key actors engaged in constructive collaboration. Systems change is about leadership, not about management. Management is about getting others to do what you want them to do. Leadership is about getting them to *want* to do what you want them to do" (Ashbaugh, 1991, p. 5). Without the active support of the leaders, specific changes cannot be brought about. It is essential for collaborators to stay in the vision and commitment stage until the leaders have demonstrated their active support; otherwise, the work will be undermined. Effort should go toward winning the leadership's support; one effective strategy might be to broaden gradually the number of consumers and families who are involved to bring the leadership to attend to their needs and desires.

Equal Footing

It is important to bring all stakeholders, as early as possible, into the collaborative process, on an equal footing. Stakeholders include not only all sectors of the service delivery system—families, service providers, funders, and advocates—but also all levels of the system—direct service and middle managers, administrators, and policy-makers. Having all participants feel equally valued and equally empowered is not an easy task, but it is essential if they are to feel ownership in the collaborative process. It may be necessary to work with some of the constituencies individually, prior to the formation of the core collaborative group, to enable them to develop a strong identity and to impart to their representative the heart of their own vision. This may be especially important for service recipients and their families and for members of the general community, who are less likely than professionals to have experience in group policy-making, but whose voice is essential. Having these preliminary vision development sessions may also make the collaborative members more forthcoming and assertive in the subsequent vision development work for the whole collaborative.

Develop a Common Vision

The first meeting of the core collaborative group should concentrate on developing a new identity and mission/vision. The key to this process is for the members to learn about one another in the context of the emerging group vision. Each stakeholder is challenged to define and describe his or her constituency in terms of the group's common goals and principles. This action builds ownership of the group's common goals and principles, which, in turn, builds ownership of the process, which is essential to reaching consensus on particular issues and steps.

Nurture the Core Collaborative

In order to keep the vision in focus, it may be necessary to "innoculate" the core collaborative members numerous times as they go deeper into the practicality of making change. Revisiting the principles of the vision cannot be done too often; this keeps the vision vibrant, meaningful, and explicit. Similarly, the collaborative should not assume that once a member is delegated the responsibility for a particular working group, the products of that group will be immediately acceptable to the larger body. It is critical that the working groups report back frequently to the core collaborative to ensure ownership of the core group in the emerging changes and to build the trust and personal connections between the working group members and the core collaborative group members.

Keep the Vision Prominent

The focus must be kept consistently on the fundamental issues, the vision of what systems change is ultimately desired. The principles of the vision should be applied constantly to whatever task is at hand. This serves continually to give greater specificity to the grand vision, giving rise to questions and conflicts at times and, thus, testing the consensus-building process. Such testing and refining is essential if the collaborative is to outlast any single leader of the moment. It pushes the members of the core collaborative group to redefine themselves in terms of the new collaborative relationships rather than in the context of the latest structural form of the service system. In addition, by not becoming too wedded to a particular change or a certain strategy, the group can allow itself to go backward at times without feeling time has been wasted.

Collaboration is necessary if any sustainable change is to occur in service systems. Climate, process, people, policies, and resources are all crucial factors directly affecting the potential for change. But to engage in collaboration is itself testimony to change; it means going against the grain of bureaucratic habit, not controlling every step but, instead, working together to realize the vision. With leadership and with patience, collaboration can, indeed, lead to fundamental systems change.

REFERENCES

Ashbaugh, J. (1991, July 16). *Progressive progressive planning*. Keynote speech to the Louisiana State Planning Council on Developmental Disabilities.

Bruner, C. (1991). *Thinking collaboratively: Ten questions and answers to help policy makers improve children's services*. Washington, DC: Education and Human Services Consortium.

Buttons, C. (1992, December 7). Remarks offered at the 1992 American Association on Mental Retardation Public Policy Forum. Washington, DC.

Flynn, C. C., & Harbin, G. L. (1987). Evaluating interagency coordination efforts using a multidimensional, interactional, developmental paradigm. *Remedial and Special Education, 8*(3), 35–44.

Guthrie, G. P., & Guthrie, L. F. (1991). Streamlining interagency collaboration for youth at risk. *Educational Leadership, September*, 17–20.

Hagebak, B. R. (1979). Local human service delivery: The integration imperative. *Public Administration Review, November/December*, 575–582.

Harbin, G. L., Gallagher, J., & Batista, L. (1992). *Status of states' progress in implementing Part H of IDEA: Report #4*. Chapel Hill, NC: Carolina Institute for Child and Family Policy.

Johnson, H. W., McLaughlin, J. A., & Christensen, M. (1982). Interagency collaboration: Driving and restraining forces. *Exceptional Children, 48*(5), 395–399. Cited in Goldenberg, P. C., & Yound, T. M. (1989). *Interagency collaboration: An annotated bibliography for programs serving children with emotional disabilities and their families*. Portland, OR: Research and Training Center on Family Support and Children's Mental Health, Portland State University.

Kimmich, M. H., & Godfrey, T. (1991). *Evaluation of the adoption-mental health collaborative project: Final report*. Bethesda, MD: Human Services Research Institute.

Kimmich, M. H., & Hutchins, A. H. (1992). *Personal assistance services for Iowa: A model and action plan*. Bethesda, MD: Human Services Research Institute.

Melaville, A. I., & Blank, M. J. (1991). *What it takes: Structuring interagency partnerships to connect children and families with comprehensive services*. Washington, DC: Education and Human Services Consortium.

Montgomery County Government R.F.F. #21017. (Issued September 11, 1991). *Analysis of developmental disabilities services in Montgomery County*. Rockville, MD: Author.

Ooms, T. (1991). *Coordination, collaboration, integration: Strategies for serving families more effectively. Part two: State and local initiatives*. Family Impact Seminar Background Briefing Report. Washington, DC: The American Association for Marriage and Family Therapy Research and Education Foundation.

Ooms, T., & Owen, T. (1991). *Coordination, collaboration, integration: Strategies for serving families more effectively. Part one: The federal role*. Family Impact Seminar Background Briefing Report. Washington, DC: The American Association for Marriage and Family Therapy Research and Education Foundation.

Pelletier, S. B. (1992). *Collaboration at the local level*. Merrimack, NH: Area Agency for Developmental Services, Region VI.

Place, P., & Gallagher, J. J. (1992). *Part H policy development for families: A case study report*. Chapel Hill, NC: Carolina Institute for Child and Family Policy.

Robison, S. D. (1990). *Putting the pieces together: Survey of state systems for children in crisis*. Denver: National Conference of State Legislatures.

Schein, E. (1988). *Process consultation: Its role in organizational development*. Reading, MA: Addison-Wesley Publishing Co.

United States General Accounting Office. (1992). *Integrating human services: Linking at risk families with services more successful than system reform efforts*. Washington, DC: Author.

25

Quality Assurance as a Tool for Change

Madeleine Kimmich and Valerie J. Bradley

If systems of support for people with developmental and other disabilities are to become a reality, then a major effort must be undertaken to transform quality assurance systems at the federal and state levels from potential obstacles to reform into vehicles for encouraging and enhancing the shift to supports. This task will require changes in both methods of monitoring and oversight and the conceptual framework that governs the vision of quality and, therefore, the content of quality assurance standards.

HISTORY

In order to understand the challenge that such a transformation entails, it is useful to review the context within which the standards that currently pertain in most states and at the federal level were developed. As noted in Chapter 2 (Bradley), quality assurance mechanisms have become highly formalized as the vision of quality has been increasingly equated with the provision of specialized services ranging over a continuum of settings. As a result, the service systems in most states are highly regulated and regimented, qualities that militate against individualization and self-determination.

The presence of such regulation also suggests, many times falsely, that compliance can, in fact, be equated with quality. The assumption that certification according to standards for intermediate care facilities for persons with mental retardation (ICFs/MR) means that quality programs are being provided was seriously questioned in a study by Reid, Parsons, Green, and Schepis (1991), reported by

Holburn (1992). The study involved 16 public residential facilities in 11 states and compared 48 ICF/MR–certified units with 12 noncertified units. According to Holburn, the following findings were reported:

> Time-sampled observations of residents involved in active treatment were obtained. Median percentages of time in active treatment were 16% for certified units and 21% for non-certified units. Even more disturbing were the graphic findings that during surveys interaction with residents and their access to leisure materials increased dramatically, then immediately dropped to presurvey levels when the surveyors left. (p. 135)

John Shea (1992) has an even more cynical view of the efficacy of rule-bound quality assurance practices:

> What . . . do we mean by *compliance with quality assurance standards*? As far as I can see, we typically mean that we expect others, in a servile or spineless fashion, at least for a day, to adhere to minimally adequate practices in institutions large and small. (p. 149)

Transforming quality assurance into a process that truly assures quality as it is newly envisioned requires inspecting the assumptions surrounding present conceptions of quality. From there the goals of quality assurance must be brought into closer alignment with the values of community inclusion and self-determination. The following questions about four key principles emerge:

1. Is the institution the appropriate frame of reference for judging the quality of community services?
2. Should professional judgments be used to define quality and customer progress?
3. Does centralized monitoring of uniform standards and use of punitive sanctions improve quality?
4. How strictly should staff skills be delineated?

Anti-Institutional Vision

To reorient quality assurance activities so that they are in line with the supports paradigm, it will be necessary not only to embrace the values that such a shift portends, but also to let go of a perspective that has driven the development of community services since the 1990s, that is, the notion that community programs are *alternatives* to institutions. The institutional alternative framework has shaped assumptions about service delivery and had a profound influence on the vision of quality.

That quality in the community has been defined in opposition to institutional conditions is apparent in both the rhetoric and the regulatory thrust from the 1980s into the 1990s. Major evaluations of community services, such as the study of deinstitutionalization at Pennhurst Developmental Center in Pennsylvania (Conroy & Bradley, 1985), have focused on the quality or effectiveness of community-based residential and day programs compared to services in the institution.

As more and more people have been placed into community programs, either because of court orders or state mandates, the fears of parents about the quality of community programs have been calmed by assertions that services in the community will be as good or better than those in the institution. This pledge can be found, for instance, in the language of the proposed settlement agreement in the five institutional class action lawsuits in Massachusetts ("Judge to End Role," May 19, 1993).

Federal policy, especially in the Medicaid HCB waiver program, has also been premised on the notion of avoiding use of institutions. In order to qualify for waiver funding, a state must certify that the recipient requires an "ICF/MR level of care." Through the strategic use of waiver funding, many states have significantly reduced their institutional populations. In the 10 years since the waiver went into effect in 1981 as part of the Omnibus Budget Reconciliation Act (PL 97-35), 49 state institutions have been closed, compared to only 13 closures in the 20 years that preceded the waiver (Lakin, Blake, Prouty, Mangan, & Bruininks, 1993). The trade-off, however, has been the application of standards—though better than those for ICFs/MR—that are still premised on the assumption that people with disabilities should reside and work in controlled, "alternative" environments.

A further reason why community programs have been evaluated in contrast to institutions has to do with the clientele of community programs. Statistics indicate that from 1973 to 1993, the number of people receiving publicly supported residential services has increased only by an average of about 1/2% per year (Gettings, 1992). Since the public institutional population declined precipitously during this same period, the growth in community programs is largely attributable to the movement of people from institutions, not by people coming from their own homes. In other words, community development during this time has been aimed significantly at providing alternatives to support deinstitutionalization. Thus, the quality of these programs has been assessed in terms of whether the services offered are superior to institutional care, and the norms that have been developed to measure outcomes have been based largely on institutional norms.

Continuing to think of quality in community services as the absence of institutional characteristics frustrates the development of resources that maximize community presence and inclusion. Rather than institutionally referenced notions, a vision of quality that is referenced to the lives and circumstances of people in general is needed. Such a vision will naturally raise issues such as choice, self-determination, and quality of life as envisioned by all citizens.

Realigning Quality Assurance Outcomes

Another traditional principle that has deterred the development of quality assurance for systems of supports is the reliance on professional and objective measures of outcomes. The deinstitutionalization focus noted above has given primacy to training, skills development, and active treatment. These activities in turn dictate a quality assurance system that measures outcomes in terms of scores on adaptive behavior scales. However, focusing on community membership places priority on individual determination and community presence. These aims lead logically to the measurement of outcomes in terms of the level of community involvement and the degree of individualization and customer satisfaction.

Quality assurance in the deinstitutionalization phase of service development not only focused on numerical measures of client progress but also emphasized the need for professional assessments of quality, including peer review and accreditation. This notion of professionally defined outcomes comes into direct conflict with a basic premise of the new supports paradigm, that is, that people with disabilities and their families should be participants in decisions about their futures and about the supports that will be required to realize their futures. In bringing quality assurance into line with these emerging participatory values, customer satisfaction should be a key ingredient in any comprehensive monitoring approach.

Learning and Enhancement

A further change in quality assurance that will foster the supports paradigm is the rejection of top-down, centralized, and heavily controlled monitoring and enforcement mechanisms. If it is assumed that the supports paradigm requires a creative and individualized approach to each person's possibilities, then such a system is best served by an open process of assessment in which learning and sharing information are priorities (Taylor, Bogdan, & Racino, 1991). In this environment, the application of uniform standards and punitive sanctions can only constrain the development of the collaborative relationships necessary to mobilize supports and to empower and support front-line staff. As noted by Holburn (1992):

> The natural reciprocity inherent in effective managing and teaching has been replaced by routine rule-based deficiency evaluations with ensuing corrective action to ameliorate the rule violations. . . . Despite our complex process of assessment, team meetings, plan development, monitoring and program documentation, very little new learning takes place. (pp. 138–139)

To retrieve this reciprocity and learning, the oversight process should be restructured to provide constructive feedback that enhances performance.

Renewed Interest in the Role of Staff

A legitimate area of examination that has been missing in most quality assurance systems has been the critical role that staff can play in facilitating the person's participation in his or her social, community, and/or work environment. When the aim of services was to teach and train, the skills required by staff could be more easily delineated. The role of facilitator and guide (as well as teacher in some instances) requires a different set of skills and sensitivities. A unitary focus on outcomes will provide a needed attention to the effectiveness of interventions but will not illuminate the variables in the interactions between staff and individual that contribute to or detract from such outcomes. If quality assurance is to serve an enhancement function, such an up close examination of what works and what does not work will be crucial to the dissemination of best practices.

Five Aspects of the New Quality Assurance

The traditional assumptions underlying current rule-bound quality assurance systems—the anti-institutional framework, reliance on professional judgments of client progress, centralized monitoring and enforcement, and strictly defined staff skills—need to be transformed to create systems that will nurture and support the view of quality as individualized, dynamic, and process-sensitive. A new foundation is needed for quality assurance activities, one that translates the reformulated assumptions into operational guidelines. Following are the five aspects of this new foundation:

1. The underlying philosophy of quality assurance must embrace enhancement as a complement to quality control elements.
2. The focus of quality assurance must move beyond process and input concerns to outcomes for individuals.
3. The role of the consumer and family must be central in the design, implementation, and ongoing maintenance of quality.
4. The vision of quality must be revisited at regular intervals rather than remaining static.
5. Quality assurance monitors should be given the discretion to respond to organizations and staff in a supportive and teaching role rather than a policing role.

The remainder of this chapter provides a description of the five operational areas in which changes are needed, with examples from specific state quality assurance efforts.

CHANGE IN PHILOSOPHY

As noted at the beginning of this chapter, the increasing formalization of quality assurance approaches in the 1970s and 1980s led to an accretion of regulations dominated by professional judgment, discretion, and control of the environments where people with developmental disabilities lived and worked. Where the supports paradigm is taking root, quality assurance is increasingly shifting from a protection orientation to an enhancement posture that is less controlling and that allows for individualized responses. This means greater focus on the primacy of choice and individuality rather than the application of blanket restrictions. Quality assurance is thus becoming less prescriptive and more of a learning experience where there are many right ways to accomplish what is needed.

Perhaps the best source of examples of this more individualized quality enhancement approach is the Community Supported Living Arrangement (CSLA) demonstration program funded through Medicaid. Many of the eight demonstration states have gone far beyond the statutory requirements to develop a wide range of enhancement approaches. For instance, Rhode Island's state office of quality assurance defines its role with respect to oversight of the CSLA program as follows: "[to] furnish training to members of the regional monitoring boards and others, . . . identify and recognize exemplary programs; and furnish technical assistance to provider agencies to enhance services" (Smith & Gettings, 1992, p. H-4). In a similar vein, Illinois quality assurance officials are conducting annual quality assurance and technical assistance visits to all CSLA agencies. The primary purpose of these visits is to "help local agencies to understand and fully implement the guiding values and principles of CSLA and current 'best practices' [quotation marks added] concepts" (Smith & Gettings 1992, p. E-5).

Changes now underway in Arizona's Medicaid waiver program also illustrate the movement toward enhancement rather than simply control. The Governor's Council on Developmental Disabilities and the Division of Developmental Disabilities are in the process of reducing the complexity of the licensing process by reducing over 300 standards to 30–40 mandatory requirements related to the physical safety of facilities and basic staff health and safety practices. Simultaneously, they are developing proactive review mechanisms to address other pressing issues that will no longer be addressed through licensure. In the meantime, state officials have revamped the licensing procedures to allow more discretion by licensing inspectors in interpreting agency compliance. These actions resemble Clarence Sundram's suggestion to "rediscover common sense" in quality assurance measurement (Sundram, 1992).

The approach taken by the Connecticut Department of Mental Retardation (DMR) represents a more mature example of the enhancement philosophy. In the late 1980s, DMR reduced its licensing process significantly and created a Service Quality Review process (SQR). The SQR process yields a report with detailed feedback but no specific recommendations, recognizing that enhancement changes should be designed by the agency itself. The SQR team is available to the agency to assist in redesign on request.

What is characteristic of all of these examples is that the emphasis on control has changed to more enhancement, but without the elimination of the quality control elements. There are and will always be threshold conditions that must be in place to ensure that the individual's safety and health are safeguarded. However, the process of guaranteeing the individual's health and safety should be clearly differentiated from programmatic oversight so that the necessary control does not negate the enhancement efforts.

CHANGE IN SUBSTANTIVE FOCUS

Along with less control and less punitive responses, emerging quality assurance mechanisms stress an outcome framework, geared to individually defined, person-centered goals to accompany—not simply replace—more traditional standards based on input (capacity), output (units of services), and process (paper compliance) standards.

Prominent among those groups moving to an outcome focus is the Accreditation Council (formerly ACDD), which has developed 30 consumer-specific outcome standards, and reduced the scope of organizational process standards from 685 to 16. To determine ratings on the outcome standards, reviewers make decisions about agency performance based on the experience and opinions of a sample of consumers. They focus on: 1) the importance of the particular outcome to the individual, 2) what the organization has done to help the individual achieve the outcome, and 3) if the outcome has not been achieved, what the organization is doing to move toward the outcome. Thus, outcomes are the primary focus, and process aspects are important only insofar as they support a desired outcome.

Since the 1980s many states have made important progress in integrating outcome measures into their quality assurance efforts, and several have made consumer-defined outcomes the primary focus. For instance, Utah conducts annual quality assurance surveys of providers based on interviews with consumers regarding their personal outcomes. The overall goal is full participation in community life, measured through four standards: 1) opportunities for personal growth and development compatible with the needs, choices, and goals of the individual; 2) program individualization especially through full participation of the individual in planning and implementation of the individualized program plan; 3) full participation in Utah life through opportunities to live, work, and associate with other people; and 4) the provider's own quality improvement plan.

Legislation in California provides another indication of the creation of accountability mechanisms based on outcomes. SB 1383, passed by the California legislature in 1992, requires the state Department of Developmental Services to develop performance contracts for the regional center system (the state's delivery mechanism for assessment, case management, and purchase of service) that are based on outcomes for people with disabilities and their families as measured by the customers themselves. The law also requires that 50% of regional center boards comprise people with developmental disabilities and their families.

CSLA sites again offer good examples of the changes that quality assurance can nurture. The focus of Illinois' CSLA monitoring is "principles of community inclusion, general quality of life, personal choice and empowerment, and independence in daily living and economic self-sufficiency" (Smith & Gettings, 1992, p. E-5). Florida's CSLA monitoring boards use their Supported Independent Living Quality of Life Outcome Measures as the exclusive assessment of the impact of services on consumers. Measures include such things as choice and control in housing, social inclusion, personal finances, and information sharing. Carrying outcomes to an even more personalized level, the Michigan CSLA program engages the consumer, during the individual support planning process, in choosing specific desired outcomes, which then become the focus for quality assurance activities, including not only monitoring of services but also, "identifying the necessary competencies of the individuals who will be furnishing supports to the consumer" (Smith & Gettings, 1992, p. G-6).

CHANGE IN THE ROLE OF THE CONSUMER AND FAMILY

To foster the supports paradigm, quality assurance must engage consumers and families in all aspects, from the definition of quality, to measurement of quality, to maintenance of quality. Inclusion of consumers and families in the design of quality assurance systems can ensure that the definition of quality is rooted in shared community values and mores and cultural sensitivity. In Michigan, consumers and families involved in the state's supported living efforts became active participants in preparing the CSLA proposal and continue to be involved as part of the governing board, which is made up entirely of consumers, families, and community members (excluding providers). In Rhode Island, regionalized CSLA monitoring boards have been developed and are administered by a statewide parent and consumer organization.

Consumers and family members are also involved in the interpretation of performance through the measurement of quality. This represents a significant change in the process of measurement. No longer does a professional simply go in to observe what is "done to" an individual. The new paradigm requires that the consumer and family be part of the monitoring team, acknowledging that they are a crucial source of assessment information. Citizen monitoring processes sponsored by Arcs have been in place for several years in many parts of the United States (see Bersani, 1990). In general, the approach employs volunteer teams of family members and consumers who conduct site visits to observe activities and interactions and to talk with staff and consumers. Only rarely, however, are the results of such citizen monitoring activities used as conscientiously and consistently by the state agency as are other sources of assessment information. Connecticut, however, does take the citizen view seriously. Its SQR process uses a volunteer team of consumers, family members, community members, and even other providers to visit a site to assess performance based on desired consumer outcomes. Agency participation in SQR is voluntary, but since it is taken seriously by regional contract managers, and since agencies have had positive learning experiences in participating, the demand for it is growing.

Even in places where consumers and families are not part of the monitoring teams, they are consistently a key source of monitoring information. As state systems have moved to a greater focus on consumer outcomes, they have recognized that no respondent can speak with greater authority than the consumer herself. Increasingly, states have adopted various types of consumer satisfaction surveys and quality of life surveys, all keyed in on the view of the consumer. Maryland is one good example. Its CSLA program provides for a Quality Assurance Review

Committee (QARC) for each individual, with membership determined by the individual and the CSLA agency. The QARC meets with participants to discuss the following simple set of questions: 1) Is your health and safety being provided for? 2) Are you getting the services named in your plan? 3) Are the services having the desired effect? and 4) Do all the services, taken together, make sense in the context of your needs and choices? Likewise, Colorado conducts a periodic consumer satisfaction survey that is administered by an independent, external organization.

There is a pervasive sense that the best way to approach consumers is through family members, friends, circle of support members, and the like. Consequently, as states have focused on consumer satisfaction and quality of life surveys, they have turned increasingly to people who play a role in the person's life to obtain the information. While Arc citizen monitoring teams have existed for many years, the new twist is that the focus of the team's interviewing work is the consumer himself; rather than using the team's view of what quality is, the new teams are striving to engage the consumer more fully in expressing exactly what she likes or does not like, what he aspires to do, and so forth, and then focusing on how the provider facilitates achievement of those personal goals. Officials in Michigan's CSLA program are serious enough about obtaining the consumer perspective that they plan to award a grant to "develop a curriculum to orient consumers, their designees, [and others] to the task of assessing consumer satisfaction with the quality of CSLA services" (Smith & Gettings, 1992, p. G-5). Florida's CSLA quality of life survey and the Accreditation Council's outcome-based performance measures are only two examples of methods that fully integrate the consumer perspective into quality measurement.

At the level of nurturing and enhancing quality, consumers and families have a major role to play. They should be kept informed about what has been done to reward or correct identified behavior, and they should be allowed to act on such information by choosing to live elsewhere or to be served by a different provider. This power, central to the CSLA demonstrations, is already being implemented (to varying degrees) in the demonstration states. In Rhode Island, for example, the state gives CSLA vouchers to individual consumers, who then choose their provider from among all the certified agencies in the state, not just from those in their local community. Here the power of consumers to choose providers makes them direct, rather than indirect, participants in creating quality.

The consumer and family role in pushing for higher quality services is not limited to CSLA demonstrations. In Oklahoma, where there is not a CSLA program, consumers choose among residential providers based on published results of an annual assessment of the programs. Volunteer teams of consumers and families, coordinated by consumer organizations, observe the sites and talk with staff and consumers about things valued by consumers such as the physical setting, the staff, regard for the individual, personal growth, and safety. These assessments are converted into "consumer ratings," which are made available on request to any consumers or family members.

In addition to being participants in quality assurance activities, people with disabilities and their families should also be involved in the oversight of agencies that provide services. One way of accomplishing this is to include customers on the governing boards of nonprofit organizations that receive public funds. While this is beginning to happen sporadically around the United States, the state of Illinois has moved one step further. The Illinois legislature passed a law requiring that all nonprofit entities in the state that receive public funding to provide services to people with disabilities have boards of directors whose membership is 50% family members and people with disabilities.

CHANGE IN THE NATURE OF QUALITY

Quality assurance should be premised on the notion that quality is not static and that any understanding of what it should be must be revisited over time. As Clarence Sundram put it, "Quality assurance is a journey, not a destination" (Sundram, 1992. p. 2). If quality is changeable, then measurements must be an ongoing process, not something that happens every year or 2. Quality assurance involves observation, followed by technical assistance, followed by observation, followed by technical assistance. In this context, annual licensure becomes an increasingly limited tool, as fewer and fewer aspects of the service or support are standardized.

Connecticut's Service Enhancement Training is a good example of an approach that acknowledges and supports the dynamic view of quality. The state makes its SQR staff available to agencies to lead discussions of what the system's values and mission mean to the staff in the organization and to help them develop more common decision-making. The process emphasizes that there is no one correct solution and that the application of particular values will change over time. As consumer situations change and staff experiences change, staff may find themselves interpreting inclusion and choice somewhat differently. The key is to keep communication channels open so that all in the agency are experiencing a similar evolution of values. In the common parlance of the new management thinkers this is referred to as a "learning organization."

CSLA quality assurance plans consistently embrace the dynamic view of quality. Just as services and supports are individualized, quality assurance concerns can also be individually tailored. Rhode Island notes that, "the exact nature of CSLA agency monitoring activities will vary, depending on the program participant and the nature of services contained in the ISP [individualized service plan]" (Smith & Gettings, 1992, p. H-4). This individualized approach to quality monitoring can work both for substantive as well as health and safety issues. For instance, New Hampshire's Home of Your Own Project (funded by the United States Administration on Developmental Disabilities), which supports home ownership among people with disabilities, has developed an agreement with the state licensing officials to allow for individually designed health and safety checklists in order to avoid licensing people's homes.

CHANGE IN ROLES OF FRONT-LINE STAFF

As quality assurance gives more attention to the views of consumers and families, it will also fundamentally alter the role of front-line staff. In order to give primacy to the consumer view, organizations must empower those in most direct contact with the consumer to enable them to respond to individual needs and desires. Such empowerment is alien to many on the front line, where managers have traditionally prescribed every action and circumscribed every decision. Now managers are saying to front-line staff that they should use their own judgment, learn from their experience, and risk being innovative. While such a shift gives front-line staff a sense of freedom and independent authority, it also can leave them somewhat fearful of the responsibility. It is incumbent upon the state to provide them with guidance and support to make this transition, and with access to knowledge to help them fill their new role.

No longer simply acting as police, the quality assurance monitor has to learn to be a helper, not one who blames, rather, one who shares the commitment to come up with a solution. Wisconsin's state quality assurance office has even moved away from the title "monitor," reserving that for compliance functions. Wisconsin now has "quality enhancers" or technical experts, who see their role as supporting the people in the field (local staff and providers) by being knowledgeable and accessible resource people. Their success is measured by the high demand for their services and by their sense of fulfillment in their work.

In terms of who best fills the role of "technical expert" or "quality assurer" or "quality assurance team member," Wisconsin uses state staff, Connecticut uses regional office staff, while Rhode Island argues that a friend or significant other of the consumer should be the key quality person, because this person has frequent contact with the individual and knows the individual intimately. The last view is held at many of the CSLA demonstration sites: "In many [of the CSLA] programs, the consumer and/or the consumer's representative is expected to be the primary monitor of services" (Smith & Gettings, 1992, p. 72). If consumers and others they select are to be the guardians of quality, they in turn need access to resources, including resource people, to make changes. In Michigan's CSLA program, the state agency trains consumers to use their Quality of Life tool and links the key quality assurance person to those with greater system knowledge and expertise in order to influence change.

SUMMARY

Many exciting changes are taking place in state quality assurance systems, including a focus on quality of life outcomes, consumer-specific measurement methods, and a reconceptualization of who should participate in the assessment of quality. Advocates of these new quality assurance approaches are not abandoning the basic moral responsibility that public developmental disabilities service systems have to ensure the well-being of people; rather, they are pointing to ways to enrich the process by encompassing the views of consumers and families.

The challenge for those attempting to transform quality assurance mechanisms so that they are in line with the assumptions described in this chapter is to make sure that the new approaches are not merely laid on top of the standards and regulations of the 1970s and 1980s. Simply grafting consumer responsive and enhancement-oriented methods on existing procedures is akin to saying that supported living is an expansion of the residential continuum. These best practices are not optional additions but should form the heart of a quality assurance system. To make room for the methods discussed here, collaborative efforts that involve customers, public officials, and providers should be mounted to review the continuing relevance of existing standards and licensing regulations in keeping with Sundram's "minimalist" approach. Unless current practices are substantially cut back, the addition of outcome-based activities will overwhelm current heavily regulated quality assurance systems.

Furthermore, a focus on enhancement activities will help to raise performance beyond the minimal, institution-referenced levels that characterize current control and sanction mechanisms. The development of community-referenced quality criteria will be greatly abetted by the increased role of consumers and families in both the definition and measurement of quality.

Another major challenge to those who are reforming quality assurance mechanisms is to maintain the dynamic character of quality assurance. This entails regarding judgments about service quality as temporal and open to change as performance and/or expectations change. This assumption has major implications for the operation and design of quality assurance systems. Specifically, formal procedures should be devised to trigger a periodic review of quality assurance criteria in order to ensure their continued relevance. The assumption also suggests that monitoring should take place more than once a year and that it should be based on the individual's unique circumstances and should involve those closest to the person.

No single state or service system has implemented all the five aspects of the new quality assurance; all are challenged to embrace additional changes. Change takes time, and, since change is the only thing that is sure, the process of finding and retaining new ways to assess and assure quality should be a continual process. To the extent that the views of people with disabilities and their families are at the center of any assessment, the continuing relevance and responsiveness of the process should be assured.

REFERENCES

Bersani, H.A. (1990). Family monitoring: Making sure a house is still a home. In V.J. Bradley & H.A. Bersani (Eds.), *Quality assurance for individuals with developmental disabilities: It's everybody's business* (pp. 77–91). Baltimore: Paul H. Brookes Publishing Co.

Conroy, J.W., & Bradley, V.J. (1988). *The five year longitudinal study of the court-ordered deinstitutionalization of Pennhurst*. Philadelphia: Human Services Research Institute.

Gettings, R.M. (1992, November). *Responding to a changing policymaking and programmatic environment*. Keynote address to the North Carolina Council on Community Mental Health.

Holburn, C.S. (1992). Rhetoric and realities in today's ICF/MR: Control out of control. *Mental Retardation, 30*, 133–141.

Judge to end role on care of retarded. (1993, May 19). *Boston Globe*, p. 4.

Lakin, K.C., Blake, E.M., Prouty, R.W., Mangan, T., & Bruininks, R.H. (1993). *Residential services for persons with developmental disabilities: Statistics and trends through 1991*. Minneapolis: University of Minnesota, Center for Residential Services and Community Living, Institute on Community Living.

Shea, J.R. (1992). From standards to compliance, to good services, to quality lives: Is this how it works? *Mental Retardation, 30*, 143–150.

Smith, G., & Gettings, R.M. (1992). *Medicaid in the community: The HCB waiver and CSLA programs*. Alexandria, VA: National Association of State Mental Retardation Program Directors.

Sundram, C.J. (1992, December). *Re-inventing quality: The role of quality assurance*. Keynote address to the 1992 Annual Meeting of the National Association of State Mental Retardation Program Directors, Alexandria, VA.

Taylor, S.J., Bogdan, R., & Racino, J.A. (Eds.). (1991). *Life in the community: Case studies of organizations supporting people with disabilities* (Vol. 1). Baltimore: Paul H. Brookes Publishing Co.

26

Managing Change Through Quality Enhancement

Making New Paradigms Work

James F. Gardner

The chapters in this book look at the changes that have taken place in the development of community alternatives for people with disabilities since the 1980s. The institutional population has declined from 194,659 in 1967 (Lakin et al., 1989) to 95,000 in 1988 (Braddock, Hemp, Fujiura, Bachelder, & Mitchell, 1989). The abiding principles of community inclusion and social participation have focused attention for future development on the community. The design and implementation of family support, supported employment, and supported living programs indicate that where people live or work depends upon the presence of supports.

These changes during the period from the mid-1970s to the late 1980s were incremental. In fact, much of the development of community programs consisted of the adaptation of institutional models within community settings. The reinvention of institutional modes of administration, clinical and educational practice, human resource management, and financial controls guided the growth of community-based services.

The institution was recreated in the half-way house, then the group home, and then the supervised apartment. While the physical setting was modified and the numbers of people residing together decreased, the organization and management models of the larger units remained (Gardner & Chapman, 1992; Smull & Bellamy, 1989). Community-based, nonprofit agencies that were set up in the 1980s and 1990s generally retained the management and organizational characteristics of the institutions. Centralization of authority, excessive formalism and layers of authority, and rigid control and supervision of staff characterized the service systems in both the institutional and community settings.

The new paradigm of supports, inclusion and participation, and individual choice and control will require new methods of administration and management. The hierarchical and authoritative management style and the centralized and formalistic structure is not compatible with decentralized, inclusive, support service programs. Service providers are searching for new modes of organization and management as services change.

Changes in the management of organizations consistent with the new paradigm must entail the realignment of the: 1) structural, 2) cultural, and 3) political systems of the organization. The management structure, the culture that binds people together, and the political coalitions that negotiate and bargain exist simultaneously within organizations. Strategic change efforts must address all three systems. Managing change in one system while ignoring the other two systems often results in organizational dysfunction. These systems must be balanced and mutually supportive rather than working at counter purposes.

THE STRUCTURAL DIMENSION

During the 1980s and 1990s the organizational structure of institutional models was reinvented in community settings. Organizations providing services to people with disabilities are commonly characterized by defined hierarchies of authority, centralized decision-making, and written policies and procedures. Human resource management, personnel supervision and evaluation, and some methods of staffing were adapted from institutional practice, which evolved in the industrial era. The field of human services is similar to other industrial and service sectors of American enterprise. Yet, as Savage (1990) noted, "Finely tuned bureaucracies with carefully defined policies, procedures, and job descriptions are no match for the next decade" (p. 65).

Formalism and Mechanistic Structure

Formalism refers to the extent of rules, policy, procedure, and regulation that have an impact on an organization. Formalism may be imposed by the outside environment, as in the case of government regulation. In contrast, organizations may design formalism into the operating structure to increase conformity and uniformity. The degree of formalism, whether internal or external in origin, is related to variables such as organization size; complex technology; vulnerable populations; and uncertain, yet critical, external forces. Thus, nuclear power plants, air traffic control systems, and blood banks have more rules and procedures than studio lofts for artisans and self-employed consultants.

The term "high reliability organization" has been applied to organizations in which mistakes or accidents can have catastrophic consequences. These high reliability organizations have internal control systems characterized by high degrees of formalism. They stress reliability more than efficiency or flexibility (Perrow, 1984). Hospitals, large residential institutions, and many community service programs for people with disabilities have organizational structures that are designed to promote high reliability.

In addition to formalism, the high reliability organization stresses centralization, clear hierarchy of authority, vertical communication, and task specialization. Organizations with these characteristics are also considered mechanistic. Burns and Stalker (1961) found that mechanistic organizations generally were large, employed a routine technology, emphasized efficiency, and existed in stable environments. The management feedback system consisted of functional structure, bureaucratic control, formal reporting, and information systems. The decision-making model was one of rational analysis. There was an articulated, though often missing, goal of cooperation between units. Burns and Stalker found little innovation in mechanistic organizations.

Mintzberg (1989) described an extremely mechanistic organization as a machine organization designed to eliminate surprises and uncertainty. The characteristics of the machine organization are listed below:

- Rules and regulation pervade the organization.
- Power is focused at the top of the organization.
- Hierarchy and line of authority are primary concerns.
- Uncertainty is minimized to minimize interruption.
- Control is an obsession.
- As a closed system, it is immune to external influence.

Mintzberg also noted the similarity between machine organizations and professional bureaucracies. While the professional bureaucracy decentralizes power among the professionals in the organization, the norms and rules of the profession perform the same function as the rules and regulations of the machine organization. The impact of both professional bureaucracies and machine organizations on people with disabilities and support staff is similar. Both types of organizational structures produce an intended conformity and control (Heffron, 1989).

The machine and professional models of organizational structure enhance the ability of organizations to develop uniform responses to significant situations. Unfortunately, their limitations are grounded in their successes. Machine and professional bureaucratic models of structure function as performance systems. They are designed for repetition and productivity. Performance systems do not promote problem-solving, adaptation, or innovation (Segal, 1974; Skrtic, 1987).

Organizations providing services to people with disabilities display many of the characteristics of machine and professional bureaucracies. From this perspective, the interdisciplinary team/individual habilitation program planning process represents an attempt to minimize uncertainty, risk, and idiosyncratic behavior. This focus on stability, predictability, and control in structural design is an outgrowth of assumptions about people with disabilities. When people with disabilities are viewed as essentially vulnerable as a group, structural design will promote protection at the expense of innovation.

Organic Control Models

Successful implementation of the new supports paradigm will require the adaptation of new structural designs that promote innovation and provide protection. An alternative to machine and professional bureaucracies is a structural design based on organic controls. Burns and Stalker (1961) described organic systems in the following words:

> [Organic systems are] characterized by fluid, nonhierarchic structures, with authority based on knowledge, competence, and expertise rather than hierarchical position. They have a "network structure of control, authority, and communication," and the content of communication consists of information and advice rather than instructions and decisions. (p. 120)

Organic control models would accommodate change and diversity offered by support programs and services in inclusive settings where task and technology will vary with individual need. Organic controls emphasize management through norms and values rather than rules alone. Organic systems stress face-to-face communication, and innovation may originate in the centers and corners of the organization. The decision process incorporates trial and error procedures and the organization tolerates conflict between work units as a cost for innovation and creativity (Robbins, 1990). Most important, an organic management structure would decentralize decision-making among employees, increase consumer autonomy, and decrease the relative role of the professional.

Mechanistic, professional bureaucratic, and organic systems are models of organizational structure. In reality, organizations seldom exhibit all the characteristics of a single model. However, the shift in paradigms in human services does suggest a shift from the mechanistic to the organic control system. This change mirrors larger trends in business and industry. Kanter (1989) indicated that managers are "watching hierarchy fade away and the clear distinction of title, task, department, and even corporation, blur" (p. 85).

The difference between how mechanistic and how organic control systems would affect anticipated changes that support the new paradigm can be explored through examination of two sets of variables (Daft, 1992). Contextual dimensions describe macro variables in the environment that influence the choice of internal control processes. The contextual dimensions determine the structural variables by which the organization is managed. Both contextual dimensions and structural variables will influence the adaptation of the new paradigm.

Following are the key contextual (Daft, 1989) dimensions that will lead to either mechanistic or organic control:

- *Environment* The elements outside the organized system of supports and services constitute environment. Natural environments are less certain and controlled than organizationally directed environments. Simple and stable environments are associated with low uncertainty. Mechanistic structures work best in these circumstances.

Organic systems are better adapted for more complex and less certain environments. Decentralized decision-making, horizontal communication, and leadership from within the organization increase adaptability in less certain environments.

- *Size* Smaller size and decentralized locations provide opportunities for organic controls that are more difficult to make workable in large organizations.
- *Technology* Individual choice, recognition of differences, and advances in technology will result in the provision of constantly changing, nonroutine technologies for supports and service. The utilization of nonroutine technology is promoted by organic structures.
- *Goals* Performance goals of productivity and uniformity favor a mechanistic control model. Goals related to individuality, adaptation, and problem-solving are promoted by organic control structures.

The primary structural variables (Daft, 1989) that will be involved in the adaptation of the new paradigm are internal structure, communication, and feedback and control. Following are elaborations on these.

- *Structure* Supports and services arising in the new paradigm should, by conscious design, contain less formalization, specialization, and standardization. Formalization, defined as the amount of written documentation, rules, and procedures, will decrease due to smaller size, personal methods of communication and control, and the implementation of nonroutine technology that varies from person to person. Specialization and standardization will decrease as the size of organized work units shrinks and staff duties and responsibilities increase in scope and sophistication.
- *Communication* There will be a shift from formal information systems to face-to-face communication and from vertical communication patterns to horizontal communication patterns. Computer technology will increase information storage and transmission, while the analysis of information is conducted by paid and unpaid advocates, friends, and service representatives.
- *Control* Organizational control will shift from forms of hierarchy, rules and regulations, and policy and procedure to controls of shared values, commitment, and tradition.

Organizational structure in the new paradigm will appear and function differently than in machine and professional bureaucracies. Organizational theory (Daft, 1992) suggests that different contextual variables should cause different organizational structures. When organic controls are used, they should not be mistaken for sloppy or ill conceived controls. Though the organic structure may look and function differently, it must maintain health and safety, prevent abuse and neglect, and maintain public support.

The structure of an organization should develop from its function or strategy. The function of community-based service and support programs is different from that of the state hospital or residential institution. However, the organizational practice of the community-based program remains rooted in the institutional model. This phenomenon is not unique to human services. Structure generally lags behind strategy (Davis, 1987).

A number of authors have pointed to the rise of new management structures in the post-industrial era. Davis (1987) noted that the mission, objectives, and strategy of a business in a mature industrial context will always be ahead of organizational structure. Davis explained, "We have industrially modeled organizations running postindustrial businesses. It is no wonder that we manage our way to economic decline" (1987, p. 6). Savage (1990) declared that the organizational assumptions and values of the industrial era are "bankrupt" (p. 65). Mills (1991) also attacked the conventional structural hierarchies as being too costly and too slow. Corporate bureaucracies and bloated hierarchies "slow responsiveness, suppress innovation, crush aspirations and retard productivity" (p. 12). The new paradigm in human services calls for new structures. The movement toward organic models is but a beginning.

THE CULTURAL DIMENSION

The change involved in a paradigm shift that centers attention on the goals and requirements of the person with a disability requires a fundamental shift in organizational culture. Culture can be defined as a set of shared values, beliefs, expectations, norms, and assumptions. Organizational culture (Duncan, 1989) is learned, shared, and transmitted, and it can be altered. Paradigms exist within the context of culture. Paradigm shifts will occur when organizational cultures are transformed (Chin & Benne, 1985). The current paradigm shift in services to people with developmental disabilities involves four significant changes in organizational culture. The changes are intimately connected with the quality of services. These changes are the empowerment of people who provide supports and services, the emergence of communities of learning within service and support systems, an evolution of new models of staff development from within the systems, and the definition of quality as continuous improvement.

Empowerment of People Who Provide Supports and Services

The empowerment of people with disabilities will occur only when organizations empower the people who provide supports and services. This change in the role and responsibility of the service worker defines the quality improvement movement in service areas. Albrecht and Zemke (1985) noted, "The organization exists to support the people who serve the customer. It has no other meaning, no other purpose" (p. 105). Zeithaml, Parasuraman, and Berry (1990) define empowerment as "pushing decision making down to the lowest levels of the company. It means granting contact personnel the authority to make important decisions about serving customers" (p. 105). One Malcolm Baldridge National Quality Award examiner (Garvin, 1991), commenting on the relationship between quality and employee empowerment, remarked, "Empowerment is in the eyes of the empowered. It's that simple" (p. 92).

Empowerment is associated with two additional characteristics that pertain to the new paradigm. The first is the need to take out layers and flatten the organization.

The second characteristic (Port & Carey, 1991) is that the "traditional American bureaucratic command and control style of management" (p. 8) is becoming a "high profile" (p. 8) victim of quality management insights. Handy (1990) refers to the organizations emerging through the new paradigm as "cultures of consent" (p. 166) where authority will be earned by an ability to help others do the job better. Xerox redefined the role of the manager from providing one-to-one supervision by telling, planning, and controlling, to being a team leader, who teaches, coaches, and facilitates.

In winning the Baldridge Award, Xerox Business Products and Services (1989) identified the following as indicators of excellence in customer satisfaction:

- Front-line employee empowerment
- Strategic infrastructure support for front-line employees
- Attention to hiring, training, attitude, and morale of front-line employees

This concern about the need for employees who can take responsibility, manage themselves, and meet customer expectations is making inroads even in the fast food industry (Schlesinger & Heskett, 1991). Through better interview and selection processes, focused and ongoing training programs, and job redesign, this industry is finding that traditional low-paying, high-turnover, poor-morale positions can be upgraded.

Communities of Learning

Defining quality as conformity with customer requirements and empowering direct staff to achieve that conformity may cause some initial discomfort for professionals. The context, content, and location for decision-making will shift to a nonprofessional dimension. This new dimension will provide fewer cues for deliberation and less clear prompts from past professional training and practice. Professionals will be called upon to perform tasks and make decisions for which they may have no direct experience.

New tasks and new decisions will not be as important, however, as defining new purposes. Academic training and the norms and practice of the professions identify the unambiguous purpose for professional practice. Training and professions also define the institutional and social context within which the purposes are fulfilled. The process of professionalization simplifies complexity and ambiguity through the design of standardized responses that represent the traditions and conventions of the various professions (Kuhn, 1970; Schein, 1972; Skrtic, 1987). This leads to the pigeonholing phenomenon wherein the professional defines the unique situations in terms of one of the standardized responses. In this way individuals with disabilities can be matched to an available slot. The new paradigm requires new thinking to sort through the complexity, uncertainty, and value conflicts that arise in professional practice. Professionals are challenged in the new paradigm to work with individuals on the individuals' terms, not theirs.

The new paradigm offers the opportunity for new forms of learning. Schon (1983) recognized that the technical rationality derived from academic training and professional norms must permit opportunities for active reflection. This reflection enables the individual to adapt knowledge and experience to new and unique circumstances, to think and then act on the basis of experience.

In the new paradigm professionals will describe their work less in terms of discipline and more in terms of "experience, trial and error, intuition, and muddling through" (Schon, 1983, p. 43). The new paradigm offers opportunities for finding new approaches by reflecting on the knowledge and experience of the past.

Senge (1990) has examined learning and reflection within the context of organizational learning. He concludes that most organizations are unable to, or incapable of, learning about their environments. More important, they are unable to examine themselves so that they can grow and respond to the complex world around them. Senge described the individual growth and organizational transformation that results from learning, and Savage (1990) defined organizational capacity for continued learning as one of the primary challenges of the next decade.

Senge connected individual and organizational learning with systems and structure. He noted that organizational structure influences individual behavior and culture. He wrote, "When placed in the same system, people, however different, tend to produce similar results" (Senge, 1990, p. 42). He warned that, because all participants are situated in a social or organizational system, they are part of the feedback process. They cannot exist outside the system as observers. This has significant cultural implication for the organization operating under the new paradigm. Both people with disabilities and other people providing services and supports can learn from the same experiences. All people share responsibility for difficulties and challenges brought about by the social or organizational system of which they are a part. Neither provider nor consumer can exist independently from the system.

This approach to experiential learning on the part of people with disabilities and those providing services and supports is consistent with organic forms of organizational control. The emphasis on reflection and learning through experience is consistent with the major thrusts of the new paradigm, that is, social inclusion, choice, participation, and community orientation.

In addition to finding solutions by reflecting on past experience and through organizational learning, practitioners can also approach the new paradigm as an opportunity for reframing. Frame flipping enables people to see situations through different perspectives. When rigid hierarchies and role and task specialization decrease, participants in social and organizational systems are able to examine a situation as others might see it. An educator can examine a situation from the perspective of a parent, a student, or an administrator. Support staff can analyze an event as a neighbor, an employer, a therapist, or as an advocate. Reframing (Bolman & Deal, 1984) promotes flexibility but protects commitments to core values. Handy (1990) noted, "Upside-down thinking, reframing, is largely a habit of mind. Those that want to learn in life, and to change comfortably, need to practice it" (p. 68).

New Models of Staff Development

Active reflection and reframing provide opportunities for new models of staff development. Mentoring emphasizes learning through experience. But learning and changing are never certain. Mentoring enables some learners to write off occasional mistakes as experience. The knowledge acquired through solving problems results in new insights and leadership capabilities (Kouzes & Posner, 1987). The mentoring process in the new paradigm develops leadership within the experiential learning community. Bennis (1989) has noted that leaders encourage dissent and tolerate error because future leaders emerge from the crucible of reflection upon failure. He has indicated the need for organizations to serve as mentors and to "provide potential leaders with the opportunity to learn through experience in an environment that permits growth and change" (p. 182).

Continuous Quality Improvement

Guided growth and learning through experience, active reflection, and empowerment of staff indicate that quality in the new paradigm is not static, especially in human services where the goal is to support and promote personal change. Quality improvement is an ongoing process because customer requirements change and evolve. Staff abilities to meet those requirements change as they learn through experience. Albrecht and Zemke (1985) have indicated that the quality of service is determined at the point when the service is rendered. Service quality cannot be stockpiled. It cannot be recalled for repair. Quality has to be achieved again and again in each support and service transaction.

The focus on continuous quality improvement requires that habilitation and rehabilitation services and supports be redefined as customer service. As such, the habilitation process does not become an end in itself. The responsibility of employees is not, for example, to provide 6 hours of vocational training or prepare a meal. The responsibility of the employee is to assist the individual with a disability in meeting his or her goals. In a similar manner, the job of the restaurant server or the car mechanic is not simply to serve a meal or fix a car. These employees' job is to satisfy the customer.

Finally, the conceptualization of human service as customer service means that there is a partnership in the service and support relationship. Staff in both aspects recognize mutual responsibilities and rights.

THE POLITICAL DIMENSION

The structural and cultural dimensions of organizational change reflect a rational approach. They rest on the premise that decision-makers have some discretion in choosing structure and culture. The political dimension of organizations can operate in an oppositional mode. Pfeffer (1978) has characterized the political process in organizations as coalitions of interests negotiating the division of power and resources.

Structure and Political Process

Organizational goals and decisions result from the process of political bargaining. From this perspective, structural decisions are reflections of political process. Dominant coalitions influence the choice for the organizational structure that furthers their interests. The range of choices is constrained by the realities of contextual variables of size, goals, technology, and external environment. However, the predominant coalition can influence the organization's choice through the planning and goal-setting process, the organization's choice of technology, the allocation of rewards, the control of information, and other organizational processes in which it has a vested interest (Cohen & Bradford, 1990).

The process of negotiation by coalitions and individuals occurs more frequently when organizations confront ambiguous goals, scarce resources, changing technology and environment, nonprogrammed decisions, and organizational change (Van Fleet, 1991). Goals in organizations often have different meanings for different organizational units. Organizational structures frequently reflect the outcome of repeated power struggles involving coalitions of internal and external players. Coalitions and individuals attempt to resolve differences over these issues through the political process.

Paradigm Shifts and Political Process

Shifts in paradigms may intensify activity in the political dimension. Without proper understanding and planning, the consensus in the structural and human resource dimension can be undone by the attending political chaos. The chaos in the political frame can be overt and direct as well as covert and indirect. Overt, direct political activity is manifest in commonly used techniques. These include the use of expert power, control of information flow, control of the agenda, appeal to authority through the hierarchy, and image control.

Covert, indirect political process is often attributed to individual employee resistance to change. The actions of individuals resisting change may actually be governed by the norms and rules of informally sanctioned political games. Allison (1971) described the characteristics of games within structural bureaucracies as interactions governed by rules:

> Some rules are explicit, others implicit. Some rules are quite clear, others fuzzy. Some are very stable; others are ever changing. But the collection of rules, in effect, defines

> the game. First, rules establish the positions, the paths by which men gain access to positions, the power of each position, the action channels. (p. 170)

Allison also indicated that the rules define the range of acceptable decisions and actions. Finally, rules define the acceptable tactics such as bargaining, persuasion, deceit, and bluff while declaring other behaviors as inappropriate.

One example of a political game in a hierarchical structure that may be of particular importance to human services organizations during paradigm shifts is the Lording game (Kanter, 1977), in which those who are powerless tend to focus and concentrate their power needs "on those over whom they have a modicum of authority. There is a displacement of control downward" (p. 189). This would be manifest in direct service staff feeling powerless and, as a result, exercising increasing control and direction over people with disabilities.

This and other political games such as empire building, budget maximizing, appeal to expertise, and insurgency by lower status staff can appear as individually motivated and irrational acts. In reality, they are socially sanctioned through group norms. Too often, organizations attempt to control game behavior though individual supervision.

Minimizing Political Process Through Structure and Culture

Some conflict, particularly conflict over goals and ideas, may be healthy and contribute to positive organizational growth. But conflict from political process can inhibit organizational growth by preventing open and clear problem identification, analysis, and solution.

The reality of scarce resources, changing goals, uncertain and changing technology, and external environments means that the potential for conflict is present in most developmental disabilities services organizations. Some degree of political activity and conflict are to be expected. The role of leadership in managing the transition to new paradigms is to minimize, rather than eliminate, conflict.

Choices about organizational structure and culture can determine the role of political process in organizations. Organizational structure can encourage political behavior when it creates units or departments that are organized around occupations or professions that then function as interest groups. Individual units of psychologists, social workers, or rehabilitation specialists, for example, attempt to promote their collective self-interest through an increase in prestige, power, resource allocation, and material rewards (Heffron, 1989).

Political activity and conflict can be minimized through participative management strategies that result in a greater balance in power within structural hierarchies. The greater balance results in less opportunity to engage in unilateral political activity. Following are five empowering strategies identified by Kanter (1977):

1. Flatten the hierarchy. This spreads formal authority to the lower levels of the organization. It also increases contact between managers.

2. Decentralize decision-making. This empowers others besides those at the top of the hierarchy.
3. Assign responsibility to teams. Work teams can dilute the power of the hierarchy.
4. Increase access to information. Access to information once reserved for high level decision-makers empowers lower-level employees and work teams.
5. Provide mentors and sponsors for lower-level employees. Linking lower-level staff to prominent senior members of the organization can increase the speed of career mobility.

STRATEGIES TO GUIDE AND IMPLEMENT CHANGE

Managing change across three organizational systems can be enhanced by the selection of strategies that are consistent with each other, are mutually reinforcing, and apply to all three systems. The search for change strategies to enhance new paradigms is a universal phenomenon. Huey (1991) warned in *Fortune* magazine that victims of paradigm shifts litter recent history, for example, buggy makers who scoffed at Ford's smelly exhaust, candle makers who never saw the light in Edison's bulb, and Swiss crafts people who failed to hear the ticking threat of Japanese digital watches.

This search for new methods of conducting business during changing times has become a national undertaking. Throughout the United States, the production and service sectors are searching for ways to increase quality and remain competitive. The 1990s is being heralded as the decade of quality. Quality is no longer an abstraction. Quality has emerged as potentially "the biggest competitive issue of the late 20th and early 21st centuries" (Shepard, 1991, p. 4). The internationalization of the economy and the continuing recession have focused attention on the quality of American goods and services. In turn, directors and managers are searching for methods to increase organizational effectiveness and quality.

The contemporary concern for quality reflects a concern about the decrease in global competitiveness of the United States economy. The interest in organizational effectiveness also represents a continuation of an earlier effort in organizational development. During the 1950s and 1960s efforts to improve organizational effectiveness were clustered under the rubric of organizational development (Chin & Benne, 1985). Organizational development emerged after World War II as a systematic and planned effort to improve organizational effectiveness by increasing the capability of small work groups to solve problems and interact (Koontz & Weihrich, 1990). Organizational development was, in part, influenced by a determination to prove that democratic societies could conduct planned change efforts without the ideology and excesses from both the right and the left. Total quality management contains many of the major characteristics of organizational development. The most significant similarity between quality improvement and organizational development is that they represent a total system effort of planned improvement. Following are other common characteristics:

- The generation of planned change
- A requirement of top management support
- A long range strategic view
- The importance of fundamental change in organizational culture
- The management of change through small work groups
- The importance of data-based decisions

The leading proponents of total quality management, Juran (1985, 1986, 1988, 1989) and Deming (1982, 1986), long familiar to Japanese business and industry, have developed a following in the United States since the early 1970s. Their work, and that of other quality theorists and practitioners, is now appearing in the management literature from human services (Albin, 1992; Lubeck & Davis, 1991; Sandow, Rhodes, Mank, Ramsing, & Lynch, 1990). In addition, the analysis of quality in the service sector (Albrecht, 1988; Albrecht & Zemke, 1985; Parasuraman, Berry, & Zeithaml, 1991; Rosander, 1989; Zeithaml et al., 1990) is beginning to generate a more specialized knowledge base with direct and immediate application to the organization and management of supports and services for people with disabilities.

The quality enhancement literature does offer a number of guides for the successful implementation of the new paradigm in human services. Following are descriptions of principles from total quality management that have a direct application to the design of administrative and management structures that will support the new paradigm.

Define the Customer

Support and service programs respond to many constituencies. State funding agencies, licensing and certification agencies, accreditation organizations, advocacy organizations, parent groups, and zoning boards make demands on the organization. Focusing on the individual with a disability as the primary customer can be difficult when confronted with the presence of state bureaucracy, organized advocacy, and parent groups.

However, the person with the disability must be the primary customer, even if a third party makes the payment. This separation of payer from service user does decrease the power of the service user and increase the power of the payer and service provider. Nonetheless, quality from the perspective of the user of services is paramount. Quality in the new paradigm will require a clear and consistent focus on outcomes of quality for individuals with disabilities.

Meet Customer Goals and Expectations

Supports and services must be designed and delivered around individual goals, aspirations, and needs. The type, time and duration, and location of the support and services should be determined by individual customer need and not the convenience of an organization or individual service provider.

This requires involved, personal, and continuous discussion, assessment, and planning. Thinking in the new paradigm must also reflect the difference between outcomes for individuals and those for habilitation programs, supports, and other educational and clinical services that are intended to produce the outcome.

Traditional service and support programs frequently confuse the means and the ends, and means become ends in themselves. For example, individuals with disabilities continue to participate in activity/training programs that focus on preparation. The tasks of "preparing for" become outcomes, and programs end up assisting individuals in increasing efficiency and effectiveness in preparing for activities.

Clarify the Mission

Based upon customer needs and expectations, a mission statement must be developed. The mission statement ensures that the organization pursues the right goals. Once the organization has established the right goals, it can pursue them efficiently and effectively. However, a focus on efficiency and effectiveness without the right goals may mean that organizations become more efficient and effective at doing the wrong thing. For example, some organizations provide very good vocational training programs for people who prefer supported or independent employment.

Quality Must Be Built-In

Quality must be built into the support and service process from the beginning. Quality results from a proactive system of quality design rather than a system of inspection. Compliance enforcement does not beget quality. Inspection may reveal instances of nonconformity to standards and expectations, but it will not yield quality. Few service organizations have ever inspected their way to quality. The few that did achieve quality through inspection incurred costs so prohibitive that the organizations ceased to exist. Standards are performance measures. They indicate an expected level of performance from individuals and programs. They must be incorporated into the system of service and support in the beginning.

The concern for quality can be found in the structure, culture, and political process of the organization. The organizational structure should be such that it stresses the role of the individual with a disability. Communication, planning, feedback, coordination, and other structural design variables should enhance the process of decision-making and control for the individual with a disability.

Values, norms, assumptions, and mental models in the culture must be derived from the mission of meeting the goals and aspirations of the person with a disability. Finally, when political issues surface, people with disabilities should have sufficient power to negotiate coalitions and make decisions.

Quality Is a Top Management Responsibility

Deming (1982) indicated, "All significant, long-lasting quality improvements must emanate from top management's commitment to improvement" (p. 281). The problem of quality is frequently defined as the inability of top management to put adequate resources on the *front* line. Leaders must demonstrate a commitment to quality in their attitude, actions, and attention to detail. The minute the responsibility for quality is delegated, it assumes a secondary importance.

In addition, quality is a leadership responsibility rather than a management task. Quality is an organization-wide phenomenon that pervades the structural, cultural, and political dimensions of the organization. The leader conveys the meaning and importance of quality.

Quality Requires Continuous Improvement

Change and improvement must be continuous and all-encompassing. Quality in a service setting exists at the moment the service is rendered. It does not exist before or after the exchange. Unlike a product, a service cannot be stockpiled, inspected ahead of time, or recalled because of a defect. As the expectations and the goals of the individual with a disability change, the requirements for quality change.

Managers Evolve from Supervisors to Team Leaders

The role of the manager must change from providing one-to-one supervision to serving as a team leader. Teaching, coaching, and facilitating replace telling, planning, and controlling. Individual workers are authorized to assume greater responsibility.

Quality Improvement Must Ward Off Undermining by Departmentalization

The quality movement strives to integrate efforts across subsystems. Deming (1986) urged organizations to scale back the barriers between departments. Departments or functional units in organizations (e.g., residential, clinical, or vocational services, or engineering, manufacturing, or accounting) often serve as corporate foxholes or silos where individuals and work units hide to escape the process of change. Very often, functional units define quality in terms of output or process within the unit and ignore the goals at the center of the system. Quality results are achieved by integrated efforts across functional units. Volunteers, senior management, the business office, the board of directors, and service staff must interact cooperatively to meet customer requirements.

In the changing paradigm, the person with a disability becomes the primary customer. People providing supports and service strive to meet the individual's requirements. However, the people providing the supports and services also become customers. Each functional unit within the organization defines itself as either a service provider or a customer for every exchange. As such, individuals and units within the organization have clear responsibilities to meet the requirements of others in the organization. In order to fulfill their responsibilities, their requirements must be met by the organization. The service personnel become the primary internal customers. Upper- and mid-level management are employed to provide resources and meet the customer requirements of the service personnel.

A Focus on Norms and Values

The focus on norms and values appears in the quality literature as Deming's (1986) call to "adopt a new philosophy." The Maryland Center for Quality and Productivity (1991) defines total quality management as "both a philosophy and a set of techniques to consistently meet internal and external customer requirements in every transaction" (p. 3).

The new paradigm in human services represents a fundamental shift in the norms and values associated with services and supports for people with disabilities. Organizational change to the new paradigm will require fundamental shifts in the norms and values of the organization.

A Focus on Small Groups

Previous work in making planned change stressed the importance of small work groups (French & Bell, 1984). Recognizing the pervasive influence of group norms on individual behavior, social and behavioral scientists targeted small groups for change.

The work group approach is evident in the quality movement's (Scholtes, 1989) emphasis on team participation and involvement in the quality improvement program. Harrington (1987) noted the importance of departmental and interdepartmental quality improvement teams. Xerox's successful effort to win the Baldridge award in 1989 was based on its ability to train all 100,000 employees to serve as members of cross-cutting problem-solving teams.

The new paradigm of supports in human services rests on the identification and operation of small groups that plan and provide supports and services. These groups and teams will, perhaps, be less formal and structured than the traditional interdisciplinary teams. However, the teams will assume greater importance in decision-making as the structure and rules of the formal system become less dominant.

CONCLUSION

Shifts in paradigms imply a fundamental re-examination of basic assumptions about how the world operates. As such, paradigms influence the operation of whole systems. Organizational structure, culture, and political behavior are altered during paradigm shifts. To expect a change in culture and political behavior without allowing a change in the structural dimension is to ignore previous experience in paradigm shifts.

The paradigm shift in the provision of services and supports to people with disabilities is addressing many of the issues that have also emerged as key elements in the total quality management movement. Flattened hierarchies, a focus on customer-driven services, motivated and empowered service staff, management by norms and values, an emphasis on work teams, and quality as a design issue suggest that the shifting paradigm in the field of disability is part of a larger paradigm shift that is also influencing the worlds of physics, biology, business, and art.

Paradigm shifts depend upon planned organizational change. In fact, the pace of the shift to the supports paradigm will depend upon how effective key leaders prove to be in guiding their organizations through the difficult structural, cultural, and political dimensions of change.

REFERENCES

Albin, J. (1992). *Quality improvement in employment and other human services: Managing for quality through change*. Baltimore: Paul H. Brookes Publishing Co.

Albrecht, K. (1988). *At America's service*. New York: Warner Books, Inc.

Albrecht, K., & Zemke, R. (1985). *Service America: Doing business in the new economy.* New York: Warner Books.

Allison, G. (1971). *Essence of decision: Explaining the Cuban missile crisis*. Boston: Little, Brown.

Bennis, W. (1989). *On becoming a leader.* Reading, MA: Addison-Wesley.

Bolman, L.G., & Deal, T.E. (1984). *Modern approaches to understanding and managing organizations*. San Francisco: Jossey-Bass.

Braddock, D., Hemp, R., Fujiura, G., Bachelder, L., & Mitchell, D. (1989). *Public expenditures for mental retardation and developmental disabilities in the United States: State profiles (3rd ed.: FY 1977–88. A working paper)*. Chicago: Institute for the Study of Developmental Disabilities.

Burns, T., & Stalker, G.M. (1961). *The management of innovation*. London: Tavistock.

Chin, R., & Benne, K.D. (1985). General strategies for effecting changes in human systems. In W.G. Bennis, K.D. Benne, & R. Chin (Eds.), *The planning of change* (4th ed.) (pp. 22–45). New York: Holt, Rinehart & Winston.

Cohen, A.R., & Bradford, D.L. (1990). *Influence without authority.* New York: John Wiley & Sons.

Daft, R.L. (1992). *Organization theory and design* (4th ed.). New York: West Publishing.

Davis, S.M. (1987). *Future perfect*. Reading, MA: Addison-Wesley.

Deming, W.E. (1982). *Quality, productivity, and competitive position*. Cambridge: MIT Center of Advanced Engineering Study.

Deming, W.E. (1986). *Out of the crisis*. Cambridge, MA: MIT Press.

Duncan, W.J. (1989). Organizational culture: "Getting a fix" on an elusive concept. *The Academy of Management Executive, 3*(3), 229–236.

French, W.L., & Bell, C.H. (1984). *Organization development: Behavioral science interventions for organization development*. Englewood Cliffs, NJ: Prentice Hall.

Gardner, J.F., & Chapman, M.S. (1992). Staffing issues in the early 21st century: Labor supply, program models, and technology. In L. Rowitz (Ed.), *Mental retardation in the year 2000* (pp. 299–315). New York: Springer-Verlag.

Garvin, D.A. (1991). How the Baldridge award really works. *Harvard Business Review, November–December,* 80–93.

Handy, C. (1990). *The age of unreason.* Boston: Harvard Business School Press.

Harrington, H.J. (1987). *The improvement process: How America's leading companies improve quality.* New York: McGraw-Hill.

Heffron, F. (1989). *Organization theory and public organizations: The political connection.* Englewood Cliffs, NJ: Prentice Hall.

Huey, J. (1991, September 23). Nothing is impossible. *Fortune,* pp. 134–40.

Juran, J.M. (1985, November). Catching up: How the West is doing. *Quality Progress,* pp. 18–22.

Juran, J.M. (1986, August). The quality triology. *Quality Progress,* pp. 19–24.

Juran, J.M. (1988). *Juran on planning for quality.* New York: Free Press.

Juran, J.M. (1989). *Juran on leadership for quality: An executive handbook.* New York: Free Press.

Kanter, R.M. (1977). *Men and women of the corporation.* New York: Basic Books.

Kanter, R.M. (1989). The new managerial work. *Harvard Business Review, November–December,* 84–92.

Koontz, H., & Weihrich, H. (1990). *Essentials of management* (5th ed.). New York: McGraw-Hill.

Kouzes, J.M., & Posner, B.Z. (1987). *The leadership challenge: How to get extraordinary things done in organizations.* San Francisco: Jossey-Bass.

Kuhn, T. (1970). *The structure of scientific revolutions.* (2nd Ed.). Chicago: University of Chicago Press.

Lakin, K.C., Jaskulski, T.M., Hill, B.K., Bruininks, R.H., Menke, M., White, C.C., & Wright, E.A. (1989). *Medicaid services for persons with mental retardation and related conditions.* Minneapolis: University of Minnesota, Institute on Community Integration.

Lubeck, R.C., & Davis, P.K. (1991). W.E. Deming's 14 points for quality: Can they be applied to rehabilitation? *Journal of Rehabilitation Administration, November,* 216–221.

Maryland Center for Quality and Productivity. (1991). *Total quality services.* College Park, MD: Author.

Mills, D.Q. (1991). *Rebirth of the corporation.* New York: John Wiley & Sons.

Mintzberg, H. (1989). *Mintzberg on management: Inside our strange world of organizations.* New York: Free Press.

Parasuraman, A., Berry, L.L., & Zeithaml, V.A. (1991). Understanding customer expectations of service. *Sloan Management Review, 32*(8), 39–48.

Perrow, C. (1984). *Normal accidents: Living with high risk technologies.* New York: Basic Books.

Pfeffer, J. (1978). *Organizational design.* Arlington Heights, IL: AHM Publishing.

Port, O., & Carey, J. (1991). Questing for the best. *Business Week Bonus Issue—The Quality Imperative,* 8–16.

Robbins, S.P. (1990). *Organization theory: Structure, design and applications.* Englewood Cliffs, NJ: Prentice Hall.

Rosander, A.C. (1989). *The quest for quality in services.* New York: Quality Resources.

Sandow, D., Rhodes, L., Mank, D.M., Ramsing, K.D., & Lynch, W.F. (1990). Assuring quality in supported employment. *Journal of Rehabilitation Administration, XIV,* 20–27.

Savage, C.M. (1990). *Fifth generation management: Integrating enterprises through human networking.* Bedford, MA: Digital Press.

Schein, E.H. (1972). *Professional education.* New York: McGraw-Hill.

Schlesinger, L.A., & Heskett, J.L. (1991). The service driven company. *Harvard Business Review, September–October,* 71–81.

Scholtes, P.R. (1989). *The team handbook*. Madison: Joiner Associates.
Schon, D.A. (1983). *The reflective practitioner: How professionals think in action*. New York: Basic Books.
Segal, M. (1974). Organization and environment: A typology of adaptability and structure. *Public Administration Review, XX*, 212–220.
Senge, P.M. (1990). *The fifth discipline: The art and practice of the learning organization*. New York: Doubleday Currency.
Shepard, S.B. (1991). Defining the Q-Word, *Business Week/Quality, 1991*, Special bonus issue.
Skrtic, T.M. (1987). An organizational analysis of special education reform. *Counterpoint, 8*, 15–19.
Smull, M.W., & Bellamy, G.T. (1989). *Community services for adults with disabilities: Policy challenges in the emerging support paradigm*. Baltimore: University of Maryland.
Van Fleet, D.D. (1991). *Behavior in organizations*. Boston: Houghton Mifflin.
Xerox Business Products and Services. (1989). *Leadership through quality*. Rochester, NY: Author.
Zeithaml, V.A., Parasuraman, A., & Berry, L.O. (1990). *Delivering quality services: Balancing customer perceptions and expectations*. New York: Free Press.

27

Bringing About Change Through Legislation

Don Wesely

This chapter describes Nebraska's role in reforming services to persons with mental retardation, how Nebraska blazed a trail to open up community-based services for persons with mental retardation in the 1960s, and how in 1991 landmark legislation was enacted to take Nebraska into the next phase of services for persons with developmental disabilities.

In the late 1960s Nebraska emerged into the light of a comprehensive system of community-based services for persons with mental retardation. Nebraska is generally regarded as the first state to take this step. As our community-based mental retardation system developed visitors from around the United States and the world came to Nebraska to examine our programs. They carried our experience back with them to begin similar programs where they lived. Nebraska's program administrators were hired or consulted around the United States to plant the seeds of system reform and to help nourish the growth of community-based mental retardation programs.

When I was elected to the Nebraska legislature in 1978 and began serving on the Health and Human Services Committee, I knew little about mental retardation services. What I did know was that Nebraska had perhaps the best programs in the United States. We were very proud of our achievement of deinstitutionalization in Nebraska. But as time passed there were problems.

Beginning with then Governor Bob Kerrey in the mid 1980s, people began asking questions about our mental retardation system. These questions concerned whether we were really doing the best we could for persons with mental retardation, whether we could improve quality, whether we could improve administrative oversight, and what we should do for persons with other developmental disabilities. Mental retardation program administrators made no substantive response.

This happened because Nebraska was in good standing in what I call Phase 2 mental retardation programs and had not evolved to Phase 3. The next section explains.

THREE PHASES OF SERVICES

Looking back at the evolution of services to persons with developmental disabilities, I see three fairly distinct phases of services:

- Phase 1 is institutional and congregate care, which began in the 1800s and was the predominant source of services until being challenged in the 1960s by advocates for persons with mental retardation.
- Phase 2 is the community-based, group home/sheltered workshop model of mental retardation services. This phase started in the late 1960s and has been implemented from state to state from the 1970s into the 1990s.
- Phase 3 is the newest evolution of developmental disabilities services. In Phase 3, services are not looked at in terms of where they originate, either in an institution or in the community, services are looked at through the eyes of persons with disabilities and their families. Services are focused on meeting the needs of the individual and his or her family, and include assisted but independent living and working, family support, and respite care.

In moving from Phase 1 to Phase 2, we moved from institutional care to community care. Moving to Phase 3 entails measuring the quality of care by the quality of life of persons served by the developmental disabilities system. This is a move from a provider-driven system to a consumer-driven system.

THE CRISIS THAT PRECIPITATED CHANGE

For years Nebraska was right to be proud of our institutional care and our community-based care, but we rested on our laurels. We did not candidly answer the question as to whether we could do better until a crisis in late 1989 forced us to face the issue.

In the fall of 1989 a great deal of controversy occurred in Nebraska involving the allocation of funds from the state to regions for mental retardation services. The dispute centered on what was promised in terms of funds from the state and what was delivered to the regions. The regions felt that they had been told one thing and the state felt that they had indicated something different. The dispute created a great deal of concern and conflict. To resolve the immediate dispute, the legislature passed budget legislation in the 1990 session mandating that the State Department of Public Institutions begin to contract for mental retardation services with local regions. Service contracts would allow us to know who was being served for how much in our mental retardation system.

The legislature was becoming concerned that the state was now spending more than $40 million a year caring for 2,300 persons in community-based programs, and still there were waiting lists and allegations of some poor quality services. Nebraska's structure of community-based programs offered little accountability on a statewide level. In Nebraska, six mental retardation regions serve 93 counties. These regions are governed by multi-county boards made up of county commissioners. The regional programs are managed by regional directors and either provide or contract for community-based programs. For a while these programs thrived. The regional directors became powerful forces in the system. In some areas it was felt that the local control that was to have been provided by the local elected officials had been usurped by the regional directors.

A 1984 study done by the Governor's Caucus on Mental Retardation showed serious inequities in resources, policies, and services between regions. A new study by the Department of Public Institutions in May of 1990 revealed that again staffing levels, that is, the actual number of staff who work with persons receiving services, varied from one region to another by 24%. When the state began funding the system in 1970, the three major funding sources, state/federal, county, and other funds, shared proportionately in the total cost of the system. Over the years county and other funds increased slightly, while state/federal funding increased substantially. Since 1988, state/federal funds for community-based mental retardation services have increased 49%, while the number of persons served has increased 12%. During this same 5-year period, special education funding increased 35% and the number of students 17.49%.

Families were told by regional office staff that the state was not providing sufficient funds. The state said that the regional offices needed to be more efficient and accountable. Other complaints expressed about community-based programs included allegations that quality had slipped. Though funding had increased, waiting lists for services were increasing. The range of services provided was too limited and varied across the state. Workers were underpaid, which led to high staff turnover rates and not enough trained staff. So the legislature faced a funding crisis in the regions, funding and service disparities among and within the regions, waiting lists that were real and growing, and a growing dissatisfaction among families and consumers with the services provided.

Legislators are faced with hundreds of issues all competing for our time and attention. It is not easy to command legislators' attention, let alone their interest or support. But legislators, as a rule, respond to crisis. And that is what Nebraska had in the spring of 1990. The legislature was asking why the system had broken down so badly, why the communication had been so poor, and how we could try to improve the system.

THE LEGISLATIVE STUDY

In order to sort out the issues and come up with an answer, the legislature appropriated $75,000 in the spring of 1990 to the Health and Human Services Committee to conduct a study of all the issues and come back to the legislature with a plan. As chair of the committee, I formed a task force in order to bring as many people as possible into the process and in an attempt to alleviate the considerable apprehension concerning the study. Interested groups were asked to make nominations to the task force. Eventually the task force members numbered 35. The task force consisted of state senators, service providers, parents, and professionals in the area of mental retardation and developmental disabilities in addition to county elected officials, state agency representatives, and advocates. It was a diverse group, and on some issues a very divisive group.

We facilitated an open process for the work of the task force by making it as inclusive as possible. Everyone who was interested was invited to the first meeting of the task force. It was open to the public and was attended by 200 people. They heard a presentation by an out-of-state leader in the field of developmental disabilities reform. This proved to be a good strategy because people who were not on the task force did not feel excluded. Then the task force itself met to begin its work.

After several meetings, the task force was organized into subcommittees. It was hoped that this would facilitate resolutions to the issues. The chairs of the subcommittees were selected with an emphasis on parents. The subcommittee meetings from the start were lively and allowed for a free exchange of ideas. Even though at times there was contention, people felt that they had the opportunity to say what was on their minds and that all ideas were considered. As one member described it, "We ruled out spitting, scratching, and hitting, but we said a lot of hard words at each other; and we came up with a task force report that I think all of us are proud of, even if we don't all agree with it." The task force used a ranking system to determine priorities and decided to focus on the issues of eligibility, systems, services, quality, and staff. Meeting as subcommittees, task force members toured facilities and asked for and examined information on programs, structures, and cost effectiveness.

Originally it had been anticipated that a consultant would be hired to do the study. However, the task force felt they did not need to bring in an outside expert to make recommendations. As it turned out, local people knew what was needed and were ready to take action. However, one of the subcommittees had a particularly difficult time, and they requested a facilitator. They were provided with a local consultant, who worked out so well that the other subcommittees requested that she work with them as well. This helped move the process along.

By September each subcommittee had presented its recommendations for changes to Nebraska's network of developmental disabilities services. A draft (Task Force, 1990) report was offered to the citizens of Nebraska for public review and comment. Eight public hearings were held across the state. The hearings were conducted by the Health and Human Services Committee. Attendance at the hearings was heavy. Some areas of the state were very supportive of the need for change in the system. However, there was not universal support. One rural area of the state was strongly opposed to any change in the system and was not at all shy about sharing their negative opinions about the proposed changes.

Following the public input provided by the hearings, a final report was prepared and broadly circulated. Legislation was drafted based on the report.

THE LEGISLATION

Five bills were introduced in the 1991 session of the Nebraska legislature. LB 830 dealt with numerous improvements to the system. It was drafted to reflect a complete administrative takeover of community-based programs by the state. LB 831 established a new Department of Developmental Disabilities rather than a separate division within the Department of Public Institutions. LBs 832, 833, and 834 increased the salaries of community-based workers, provided for training of workers, and established a certification and training program for community-based workers. In Nebraska, every bill has a public hearing. The hearing on the package of bills was packed. Altogether, 35 people testified, 23 in favor and 12 opposed.

Why would there be opposition to such legislation? First and foremost, change is always hard. Even those who have the most to gain become uncomfortable. Much of the opposition came because of the long-time tension between the community-based mental retardation programs and the Department of Public Institutions. The system had a history of misunderstandings, which made people suspicious of each other. The regional directors saw the bills in light of their worst fear, that the regions would be eliminated.

The hearing provided vivid testimony as to why changes were needed. One parent testified that her daughter had had 72 different staff persons in a 1-year period, and she lived in an apartment with just two other persons. Another person testified, "I think it is fair to say that the MR system in this state is developmentally disabled. That is to say, we've come a long way from institutionalizing every retarded person. The Nebraska MR system of options, community-based programs, and institutional programs has developed, and it has grown, and it still has much good in it. But at this point it is stronger in potency than in act. Isn't that what it means to be developmentally disabled?"

Another parent with a long involvement in the system testified:

> As a parent and also as someone who has advocated for people throughout this state, I will tell you what the [current] system creates. You can get in your car or get in the plane, as the senators did in the task force, and you can drive from one end of the state to the other, and as you pass an imaginary boundary, you're going to see a different service delivery system. One place serves children, those under 21. Another place does not serve children. One place serves people with this type of handicap. Another place serves people with that type of handicap. These are tax dollars that are being spent. I make it akin to a situation if you started a program in the State of Nebraska with tax dollars, whatever that program would be, and you let individuals other than the state determine who would use this program and who would not, that would be, certainly in legalistic terms, denial of due process and equal protection of the law, as you're spending tax dollars for the benefit of all people of the State of Nebraska, but

> you're letting other people make determinations as to who gets it and who does not. Is this going to cost more money? I think the presumption that it is, is not warranted. You're going to have people come up here and talk to you about the fact that they are concerned about terminating services for people or for their loved ones that are on services. What we have here is a system of haves and have nots. . . .

A number of others testified regarding their inability to obtain services at all.

The hearing presented a good opportunity for airing all sides of the issues. County commissioners testified about their county funding limitations. Supporters of the status quo expressed their opposition to proposed changes.

The Director of the Department of Public Institutions testified in strong support of the Developmental Disabilities Act (LB 830, 1991) at the hearing. Among his comments was, "When I reflect back on the last 20 years, I realize that the word I heard most often has slowly changed, from client to money." It was also surprising to some that he also testified, "It is my belief that creative solutions can evolve even without additional funding."

One important section of LB 830 expanded the system to cover all persons with developmental disabilities. The Nebraska service delivery system was for persons with mental retardation. That meant either that persons with other developmental disabilities did not have access to services or if they did receive services, they were basically designed for persons with mental retardation.

Surprisingly, not everyone favored an expanded definition of those eligible for services. Some feared that some persons currently in service would be dropped to meet the needs of those newly eligible under the expanded definition.

THE POLITICS

With so many issues to address, it was clear that priorities would have to be set and compromises made. Of the five bills introduced, the three bills concerning staff were held by the committee mostly because of their costs. I personally came to the conclusion that additional funding for staff salaries or an expanded level of services or staff should not be supported until structural and operational changes were made to improve efficiencies in current expenditures. The Health and Human Services Committee also determined that improvements in the system were needed and that this should be the first priority. LB 830, which contained a host of improvements to the system, became the vehicle for reform of the mental retardation service system in Nebraska.

The bill was advanced from committee on a vote of five to two. It was amended by the committee to provide for a phase-in of its provisions. Other changes were made as well. Originally LB 830 provided for an increase in the rate of county financial participation in the local programs. Across the state, county funding varied but averaged about 4% of the total cost. Despite this miserly level of funding, the counties vigorously opposed an increase in the amount that they paid, and, ultimately, it was dropped from the bill. This was due mainly to the fact that, in 1991, counties were facing a potential loss of revenue due to a lawsuit that limited their ability to collect taxes on certain property. The uncertainty of the tax situation was too much, and an increase in county participation was not feasible.

I called in the key players to emphasize the critical stage that we were in. Crisis had focused the legislature's attention on the need for reform of the mental retardation system. We were looking at ground-breaking improvements in developmental disabilities programs in Nebraska. It was a situation that needed to be acted upon. Even then there was limited consensus. The Association for Retarded Citizens (Arc) was positive and very helpful overall but divided in terms of support from local chapters. The Developmental Disabilities Council did not endorse the legislation until the very end. The various advocacy groups for persons with autism, epilepsy, cerebral palsy, and spina bifida provided limited help, as did the Mental Retardation Association. The private service providers at first liked the bill, then they did not, and then they did. Many of the counties that had vigorously opposed the bill dropped their opposition when the provision for increasing the funding from the counties to support the programs was dropped from the bill. Only one of the six regions that controlled the community-based programs publicly opposed the bill. The rest were working quietly against the bill with one possible exception. The Vocational Rehabilitation program fought the bill until an understanding was reached and some amendments were adopted. The bill was strongly supported by the State Department of Public Institutions, by Nebraska Advocacy Services, and by individual parents who had had enough of the current system and wanted change. It was these parents who ultimately prevailed. They would not give up no matter how discouraging the situation looked.

A number of meetings were held throughout the process, with interested parties to try to work out problems. Some of the meetings involved going over the bill word by word. Hidden meanings were seen by some. Others used these tactics simply as a way to delay and confuse.

Finally, much of the opposition to the bill centered on the provisions that case management for individuals and their families would become a state responsibility. In response to this concern, a provision was established that set up a committee to provide input into the case management system, effectively delaying its implementation.

This issue was complicated, and yet the floor debate on the bill was not lengthy. Ultimately, the bill passed on a vote of 29 in favor and 14 opposed. Then the bill went to the governor to sign. Governor Ben Nelson had concerns about the fiscal impact of the bill. However, I worked with the governor, and he put aside his concerns and signed the bill on June 7, 1991. LB 830 became law.

Still there were problems. The new task force working with the State Department of Public Institutions on the implementation of the case management system was off to a rocky start. Although the situation improved, this continuing friction was used by people uncomfortable with the law to try to delay its implementation during the next legislative session. Legislation was introduced in the 1992 Legislative Session, LB 1169, to require the legislature itself to approve the service coordination (case managment implementation) plan prior to its implementation. This bill was viewed by many of us as a tactic to delay or even repeal the 1991 act. The regional directors were very supportive of LB 1169. In fact, it had 27 co-sponsors, two more than needed to pass the bill. However, LB 1169 proved to be a rallying point for supporters of the 1991 Reform bill. People who might have taken LB 830 for granted did not want to lose the gains made through it. A fight was launched to keep them. The hearing on LB 1169 was long and somewhat heated. Ultimately, the Health and Human Services Committee held the bill, and it died at the end of the 1992 session. LB 830 was saved, and mental retardation reform in Nebraska could move forward. Still the battle continued.

THE FUTURE

Now and forever more, there will be more work to be done. If the dream of good quality service provision to persons with disabilities is to be met, a state funding increase of up to 40% will be needed. Funding will be needed for other elements of the bill. The budget is tight in Nebraska as it is across the United States.

The situation in Nebraska points out that the effort to improve services for persons with developmental disabilities never ends. Even successes such as the passage of LB 830 in 1991 is but one more step forward in a long journey to improve the lives of persons with developmental disabilities. Now that the bill is passed, we must defend it against those who would diminish it. We must find funding to implement it. We must see that the legislative vision is instilled in rules and regulations. But the blueprint has been passed, and the path we must take is clear.

A consensus has been forming around the United States that developmental disabilities programs need to move into this Phase 3 of services. Phase 2, community-based programs, brought the United States into the light of needed reform. Phase 3, services focused on the individual and family, can make that light shine brighter and farther. Judicial decisions have pointed in this direction. Mental retardation program directors have embraced this concept. The National Conference of State Legislatures has given its blessing to this phase of developmental disabilities services with a 1991 report of its Task Force on Developmental Disabilities about policy directions for the states.

The primary reluctance to change from Phase 2 to Phase 3 services comes from the mental retardation bureaucracy of service providers. The status quo is comfortable to them, and adjusting programs to meet the needs of those using services rather than requiring those using services to fit the slots available in programs is worrisome to service providers. But this change must and will occur, just as the transition from Phase 1, institutional care, to Phase 2, community-based programs, has occurred. That change is still in progress; it, too, was strongly opposed. Bureaucratic intransigence was part of that opposition but even more so, some older parents who fought hard for institutional care for their children with mental retardation opposed moving them into community-based programs. They did not want to see their victories on behalf of people with mental retardation diminished by people being moved into community-based programs, which they felt had a lower quality of care. Phase 3 reform can bring older people and younger people and those who are pro-institution and those who are pro–community-based services together to improve services to persons with developmental disabilities. That is what we saw in Nebraska. We also saw advocates for persons with mental retardation reach out to work with the advocates for persons with other developmental disabilities to broaden programs to cover all persons with developmental disabilities.

We are witnessing in the United States a new sensitivity as to how we serve the needs of persons with developmental disabilities. We see this new sensitivity in how we describe the people served by the system. No longer are they "retardates" or "the mentally retarded." They are people first and are now referred to as persons with developmental disabilities.

REFERENCES

Department of Public Institutions. (1990, May). Lincoln, Nebraska.

Governor's Caucus on Mental Retardation. (1986). Lincoln, Nebraska.

Task Force on Developmental Disabilities. National Conference of State Legislators. (1991). *Americans with disabilities: Policy directions for the states*. Denver: Author.

Task Force of the Health and Human Services Committee. (1990, September). *Services to Nebraskans with mental retardation: Two decades in the light*.

28

Creating Individual Supports for People Moving Out of Nursing Facilities

Supported Placements in Integrated Community Environments (SPICE)

Kathleen Carmody

Illinois, like many other states, has relied upon nursing facilities to provide care for people with developmental disabilities. This practice has led to a significant concentration of people with developmental disabilities, and particularly those with multiple and severe disabilities, living in nonspecialized nursing facilities across the state. In 1987, the Supported Placements in Integrated Community Environments (SPICE) Project was initiated in an effort to address the needs of these individuals. Through this project, 38 people diagnosed as having severe mobility impairments and/or cognitive impairments were assisted in moving from nursing facilities into homes in the community (two additional project participants moved from an aging parent's home, rather than a nursing facility). These 40 participants were selected from a pool of over 2,600 people with developmental disabilities living in nursing facilities. In addition to affecting the lives of

The author wishes to acknowledge Cathy Ficker Terill, Director of the Illinois Planning Council on Developmental Disabilities, for her assistance and guidance in preparing this chapter.

SPICE participants, this project contributed toward the development of a new approach to services for all people with disabilities in Illinois. This new approach, introduced in Illinois through the SPICE Project, emphasizes the qualities of choice, integration, and individualized services to address each participant's unique circumstances, abilities, and preferences.

BACKGROUND

The SPICE Project was initiated in response to several factors. Among the most significant were the results of a statewide evaluation of people with developmental disabilities living in nursing facilities, and an increasing sense that the dominant service paradigm, that is, the developmental continuum of care, imposed severe and unnecessary restrictions upon the opportunities available to people with multiple and severe disabilities in Illinois. Additionally, as the SPICE Project progressed, states became aware of impending federal legislation that would severely limit the use of nursing facilities as a residential service option for people with developmental disabilities.

Responding to concerns regarding the quality and appropriateness of services being provided to persons with developmental disabilities living in intermediate care and skilled nursing facilities (since re-classified as nursing facilities), the Illinois Planning Council on Developmental Disabilities awarded the Taylor Institute a grant in 1985 to conduct the Evaluation and Service Identification Project for Developmentally Disabled Residents of Intermediate Care Facilities (ICFs) and Skilled Nursing Facilities (SNFs) (Davis, Silverstein, Uehara, & Sadden, 1987). The goal of the Taylor Institute study was to identify the habilitation and residential needs of the people with developmental disabilities assessed during the study and to recommend policies and procedures that would enable the state to ensure the provision of appropriate placement and active treatment services (Davis et al., 1987).

Based upon information yielded through psychological, behavioral, functional, and medical assessments, as well as input provided by an interdisciplinary team that had been established for each resident, service recommendations were made for 2,721 persons identified during the study period. The study showed that only 10% (n = 277) of the people with developmental disabilities living in nursing facilities were actually in need of that level of care. The majority of the population assessed (n = 1,899) were recommended for placement into ICFs/MR, which, in Illinois, typically range in size from 15 to over 100 beds. Rather than this being the only setting in which people's needs could be met, the heavy reliance on this placement option was strongly influenced by the lack of community-based alternatives to the ICF/MR setting. That is, consistent with the continuum approach to services, people were fit into an existing service category, rather than services being designed to meet the specific and unique needs of individuals.

The researchers found that the people assessed through this study "tended to be lower functioning and require more staff assistance than is the norm for the population currently served in DD residential facilities" (Davis et al., 1987, p. 35). Given this finding, the Taylor Institute's conclusion that the fact that ". . . the community residential system in Illinois has not generally been organized and staffed to serve the severely or profoundly handicapped with neuromotor problems or other problems in basic sensory or motor systems" (Davis et al., 1987, p. 33) caused great concern. Illinois now had indisputable evidence that the vast majority of people with developmental disabilities living in nursing facilities should not be in these settings. Furthermore, the system of community-based services was either unprepared or unwilling to address the needs of many within this group.

A second factor that contributed to the initiation of the SPICE Project was an increasing awareness that the current system of services was not flexible enough to accommodate the needs of all those whom it was intended to serve. Specifically, people with multiple and severe disabilities were routinely denied access to the most desirable and least restrictive services. Though there were regulatory and financial limitations that contributed to this practice, an equally important cause was the attitude that somehow nursing home residents and others with severe disabilities did not belong in community-based residential programs.

An important circumstance that emerged during the early stages of the SPICE Project was impending federal legislation that would impose severe restrictions upon the state's use of nursing facilities as an integral component of their residential services continuum. This legislation was contained within the Omnibus Budget Reconciliation Act of 1987 (OBRA-87, PL 100-203). Illinois would be particularly affected by this legislation, in part because of a heavy reliance upon nursing facilities during earlier deinstitutionalization efforts, and in part because the scope of OBRA-87's impact in regard to people with developmental disabilities was well documented.

The combined impact of these factors made it clear that Illinois needed to expand its array of service options. However, it was equally clear that merely increasing the capacity of the existing community system would not address the problem facing the state. Not only did services need to be expanded, they also needed to be restructured so that the diverse needs and preferences of people with all types and degrees of disabilities could be accommodated. The SPICE Project was expected to play an important role in this process by demonstrating that services could be flexible and individualized enough to meet the needs of all people with disabilities in the most desirable setting—their own homes.

STATE-WIDE COORDINATING ACTIVITIES

The SPICE Project was coordinated by United Cerebral Palsy of Illinois (UCPI), through a grant from the Illinois Planning Council on Developmental Disabilities. This grant was awarded to UCPI for a pilot project to demonstrate that residents with developmental disabilities in nursing facilities could live in the community when provided with appropriate services and supports and the opportunity to exercise choice and control in their lives. Through SPICE, a more individualized and innovative approach to residential supports could be tested in Illinois. Furthermore, this approach would be implemented with people who were considered to have the most severe disabilities, ensuring that future services could not be denied to this group with unfounded claims that they were "too disabled" to live in the community.

An important factor contributing to the success of the project was that, since its inception, SPICE received strong support from a variety of state agencies, whose assistance would be critical to successfully implementing services. These agencies included the Illinois Department of Mental Health and Developmental Disabilities, the Illinois Department of Rehabilitation Services, the Illinois Department of Public Aid, and the Illinois Planning Council on Developmental Disabilities. Collectively, these departments enabled SPICE participants to gain access to funding for ongoing support services through the Medicaid Home and Community-Based waiver, Personal Attendant Services, and reimbursement for adaptive equipment. Additionally, state departments demonstrated their support by intervening with other entities (e.g., nursing facilities) when necessary, as well as accommodating their referral, regulatory, and monitoring practices to the goals of the SPICE Project.

The systemic change that was initiated by the SPICE Project was driven by strong advocates who refused to allow services to continue in the disparate manner that often typifies state systems. These advocates, led by executive staff and members of the Illinois Planning Council on Developmental Disabilities, along with executive staff from the United Cerebral Palsy Association Governmental Affairs Division in Washington, D.C., provided direction and support to the statewide activities described above. These advocates, and their continuous message that the system could and should change, were essential to the task of eliciting cooperation among various state-wide agencies and service providers.

The first major activity of the SPICE Project was to identify potential project participants. Referrals were received through several sources: the Taylor Institute Study, case management agencies, day service agencies, and family and friends of eligible people. The only reasons for which a person referred would not be interviewed were that the person did not have a developmental disability or the person was not a resident of a nursing facility.

Throughout the course of the project, more than 50 nursing facilities and day service agencies were visited for meetings with people who had been referred. Each of these meetings was conducted by the project director and involved an explanation of the SPICE Project, as well as the completion of the Interview Guide. This tool was developed during the SPICE Project to assist in gathering information relevant to people relocating from nursing facilities into the community. This process was not intended to replace the formal assessment and evaluation to which people with disabilities are routinely subjected. Rather, it was carried out in recognition of the need for more qualitative and personal information regarding people's interests, hopes, fears, and choices. These responses, rather than test scores and achievement results, would guide the development of individualized services and supports.

During the interview process, people were asked many questions pertaining to the kind of lifestyle they would like to achieve and the types of supports they felt were necessary to assist them. Among these questions was whether there was another person with whom the participant wanted to live. Many people identified a friend; while others chose to live alone. Some indicated that they did not have someone in mind with whom they wanted to live but would be willing to meet other SPICE participants who might be potential housemates. Additionally, people were asked if they wanted to remain in their current geographic area, or if they would be willing to relocate in order to participate in SPICE. Given the magnitude of this decision, great effort was made to ensure that it would be as informed a choice as possible. Where people would need to relocate in order to participate in SPICE, they were taken to visit the area, meet with the service providing agency, and look at housing options.

People served through SPICE, similar to many who remain in nursing facilities, depend upon mobility and other equipment for whatever amount of independence they have. Typically, people in nursing facilities have not been properly evaluated and fitted for wheelchairs. Furthermore, there are often many problems with the equipment that people use, including it being inappropriate to meet individual people's needs, antiquated, scarce, or in such an advanced stage of disrepair as to render it unsafe. It was clear that an important component of the SPICE Project would be to ensure that participant's were properly evaluated for and received adaptive equipment that was necessary for living outside of an institutional setting.

Given these concerns, grant funds had been allocated for sophisticated seating, positioning, and augmentative communication evaluations. These were coordinated through the SPICE Project and carried out by staff of the Rehabilitation Institute of Chicago. In addition to on-site clinical evaluations, the Rehabilitation Institute, together with the SPICE Project, organized a mobile assessment team to enable project participants from across the state to be evaluated for appropriate equipment. This activity was critical to ensure that equipment would maximize independence, comfort, and function.

While SPICE participants were being identified and evaluated, a competitive Request for Proposals process was initiated to identify community agencies that would provide direct services to SPICE participants. This process was open to private for-profit and nonprofit community service agencies throughout the state. Selected agencies would receive start-up grants and ongoing contracts to provide support services through SPICE.

During this process, bidder's conferences were held across the state featuring national experts on supported living, as well as representatives of the SPICE Project and key state administrators. This process was critical to ensure that potential providers understood the goals and expectations of the SPICE Project. Previous to these conferences, there had been limited opportunities in Illinois for service providers to be exposed to concepts similar to those that drove the SPICE Project. The conferences provided an important foundation upon which agencies could begin to develop service plans consistent with the values and goals of the SPICE Project.

These values included the following four basic tenets about people:

1. People want to live in a home. They do not want a facility, or residential arrangement, or least restrictive environment, or normalizing atmosphere, but a home. Most adults in society do not live with many other unrelated adults. People with disabilities should have options beyond this as well.
2. People want to be surrounded by family and friends. They do not want to be involved only with people who are paid to be with them, or whom they know only due to the similarity of their circumstances, whether it be others residing in a nursing facility, attending a day program, or participating in special recreation events. People want friends with whom they share more than just a label.
3. People want to feel productive. There are many avenues for demonstrating productive capacity, for example, at work, at home, by volunteering, or through advocacy activities. Each of these opportunities allows people to give, rather than receive, service.
4. People want to have some control over their lives. They do not want to be told with whom they will live, what they will wear, when they will eat, where they can and cannot go, and why all of these restrictions are in their best interest.

The most important value that drives the SPICE Project is that people with disabilities are no different from anyone else in wanting these qualities in their lives. It was with these values as a guide that individualized services and supports were developed for SPICE participants.

SERVICE DELIVERY ACTIVITIES

Five community-based agencies were selected to provide services through the SPICE Project. Each of these agencies served between six and 10 SPICE participants. Following are descriptions of the major activities that these agencies undertook in order to assist SPICE participants in moving from the nursing facility into their homes.

First, agency personnel met and began to establish a relationship with the SPICE participants they would be serving well before they moved into the community. Typically, there are many activities necessary before a person can move from an institution into the community; these same activities were necessary in SPICE. However, rather than excluding the very people whose lives would be most influenced by the decisions made during this time, SPICE participants were as involved as possible in this process. Because many of the participants had limited experiences and opportunities upon which to base decisions, an important role for staff during this period was to help people explore their options, consider the consequences of various decisions, and make choices that were in the participant's own best interest.

Following are the activities in which SPICE participants were involved during this period:

1. Staff identified homes in the community that were affordable and either were accessible or could be made accessible. The staff accompanied participants as they visited the homes to select the ones in which they wanted to live.
2. Participants who wanted to share a home but did not know someone with whom they wanted to live met other SPICE participants to select a housemate mutually.
3. Staff accompanied participants shopping to select furnishings for their homes. Each agency had received grant funds from the Illinois Planning Council on Developmental Disabilities to enable participants to purchase furniture and other needed items for their homes, as well as pay for modifications if necessary. This experience provided an important learning opportunity because many SPICE participants had never been given the opportunity to make major purchases in the past.
4. Participants were involved in interviewing potential direct service staff who would be working with them in their homes. Though all participants had been receiving staff support for most of their lives, this was the first opportunity they had had to be involved in selecting who would work with them and to provide direction to staff who would be assisting them.
5. Participants were actively involved in developing their individual service plans, which outlined the types of support and training they would receive.
6. Staff assisted participants in becoming familiar with the community in which they would soon be living. For some participants this activity involved day trips to visit agency programs, going shopping, or meeting at restaurants. Other participants, whose facilities were some distance from where they would be moving, stayed overnight. Family members were also welcome to accompany SPICE participants on these outings.

These are just a few of the pre-move activities in which SPICE participants were involved. Other decisions that must be considered before a person moves from a nursing facility into the community are outlined in Figure 28.1.

Once people moved from nursing facilities into the community, it was important to ensure that they did not become "institutionalized" within their own homes. This concern led to programmatic emphasis being placed on promoting the qualities of choice and inclusion.

Similar to others who live in institutional settings, many of the SPICE participants had few opportunities to make choices while living in nursing facilities. Additionally, many had generally limited experiences and did not know what options were available to them. While SPICE participants were involved in making major

- Will you stay living where you are now, or will you move?
- If you choose to move, will you move to an institution, apartment, or house?
- What city/town will you live in?
- Which agency(ies) will provide you with support services?
- What other service providers (generic or specialized) will contribute to your support?
- How many other people will live with you?
- Will your home be single gender or have both genders?
- Will everyone know each other before moving in together?
- Will you have a roommate?
- Who will your roommate be?
- How will your home be furnished/ decorated?
- Which staff will work with you?
- How will these staff be selected, and how will their performance be evaluated?
- What type of staff training will be conducted?
- When will you move?
- Will you get a job?
- Will you be involved in a formal day training program?
- Which chores will be done, and when must they be done?
- Can you decide that you do not want to go on an outing?
- Who will plan the menus for meals?
- Who will do the shopping?
- Can menus be changed?
- What training goals will be included in your program plan?

Figure 28.1. Choice-making for persons moving out of nursing facilities.

life decisions (e.g., whether to leave the nursing facility, whom to live with), an equally important area of decision-making was daily, routine choices (e.g., what to eat for dinner, when to wake up in the morning). Often, in residential support programs, the importance of participants making these kinds of choices is overlooked. The result is that routine issues, such as having established bedtimes, participants asking permission to use the telephone or have a snack, or staff paying bills and doing the shopping, become regimented and institutionalized.

The SPICE Project attempted to avoid this pattern by involving participants as much as possible in managing their homes and personal affairs. Of course, some people are more skilled and experienced in these matters, while others may initially require a great deal of support and guidance from staff, friends, or advocates.

Assisting participants in making choices is a challenging and individualized process. It is not accomplished by staff simply abandoning people to whatever ill-conceived decisions they may make; rather, it requires ongoing support and training. Additionally, staff and friends must expose people to the options available to them and rely upon intervention guidelines that respect the principle of "dignity of risk," but do not imperil the well-being of participants. Most important, the ability to make choices that are in one's own best interest must be recognized as among the most important "Activities of Daily Living" that a person can perform. Once this recognition is made, making decisions for, rather than with, participants becomes a more uncomfortable and unnatural activity for staff.

The second critical component of ongoing services is assisting participants in becoming as involved in the community as possible. Typically, this activity has not been emphasized in services, not even in those that are community-based. While people with disabilities have been living in the community, they have not been assisted in becoming part of the community. Though some people may naturally acclimate to living in the community, others just as naturally may find themselves overwhelmed and ill at ease. Through SPICE, support was provided to assist participants in overcoming this anxiety. Many SPICE participants were unaware of opportunities in the community. An important function for staff was to assist people in trying new activities so that they could develop preferences. Additionally, staff relied on what they knew about participants and their interests to link them with groups and organizations in the community. Through SPICE, participants have become active members in civic and religious groups, community colleges, jobs, and volunteer and advocacy activities.

Supporting people to participate in these activities did not require extra resources; rather, it required a new way of thinking that supports a re-direction of existing resources. Most important, there needed to be a strong commitment to promoting choice and community involvement, persistent and creative staff and friends to facilitate exploring and making opportunities, and the expectation that participants were going to become involved in their community.

OUTCOMES

The Illinois Planning Council on Developmental Disabilities funded Corporate Alternatives, Inc., (CAi) to conduct an independent evaluation of the SPICE Project. The purpose of this study was ". . . to determine whether people with severe disabilities were better off in small, community homes, and to identify the variables that contribute to quality residential care" (Wilson, Huffman, & Conroy, 1991, p. 4). This study included pre- and post-move interviews and assessments with SPICE participants, and pre- and post-move interviews with family members. Additionally, a consumer-focused residential review was conducted within each person's home.

The results of this study show that upon moving into their own homes, SPICE participants made significant gains in personal and community living skills. Using the Inventory for Client and Agency Planning (ICAP), the researchers showed that SPICE participants gained 19.38 points on the Personal Living Scale, in the 9–10 months after moving into their own homes in the community (Wilson et al., 1991). The researchers found this increase highly significant by paired t-test, and it was the group's greatest comparative gain ($t = 4.99$; 36 df; $p < .001$).

Another area in which SPICE participants showed strong growth is Community Living Skills. Upon living in their own homes for nine to 10 months, SPICE participants' average domain scores in this area increased from 468.22 to 480.02. (A perfect score on this scale would be 569; the lowest possible score is 312.)

Again, the researchers found the increase of 11.88 points very significant by paired t-test ($t = 3.04$; 36 df; $p = .004$). These two scales, along with scales measuring motor and social/communication skills, combine to create a Broad Independence score. The average Broad Independence score for the SPICE participants rose from 438.86 pre-move to 447.05 post-move. Again, the researchers found this increase highly significant by paired t-test ($t = 2.53$; 36 df; $p = .016$).

SPICE participants were interviewed before and after moving regarding their satisfaction with their current living arrangement and services. In response to the question, "Do you like living here?" 24.1% of participants responded "yes" while living in the nursing facility. When asked the same question 9–10 months after moving, 91.4% of participants responded "yes." Participants were asked the question, "Are staff people mean or nice to you?" Pre-move responses showed 55.2% of participants said staff were nice to them, and 37.9% said staff were some place in between mean and nice. Post-move responses indicated that 88.5% of participants said staff were nice to them, while 8.6% felt they were some place in between mean and nice. Participants were also asked the question, "Is there someplace else you would rather live?" Prior to moving, 85.7% of participants said "yes," while only 8.8% responded "yes" after moving into their own homes. Similarly, family members showed an overwhelming increase in satisfaction with SPICE participants' living arrangements and services upon their moving into the community.

The final component of the evaluation study was a residential review. This review consisted of trained interviewers conducting on-site reviews in SPICE participant's homes. Through a combination of interviews, record reviews, and observations, researchers used the "SPICE Review Instrument" to rate the following 13 items that they felt were necessary for a community-based support program to be successful:

- The residence being appropriately least restrictive
- Physical quality
- Safety of the individuals who live there
- Encouragement of integration
- Quality of staff/consumer interaction
- Training for residential supervisory staff
- Training for residential direct service staff
- Client services
- Behavior management techniques
- Quality of direct service staff
- Quality of client files
- Individual habilitation plans (IHPs) being complete, updated, and based upon the needs of the individuals served
- The overall quality of the residential management (Wilson et al., 1991)

Each item was rated on a 1–10 scale, with 10.0 being the highest possible rating, 1.0 being the lowest, and 5.5 being average.

Using this scale, Wilson and her colleagues compiled scores for individual homes, average overall agency scores, and individual item scores. Their findings show that individual home scores ranged between 7.62 and 9.38, with an average score of 8.86. Overall average agency scores ranged between 8.32 and 9.27. The range and average scores on individual items are detailed fully in CAi's Final Report (Wilson et al., 1991).

The authors note that a variation of their "SPICE Site Review" instrument was used in an earlier state-wide evaluation of community residential programs in Illinois. While an exact comparison cannot be made between the results of these two studies, the researchers note that a comparison of overall scores is worthwhile. Individual home scores from the earlier study ranged between 2.0 and 10.0, with an overall average score for the 20 homes in this study of 5.63. Individual home scores for the SPICE participants ranged between 7.62 and 9.38, with an overall average score for the 22 SPICE homes of 8.86 (Wilson et al., 1991). While the researchers cannot fully account for the dramatic variation in comparison scores, it is possible that the input participants gave in the design of their home and services, as well as the priority given to services that enhance participant's lifestyle, contribute to the overall increase in objective measurements of quality.

The results of this study show that SPICE participants' quality of life have dramatically improved upon moving into the community. Furthermore, the services and supports being delivered through the SPICE Project are judged to be of significantly higher quality than those provided through other community residential programs.

LESSONS LEARNED

During the 3 years after SPICE participants began moving into their own homes many lessons have been learned about assisting people in moving from nursing facilities into the community. The experience has taught not only what was done well during this process, but also how participants and agencies could have been supported better during this time.

First, it has become clear that self-advocacy training for people with disabilities is an essential element to any individualized, community-based support program. Self-advocacy must be broadly defined to include not only the areas of rights and responsibilities, but also personal and community safety, effective communication skills, futures planning, and interpersonal relationships. These are all areas in which people coming from a nursing facility environment may have limited experience. Self-advocacy training must be geared toward helping people learn to make good decisions for themselves in these areas, and helping them to be able to communicate their decisions effectively. It must be an ongoing activity, and people must be allowed to incorporate what they are learning into their everyday lives. This means that once they have learned safety skills, participants can expect to go into the community alone, or that participants can expect staff to listen and respond to them when they are advocating for themselves.

Changes such as these represent a dramatic departure from traditional practice for many agencies. Typically, people with disabilities are expected to act as service recipients, following agency rules and accepting agency services, rather than becoming active participants in the design of their own services. It has become clear that not only do participants need training in order to fulfill their role, but staff and agencies must also receive training so that they understand and are able to carry out their new responsibilities.

Staff training must be broadened beyond topics such as first aid, behavior management, and emergency procedures. SPICE showed that staff must understand and accept the values underlying individualized, community-based supports and then be taught strategies for operationalizing these values. It is now understood that it cannot be assumed that all staff feel people with disabilities should have equal opportunity in the community, or should be allowed to make important choices for themselves. Likewise, it cannot be assumed that staff who do support the values of integration and choice will know of strategies to assist people in gaining access to community opportunities or learning to make good choices. Both issues—values and strategies to live up to them—must be addressed during staff training.

Similarly, management-level staff must receive training to assist them in administering programs such as SPICE. The project showed that agencies cannot expect to provide individualized supports in a manner similar to SPICE without changing agency policies and practices. Three specific issues that emerged during the project were hierarchical structure, the effect of SPICE on other agency programs, and existing agency policies.

First, the project showed that a service that encouraged participation and feedback from people with disabilities had to also encourage participation and feedback from staff at all levels. Clearly, staff who worked directly in participants' homes were among the most knowledgeable people regarding participants' preferences, needs, abilities, and interests. Too often, agency practice fails to recognize the expertise of staff at the direct service level and does not involve them in important decision-making or program planning activities. Assisting agencies in transforming their staff structure from a hierarchy into a team that encourages input and feedback and shares responsibility across all staff positions is an important area of training, with enormous impact upon the quality of services provided.

The second administrative issue that emerged was the influence of SPICE services upon other agency programs. As agencies began implementing the SPICE program, they found methods used in other agency programs, and indeed the programs themselves, to be increasingly called into question.

Agencies found that the SPICE Project did not fit neatly into their structure of services and programs. SPICE required a different way of thinking and acting, which often challenged existing agency practice. With the introduction of SPICE, some agencies now maintained traditional programs, such as group homes, workshops, and special recreation activities, in addition to SPICE. Clearly, the values and philosophy that support these services were distinct and often in conflict with those that support SPICE. Attempting to maintain both sets of values was a challenge that could not be managed. Yet, abandoning established and well-rehearsed practices in favor of untested and unfamiliar ones was also a challenge to agencies.

The struggle to transform traditional agency-based services into individualized supports consistent with the values and approach adopted by SPICE is one that will likely go on for some time, as more people with disabilities and their advocates refuse to accept traditional, agency-centered (versus individualized) services. As shown through SPICE, agencies must be supported during this process with training and technical assistance. Just as staff must be taught strategies and techniques for living up to the values of choice and integration, agency administrators must be taught management practices and organizational approaches that will facilitate restructuring services.

A related area that agencies must address is the policies that guide the organization. As the SPICE Project began assisting people in moving from nursing facilities, it became apparent that some agencies' internal policies would require modification or change to accommodate the goals of the SPICE Project. Some agencies, for example, had policies or long-established practices of not allowing people to go into the community unaccompanied by staff, or not allowing people to stay alone in their own homes. A further issue is that if staff are told to disregard certain policies or told that policies do not apply to a particular program or group of participants, then staff are left with nothing to guide them in performing their job. This situation can be as detrimental to participants as the over-restrictive policies that it replaced.

Because the nature of SPICE and similar support programs is individualized, developing policies to guide staff actions is challenging. Policies must be broad enough to address all the people whom the program serves, or potentially could serve, yet prescriptive enough to actually provide direction to staff. Areas in which agencies have had to re-examine current policies include the selection of home sites and housemates, staff interviews, hiring and supervision processes, quality assurance, the individual program planning process, staff training, grievance protocols, active treatment, and choice. Figure 28.2 shows the policy developed through SPICE to address the issue of choice.

A final effort that needs to be expanded for SPICE participants is assisting them in obtaining jobs and training programs. Nearly all of the SPICE participants want to be employed, yet few have actually attained this status. Through the SPICE Project, some advances have been made in assisting people in gaining ac-

CHOICE POLICY

[Agency] is committed to soliciting and respecting the choices of persons served. Persons will participate in designing their own service package. This includes participating in the selection of their home, house mates, furnishings, staff, day time activities and goals/objectives. No person will move into a home which they have not yet visited and approved, nor will they live with someone whom they have not met.

Recognizing that many persons with disabilities have had limited opportunities to make choices in the past, an important goal of [Agency's] services is to create opportunities for people to develop skills in this area. This includes exposing people to the different options available to them in the community (e.g. jobs, recreation, education, etc), as well as using everyday situations to teach decision-making skills.

Staff will assist people in carrying out their choices by analyzing the consequences of actions, assisting people in attaining skills necessary to implement choices and discussing other possible options available to the person. The distinction between "risk" and "harm" will be discussed with each participant. [Agency] will not support people in carrying out choices which are considered likely to bring harm to the person or others.

When it is necessary for staff to make choices on behalf of participants, they will do so in the best interest of the person. This means they will respond to situations and opportunities in the manner which they think the participant would want. Choices made in the best interest of a participant will be based upon staff's knowledge of and experience with the person. These choices shall be consistent with the goal of assisting and supporting people to become as capable as possible.

Figure 28.2. Policy on choice developed through SPICE. Used by permission.

cess to meaningful training programs and volunteer opportunities, and in redirecting funds from work activity to supported employment. However, these efforts have yet to translate into jobs for all the SPICE participants who desire them. This is among the largest missing piece of an adult lifestyle that remains for SPICE participants.

CONCLUSION

Through the SPICE Project, Illinois demonstrated that people with multiple and severe disabilities who have spent the majority of their lives in institutions can be supported in the community. Furthermore, SPICE participants showed that despite years of institutionalization and often little or no active treatment services, they were able to gain skills and become active decision-makers in their own lives.

SPICE has been an important step toward the expansion of individualized support services for people with developmental disabilities moving out of nursing facilities. The lessons learned through this effort have assisted other agencies in designing programs to address the circumstances of these individuals. The experience has shown that anyone with disabilities can live in the community and that the community has the capacity to meet the needs of anyone, including people for whom nursing facilities had been thought to be the only "appropriate" residential option.

Living in their own homes, experiencing people and opportunities around them, and facing everyday challenges is more than many of the SPICE participants had dared to expect from life. Through SPICE, 40 people who would otherwise have spent the rest of their lives in institutions of one type or another now have a future that promises more than they or most who knew them thought possible.

REFERENCES

Davis, R., Silverstein, B., Uehara, E., & Sadden, L. (1987). *Evaluation and service identification project for developmentally disabled residents of intermediate care and skilled nursing facilities.* Report prepared for the Illinois Department of Public Aid and the Illinois Planning Council on Developmental Disabilities. Chicago: Taylor Institute.

Wilson, L., Huffman, C., & Conroy, J. (1991). *Final report: Evaluation of supported placements in integrated community environments project (SPICE).* Report prepared for the Illinois Planning Council on Developmental Disabilities. Springfield, IL: Corporate Alternatives, Inc.

29

Paying for Supports

Dollars, Payments, and the New Paradigm

Gary Smith

The premises of public developmental disabilities service delivery systems are being challenged by a "new way of thinking" (Minnesota Governor's Planning Council on Developmental Disabilities, 1987). Instead of developmental, continuum-based systems defined by preconfigured niches into which people with disabilities are slotted, the supports paradigm demands the reconfiguration of these systems around flexible, customer-driven services and supports. The developmental model viewed people with developmental disabilities as passive subjects of care and treatment prescribed and managed by professionals. The new supports paradigm calls for helping people live in ordinary places, engage in lifestyles of their choosing, and be included in community membership (Bradley & Knoll, 1990).

Weaving the supports paradigm into public service delivery systems dictates rethinking their core features: how services are planned, organized, managed, and regulated. The developmental model is embedded in federal and state laws, regulations, policies, and practices governing nearly every aspect of the interaction between public systems and people with developmental disabilities. Entire service delivery systems (and the policies and practices that undergird them) will need to change radically if the supports paradigm is to prosper.

This change has begun. Family-driven family support legislation is being enacted in more and more states. Supported living is being worked into a growing number of service systems. More people with severe disabilities are being supported in real jobs for real wages.

Yet, however compelling the case may be for the supports paradigm as the most satisfactory means of fostering independence, productivity, and inclusion, reorienting our systems to practice its principles will be no easy task. While the new paradigm already has had enormous ideological impact, the great bulk of public dollars spent on behalf of people with developmental disabilities pay for services framed under the developmental model. This model defines quality in terms of improving client living skills, social competencies, and behavior management, which is done through professionally defined active treatment regimens.

As Rudolph Goldscheid (1992) observed, "The budget is the skeleton of the state stripped of all misleading ideologies." The supports paradigm may have laid claim to the heart and the mind; thus far, its impact on the public purse has been less dramatic, as illustrated by the following:

- Spending for family supports in 1989 ($172 million) amounted to only 1.5% of *all* state spending for mental retardation/developmental disabilities services that year (Knoll et al., 1990).
- Medicaid's intermediate care facility for people with mental retardation (ICF/MR) program is regarded by many as the antithesis of the supports paradigm. Yet, in 1993, ICF/MR outlays reached an estimated $9.7 billion, $3.1 billion or 47% more than in 1989 (Smith & Gettings, 1993b). This massive, 4-year jump in ICF/MR outlays (equivalent to 18 times state spending for family supports) failed to yield any significant increase in the number of people served in such facilities.
- Between 1988 and 1993, the number of people supported by the Medicaid Home and Community-Based (HCB) waiver program more than tripled (Smith & Gettings, 1993a). While this program has emerged as a key financing tool for community supports, HCB waiver outlays still make up only 15% of all state–federal Medicaid outlays for developmental disabilities services.
- Despite the rapid expansion of supported employment services for people with developmental disabilities since 1985, fewer than one in every seven adults served in state-funded daytime programs holds an inclusive job (McGaughey, Lynch, Morgenstern, Kiernan, & Schalock, 1991).
- From 1987 to 1992 there has been a flurry of activity by states to initiate supported living programs. Still, in only a few cases has supported living emerged as a dominant service option in state community residential service systems (Smith, 1990).

The old way of thinking continues to command the vast majority of public dollars spent on developmental disabilities services.

Nonetheless, a shift is occurring. States have stepped up their spending for supports, an important change from only a few years ago when state agendas consisted largely of plans to expand facility-based models. Still, there remains a wide gulf between the ideology of the supports paradigm and the reality of how the state and federal governments spend their dollars for developmental disabilities services.

For the supports paradigm to take hold to any significant degree, its financial feasibility must be clearly established. This involves two fundamental issues: 1) demonstrating to federal and state policy-makers that the new way of thinking is *affordable,* and 2) rethinking how public systems manage dollars. Putting flesh on Goldscheid's "skeleton" through shifting dollars from services framed by the developmental model to person-centered supports demands more than ideological fervor. There must be confidence that the new paradigm yields economical solutions to the needs of consumers and families. Moreover, traditional payment systems are ill-suited to the task of tailoring supports to the particular circumstances and preferences of each consumer. Unless such systems are fundamentally retooled, the basic premises of the supports paradigm will be undermined.

AFFORDABILITY

Dollars will shift to person-centered supports only if state and federal policy-makers are convinced that the new paradigm is affordable. Demonstrating affordability answers two key issues: 1) how the costs of such supports compare to outlays for serving individuals through traditional service models, and 2) to what extent the federal government will share in such costs. The question is addressed in Chapter 9. The federal and state fiscal climate during the 1990s dictates that there will be no paradigm shift if the price tag is out of line.

For better or worse, the yardstick against which the affordability of supports will be measured is the cost of furnishing services via traditional models. Is supported living more or less costly than serving an individual in a group home? Are inclusive employment supports more or less expensive than sheltered employment?

From a fiscal perspective, person-centered supports offer two potential advantages over traditional models. The first lies in tailoring services to each person's needs and, thereby, making the most efficient use of available dollars by purchasing only what is needed rather than a predetermined package of services. The second advantage lies in the reduced reliance on paid staff through the integration of natural supports into person-centered support strategies.

However, person-centered supports also evoke considerable uncertainty concerning costs. In part, these concerns stem from the paradigm's fluidity, that is, that the resources needed to support people will vary from person to person, depending on a wide variety of factors, only some of which stem from disability-related consumer characteristics. Hence, definitive answers to the question of how much supports will cost can be elusive. Moreover, the principle of doing whatever it takes to make supports work can be interpreted by policy-makers as a request for a blank check. Finally, individualizing services appears to contradict evidence that smaller settings are more costly.

There is little doubt that these concerns have led policy-makers to focus supports on individuals whose needs are less intensive. In some quarters, the view has emerged that person-centered supports might work for people who do not need complex, wraparound services but will not be affordable for individuals with significant, multiple disabilities. In supported employment, for example, the chief beneficiaries have been individuals diagnosed as having mild and moderate levels of mental retardation (Wehman, 1992). Individuals with multiple, severe disabilities have been judged (implicitly or explicitly) to need traditional services, which are regarded as more economical to furnish than personalized, inclusive supports.

However, at this stage in the evolution of person-centered supports, there is solid and steadily mounting evidence that the new paradigm is at least as affordable as traditional residential and day program models for individuals requiring any level of support. Following are examples:

- In relative terms, North Dakota's Individualized Supported Living Arrangements (ISLA) program is the United States' largest supported living program. Since its inception, ISLA has consistently demonstrated average costs 20% or more below the costs incurred on behalf of its participants prior to their entry into the program (Smith, 1990). While the costs of serving some participants has reached as much as $300 per day, the overall average costs are below those in traditional models. In other supported living programs similar evidence has accumulated that *average* costs across all consumers are competitive with those under conventional models. In fact, in Colorado the mix of people who participate in "personal care alternatives" is very similar to other, traditional residential services recipients (Smith, 1990). Yet, these supports are no more (and frequently less) costly than traditional models.
- More broadly, the supported living programs fostered under the Medicaid HCB waiver programs in more than 20 states reveal costs significantly below those for ICF/MR services (Smith, 1990; Smith & Gettings, 1993b). HCB waiver participants must meet exactly the same eligibility criteria as apply in the ICF/MR program.
- Supporting children with severe disabilities (including significant medical challenges) in the family home has been demonstrated to be significantly more economical than paying for long-term institutional services (Ellison & Ashbaugh, 1990).
- Time and again, family support programs have demonstrated that spending dollars in such programs produces more than does paying for facility-based options (Ellison & Ashbaugh, 1990; Knoll et al., 1990). The dollars needed to serve one person in an institution typically can support 25 or more families in a family support program.
- Study after study reveals that the longitudinal costs of supported employment services are well below the long-run expenditures needed to sustain people with developmental disabilities in traditional day treatment, work activity, and sheltered work settings.

Experience with the supports paradigm does not so much negate concerns regarding its cost implications as provide a clearer perspective regarding its underlying dynamics. The following illustrate:

- By and large it is true that person-centered support strategies can be a costly proposition in meeting the needs of people with particularly complex needs. For some individuals, costs will significantly exceed those of traditional, congregate service models. Considered in isolation, the costs of supporting these individuals through supported living or other strategies appears to be unaffordable. However, considered from the perspective of *average* costs, inclusive strategies—premised on the principle that supports should be for all—are highly competitive with traditional models.
- Where there have been breakdowns in the affordability of person-centered supports, the root causes appear to lie in the failure to fully embrace the paradigm's essential principles. For example, an essential principle of the supports paradigm is that paid services *complement* but do not displace natural supports (which, in turn, are critical to building interdependence and community membership). When, however, natural supports are relegated to a secondary or incidental role, it becomes an extremely expensive proposition to rely exclusively on paid, specialized services for consumers.
- Moreover, it is clear that, over the long haul, the supports paradigm proves to be a costly proposition when it is implemented as merely dressing up the developmental model in new clothes. Supported living is unaffordable if it is managed as a smaller version of traditional group home models. Moreover, unless functional programming is embraced as the basic strategy for equipping individuals with the skills needed to deal with the day-to-day realities of community life, the long-term costs of supports will not decline. The costs of services are persistent and high. Without functional strategies, supports can be unaffordable.
- Finally, supports will be costly if there is not a concurrent shift in the regulatory climate under which public services are furnished, particularly removing the traditional bias that paid staff afford consumers the only measure of reliable protection against potential harm. Staff presence and interventions are the single most decisive factor in determining the costs of nearly any developmental disability service. Dictating high levels of paid staff presence works against the affordability of supports.

The costs of developmental disabilities services are the product of a host of factors. Person-centered supports can be affordable or, due to regulatory or other factors, can be made unaffordable. It seems clear that fully embracing the new paradigm enhances the affordability of person-centered supports.

On the whole, the evidence is most encouraging that the supports model is affordable, considered either from a cost or federal financing perspective. Indeed, the accumulating evidence for this is far more encouraging than the recent track record for traditional services. Annual increases in the per capita costs of ICF/MR services, for example, persistently have been in the range of 9%–10% per year from 1982 to 1993, well above the overall rate of inflation. For a variety of reasons, there is enormous upward pressure on the costs of traditional service models. The supports paradigm is emerging as the best opportunity to restructure service delivery systems to cope with these rising costs constructively.

MANAGING PAYMENTS

Shifting to the supports paradigm also requires rethinking how payments for developmental disabilities services are managed. Payment systems (e.g., rate determination, reimbursement methods, and dollar allocation strategies) dictate the flow of resources in community service systems. By their very nature, payment systems have a powerful influence over the scope, nature, and quality of services (Smith & Aderman, 1987). Such systems contain implicit and explicit incentives and disincentives that affect the delivery of services. It is important to look at the payment policies and practices and their interaction with support strategies.

Under the precepts of the developmental continuum of care model, state payment systems for specialized developmental disabilities services became more or less organized along hierarchical lines. The continuum of care held that preconfigured service models would play particular roles in meeting the needs of specific categories of individuals. In this context, paying for services could be viewed as fixing a price for each of these various models or tiers along the continuum. In order to contain costs, such pricing systems have conditioned payment on consumers meeting predefined entry criteria, usually based on assessed disability. Payment levels are scaled against severity of disability.

Pricing developmental disabilities services in the foregoing fashion has given rise to some thorny issues, including dealing with outcomes such as the creation of significant disincentives to promoting independence; service system rigidity; and serious compromises of key principles, including individualization and affording people with disabilities real choices about where they live.

Moreover, it is important to keep in mind that conventional payment systems have been designed as essentially two party (funder–vendor) transactions. The aim of such systems is to furnish the provider agency with sufficient resources to maintain the capacity for a set number of slots. These funding systems are facility-based; they purchase the capacity to serve a set number of consumers who meet certain characteristics. The supports paradigm enhances the principle that consumers will have a large say in how public dollars are expended. Consumer choice and empowerment introduce a third party to the payment equation. The supports paradigm and its underlying values presume that the tie between public dollars and particular vendors will be severed and that dollars will follow the person.

The supports paradigm casts aside the notion of a hierarchy of services in favor of considering the needs of people one person at a time. Prejudging needs by preconfiguring a continuum of care is rejected in favor of taking into account each individual's circumstances, dreams, and natural support network in crafting person-centered support strategies. The role that paid staff and specialized services might play in the lives of individuals is expected to differ, even though the individuals, on the surface, may have similar disability labels.

The supports paradigm presumes that the dollar resources needed to meet the needs of each individual consumer will differ. The expectation that people's needs will change over time argues for funding approaches that are far more flexible than those that emerged under the continuum of care.

Personalized, flexible funding strategies coupled with shedding provider-oriented systems in favor of consumer-centered systems turn existing approaches to payment management on their heads. The outlines of new approaches that might take their place are only now beginning to come into focus. The following are notable:

- Rate determination methods in place in states including North Dakota, Missouri, and Nevada yield individualized payment rates driven by an individual's support plan. Customized payments are being managed successfully in these states.
- The use of vouchers in Maine's school-to-work transition program is giving families the ability to shop among service provider agencies.
- The growing number of cash subsidy and voucher-based family support programs are allowing families to decide which supports will be of most benefit and to select the individuals/agencies to provide such supports.
- Oklahoma's initiatives to equip families and consumers with information concerning the quality of services furnished by provider agencies is introducing competitive marketplace concepts into its service delivery system.
- Wisconsin has decategorized its HCB waiver funds in order to maximize the opportunities for counties to individualize funding on a consumer-by-consumer basis under an overall dollar constraint.

Such steps represent distinct departures from the past practices that have been dominated principally by funder–provider negotiations over payments independent of the specific needs of individual consumers.

Sorting through these and efforts by other states to realign payment systems to undergird the supports paradigm, one finds certain themes emerging that may ultimately define a new way of thinking in this arena. The following are among these themes:

- There is a shift from managing payments on a service-by-service basis to less categorical strategies that permit decisions about specific services and supports to be made locally or personally. More states seem prepared to manage payments at a more global level rather than lock in preemptive payment strategies.
- Consumers and families are having a far stronger voice in the selection of vendors as dollars are being more readily transportable as part of the unlinking of funding from specific provider agencies.

- There is a shift from model-driven rates to support–plan-driven payments which directly tie payments to a consumer's plan while containing outlays through the imposition of overall caps and/or service specific caps.

How exactly these themes will be played out remains to be seen.

Ultimately, in redefining payment systems from facility-based to customized funding strategies, states must confront a number of thorny issues. Among these are dealing with provider agency concerns that such strategies threaten their operational stability and, thus, the quality of services they furnish. Also, schemes must be devised for allocating funds to substate areas on a non–service-specific basis. No longer can funds be allocated on the basis of service-by-service slots and related rates as is commonly done now. Moreover, it seems certain that the role of today's case manager must be transformed from gatekeeper for the continuum to service coordinator/service broker.

CONCLUSION

There is solid evidence that the supports paradigm is practicable and affordable. Fund allocation and payment systems are being realigned in order to decouple dollars from traditional facility-specific, provider-specific, or service-specific categories. While much still needs to be learned about the interconnections between funding and supports, there is some basis for optimism.

Considerable challenges remain. The following three merit specific mention:

- Progress in infusing the new paradigm into state service delivery systems will mean confronting what is to be done with the considerable investments that have been made in facilities and programs developed under the old way of thinking. As noted earlier, such facilities and programs continue to lay claim to the lion's share of resources in public service delivery systems. If the new paradigm is to work for everyone, then serious thought must be given to its implications for current programs.
- In this light, it seems clear that better strategies are needed to assist agencies in the transition to the new way of thinking. These strategies must confront the financial realities inherent in such transitions. Successes have been recorded in this arena. In New Hampshire, the collaboration of state officials and private program managers cleared the way for the closure of several sheltered work programs in favor of inclusive employment. Some states, including Minnesota and New Hampshire, have made provisions to cover operational losses (e.g., the fixed costs of facilities for a limited period of time until the transition from facility-based to support arrangements can be accomplished). In Colorado and Oregon, state officials and provider agencies have been able to work out the closure of large, private ICFs/MR in favor of supported living services. If the supports paradigm is to reach more consumers (rather than grow at the margins of state systems), then collaborative transition strategies will be vital.

- There seems little doubt that federal policies must be restructured if the supports paradigm is to flourish. Such policies must be redefined to shed their linkages with the developmental model with its emphasis on treatment as the only legitimate offering federal Medicaid makes to people with developmental disabilities.
- Finally, the emergence of the supports paradigm means thinking about funding services in ways radically different from those linked to the developmental model. If consumer empowerment is a critical aim, then breaking out of the dominant vendor payment framework in favor of vouchers or income assistance strategies must be entertained more seriously. In turn, this implies creating a radically different marketplace of services and supports than emerged as a result of the states' efforts to foster the development of the continuum of care, based as it was on carefully controlling the entry of provider agencies into the service delivery system. Past experience provides only limited clues for organizing a marketplace that will be controlled less by licenses and more by consumers making choices.

From many different, compelling perspectives, using the supports paradigm is the right thing to do. Unlike the developmental model, the supports paradigm offers the hope of achieving the integration of public policy, long-articulated values, and practice, in order to provide supports to people with developmental disabilities.

REFERENCES

Bradley, V.J., & Knoll, J. (1990). *Shifting paradigms in services to people with developmental disabilities*. Cambridge, MA: Human Services Research Institute.

Ellison, M.L., & Ashbaugh, J. (1990). *The dollars and sense of promoting the self-sufficiency of persons with disabilities through programs of independent living, in-home and family supports*. Cambridge, MA: Human Services Research Institute.

Goldscheid, R. (1992). *A call for change: Empowering consumers, families and communities*. Atlanta: State Commission on Mental Health, Mental Retardation, and Substance Abuse Service Delivery.

Knoll, J.A., Covert, S., Osuch, R., O'Connor, S., Agosta, J., & Blaney, B. (1990). *Family support services in the United States: An end of the decade report*. Cambridge: Human Services Research Institute.

McGaughey, M.J., Lynch, S., Morgenstern, D.R., Kiernan, W., & Schalock R. (1991). *National survey of day and employment programs for persons with developmental disabilities: Results from state MR/DD agencies*. Boston: Training and Research Institute for People with Disabilities.

Minnesota Governor's Planning Council on Developmental Disabilities. (1987). *A new way of thinking*. St. Paul, MN: Author.

Smith, G. (1990). *Supported living: New directions in services to people with developmental disabilities*. Alexandria, VA: National Association of State Mental Retardation Program Directors.

Smith, G., & Aderman, S. (1987). *Paying for services*. Alexandria, VA: National Association of State Mental Retardation Program Directors.

Smith, G., & Gettings, R.M. (1993a). *Medicaid-funded home and community-based waiver services for people with developmental disabilities*. Alexandria, VA: National Association of State Directors of Developmental Disabilities Services.

Smith, G., & Gettings, R.M. (1993b). *Medicaid's ICF/MR program: Present status and recent trends*. Alexandria, VA: National Association of State Directors of Developmental Disabilities Services.

Wehman, P. (1992). *Achievements and challenges: A five-year report on the status of the national supported employment initiative: FY 1986–1990*. Richmond: Rehabilitation Research and Training Center on Supported Employment, Virginia Commonwealth University.

30

Implications for Future Practice and Systems Design

John W. Ashbaugh, Valerie J. Bradley, and Bruce C. Blaney

In a book as diverse and wide-ranging as this one, it is a challenge to distill the major implications that arise from the varied analyses and apply them to practice. Though the reader will certainly draw his or her own lessons from the perspectives presented, the editors also offer the following observations.

THE SUPPORTS PARADIGM

In order to design implementation strategies that will facilitate the development of supports, it is first important to understand the underlying paradigm shift and the types of practices that such a shift implicates. Drawing on her earlier work and that of others (Bradley & Knoll, 1990, Ferguson & Olson, 1989; Taylor, 1988; Taylor, Racino, Knoll, & Lutfiyya, 1987), Bradley (Chapter 2) described a movement in which the prominent value is individual choice and self-determination. This suggests a system in which people with developmental disabilities should be given the option of choosing among available supports and providers and in which friends, family, and service coordinators provide support and guidance when necessary. To realize the ideals laid out by Bradley, self-advocacy training and case management support will be needed to inform these choices, and a conscious effort should be made to develop multiple sources of supports from which to choose. Furthermore, specialized systems must be transformed to more holistic enterprises that, instead of surrounding people with services in specially designed and constructed facilities, provide supports where the individual works and lives. Rather than "fixing people" with disabilities, the emphasis should be on integration and inclusion.

These values are interlaced throughout the book, and each author adds her or his own particular interpretation. Racino (Chapter 10) defined the emergence of the supports paradigm in terms of social justice, specifically as a move toward an inclusive society where power is shared among people. Blaney (Chapter 8) and Kendrick (Chapter 21) saw the emerging supports paradigm as building socially valued roles for people who have long been denied them. Mount (Chapter 6), Kiracofe (Chapter 16), and Smull and Danehey (Chapter 4) discussed how the supports paradigm transforms the fundamental nature of the professional's relationship to consumers from that of expert to the more humble role of partner. Nisbet, Jorgensen, and Powers (Chapter 12) identified long-standing rationales that form the foundation of inclusion in education: civil rights, the belief that schools should reflect a pluralistic society, the potential for the development of social relationships, and the preparation for optimum functioning in inclusive adult communities. She listed a number of beliefs, among them: "1) that children who have disabilities are full human beings whose presence enriches our schools, and 2) that people with disabilities do not need to be 'fixed' before they are allowed to participate in the mainstream of school and community life." Finally, Luckasson and Spitalnik (Chapter 5) discussed the influence of the new paradigm on the definition of mental retardation and the ripples that this new definition will have throughout the service system.

Particularly compelling are the first person accounts of individuals—some of whom spent earlier parts of their lives in institutions—who are being supported in the ways outlined in the book. Regina DeMarasse and Cathy Ludlum (Ducharme, Beeman, DeMarasse, & Ludlum, Chapter 20) had big dreams, a lot of persistence, and, finally, circles of friends to help secure the supports they needed to live in the community. Judith Snow's statement in that same chapter captures their battles for independence and community involvement: "The dream will be changed by reality, but the dream will also change reality."

Ray Gagne's struggle for independence and inclusion was longer and harder (Chapter 18). He described the enormity of the struggle he faced after living 18 years in an institution and moving into the community: "When I left the institution, it took awhile for my family to understand that I could live successfully on my own. For a number of years, changing their beliefs was hard, but they slowly began to see me as a person."

IMPETUS FOR CHANGE

In reading about the professional as a partner to the consumer, in Kiracofe's chapter, one cannot help but feel that the supports paradigm concerns simply doing the right thing. It is a paradigm driven by unassailable values and principles. Yet, what is also apparent, especially in the chapters by Bradley (Chapters 1 and 2),

Ashbaugh (Chapter 23), Kendrick, and Smull and Danehey, is that the paradigm shift is being propelled as much, if not more, by the need to find answers to some of the more intractable problems currently confronting state developmental disabilities systems as it is by these higher order values and beliefs. This is consistent with the common sense understanding of paradigms and paradigm shifts laid out by Ashbaugh, who noted that paradigms are sets of rules and regulations (written or unwritten) for problem-solving. Sooner or later, problems begin to surface that the rules of the paradigm cannot solve. These are the catalysts that trigger the paradigm shift.

The catalytic problems in the developmental disabilities field surfaced during what Bradley called the deinstitutionalization era, when professionally run, facility-based residential, day and therapeutic programs were the dominant service modality. Smull and Danehey, and Ashbaugh described the bind in which most state systems for people with developmental disabilities now find themselves: heavily invested in expensive facility-based services that, by their very nature, limit choice and community inclusion, facing ever-increasing demands for services, and experiencing diminishing revenues.

Facility-based services are not working. As Bradley observed, much of facility-based programming is aimed at helping consumers to adapt to their environments and eliminate maladaptive behaviors that interfere with their adaptation. Yet, from the individual's viewpoint, it is not hard to understand why they may "maladapt" to a set of expectations that are, in many ways, far from normal and that they themselves have not participated in developing. Likewise, attempts to integrate consumers into the life of the community from these facility bases are often contrived and superficial. As Blaney emphasized, such programming can only deliver variations on a client role and will not lead to valued roles and relationships.

Costs continue to escalate. States have been compelled to continually increase intermediate care facility for persons with mental retardation (ICF/MR) rates as regulatory demands from the United States Health Care Finance Administration have escalated and as provider costs have gone up with other health industry costs. Rate increases have averaged over 10% each year since 1983—well above the level of inflation. In many cases, these increases are on the backs of the other providers. Most states have been under-funding the state-funded segments of their service systems for years as they have been unable to keep rates in line with inflation. Providers have responded by thinning front-line staff and holding down wage increases. The result has been an increase in staff burnout, turnover, and shortages, and decrease in quality, with fewer trained and experienced staff supporting more individuals.

Waiting lists continue to build. Their growth reflects the pent-up demand of people with developmental disabilities living at home whose needs for out-of-home placement have been subordinated to the need to move people from increasingly expensive institutions. Such lists have also been swelled by people whose parents have aged to the point where they are no longer able to look after them, and by the waves of students graduating from school systems and who are prepared for a more inclusive life in the community than the adult service system can offer.

Revenues in most states continue to decline. In 1992 nearly two thirds of the states reported budget deficits. Certainly this is an outgrowth of the recession. However, it is also a reflection of the rising costs of health and long-term care systems, with Medicaid overruns accounting for a large part of many of these deficits. That federal and state caps will soon be placed on health and long-term care spending generally and on Medicaid spending specifically is almost certain.

Smull and Danehey referred to this set of circumstances as the "trap of the 1980's" Indeed it has been. It is unrealistic to expect that state officials will enmesh themselves any further in the trap of professionally controlled, facility-based models of service characteristics of the community and institutional paradigms. A study at the University of Minnesota (Hayden, 1992) conservatively estimates the numbers of persons on waiting lists for residential and day services at 200,000, roughly 133,000 for residential services and 67,000 for day services. The added cost of serving these persons under facility-based paradigms would run into the billions and would escalate state developmental disabilities budgets by 20% for the residential portion above.

In the 1990s and beyond, supported arrangements should move front and center. Indications are that for many individuals they are less expensive than facility-based arrangements. North Dakota's Individualized Supported Living Arrangements Program, the largest in the United States relative to the size of the population served, has consistently demonstrated average costs 20% or more below the costs incurred on behalf of participants prior to their entry into the program (Smith, 1990). In Minnesota (Minnesota Disability Law Center, 1991), the savings associated with the concerted effort to move children from facilities to homes with supports amounted to over $20 million. Family support programs have been demonstrated time and again to be far more economical than facility-based options (Ashbaugh & Ellison, 1990). And the longitudinal costs of supported employment and community-based activity services are consistently reported to be at or below those of the traditional sheltered work and day activity programs for most individuals (Smith, Chapter 29).

More important, supported arrangements are high in customer satisfaction. This is not surprising as the supports paradigm is designed to give customers what they want, within reason. Supports are tailored to the preferences of consumers, allowing them, where at all possible, to live and work where and with whom they wish and to spend their spare time in activities that they enjoy and with people with whom they wish to associate.

WHAT NEEDS TO CHANGE?

The notion that customers should drive services is hardly a breakthrough concept. It is at the heart of what is commonly termed the Total Quality Management approach to organizational management, an approach seen by corporations worldwide as the key to their success and survival in the highly competitive business environment of the 1990s. There is widespread agreement today among management and organizational design thinkers generally, and in the developmental disabilities arena specifically, that success will come to those organizations that are consumer driven, where every employee is either serving the customer directly or actively supporting those who do (Albrecht, 1992).

Yet, the supports paradigm is still functioning only at the margins of most state developmental disabilities systems. Specifically, spending for family supports in 1989 amounted to only 1.5% of state spending for mental retardation/developmental disabilities services (Knoll et al., 1992). Fewer than one in seven adults served in state-funded day programs has inclusive employment (McGaughey, Lynch, Morganstern, Kiernan, & Schalock, 1991). Supported living has emerged as a dominant service option in very few states (Smith, 1990).

In order for the supports paradigm to take center stage, state developmental disabilities systems and provider agencies must change. As Gardner (Chapter 26) explained, current organizational structures, cultures, and political environments are designed to make the institutional and community paradigms work; they are not designed to further the supports paradigm.

Systems Must Become Consumer-Centered

It is widely agreed that if the supports paradigm is to work as envisioned, consumers and families must step into the driver's seat. There must be ways for consumers to be heard and to assert themselves at both the service agency level and the system level. The channels through which consumers and their families have traditionally weighed in have allowed consumers only limited influence, and even some of the most influential channels have been compromised.

The effectiveness of case managers/service coordinators as consumer and family advocates has been compromised in most states. Good case management has been touted as the way to protect consumer and family interests. However, the case management function has become increasingly administrative in nature with the Medicaid-fueled buildup of the developmental disabilities service industry, and increasingly mechanical with the rise of the developmental model of the continuum of service.

In line with the developmental model of services, case managers were expected to prepare formal individualized service plans coordinating input from an interdisciplinary team of professionals, to coordinate the range of services planned, to monitor client progress through the continuum, and to document all. Case files have grown as has the amount of time spent papering the process.

With Medicaid came intake and eligibility determinations, service verifications, and the updating of client and service information for payment and accountability purposes. And, as the numbers of people in service and awaiting service grew, so did the caseloads. As the numbers of services and related rules and regulations grew, so did the specialized knowledge required of service offerings and limitations.

Administrative responsibilities for intake and eligibility determination, service documentation, and other payment related activities have taken precedence over face-to-face activities in which the case managers were actively engaged with families and consumers. Larger caseloads have exacerbated the situation. Most case managers have become minions of the service system. Their roles as gatekeepers, fiscal agents, and paper processors have supplanted their roles as consumer and family advocates. They have lost touch.

Mount, Smull and Danehey, and Kiracofe saw person-centered planning processes that are based on the person and his or her social, vocational, and living preferences as the way to redirect the efforts of case managers and providers. They saw it as the cornerstone of the paradigm shift. As Mount explained, "It moves the locus of change away from the person with a disability toward a focus on changing social roles, responses, and existing organizational structures and cultures. It is nothing more than coming to know the customer." Smull and Danehey noted, "We cannot plan for someone we do not know." Also significant is the role of person-centered planning in developing a motivating vision, a far more powerful prod to action than compliance mandates or programmatic goals.

Creating the organizational environment needed for person-centered planning and supports coordination is not a simple undertaking. It means giving case managers and support workers more authority to act in the best interest of consumers and families, freeing them of needless regulation and paperwork, lowering caseloads to a manageable size, raising pay to a competitive level, and helping them reclaim lost attitudes, skills, and spirit through training, recognition, and competency building in partnership with families and consumers.

A number of states are taking dramatic steps to put case managers back into the service of consumers and their families. In Florida, as part of their Medicaid waiver, state officials are funding independent service coordinators as a purchased service. These individuals, who serve at the pleasure of the consumer, are trained and certified by the state.

Others are moving beyond formalized case management arrangements in their person-centered planning efforts. Ducharme, Beeman, DeMarasse, and Ludlum provided some first-person accounts of circles of support, in which people who care about an individual come together to help the person work toward his or her dreams. Parent-to-parent groups, family resource centers, and consumer groups have been formed across the country to share information about how to gain access to needed resources and to provide mutual support.

Changes Must Take Place in System and Agency Governance

Private providers dominate most community-based service systems, and yet consumers and families are often a minority or nonexistent on the governing boards of these corporate enterprises. Some of the largest corporations are nominal advocacy organizations that have become sophisticated provider enterprises. No longer advocates, now their primary charge is to maintain and expand the programs in which they have become invested.

In recognition of this, some states, such as California and Illinois, have recently enacted legislation requiring that the majority of the members of governing boards of administrative or service providing agencies be made up of people with developmental disabilities and their families. Still other states, like Colorado, are surveying individuals and families directly in order to obtain feedback of the sort once obtained through intermediaries such as The Arc and United Cerebral Palsy Associations.

Bowen (Chapter 19) described the progress being made in building one of the better known advocacy organizations, People First, to step into the breech and become a fresh voice for people with disabilities. Finally, Kendrick described the importance of developing such direct leadership but also noted that such leadership must be nurtured if the promise of participation is to be realized.

System and Service Agency Structures and Cultures Must Change

Bradley and Gardner contrasted traditional organizational structures and cultures with those suited to making the supports paradigm work. Gardner contrasted the heavily centralized, formalized, and mechanistic structures still characteristic of most organizations and systems with the more decentralized, less formal, and more fluid (organic) structures required to foster the development of consumer-driven supports for people. The mechanistic structures are designed to eliminate surprises and uncertainty and, thus, are a natural scheme for public and private institutions and systems responsible for the health and welfare of vulnerable people. Characteristically, rules and regulations pervade these organizations; power is focused at the top; and there is a strict hierarchy, there is more vertical communication, there are more specialists, and a "command and control" style of management prevails. These systems are designed for repetition and productivity; they promote uniformity. Staff look to rules and professional conventions for answers to problems. They are not expected to do problem-solving, adapt, and innovate; they are not expected to make mistakes.

The organic control models are nonhierarchical, with authority based instead more on knowledge, competence, and expertise. Generalists outnumber specialists. They are decentralized, with more horizontal, face-to-face communication. Rules and regulations take a back seat to shared values; uniformity takes a back seat to individuality and adaptation. Front-line staff are empowered to do problem solving. The organic models are clearly more appropriate in building individualized, community-based supports. As O'Brien and O'Brien (Chapter 7) observed, organizations that seek to build community are themselves best organized in terms of the equalitarian and mutual relationships that characterize community.

A shift to the supports paradigm will require a transformation of organizational structures and cultures. A number of obstacles and corresponding requirements have been identified for achieving this fundamental shift. First, financing and payment systems must become more flexible and consumer-directed. Gettings (Chapter 9) spoke to the most challenging fiscal reconfiguration needed to fund supports: the transformation of the Medicaid program. As he pointed out, 3 of every 5 dollars that the states expend on specialized developmental disabilities services come through Medicaid, and this does not include acute health care payments made on behalf of individuals eligible through Title XIX (of PL 74-271, the Social Security Act of 1935 as amended). The ICF/MR coverage option has led states to place and maintain nearly 150,000 persons in ICFs/MR. According to Gettings, the ICF/MR regulations have led ICF/MR providers to adhere to a facility-based, 24-hour programming model that is unnecessary and inappropriate for the vast majority of people with developmental disabilities who require ongoing assistance. Increasingly, states are opting to serve individuals through the more flexible Medicaid waiver option now involving nearly 65,000 persons. More aggressive states are creating individual support models under the waiver; however, the waiver still limits access to many types of supports and services and contains incentives to fashion service packages that approach the cost of ICFs/MR rather than more cost-effective packages.

As Smith explained, most state and federal payment schemes work against the funding of individualized supports. One common constraint is varying rates for different preconfigured service models and different levels of consumer functioning. In other words, these financing and payment systems are tied to traditional service models and contain inherent disincentives to promoting independence.

Untying financing and payment systems from existing service models, unbundling the various services often bound within these models (Smull & Danehey), and opening them to innovative arrangements are prerequisites for truly individualized supports. Smith suggested the use of vouchers and income assistance strategies, allowing consumers to choose among services and providers. He referenced Maine's use of vouchers as part of their school-to-work transition program and the cash subsidy programs now available to families in Michigan, Texas, Massachusetts, and numerous other states as cases in point. Voucher systems covering a wide range of supports are also being piloted in New Hampshire, Arizona, and California, among others.

Quality Assurance Systems Must Empower Consumers

Gettings, along with Kimmich and Bradley (Chapter 25), and Gardner (Chapter 26) addressed approaches to quality assurance and quality enhancement. Gettings defined the central question of how one ensures that the rights and interests of program participants are adequately safeguarded without violating the fundamental goal of allowing individuals to control their own lives and take their rightful place as participating members of the community. He described as promising the quality assurance provisions in the legislation creating the Community Supported

Living Arrangements program under Medicaid that allows state and local officials considerable latitude in "constructing quality assurance strategies that are molded to the particular strengths, needs, and aspirations of each program participant." However, he noted that later amendments to the legislation added explicit federal statutory and regulatory requirements and enforcement provisions indicating that there remains a core of federal officials who are not yet ready to entrust further quality assurance responsibilities to state and local officials.

Kiracofe would argue that these officials have not yet recognized and accepted the delimited role that the supports paradigm holds for public officials. Unlike providers in the institutional and deinstitutional eras who assumed total responsibility for individuals in their care, providers of supports are responsible *to* the individuals they serve, not *for* them. Thus, the principal assurer of quality is people with developmental disabilities, their families, or guardians.

As Gardner observed, quality should be defined as conformity with customer requirements, and expecting and empowering direct service workers to respond to this notion lies at the heart of the quality improvement movement under the supports paradigm. Quality improvement in this context is essentially a partnership in which both the service workers and customers have mutual rights and responsibilities. The basis and assumptions that underpin the partnership are constantly changing as customer requirements change and evolve. This continuous quality improvement approach, long touted by Deming (1986) as part of the Total Quality Management approach to corporate governance, appears to make eminent sense. After all, the traditional licensure and certification surveys have been shown to have little influence on provider performance day to day (Ashbaugh, Bradley, & Allard, 1980; Conroy & Lemanowicz; 1981 Mathematica Policy Research, Inc., 1977). At best, such monitoring mechanisms might be viewed as secondary or back-up mechanisms, certainly not as primary. Moreover, such regulations retard the ability of the system to innovate. The oversight of services has come into relief as regulations from each era of reform are heaped on top of the requirements of the previous period. This exponential expansion of regulations provides the political anthropologist with an extraordinary laboratory within which to view the assumptions and mistakes of the past 20 years. An alternative to heavily input- and process-oriented regulations is the assessment of outcomes for individuals with disabilities. As Kimmich and Bradley noted, a focus on outcomes means determining whether services and supports contribute to the enhancement of the individual's quality of life and whether they facilitate the exercise of individual choice.

Bureaucracies Must Be Trimmed

Gardner explained that it is difficult for bureaucracies to move from the traditional command and control styles of management, in which authority derives from organizational position, to "cultures of consent," where authority derives from performance. Such resistance is understandable since it implies that upper and particularly middle management staff cede descion-making power, and perhaps even their jobs, to front-line staff.

Kendrick explored the various ways in which bureaucracies work to impede and distort the aims of the supports paradigm. The nature of bureaucratic hierarchies is to "seek advice at their own pleasure" and to grow increasingly distant from the communities they serve. He also expressed concern over the tendency of these growing agencies to envelop and isolate the persons they serve in a web of agency-centered activities designed ultimately in the agencies' interest, rather than in response to the preferences of those served. He argued for nonbureaucratic arrangements, and recognized the need for leaders to break the grip of "dysfunctional bureaucracies" on the service system. Bradley, likewise, lamented the loss of community connections as agencies grow apart from the communities they serve: "Agencies that began as indigenous local organizations are now covering large geographical areas with management that is many times located outside of the community."

Gardner remarked that bureaucracies tend to compartmentalize operations in the interest of manageability. He noted that this trait is yet another barrier to the supports paradigm in that these divisions represent a fragmented response to consumer needs. He suggested that, as a result, large agencies may be unable to manage the horizontal communication needed to generate the coherent response to consumer needs called for under the supports paradigm. Bradley held out hope that interagency collaboration could be used to develop truly person-centered supports. Evidence of fulfillment of this hope is the mushrooming number of successful consumer- and family-centered interagency collaborations in the literature (Ashbaugh & Bergman, 1992; Goldenberg & Young, 1989; Swan & Morgan, 1993).

Staff Must Become More Humble, Knowledgeable, and Resourceful

The organizational changes needed to facilitate the supports paradigm have many implications with respect to staff development. Gardner pointed to the major adjustment that will be needed to ensure that staff accept direction from customers, a significant change from the traditions and conventions of their professional disciplines and the established rules. It will require learning through experience and will demand a new level of resourcefulness. It will mean that there will be fewer specialists and more generalists knowledgeable and skilled in securing access to a wide range of information, technology, and supports.

Bradley, borrowing from the work of the Family Empowerment Project at Cornell University (Cochran, 1990), listed a variety of competencies for effective support workers and collaborators, such as the capacity to listen and reflect, the ability to analyze power relationships and help others do so, and skills in helping people and groups to recognize and gain confidence in their abilities. Nisbet, Jorgensen, and Powers referred to the wealth of literature supporting the notion that the most successful inclusive school programs are those in which there is heavy collaboration between the regular classroom teachers and other support staff. In the same vein was Smull and Danehey's reminder of the importance of collaborating with families and communities to retain existing natural supports and build still more.

Knoll and Racino (Chapter 17) noted the absence of the degree programs needed to train resourceful, socially competent, transdisciplinary support workers. They explored the pros and cons of establishing a program within the traditional disciplines, as part of the interdisciplinary (nondegree) programs offered through University Affiliated Programs (UAPs), or elsewhere.

However it is accomplished, it is clear that the jobs of front line workers will be enlarged. They must have the basic knowledge, temperament, and capacity to grow in their jobs through experience, sharing, and collaboration. And they must be well supported by other staff in the organization up and down the line. As Gardner pointed out, the most important training, in fact, given the wide-open nature of the supports paradigm, will be the mentoring of inexperienced staff by experienced staff.

WHAT WILL IT TAKE TO MAKE THE SHIFT?

Shifting from the institutional and deinstitutional eras to the community membership era will involve changes in statute and regulation, changes in financing and payment systems, changes in organizational structure and culture, and changes in staff and consumer roles and responsibilities. Fundamentally, it will involve shifts in power from providers to consumers, from top and middle management to frontline workers, and from public agencies to private communities. Engineering these changes involves planning, organizing, and collaborating. It involves politics.

Section III of this book provided accounts of systems change efforts around the United States that are telling and instructive, offering insight into what it takes to effect such basic and far-reaching change. Some described efforts within provider agencies; others described efforts system-wide. Following are some common threads:

- The importance of leadership and commitment to a shared vision;
- The need for an action bias and learning environment that allows for continual reflection, conflict resolution, and adjustment;
- The importance of consumers and families as agents of change.

Committed Leadership

As Barker (1992) posited, "You manage within a paradigm, [but] you [must] lead between paradigms" (p. 164). This is as true at the systems level as it is at the agency level. At the agency level, Magis-Agosta (Chapter 14) identified strong leadership keyed to the supports vision as essential to the organizational transformations required in shifting paradigms. Nisbet, Jorgensen, and Powers, likewise, emphasized the importance of having strong school district leadership in order to move to inclusive education programs. Kiracofe rated the importance of obtaining the commitment of the agency director and key stakeholders to the process of change as second to none. He referred to these committed individuals as "paradigm pioneers." The organizational change strategy is to bring others in the agency along by having the paradigm pioneers demonstrate the feasibility and efficacy of person-centered supports.

Ashbaugh pointed out that, at the systems level, the interests vested in professionally dominated and provider-centered service systems are politically powerful. They cannot be expected simply to see the light and follow the leader as might be the case in agencies with committed leadership. There must be compelling reasons for the service industry to change. Ashbaugh explained how family and consumer-energized, interagency collaboratives can be used to identify and develop that leadership and to mobilize the political power needed to effect the paradigm shift.

At the agency level, the leadership has the power and reach to shepherd the change process. At the systems level, this power must be generated. The opportunity to do so may arise in different ways. Covert, MacIntosh, and Shumway (Chapter 11) described how in New Hampshire the opportunity grew out of a suit brought by the New Hampshire Association for Retarded Citizens against the state concerning conditions at the Laconia State School and Training Center. The trial generated public support for the basic notion that people with disabilities should be included in community life. Thanks to some insightful behind-the-scenes leadership, which enjoyed a long-term tenure, it eventually led to the development of community-based programs and to the development of a family support program and related family constituency. This constituency has been instrumental in pushing the developmental disabilities system toward the supports paradigm. Wesely (Chapter 27) described how in Nebraska it was the mounting dissatisfaction among families and consumers and a funding crisis that drew legislators' attention to the need for major systems change. Carmody (Chapter 28) described how in Illinois the federal nursing home reform legislation, which limits the use of nursing facilities as a residential option for people with developmental disabilities, helped convince the key state agencies involved in funding and administering nursing homes and developmental disabilities services to collaborate in the development of individual supports for people moving out of nursing homes. In Louisiana, the State Planning Council on Developmental Disabilities prompted and supported a grassroots organizing effort by families of children with developmental disabilities. The families, with council guidance and assistance, essentially created their own opportunity, drafting and lobbying successfully for a community and family support bill.

An Action Bias, a Learning Environment, and a Process for Conflict Resolution and Adjustment

In the descriptions of paradigm change at the service agency level, there is repeated reference to the need for continual reflection, organizational and procedural adjustment, and conflict resolution. In describing the transformation of two sheltered work agencies into integrated employment agencies, Magis-Agosta characterized the movement to the new paradigm as successive approximations of the vision with corresponding realignments to the agency's administrative and programmatic systems. Some changes settle in during the alignment; others do not. During these adjustment periods, reflective analysis occurs, and decisions are made about how best to proceed.

Kiracofe, in describing the steps involved in transforming residential service agencies to supported living agencies, likewise referred to planned periods of reflection and sharing during which the participants in the change process share what they have experienced and learned. They "celebrate their successes, share their frustrations, identify the obstacles and challenges they face, and renew their commitment to carry on." Kiracofe's agency facilitates this process and provides related training and consultation. Nisbet, Jorgensen, and Powers, in describing the transformation of segregated school districts to inclusive districts, stresses the importance of frequent collaboration and in-service training time in order to ensure the learning needed to effect the change and explained how successful districts serve as mentors (trainers) to others.

All allude to the action-oriented nature of the process, describing it as a journey not a blueprint, during which action precedes planning, where people are learning as they go. They also cite the inevitability of conflict and resistance, and the need to surface and deal with this conflict in a timely fashion.

At the systems level, the action bias involves initiating those systems level changes needed for these agency transformations to occur. As indicated earlier, this means empowering front-line workers and consumers through modifications to financing and payment systems by loosening the grip of hierarchical system administrations through decentralization and deregulation, and by relaxing the micro-managerial bent of administrative and quality assurance systems.

The scale and complexity of the collaborative arrangements needed to drive the paradigm shift are considerable, and the ability to use these collaboratives to bring to the surface and resolve conflict is critical, as Kimmich's examples of collaborative systems change illustrated (Chapter 24).

The Importance of Consumers and Families as Agents of Change

Universally emphasized in the accounts of systems change in this book is the central importance of consumers and families in galvanizing the actions needed to bring about the paradigm shift. The importance of individual consumer persistence in prodding service systems to support their choices is eloquently reflected in the personal accounts of Gagne, Bowen, Ducharme, Beeman, Ludlum, and DeMarasse, who have taken on the system. Carmody referred to self advocacy training as "an essential element to any individualized community-based support program, . . . geared toward helping people learn to make good decisions for themselves and [learn] to communicate those decisions effectively." In describing the People First self-advocacy organization in Connecticut, Bowen explained the importance of this organization as a support group helping individuals think for themselves and think of themselves as valued persons and discriminating customers who have every right to demand good service.

The success that comes from family- and consumer-rich collaboratives organizing for systems change is also clear. Covert, MacIntosh, and Shumway credited the family constituency built around the family support program as instrumental in closing the state's sole publicly administered institution and developing strong supported employment and living programs in New Hampshire. Wesely pointed to the organized uprising of families and consumers in Nebraska as the impetus for the overhaul of the developmental disabilities system in that state. Farber and Marcel (Chapter 22) related how families were able to build a sophisticated grassroots campaign that eventually led to the authorization and funding of an individual and family support program in that state.

WHAT LIES AHEAD?

By the accounts in this book, it would seem that the developmental disabilities field is poised on the cusp of the community membership era. Ashbaugh noted that, as Barker (1992) saw it, there is about to be a move from the pilot and demonstration stage to the operational stage. The field has been building a solid base of knowledge about what works and what does not since 1988. The amount of implementation literature on family support (e.g., Bradley, Knoll, & Agosta. 1992) supported living (e.g., Racino, Walker, O'Connor, & Taylor, 1993; Taylor, Bogdan, & Racino, 1991), and inclusive employment (e.g., Nisbet, 1992) is sizeable. A number of states, including Louisiana, Colorado, New Hampshire, West Virginia, and Ohio, have already passed landmark legislation designed to build individual and family support programs as centerpieces of their systems.

And yet, even as state officials are beginning to restructure and retool, they are bumping up against some sticky and seemingly intractable problems that will require serious attention if the community membership era is to become a reality. Some of these problems indicate that there will be a great deal of problem-solving necessary in addressing the following issues to make the supports paradigm work:

- *Ensuring that people with developmental disabilities are able to exercise choice will sometimes be a challenge*. How do we expand the opportunities for meaningful choice among people with developmental disabilities who have limited communication skills and limited experience from which to identify possible options?
- *Gaining access to public and private resources and supports is a challenging and time consuming proposition*. How do we inform and empower disadvantaged families heavily occupied with other demands on their time and resources or who simply are not up to the challenge? How do we identify and

secure the support of guardians and other consumer advocates? How do we promote, nurture, and cement friendships with the strength and endurance necessary to establish and maintain circles of friends?

- *There is a fine line between the interests of family and consumer*. Where should the line be drawn, if at all, between what the family wants for an individual and the individual's own hopes and dreams? Families, and parents in particular, may feel more protective of the individual and less inclined to tolerate risks that the individual may be willing to assume. How are these differences to be resolved? How do we build a system that protects individuals with disabilities when their families are not operating in their best interests?
- *The definition of quality should no longer be the sole purview of the state or the agency*. Kiracofe made the point that under the supports paradigm, the responsibility of the support agency and government sponsor is *to* the consumer and not *for* the consumer. Their responsibility is limited, and as Gettings, and Kimmich and Bradley implied, so is the government's role in defining service quality. Under the supports paradigm, it is the customer who should be the final arbiter of service quality. How can systems ensure this?
- *For the supports paradigm to work, developmental disabilities systems and service organizations can and should be decentralized, flexible, and driven by shared values*. This is an important tenet but will require the development of "community competence" and the development of grassroots, rather than centralized, advocacy entities. Such entities will be necessary to influence increasingly decentralized decision-making and to ensure that resources are equitably distributed.
- *Implementation of supports entails a change from the disparate aspect of categorical disability services*. In the 1970s, Karl Grunewald (1971), the former head of the Swedish mental retardation system, predicted that the full realization of the normalization principle would come in four stages and that the fourth and final stage would be decentralization and integration. This would require moving out of more narrow categorical services to more collaborative and interagency relationships. This "genericizing" of disability services has the advantage of removing the stigma associated with "special" services, but it also runs the risk of de-emphasizing the significant and intensive support needs of many people with developmental disabilities.

Additional caveats were also raised that may be less amenable to policy reform and problem-solving. For example, as Blaney explained, the quality of life for older people with developmental disabilities will be constrained by the societal roles for older persons in society which have led to patterns of age-segregation and exclusion from community life. To emulate these roles for older adults with disabilities in the interest of normalization would be a major step backward.

Kendrick questioned the romantic vision of community life held by many reformers. He challenged the assumption that community life will provide a refuge for people with disabilities. He could foresee "continued social devaluation, rejection, exploitation, disregard and neglect, abuse, segregation, abandonment, poverty, powerlessness, . . . [as more or less] predictable constancies in the human condition."

Racino identified the limited availability of services, including health and social services. She asserted that issues regarding access to health care, social services, and other resources by persons with disabilities cannot be truly addressed until they are addressed for society at large. In this connection, as persons with disabilities and their advocates battle for inclusion, they must recognize that with inclusion comes the loss of a disability identity and any special treatment that may afford. Is the real aim for equal treatment and social justice or for special consideration and human caring? Can people with disabilities thrive in anonymity, or is the special identity needed to avoid benign neglect?

CONCLUSION

As Boggs (Chapter 3) noted, no one generation has a lock on the truth. It may be unthinkable to some disciples of this new paradigm that there could be a better approach. However, in Boggs' view, that another paradigm is looming is a foregone conclusion. Her insightful account of the long line of paradigm changes that have characterized the developmental disabilities field in the twentieth century is broadening and convincing in terms of how it tells us what we cannot help but know deep down: that problems are bound to keep coming, and they will continually demand new approaches. Whether, as Boggs posited, it is the oscillation between compassion and remediation, paternalism and autonomy, or cacophony and consensus, another change inevitably will occur.

However, as Racino reminded us, truly fundamental change is not that which occurs with the passage of new legislation and the advent of new programs, but that which occurs with societal change reflected in the disability-based assumptions that permeate daily life. What matters is holding to the basic human values and principles that are associated with the supports paradigm, so that people with disabilities are seen as people first, as deserving customers second, and as accepted community members always. Regardless of the relative success of one paradigm or another, we are sure to be moving in the right direction.

REFERENCES

Albrecht, K. (1992). *At America's service*. New York: Warner Books, Inc.

Ashbaugh, J. (1992). *Collaborative planning: Selected references. Technical Bulletin 92*(1). Cambridge, MA: Human Services Research Institute.

Ashbaugh, J.W., & Bergman, A.I. (1992). The demonstration of resource acquisition and capacity building strategies in support of coordinated, family-centered, community-based services for children with disabilities. *Office of Special Education and Rehabilitative Services: News in print.*

Ashbaugh, J.W., Bradley, V.J., & Allard, M.A. (1980). *Assuring the quality of human services: A conceptual analysis*. Cambridge, MA: Human Services Research Institute.

Ashbaugh, J.W., & Ellison, M.L. (1990). *The dollars and sense of promoting the self-sufficiency of persons with disabilities through programs of independent living, in-home and family supports*. Cambridge, MA: Human Services Research Institute.

Barker, J.A. (1992). *Future edge: Discovering the new paradigms of success*. New York: William Morrow & Company, Inc.

Bradley, V.J., & Knoll, J. (1990). *Shifting paradigms in services to people with developmental disabilities*. Cambridge, MA: Human Services Research Institute.

Bradley, V.J., Knoll, J., & Agosta, J.M. (Eds.). (1992). *Emerging issues in family support*. Washington, DC: American Association on Mental Retardation.

Center on Residential Services and Community Living. (1992). *Policy research brief. Adults with mental retardation and other developmental disabilities waiting for community-based services in the U.S.* Minneapolis: Institute on Community Integration, University of Minnesota.

Cochran, M. (1990). The transforming role. *Networking Bulletin, 1*(3), p. 25.

Conroy, J., & Lemanowicz, J. (1981). *Developmental growth among the residents of Pennhurst: What factors are related to growth? Pennhurst study brief report No. 8*. Philadelphia: Temple University Developmental Disabilities Center.

Deming, W. (1986). *Out of the crisis*. Cambridge, MA: MIT Center of Advanced Engineering Study.

Ferguson, P.M., & Olson, D. (Eds.). (1989). *Supported community life: Connecting policy to practice in disability research*. Eugene: Specialized Training Program, Center on Human Development, University of Oregon.

Goldenberg, P.C., & Young, T.M. (1989). *Interagency collaboration. An annotated bibliography for programs serving children with emotional disabilities and their families*. Portland: Portland State University, Research and Training Center on Family Support and Children's Mental Health.

Gruenwald, K. (1971, March 27–April 1). *The guiding environment: The dynamic of residential living*. Paper presented at the first regional conference of the United Kingdom Committee of the World Federation on Mental Health, in association with the National Society for Mentally Handicapped Children, Dublin.

Hayden, M.F. (1992). Adults with mental retardation and other developmental disabilities waiting for community-based services in the United States. *Policy Research Brief, 4*(3).

Knoll, J., Covert, S., Osuch, R., O'Connor, S., Agosta, J., & Blaney, B. (1990). Supporting families: State family support efforts. In V.J. Bradley, J. Knoll, & J. Agosta (Eds.), *Emerging issues in family support* (pp. 57–98). Washington, DC: American Association on Mental Retardation.

Mathematica Policy Research, Inc. (1977). Impact of the FIDCR on children, families and caregivers. In *FIDCR appropriateness study: Chapter IV, final report: Volume I*. Washington, DC: Department of Health Education and Welfare, Office of Assistant Secretary for Planning and Evaluation.

McGaughey, M.J., Lynch, M.A., Morganstern, D.R., Kiernan, W.E., & Schalock, R.L. (1991). *National survey of day and employment programs for persons with developmental disabilities: Results from state MR/DD agencies*. Boston: Training and Research Institute for People with Disabilities, The Developmental Evaluation Center, Children's Hospital.

Minnesota Disability Law Center. (1991). *Optimizing reduced in financing in support of coordinated, family-centered, community-based services for children with disabilities, a tutorial seminar* (9/30/92–10/2/92). Chicago, IL: United Cerebral Palsy Associations and Human Services Research Institute.

Nisbet, J. (Ed.). (1992). *Natural supports in school, at work, and in the community for people with severe disabilities*. Baltimore: Paul H. Brookes Publishing Co.

Racino, J.A., Walker, P., O'Connor, S., & Taylor, S.J. (Eds.). (1993). *Housing support and community: Choices and strategies for adults with disabilities*. Baltimore: Paul H. Brookes Publishing Co.

Smith, G.A. (1990). *Supported living: New directions in services to people with developmental disabilities*. Alexandria, VA: National Association of State Mental Retardation Program Directors.

Swan, W.W., & Morgan, J.L. (1993). *Collaborating for comprehensive services for young children and their families: The local interagency coordinating council*. Baltimore: Paul H. Brookes Publishing Co.

Taylor, S.J. (1988). Caught in the continuum: A critical analysis of the principle of the least restrictive environment. *Journal of The Association for Persons with Severe Handicaps*, *13*, 41–53.

Taylor, S.J., Bogdan, R., & Racino, J.A. (Eds.). (1991). *Life in the community: Case studies of organizations supporting people with disabilities*. Baltimore: Paul H. Brookes Publishing Co.

Taylor, S.J., Racino, J., Knoll, J., & Lutfiyya, Z. (1987). *The nonrestrictive environment: On community integration for people with the most severe disabilities*. Syracuse: Community Integration Project, Center on Human Policy, Syracuse University.

INDEX

Page numbers followed by *t* or *f* indicate tables or figures respectively.